THE ASTRONOMICAL AND MATHEMATICAL
FOUNDATIONS OF GEOGRAPHY

The
Astronomical & Mathematical
Foundations of Geography

CHARLES H. COTTER

EX.C., B.SC., M.I.N.

*Senior Lecturer in the Department
of Maritime Studies at the
Welsh College of Advanced Technology*

Skilled in the globe and sphere,
He gravely stands
And with his compass, measures seas and lands.
DRYDEN, *after* JUVENAL

NEW YORK
AMERICAN ELSEVIER PUBLISHING COMPANY, INC.

© Charles H. Cotter 1966

First published in the United States 1966

AMERICAN ELSEVIER PUBLISHING COMPANY, INC.
52 Vanderbilt Avenue
New York, New York 10017

LIBRARY OF CONGRESS CATALOG CARD NUMBER 66 22459

Made and printed in Great Britain by
William Clowes and Sons Limited, London and Beccles

THE ASTRONOMICAL AND MATHEMATICAL
FOUNDATIONS OF GEOGRAPHY

CONTENTS

CHAPTER ONE

Ideas on the Size and Shape of the Earth

1. *The earliest theories*

A civilized person of the present time who does not know that the Earth on which we live is spherical is indeed something of a *rara avis*. Small children, soon after they learn to talk, are informed by their teachers that our Earth is a great spinning ball that traces out, as she spins, an elliptical orbit round the Sun. All of us grow up with these ideas, and we have no reason to question their truth.

But not all children—and indeed not all adults—of all ages have known that the Earth is a spherical satellite of the Sun. This grand knowledge was acquired little by little, and many centuries of human history were to pass before the relevant scraps of evidence were pieced together to provide—even for children of our day—the true knowledge of the character of our terrestrial home.

In the prehistorical period of human progress, for which written records do not exist, it is not unlikely that every man thought of himself, or at least the group with whom he lived, as occupying the very centre of the universe. This egocentric viewpoint is not perhaps unnatural; and we find folk, even at the present time, who find it difficult to think otherwise.

Records dating from the earliest period of history reveal that the Earth was regarded as being a disc surrounded by water. This again was not an unnatural assumption, for whichever way a man travelled, he ultimately reached the sea. The imagined extent of the world-disc varied with one's way of life; and wandering folk such as nomadic hunters and herders, seeing more of the world than did settled peoples who cultivated crops, doubtless regarded the Earth as having a size commensurate with the extent of their travels.

Ideas on the structure of the universe according to the Greeks of antiquity were geocentric. The Earth was believed to be circular in shape and to be bisected from east to west by the 'middle-earth' or 'mediterranean' sea, which divided the land into two continents.

Surrounding the Earth was the river Ocean, which was believed to flow northwards on the western sides of the continents and southwards on the eastern sides. 'The Sea'—as the Mediterranean was called—and all rivers and streams were regarded as being nourished and sustained by the mighty river Ocean, which was thought to flow smoothly and inexorably on its never-ending journey, unaffected by storm or tempest.

According to Greek mythology, before the Earth was peopled by man it was inhabited by a race of giants known as Titans. The Titans were the offspring of Uranus and Ge, the Olympian gods respectively of Heaven and Earth. Uranus and Ge, after rebelling against the remaining twelve higher gods of antiquity, were vanquished and thrust down to Tartarus, the abysmal place of punishment in the nether world.

The oldest of the Titans was Oceanus, the god of the Ocean, whose wife Tethys was mother of the 3,000 sea-nymphs or Oceanids.

The Sun, Moon, planets and Dawn, were believed to rise out of the ocean in the east, and to perform their daily drives westwards across the sky to give light, warmth and pleasure, to earthly beings.

According to Greek cosmogony, before the creation of the world, there existed a confused agglomeration of the four elements, fire, air, water and earth. This distorted mass was known as Chaos. The action of God the creator ended chaos and gave order to the universe, which henceforth became known as Cosmos.

Fire, the lightest of the four elements, was believed to have sprung upwards, when chaos ended, to form heaven—the abode of the gods. Air, being the next lighter element took its place immediately under heaven. Earth, being the heaviest element was supported by water on which it was supposed to float.

It is interesting to compare the classical Greek cosmogonic ideas with the account of the Creation written by Moses and supposed to have occurred some forty centuries before the birth of Christ. The opening chapter of the Book of *Genesis* contains a wonderful and truly remarkable story. 'In the beginning,' we are told, 'God created the earth and the heaven; and the earth was without form and void, and darkness was upon the face of the deep.' A vivid word-picture of chaos, to be sure.

2. First scientific approach: the Greek philosophers and mathematicians

Anaximander, who is often credited with the distinction of being the inventor of maps, so entitling him to the appellation Father of Geography, is thought to have been the first of the Greek philosophers to attempt the determination of the compass of the Earth. It is recorded that Anaximander—who flourished during the 6th century BC—after noting that the stars appear to revolve around the celestial pole, concluded that the Earth was at the centre of a vast sphere on the inside surface of which the stars, he thought, were fixed.

At the time of Anaximander, travellers had become aware that the boundary of the Earth was by no means a regular circle. Democritus, the Greek philosopher who propounded the theory that all substances are composed of moving atoms, and who flourished c. 450 BC, constructed a map on the basis of his own travels. Democritus is thought to have been the first to have produced a rectangular map. He claimed that the Earth is one-and-a-half times as long in the east–west direction, as it is broad in the north–south direction. Reminders of this supposed difference between the east–west and north–south extents of the Earth are to be found in the terms *latitude* and *longitude*, which are derived from the Latin *latus* and *longus* signifying respectively broad and long.

Who it was who first thought the Earth to be spherical is not known. But it is recorded that during the 6th century BC, Thales of Miletus—the sea-port of Ephesus—believed the Earth to be spherical in shape.

In the 5th century BC, the notable Pythagoras held and taught that the Earth is a sphere, a clear proof being provided by the appearance of ships, as they heave into the sight of, or sail away from, an observer standing on the shore.

Aristotle and Plato, who flourished during the 4th century BC, also regarded the Earth to be spherical in shape. 'The sphere is the most perfect geometrical shape,' they argued, 'and the Earth, being the home of man, must of necessity be the perfect production of its creator; therefore the Earth must be a sphere.'

The beliefs of the philosophers who lived during the time of Aristotle and Plato were based, not on knowledge gained from observation or experiment, but on personal views thought to be appropriate to particular beliefs. The Earth and the universe, they thought, were modelled on the most perfect of geometrical forms. According to Aristotle, the sphere of the Earth was surrounded by a series of concentric spheres. Above the four innermost spheres of water, earth, air and fire, were the spheres of the five ancient planets: Moon, Mercury, Venus, Mars and Jupiter; and beyond these was the sphere of the stars.

Aristotle mentioned in his writings that the Earth's circumference 'as determined by the mathematicians' was 400,000 stadia, the stadium being a unit of which there were many varieties. As the particular stadium mentioned by Aristotle is not defined by him, it cannot be known how near to, or wide of, the truth is Aristotle's measure of the Earth's circumference.

Eratosthenes (c. 276–c. 195 BC), one of the most learned men of antiquity, is credited with making the first scientific attempt at measuring the Earth's circumference. The simple method employed by Eratosthenes is essentially the same as has been used for the same purpose in more recent times. To understand the method requires some knowledge of the motions of the Earth and the concepts of latitude and longitude.

It is recorded that one of the followers of Pythagoras propounded the idea, as far back as the 5th century BC, that the spherical Earth rotates about one of its diameters. Moreover Pythagoras himself suggested that the Earth revolves around the Sun. But, as we have noted, Aristotle and Plato regarded the Earth as being fixed at the centre of a series of concentric spheres. Their word on the matter being regarded as final, no one would argue against the views of these princes of philosophy. And so it was that the notions that the Earth rotates about a diameter and revolves around the Sun were renounced, and the cause of science was set back for many centuries until Copernicus revived the ideas in the 16th century of our present era.

3. The Earth as a rotating sphere; latitude and longitude

We now know that the Earth rotates: she spins slowly and uniformly about her polar axis. One manifestation of this real motion is the apparent diurnal movements of the heavenly bodies.

In general, during the course of a day, every celestial object rises out of the eastern half of the horizon of any terrestrial observer; crosses the north–south vertical plane, at which instant it is said to *culminate*; after which its altitude decreases until it sinks below the observer's horizon in the western half of the sky.

Our fundamental ideas of horizontal direction are related to the spin of the Earth. Every point on the Earth's surface is continually being carried in a direction called *east*. The horizontal direction opposite to, or 180° from, east is *west*. The directions *north* and *south* are 90° to the left and right respectively of east. The natural compass of an observer located on the Earth is his celestial horizon—the circle on the celestial sphere which divides the heavens into the *visible* and *invisible hemispheres*.

The celestial horizon of an observer—unless he be located at either of the Earth's poles, in which event his horizon would lie in the plane of the Earth's spin—swings around the celestial sphere towards the east. It appears, of course, that the Earth is stationary and that the heavens revolve around the Earth towards the west; and it is not, therefore, difficult to appreciate the ideas of ancient people who regarded the Earth as being fixed at the centre of the universe.

The axis of the apparent daily revolution of the celestial sphere is coincident with the axis of the real rotation of the Earth.

The stars are so far distant from the Earth that their real motions are not readily observable. They are, therefore, said to be *fixed*; and their positions on the celestial sphere relative to one another remain constant for long periods of time. The stars, and indeed all other celestial bodies including the Sun, Moon and planets, are often regarded as lying on the inside of a vast sphere known as the *celestial concave* or *celestial sphere*. The radius of the celestial sphere is considered to be infinite, and the Earth is usually regarded as occupying its central position.

A circle on the Earth's surface that lies in the plane of the Earth's spin is known as the *equator*. This divides the Earth into the *northern* and *southern hemispheres*. The two points on the Earth's surface that are located 90° from every point on the equator are known as the *Earth's poles*: the *North Pole* in the northern hemisphere and the *South Pole* in the southern.

The Earth's North and South Poles lie at the extremities of the Earth's axis of rotation.

Semicircles which lie on the Earth's surface and which extend between the Earth's North and South Poles, cross the equator at an angle of 90°. These semicircles are known as *meridians*.

Circles on the Earth which are parallel to the equator are known as *parallels of latitude*.

To define a terrestrial position we state which parallel of latitude and which meridian locate the position. These circles are described by two angles known respectively as *latitude* and *longitude*.

Treating the Earth as a sphere, the latitude of a place is the angle at the Earth's centre measured in the plane of the meridian of the place between the radii which terminate at the place and the equator respectively.

All places on the Earth's surface having the same latitude in either the northern or southern hemisphere, lie on the same parallel of latitude. Thus the latitude of a place defines the parallel of latitude on which the place lies.

The plane of reference from which latitudes are measured is that of the equator, which is the datum parallel of zero latitude. The latitude of either pole is 90°. Latitudes of points on the Earth's surface are named north or south according to the hemisphere in which the points lie.

The longitude of a terrestrial position defines the meridian on which the position lies. The meridian from which longitudes are measured is known as the *prime meridian*. The confusion that arose from having many prime meridians was ended in 1889, when the members of an international conference held in New York decided that the meridian in whose plane the transit instrument at the Royal Greenwich Observatory at Greenwich rested, should be adopted universally as the prime meridian. The prime meridian is sometimes called the *Greenwich meridian* or *zero meridian.*

The word meridian is derived from the fact that when the Sun, in his apparent diurnal journey around the Earth, crosses the vertical plane of the meridian of a place, the local time at the place is midday or noon. At noon the Sun is said to *culminate* or *transit*; and at this instant of time, his altitude during each and every day is greatest.

The prime meridian and the antipodal or 180th meridian, divide the Earth into two hemispheres; known respectively as the *eastern* and *western hemispheres.* All places on the Earth's surface which lie east of the prime meridian and west of the 180th meridian are in the eastern hemisphere. All places on the Earth which lie west of the prime meridian and east of the 180th meridian are in the western hemisphere.

All places in the eastern hemisphere have *east* longitude, and all places in the western hemisphere have *west* longitude. The *longitude* of a terrestrial position is the smaller angle contained between the planes of the meridians of Greenwich and the position itself. It is the smaller angle at either of the Earth's poles, or the smaller arc of the equator, between the prime meridian and

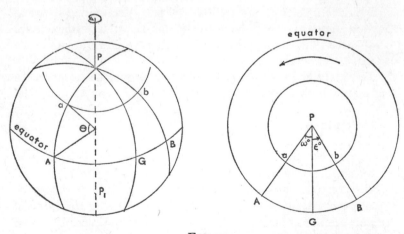

2   FIG. 1

the meridian of the place, named east or west according to the hemisphere in which the place is located.

Fig. 1 illustrates the Earth. P and P_1 are the North and South Poles respectively, and the circle through A, G and B, is the equator. The circle through a and b is a parallel of latitude, and the latitude of every point on this parallel is $\theta°$. PG is the Greenwich meridian, and the longitudes of b and a are $\epsilon°$E., and $\omega°$W., respectively.

4. *The celestial sphere; principal arcs, angles and circles*

An observer located at either of the Earth's poles would see the heavenly bodies that are visible to him describe their apparent daily motions along paths which are parallel to his horizon. Each star, during the course of a day (which is the time taken for the Earth to make one rotation), describes an apparent path around the Earth, which is known as the star's *diurnal circle*. The diurnal circles of all stars are parallel to the horizon of an observer located at either pole. All stars, therefore, at either of these terrestrial positions, maintain constant altitudes.

The *altitude* of a celestial body is the angle at the centre of the celestial sphere contained between two radii, one terminating at the body and the other at the point on the observer's horizon vertically beneath the body. Alternatively, the altitude of a body is the arc of a celestial great circle (cf. p. 33) contained between the body and the horizon vertically below it. Celestial circles which cross the celestial horizon of an observer at right angles are called *vertical circles*. All vertical circles terminate at a point on the celestial sphere which lies vertically above the observer—a point known as the observer's *zenith*. A point on the celestial sphere diametrically opposite to an observer's zenith is called the observer's *nadir*.

The complement of the altitude of a celestial body, that is to say, the angular difference between the altitude and 90°, is a measure of the angular distance between the body and the observer's zenith—an arc referred to as the *zenith distance* of the body.

Circles on the celestial sphere that are parallel to the celestial horizon are known as *parallels of altitude*. All points on a given parallel of altitude have the same altitude.

One method of defining a celestial position, known as the *horizon system*, is to describe the parallel of altitude and the vertical circle on which the position is located. These are described by stating two angles: the altitude to describe the parallel of altitude, and an angle known as *azimuth* or *bearing*, to describe the vertical circle.

The *azimuth* of a heavenly body is the smaller angle at the observer's zenith, or the smaller arc of the observer's celestial horizon, contained between the vertical circles through the elevated celestial pole and the heavenly body respectively.

The vertical circles which link the east and west points of an observer's horizon form a semicircle known as the *prime vertical circle*. Every point on the prime vertical circle which lies between the observer's zenith and the east point of his horizon, has an azimuth of 090°. The azimuth of any point on the remaining half is 270°.

Fig. 2 illustrates the horizon system of defining a celestial position, the coordinates being altitude and azimuth.

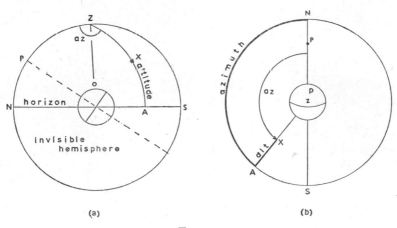

(a)   (b)

FIG. 2

Diagram (a) of Fig. 2 is a projection of the celestial concave on to the plane of an observer's meridian The observer's zenith is at Z and his celestial horizon is NAS. P is the celestial pole and X is a star or other celestial body whose altitude and azimuth are arcs

AX and NA respectively. Diagram (b) of Fig. 2 is a projection of the celestial sphere for the same observer and star on to the plane of the observer's horizon.

To an observer located at any point on the equator, the diurnal circles of all stars are perpendicular to the observer's horizon, because the horizon will appear to revolve westwards around the observer about a diameter along which the earth's spin axis lies. This is evident from Fig. 3.

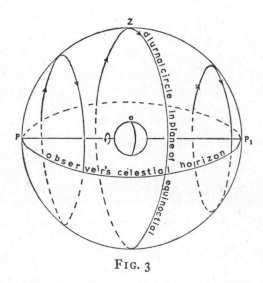

FIG. 3

At the equator, all celestial bodies rise out of and set into the horizon of an observer vertically. It follows that the altitudes and azimuths of all celestial bodies continually change to any observer located on the equator. To an observer at either pole of the Earth, the altitudes of the visible heavenly bodies will remain constant, but their azimuths will change at the rate of 360° per day at a constant angular rate of 15° per hour.

A circle on the celestial sphere which is co-planar with the equator is known as the *celestial equator* or, more generally, as the *equinoctial*.

The two points on the celestial sphere which are the positions of the Earth's north and south poles projected on to the celestial sphere from the Earth's centre, are the extremities of the axis of the celestial sphere about which the celestial bodies describe their diurnal motions. These points are known as the *north* and *south celestial poles.*

Semicircles on the celestial sphere which terminate at the celestial poles cross the equinoctial at an angle of 90°: these semicircles are known as *celestial meridians.*

Circles on the celestial sphere which are parallel to the equinoctial are known as *parallels of declination.*

Celestial meridians and parallels of declination correspond to terrestrial meridians and parallels of latitude; and, just as a terrestrial position is defined by stating the particular meridian and parallel of latitude on which the position lies, so a celestial position may be defined by stating which celestial meridian and which parallel of declination pass through the position. The two circles are defined by stating two angles known respectively as *right ascension* and *declination.*

The right ascension (R.A.) of a celestial point is the angle at either celestial pole, or the arc of the equinoctial, contained between the celestial meridian on which lies a point known as the *First Point of Aries* (♈) and the celestial meridian on which the point lies. R.A. is always measured eastwards from the celestial meridian of the First Point of Aries.

The declination of a celestial point is the angle at the centre of

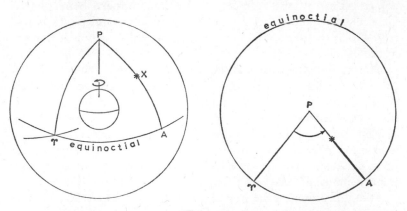

FIG. 4

the celestial sphere contained between the radii terminating at the celestial point and the point on the equinoctial nearest to the point. It is the smaller arc of a celestial meridian contained between the celestial point and the equinoctial. The declination of a celestial position is named north or south according to whether the position lies in the northern or southern celestial hemisphere respectively. The declination of any point lying on the equinoctial is 0°; and that of the celestial pole is 90°.

The declination and R.A. of a celestial body define the body's position in terms of a system of coordinates known as the *equinoctial system*. Fig. 4 illustrates the equinoctial system of defining celestial positions.

5. *Finding latitude by star observation*

The principle of finding a terrestrial position by astronomical means is related to the connection between the position, at a given instant of time, of a celestial body which is observed for the purpose, using the horizon system of coordinates (altitude and azimuth), and the equinoctial system of coordinates (declination and right ascension). We shall deal with this more fully in Chapter Five.

To an observer located at any position on the Earth's northern hemisphere, the north celestial pole will lie above his horizon, and the south celestial pole will lie below it. The reverse will be the case for any observer located on the southern hemisphere. The celestial pole that lies within the visible hemisphere is referred to as the *elevated pole*; and the other celestial pole is known as the *depressed pole*.

The angle at the centre of the celestial sphere, or the arc of the celestial meridian, contained between a celestial body and the elevated pole is known as the *polar distance* of the body. The polar distance of a celestial body is 90° ± declination of the body. If the elevated pole and the body's declination have the same name, that is to say if they are both north or both south, the polar distance is 90° − declination of the body. If the names are different, the polar distance of the body is 90° + declination of the body.

At any position on the Earth, other than either of the poles or any point on the equator, the diurnal circles of the heavenly bodies are oblique to the horizon. This may readily be seen from Fig. 5.

From Fig. 5 it is evident that the angle θ at which the diurnal circles cross the horizon of an observer O, is equal to the complement of the observer's latitude. At latitude 90° the angle is 0°; whereas at any point on the equator, where the horizon of an observer bisects all diurnal circles, the angle is 90°.

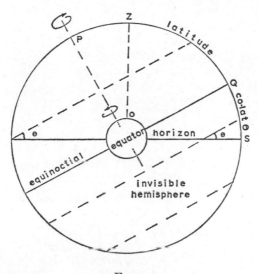

F IG. 5

It follows from the foregoing remarks that the greatest daily altitude of any celestial object—an angle known as the *meridian altitude*, for it is attained when the object culminates at meridian passage—depends upon the observer's latitude and the object's declination. If the declination of a celestial object at the time of its meridian transit is known, and the meridian altitude is measured, the latitude of the observer may readily be found.

Fig. 6 represents the celestial sphere drawn on the plane of the meridian of an observer O. The small circle represents the Earth and the large circle represents the celestial concave. p is the Earth's North Pole and P is the elevated celestial pole. Z is the observer's zenith, and N and S are the north and south points of the observer's celestial horizon. Q is a point on the equinoctial which lies on the observer's celestial meridian; and X_1, X_2 and X_3, are three celestial objects at meridian passage.

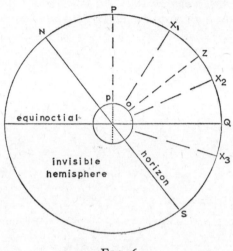

.FIG. 6

Meridian altitude of X_1 = arc NX_1 north
$\qquad X_2$ = arc SX_2 south
$\qquad X_3$ = arc SX_3 south

Declination of $\qquad X_1$ = arc QX_1 north
$\qquad X_2$ = arc QX_2 north
$\qquad X_3$ = arc QX_3 south

Latitude of observer = arc QZ north
$\qquad\qquad\qquad$ = arc NP north

Considering X_1: $\qquad QZ = QX_1 - ZX_1$
$\qquad\qquad\qquad = QX_1 - (90 - NX_1)$
$\qquad\qquad\qquad = $ Dec. $X_1 - $ Mer. Zen. Dist. X_1

Considering X_2: $\qquad QZ = QX_2 + ZX_2$
$\qquad\qquad\qquad = QX_2 + (90 - SX_2)$
$\qquad\qquad\qquad = $ Dec. $X_2 + $ Mer. Zen. Dist. X_2

Considering X_3: $\quad\quad QZ = ZX_3 - QX_3$
$$= (90 - SX_3) - QX_3$$
$$= \text{Mer. Zen. Dist. } X_3 - \text{Dec. } X_3$$

In general:
    Latitude of observer
        = Dec. star on meridian $\pm$ Mer. Zen. Dist. of star

An observer travelling due east or due west over the Earth's surface along any parallel of latitude, would observe that the greatest altitude attained by any fixed star would remain constant night after night. An observer travelling due north or due south along any meridian, would observe that the greatest altitude attained by any particular fixed star would change night after night.

As we have seen, to an observer located at either pole of the Earth, the diurnal circles of all stars and other celestial bodies whose declinations have the same name as the latitude of the observer, will be parallel to the horizon and will lie within the visible hemisphere. Their altitudes will remain constant and will be equal to their respective declinations.

Celestial objects whose diurnal circles are wholly above the horizon of an observer, are known as *circumpolar objects*. At either pole all visible stars and other celestial bodies are circumpolar; but at the equator, no stars are circumpolar because the planes of all diurnal circles cut the horizon at 90°. At any intermediate latitude some celestial objects are circumpolar, the number increasing as the angle of latitude increases.

Fig. 7 illustrates the celestial sphere. Diagram (a) is drawn on the plane of the meridian of an observer at o, and diagram (b) is drawn on the plane of the observer's celestial horizon. N, E, S and W are the north, east, south and west points of the observer's horizon, and Z is his zenith. Q is a point on the equinoctial where this circle crosses the observer's celestial meridian, and P is the elevated pole.

NBC represents the diurnal circle of a star which grazes the north point of the horizon of the observer. The polar distance of this star is equal to the observer's latitude. The declination of the star is equivalent to arc QC; and it should be clear from the diagrams that all stars which have northerly declinations exceeding arc QC are circumpolar. For a star to be circumpolar the names of the declination of the star and the latitude of the observer must be the same, and the declination of the star must be such that its polar distance is less than the latitude of the observer.

That part of the celestial meridian of an observer which extends from the elevated pole and which crosses the observer's horizon vertically below the elevated pole is known as the observer's *inferior* or *lower celestial meridian*. The part which extends from the elevated pole and which passes through the observer's zenith, is known as the observer's *superior* or *upper celestial meridian*.

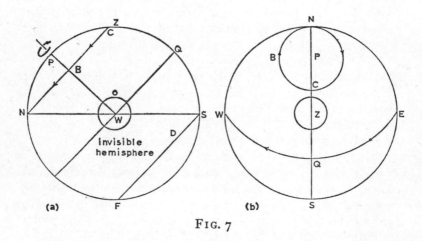

Fig. 7

When a heavenly body is on the *upper celestial meridian* of an observer it is said to be at *superior* or *upper transit*; and when it is on the observer's *lower* or *inferior meridian* it is said to be at *inferior* or *lower transit*.

Circumpolar bodies are above the horizon at both superior and inferior transits. When a circumpolar body is at lower meridian passage, its altitude is less than that of the elevated pole. For this reason when a circumpolar body is at lower transit it is said to be on the meridian *below the pole*. Similarly, when a heavenly body which is circumpolar is on the upper meridian of an observer it is said to be on the meridian *above the pole*.

Stars whose declinations have a different name from that of the latitude of the observer, and which have values exceeding the complement of the observer's latitude, never rise above the observer's horizon. Referring to Fig. 7, all stars whose declinations exceed arc QS never rise above the horizon of the observer at O.

If a star is visible at both upper and lower transits, a stationary observer may ascertain his latitude readily, even if the declination of the star is not known, and if the altitudes at upper and lower transits are measured. All diurnal circles are centred at the celestial pole, so that the mean of the upper and lower meridian altitudes of a circumpolar star is equal to the altitude of the celestial pole, which is equal to the latitude of the observer.

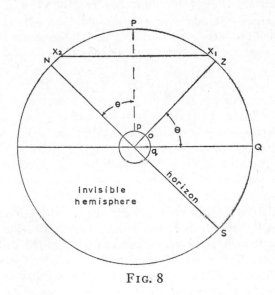

FIG. 8

Referring to Fig. 8,

Latitude of observer O = arc oq = arc QZ

Now   PQ = NZ = 90°

and   ZQ + PZ = 90°

Therefore   ZQ = NP

But   NP = Altitude of pole

Therefore:

Latitude of observer = Altitude of pole.

If X_1 and X_2 are the positions of a circumpolar star when at upper and lower transits respectively, then $(NX_1 + NX_2)/2 = NP$, that is:

Mean of altitudes at lower and upper transits

= Altitude of celestial pole
= Latitude of observer

It follows, therefore, that the altitude of a star which is located at the elevated celestial pole is equal to the latitude of an observer. No star exists at either of the celestial poles; but a bright second-magnitude star—α Ursae Minoris—does lie near to the north celestial pole. This star is named Polaris. Its declination is about 88° 45′, so that its angular distance from the celestial pole is about 1° 15′.

When Polaris is at upper meridian passage its altitude is equal to (lat. of observer + polar dist.). When it is at lower meridian passage its altitude is equal to (lat. of observer − polar dist.). In other words the altitude of Polaris at any time is within about $1\frac{1}{4}°$ of the latitude of the observer.

Because of the proximity of Polaris to the north celestial pole, and because of the phenomenon known as precession of the equinoxes (p. 105), the declination and right ascension of Polaris undergo relatively rapid changes. However, within recent historical time, Polaris has been sufficiently near to the north celestial pole for it to have been regarded as lying at the hub of the celestial sphere. It has, therefore, provided northern seamen with the simple means of finding latitude and direction within close limits of accuracy. Pole star tables, which furnish the necessary correction to apply to the altitude of Polaris to obtain the latitude of an observer, have formed part of the navigational equipment of seamen since the days of the great discoveries initiated by the Portuguese navigators of the 14th century.

6. *Measuring the Earth's circumference: attempts in the Ancient World*

To ascertain the size of the Earth from astronomical observations, the meridian altitudes of a fixed star at two places lying on the same meridian are measured. The difference between the zenith distances or meridian altitudes is equal to the angle at the spherical Earth's centre contained between radii terminating at the two places at which the observations were made. If the distance between the two places is known, the measure of the Earth's circumference can be found by simple proportion. This principle is illustrated in Fig. 9.

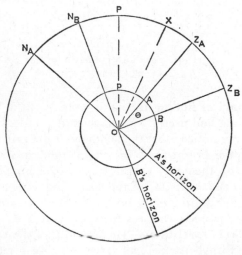

FIG. 9

In Fig. 9, A and B are two observers located on the same meridian. O is the centre of the Earth and p the Earth's North Pole. P is the elevated celestial pole and Z_A and Z_B are the zeniths of A and B respectively; and N_A and N_B are the north points of their respective horizons. X is a star at meridian passage, whose altitude is measured at A and B.

$$\text{Mer. Alt. of X at A} = N_A X$$
$$\text{Mer. Alt. of X at B} = N_B X$$

$$\text{Zen. Dist. of X at A} = Z_A X$$
$$\text{Zen. Dist. of X at B} = Z_B X$$

Diff. between Mer. Alts. at A and B

$$= \text{Diff. between Zen. Dists. at A and B}$$
$$= N_A N_B$$
$$= Z_A Z_B$$

now, $Z_A Z_B = AOB = \theta$

If θ is found and the arc length AB is measured, then the circumference c of the Earth is readily found, for:

$$\frac{c}{360} = \frac{\text{Arc AB}}{\theta}$$

whence, $c = \frac{360 \times \text{arc AB}}{\theta°}$

This method of finding the size of the Earth is basically the same as the method used by Eratosthenes.

Eratosthenes noticed that the noonday Sun was in the zenith of Syene in Upper Egypt (now the site of modern Aswan) on the longest day of the year, at which time the buildings cast no shadows. On the same day of the year—the day of the summer solstice—at Alexandria, to the north, the Sun's greatest altitude—his meridian altitude—was less than 90°, and at noon the buildings, therefore, cast shadows. He argued that the rays from the very remote Sun, being parallel at the two places, meant that the zenith distance of the Sun at Alexandria on the longest day of the year, was equal to the angle at the spherical Earth's centre contained between the two radii terminating at the two places. The ratio between the arc distance between Alexandria and Syene, and the circumference of the spherical Earth, is equal to the ratio between the Sun's meridian zenith distance in degrees at Alexandria at the time of the summer solstice, and 360. This argument is not quite sound as Alexandria and Syene are not on the same meridian, although the difference of longitude between them is small. The distance between Alexandria and Syene was estimated and the Earth's circumference was found scientifically for the first time.

Fig. 10 illustrates the method used by Eratosthenes to ascertain the length of the circumference of the Earth. In the small triangle

ABC, AB represents a vertical building at Alexandria and AC represents the length of its shadow at noon on the day of the summer solstice when the Sun's declination is $23\frac{1}{2}°$N. Knowing the lengths AB and AC, the angle θ may be computed. This angle is equal to the angle at the Earth's centre O, between the radii terminating at Alexandria and Syene. If the distance between Alexandria and Syene is d, and the length of the Earth's circumference is c, then, $c/d = 360/\theta°$ and $c = (d \times 360)/\theta°$.

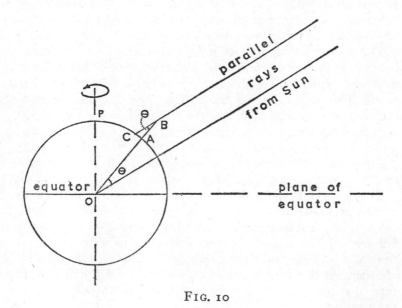

FIG. 10

The result of the attempt of Eratosthenes at finding the length of the Earth's circumference, although approximating to the truth, was reached by relatively crude methods. According to Eratosthenes the length of the Earth's circumference is 250,000 stadia. The unit used for most of the earliest estimates of the Earth's size, viz., the stadium, was, as we have noted, by no means a standard unit; and, as with most other ancient measures, we cannot be sure which particular stadium was used by Eratosthenes.

Another classical attempt at measuring the Earth's dimension was made by Posidonius at about the beginning of the Christian era. Posidonius used the bright star Canopus for his attempt. Canopus, whose declination is about 53°S, was just visible at lower passage at Rhodes, which lies in latitude 36°N., it being just circumpolar. At Alexandria, to the south of Rhodes, Canopus has a meridian altitude of several degrees. The difference between the meridian altitudes of Canopus at the two places, together with an estimate of the distance between Rhodes and Alexandria, which were believed to lie under the same meridian, enabled Posidonius to estimate the size of the Earth. The result of the attempt of Posidonius was not materially different from that of Eratosthenes which had been made two centuries earlier.

The earliest attempts at estimating the compass of the Earth were crude by modern standards. Accordingly there was no great measure of agreement amongst geographers and philosophers as to the true dimension of the Earth. The famous Claudius Ptolemy, who flourished during the 2nd century AD, and who is renowned for basing the science of geography on that of astronomy, and for explaining the mathematical principles of mapmaking, assumed the circumference of the Earth to be 180,000 stadia—a measure much too short of the true value.

The great Greco–Egyptian culture, which was centred at Alexandria, came to an end during the middle part of the 7th century AD, when the great centre of learning was overrun by the followers of Mohammed. Its famous library, with its enormous store of knowledge, was almost completely destroyed at the hands of Islam. At this period in human history, the Christian world entered an age from which it did not emerge for three quarters of a millennium.

At the beginning of the 9th century AD, the surviving works of Aristotle and other Greek scholars and philosophers were translated into Arabic; and the lamp of learning, having been rekindled by the Arabs, was to illuminate the world of Islam during the period of European history known as the Dark Ages.

There is an interesting record of an attempt to measure the length of the Earth's circumference in the year AD 814 under the order of the Caliph Abdullah al Mamun. From a point in the plains of Mesopotamia—believed to have been on the plain of Shinar on which the families of the sons of Noah built the tower of Babel—parties of astronomers were sent northwards and southwards each measuring its progress by means of measuring rods, to positions at which the altitudes of the Pole star differed by exactly one degree from its altitude at the point of departure. From the observations the length of a two-degree arc of the meridian was found and the length of the Earth's circumference thereby determined.

During the Dark Ages the belief that the Earth was spherical was considered to be unscriptural and, therefore, heretical. During the early Middle Ages scientific doctrines were regarded as being unnecessary. As a consequence, scientific thought and effort were not encouraged. The maps of the period, which were doubtless in great demand by religious pilgrims, were predominantly Christian in concept. The T and O world maps, typical of the period, were probably Greek in origin. Such a map is circular, the area portrayed being divided into three by the arms of a letter T. Jerusalem is plotted at the centre of the map to conform with the idea expressed in verse v of the 5th chapter of the Book of the prophet Ezekiel. The three arms of the T represented the Mediterranean Sea, the River Nile and the River Don. East is placed at the top of the map, and the three land areas, into which the circle is divided, formed the three known continents— Europe, Asia and Africa. Fig. 11 illustrates diagrammatically a typical T and O map.

In the eyes of a prospective Christian pilgrim, especially one who was to voyage by sea from North-west Europe to the Holy Land, the T and O map seemed fine. All one had to do was to sail southwards to the Pillars of Hercules at the western entrance to the Mediterranean Sea, and then due east to the Holy Land located at the centre of the world. Having embarked on his pilgrimage, the crusader was quickly disillusioned: he was soon to discover that the simplicity of the map was quite false and misleading. The need arose for more accurate sea charts on which coastlines, islands and navigational dangers, were portrayed accurately.

Improvements in mapping during early times followed closely on the heels of improvements in astronomy and geography. The fixing of terrestrial positions can be done satisfactorily only by astronomical methods. This was recognized by the great Hipparchus, the most famous of the astronomers of antiquity and the inventor of both plane and spherical trigonometry.

Hipparchus, who flourished during the 2nd century BC, demanded that positions of places to be mapped be verified astronomically. He suggested that lines of latitude depicted on the map should be equidistantly spaced, and that lines of longitude should likewise be regulated, preferably by observations of eclipses. Hipparchus, who rejected the map of Eratosthenes because, he claimed, much of it was based on conjecture rather than on observed facts, devised an excellent star catalogue, and also a map of the heavens, but he never attempted to produce a map of the

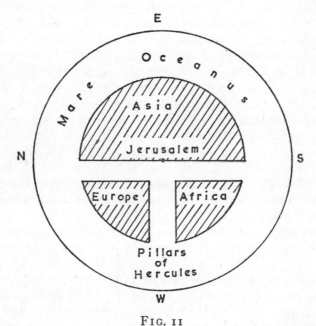

FIG. 11

Earth. This is not surprising in view of his stated ideas on the subject: many centuries were to elapse before the positions of a sufficiently large number of places had been determined astronomically, so making it possible to construct an accurate world map.

7. Modern attempts to measure the Earth's circumference. The establishment of the nautical mile

Following the attempt at measuring the length of an arc of the

Earth's surface made by Al Mamun in the 9th century AD, for a long period of six or seven centuries the problem appears to have attracted little or no attention.

At the beginning of the 16th century a French surveyor named Fernel measured the length of an arc of a meridian near Paris, by counting the revolutions of the wheel of a carriage, an early illustration of the principle of the surveyor's measuring wheel or perambulator.

An important attempt to determine the length of a degree of a meridian was made by the Dutch philosopher Willebrord Snell in 1619. The attempt of Snellius' is noteworthy as it marks the first use of the surveyor's method of triangulation, in which a chain of triangles is substituted for linear measurement. Snellius measured, with great accuracy, the length of a base line on the flat meadows near Leiden, and his chain of triangles extended from Alkmaar to Bergen-op-Zoom.

Another noteworthy measurement of an arc of a meridian was that made by our countryman Richard Norwood. Norwood spent his early life at sea, and later set himself up in London as a teacher of navigation and a surveyor. He found the latitude of a point in London with a high degree of accuracy using a quadrant of many feet radius. Two years later, in 1635, he determined the latitude of a point in York in the same way. On his return journey to London, he measured the distance by chaining, perambulating or pacing, making allowances for all the twistings of the way, and the changes of slope along the route. With a knowledge of the latitudes of London and York (which lie almost on the same meridian), and the distance between them, Norwood found the number of feet in a minute of arc of the meridian between York and London to be 6,120. This figure compared favourably with the result of Snellius' measurement made some two decades earlier.

Norwood published, in 1637, his results in a book entitled *The Seaman's Practice, containing a Fundamental Probleme in Navigation, experimentally verified, namely, touching the Compasse of the Earth and Sea, and the Quantity of a Degree in oure English Measures.*

The fundamental problem referred to in the title of Norwood's book related to the length of a nautical mile and the marking of the log-line used for measuring the rate of progress of a ship through the water. The nautical mile as distinct from the land mile, and which we shall describe presently, may be considered to have been introduced by Richard Norwood.

The unit of distance—the mile—used ashore, was derived from the Roman mile, a unit of 1,000 Roman paces, the word mile coming from the Latin *mille* meaning thousand. The mile was an arbitrary measure, and was not related to the size of the Earth. The statute- or land-mile used in Great Britain is a unit of 5,280 feet, the foot being one third of the arbitrary unit of length known as the yard. The nautical mile is a unit of distance related intimately to the size of the Earth.

Treating the Earth as a sphere, the nautical mile is equivalent to the length of a minute of arc of the Earth's surface. That is to say, an arc of the Earth's surface subtended by an angle of one degree at the Earth's centre, contains 60 nautical miles. Such a unit of distance for navigational purposes has an obvious advantage over an arbitrary unit of length such as the land mile. How confusing it must have been for the navigators who lived at the time of the early ocean voyaging when the unit of distance was unrelated to angular measure of an arc of the Earth's surface. An interesting account of the 'whole quantity of the Earth' appears in the famous work by Edward Wright published at the end of the 16th century and entitled *Certaine Errors in Navigation Detected and Corrected*.

'And albeit the Globe of the earth and water, compared with the sphaeres of the starres, is as it were a centre or prick; yet being considered by itself, it conteineth in the greatest circle 6300 common Spanish leagues. Which a man may easilie perceive by taking two such points or headlands of the earth, as are under the same meridian and which differ in distance one from another so much as one of those parts is, whereof the compasse of the whole world conteineth 360; and it is found both by navigation at sea, and also by travel on land, that the two foresaid points are distant each from other 17 leagues and ½: of which leagues, each one conteineth 4000 pases, each pase 5 foote, every foote 16 fingers and every finger 4 graines of barley.'

The figure for a one-degree arc of the Earth's surface adopted by Claudius Ptolemy, the last of the great astronomers of antiquity, and who flourished during the 2nd century of the Christian era, was 30,000. This gave 5,000 feet per minute of arc. Ptolemy used the equivalent of this figure in his monumental *Geographia*, a work first published in AD 150 in which the author laid down the foundations of modern geography and cartography.

Ptolemy's *Geographia*—a work in eight parts—contains detailed notes on mathematical geography and the problems related to projecting the spherical Earth's surface on to a plane surface, and also a comprehensive list of positions of numerous places, by means of which maps could be constructed. Ptolemy ranks as one of the princes of ancient geography.

The invention of the printing press in the 15th century, coming at a time when western Europe was aflame with the idea of exploration, led to the printing of several editions of *Geographia*, not only in the Latin, but also in the vulgar tongues of Europe, notably German, French and English.

Ptolemy's figure of 5,000 feet per minute of arc gave 69 land-miles per degree of arc of the Earth's surface. This figure was adopted by seamen as a basis for marking their log-lines. Using a 30-second glass, the distance between the knotted cords on the log-line was reckoned to be $41\frac{2}{3}$ feet: this distance in 30 seconds being equivalent to 5,000 feet per hour.

The common log used for measuring a ship's speed through the water is sometimes thought to have been invented by Humphrey Cole, an instrument-maker of the 'mint in the tower', who flourished c. 1570–1580. An early—probably the first—written account of the common log appeared in *Inventions and Devises very necessaries for all Generalles and Captaines or Leaders of Men, as wel by Sea as by Land*, published by its author William Bourne in 1574.

The common log did not come into general use until the middle of the 17th century, and was not entirely replaced by the mechanical or *patent log*—as it is called—until the beginning of the present century. The outfit consisted of a log-ship, -reel, -line and -glass.

The log-ship was a flat piece of wood in the form of a quadrant, and about 5 inches in radius and $\frac{1}{2}$ inch in thickness. The rounded edge of the log-ship was weighted with lead so that it just floated with its face in the vertical plane. At each of the three corners of the log-ship was a hole, by means of which the log-line was secured to it by a threelegged bridle or crowsfoot. The other end of the log-line was secured to the log-reel around which the log-line was wound. The log-line was divided into equal parts, the limits of which were marked by small lengths of knotted cords. The divisions commenced at a point about ten fathoms from the log-ship, this length forming the so-called stray line. The log-glass was merely a sand glass which ran out in a specified duration of time—the *long glass* running out in 30 seconds and the *short glass* in half this time. The long glass was used for slow speeds, and the short glass was used for speeds through the water of more than about five knots, in which case the number of knotted cords which ran out when the log was hove, was doubled in order to give the vessel's speed through the water.

The log-ship was hove from the weather quarter of the vessel and the glass was turned when the stray line had passed over the stern, after which the log-ship was reckoned to lie in still water abaft the wake or dead water which was dragged along by the vessel through frictional resistance. The number of knotted cords that ran overboard during the running time of the glass, was a measure of the ship's speed through the water in miles of 5,000 feet per hour or 'knots'.

The accurate division of the log-line into 'knots' presented a problem which was impossible of solution until an accurate determination of the dimension of the Earth's circumference and, accordingly, the length of a minute of the arc of the Earth's surface, had been made. Many writers on navigation had stressed the error in the division of the seaman's log-line, and it was in quest of the solution to this fundamental problem in navigation that Norwood and others carried out their measurements of the arc of a meridian.

An account of the measure of the arc of a meridian, made by the French philosopher Jean Picard, appeared in the *Philosophical Transactions of the Royal Society of London* for the year 1669. Picard applied the telescope to his surveying instruments, and measured the length of an arc of a meridian with an accuracy hitherto not possible. Picard concluded that one degree of the

Earth's surface contained 365,184 feet, a figure with which Norwood's value of 367,200 feet, compared favourably. It is interesting to note that Picard's measure of the size of the Earth was used by Newton in his calculations to prove that the gravitational attraction of the Earth on the Moon was largely responsible for the orbital motion of the Moon.

8. The figure of the Earth and the International Ellipsoid of Reference

In 1673, the French scientist Jean Richer, whilst in French Guiana investigating astronomical refraction on behalf of the Academy of Sciences of Paris, noticed that his pendulum clock, which had been regulated to beat seconds at Paris, lost about two and a half minutes per day. The fact that the length of a seconds pendulum varied with the latitude, discovered by Richer, was subsequently verified by pendulum observations in many parts of the world. The reason for this phenomenon was first given by the illustrious Sir Isaac Newton who, in his *Principia*, explained that the reduction in the Earth's force of gravity in approaching the equator is due to a protuberance of the Earth's mass in equatorial regions, and by a counteracting effect of centrifugal force (first explained by Huygens), due to the Earth's rotation.

Attention was now focused on the determination of the true shape of the Earth, and the expressive term '*figure of the Earth*' appears to date from this period. According to Newton the shape of the Earth is that of an oblate spheroid whose shortest diameter is the axis of the Earth's rotation.

An oblate spheroid is a solid produced by rotating an ellipse about its minor diameter. The Earth's shape, being that of an oblate spheroid, introduces a problem related to the nautical mile.

The modern definition of a nautical mile is that it is the length of an arc of a meridian the latitudes of the end points of which differ by one minute of arc. In other words it is the length of an arc of a meridian between two points at which the verticals make an angle of one minute with one another. That is to say, it is the length of an arc of a meridian subtended by an angle of one minute at the centre of curvature of the arc. The length of the

nautical mile is greatest where the curvature of the Earth's surface is least, that is at either pole. At the equator (where the
curvature is greatest) the length of the nautical mile is least.

$$\text{Length at equator} = 6,046 \text{ feet}$$
$$\text{Length at lat. } 90° = 6,108 \text{ feet}$$

A standard nautical mile of 6,080 feet is adopted in Great
Britain. This is derived from the arithmetic mean of the maximum and minimum lengths—which is 6,077 feet—rounded off to
6,080 feet.

The renowned Italian astronomers father and son J. and
D. Cassini, during the years between 1684 and 1710, carried out
a meridian survey extending through Paris to Dunkirk in the
north and Collioure in the south. They found from their observations that the length of a degree arc of the meridian increased
equatorwards. Accordingly they advanced the idea that the Earth
is a prolate and not an oblate spheroid. As a result of the controversy that arose between the so-called Earth-elongators and
the Earth-flatteners, the Academy of Sciences of Paris organized
expeditions to Peru and Lapland in order to measure arcs in high
and low latitudes so that a decisive test would settle the controversy as well as gain more knowledge of the true size and shape of
the Earth. The results of the observations which were made during the years between 1735 and 1743 by the members of these
expeditions were published by the philosopher Maupertuis.
They proved conclusively that the Earth's shape is that of an
oblate spheroid.

The figure of the Earth is expressed in terms of the equatorial
radius and the *compression* or *ellipticity*—this being the ratio
between the difference between the equatorial and polar radii,
and the equatorial radius itself. That is, if the lengths of the
equatorial and polar radii are a and b respectively, and the
ellipticity is c, then: $c = (a-b)/a$.

The geodesist, whose study is the science of surveying extended
to large areas of the Earth's surface, has in mind, not only the
production of accurate maps, but also the determination of the
figure of the Earth.

The geodesist is not concerned with heights of land and depths
of the sea bed: these are the concern of the topographer and

hydrographer. Heights and depths are referred to a surface which forms the figure of the Earth. This surface is that of the mean sea level over the sea, and a corresponding level surface under the land marking a boundary surface of an ellipsoid of rotation.

The actual irregular surface of the solid Earth is referred to as that of the *geoid*, a term meaning simply 'earth-shaped', and used so that any commitment in advance, of knowledge of the exact shape of the Earth, is avoided. The surface of the geoid is defined by heights above or depths below a particular *ellipsoid of reference*: that is to say a particular *figure of the Earth*.

The figure of the Earth derived by Delambre in 1806, from which the length of the metre (intended to be a ten-millionth part of a quadrant of a meridian extending from pole to equator) was determined, is 1/334. That computed by Airy the Astronomer Royal in 1830, and which was used as a basis for the Ordnance Survey of Great Britain is 1/299·3. The figure used by Everest in 1830 in the survey and mapping of the Indian subcontinent is 1/300·8. That of Bessel derived in 1841 is 1/299·3, this forming the basis of much continental mapping.

The Clarke spheroid of 1866 derived by the English geodesist Colonel A. R. Clarke, has an ellipticity of 1/295. Clarke investigated the problem by comparing numerous figures of the Earth, determined by meridian measurements, pendulum observations and astronomical methods. Clarke's figure was used as a basis for mapping North America. British Admiralty charts are constructed on the basis of a figure of the Earth known as the Clarke 1880 figure the ellipticity of which is 1/293·5.

The figure of the Earth considered to be most near to the truth is that of the *International Ellipsoid of Reference* which was formulated in 1924.

Equatorial radius of the International
Ellipsoid of Reference = 6,378,388 metres
Polar radius = 6,356,912 metres

$$e = \frac{1}{297}$$

The accuracy of the measure of the equatorial radius of the International Ellipsoid of Reference is considered to be within ± 50 metres, and that of the reciprocal of *e* to ± 0·5 units.

The topographical or relief features of the geoid may be shown on a model globe of the Earth, provided that the globe is sufficiently large. Represented accurately on a large model globe of 3 ft. 6 in. diameter, the relief features of the ocean basins and the continents would be confined within a layer no greater than 1/16 in. thick. Considered in this way the relief features are insignificant; yet were the Earth's surface perfectly smooth and her shape that of a perfect ellipsoid, the seas would cover the solid Earth to a depth of no less than 1,450 fathoms or nearly 2 miles.

Apart from its importance to map- and chart-makers, the figure of the Earth is of the highest importance to astronomers, inasmuch as the Earth's diameter is the unit to which all celestial distances are ultimately referred.

CHAPTER TWO

The Sphere and the Ellipsoid

1. *The sphere and formulae for its measurement*

For most purposes it is sufficiently accurate to suppose the Earth's form to be perfectly spherical. Her very small ellipticity of about 1/300 warrants this supposition. Nevertheless, for certain purposes of navigation and mapping, it is necessary to allow for the spheroidal shape of the Earth.

A sphere is a three-dimensional figure every point on the surface of which is the same distance from a fixed point called the centre of the sphere. If a circle is rotated about any of its diameters, it will trace out a sphere. Any such circle of rotation is the largest possible circle that may be described on the sphere's surface, and it is known as a *great circle*. The boundary edge of every plane section of a sphere is a circle. Circles of section of any sphere are divided into two types known respectively as *great circles* and *small circles*. A great circle is one on whose plane the centre of the sphere lies. Any other circle of the sphere is a small circle. The equator and all meridians are examples of terrestrial great circles; and the equinoctial, vertical circles, rational horizon and celestial meridians, are examples of great circles on the celestial concave. Examples of small circles on the Earth are parallels of latitude; and examples of celestial small circles are parallels of declination and parallels of altitude.

Every great circle of a sphere divides the sphere into two *hemispheres*. Any small circle divides a sphere into two *spherical segments*, the larger being the *major segment*, and the smaller, the *minor segment*.

If a straight line is rotated about one of its ends in any given plane, the line is said to describe a *plane angle*. The plane angle swept out by a line which describes a circle is divided into 360 equal parts each of which is known as a *degree*. Each degree (°) is divided into 60 *minutes of arc* ('), and each minute is divided into 60 *seconds of arc* (").

If three or more planes taken in order intersect with the next, in lines which meet at a point, a *solid angle* is formed. The point is called the *vertex* of the solid angle, and the lines of intersection of consecutive planes are known as the *edges* of the solid angle. The plane angles between consecutive edges are known as the *face angles* and the angles between consecutive planes are known as *dihedral angles*. In Fig. 1, the planes AOB, BOC and AOC, intersect to form a solid angle denoted by (O, ABC).

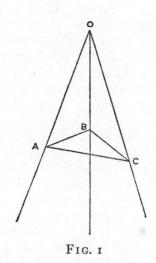

Fig. 1

The vertex of the solid angle illustrated in Fig. 1 is at O. A solid angle, such as the one illustrated in Fig. 1, which is formed by three intersecting planes is known as a *trihedral angle*.

If more than three planes intersect to form a solid angle, the angle is known as a *polyhedral angle*.

In a trihedral angle the sum of any two of the face angles is greater than the third. The proof of this proposition is as follows.

Referring to Fig. 2, let (O, ABC) be any trihedral angle and let BOC be the greatest of the three face angles BOC, AOB and AOC. If we consider a plane angle BOD in the plane BOC which is equal to the face angle BOA then, if OD is equal in length to

OA, it is a simple matter to prove that BA has the same length as BD, for the triangles OBA and BOD are congruent. In the triangle ABC, C lies on the straight line through B and D. (BA + AC) is greater than BC, for the sum of any two sides of a triangle is greater than the third. Thus,

BA + AC > BD + DC, but because BA = BD, therefore, AC > DC.

In the triangles AOC and DOC, AO = DO (given), OC = OC (common), AC > DC (proved); therefore,

AOC > DOC, and hence AOB + AOC > BOD + DOC, and AOB + AOC > BOC.

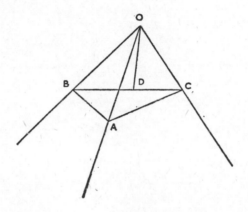

FIG. 2

Therefore the sum of any two face angles in a trihedral angle is greater than the third face angle.

The arc of a great circle is measured in angular units. The minor arc of a great circle between two given points on the surface of a sphere is known as the *spherical distance* between the two points. Since all great circles of a given sphere are equal, an arc of a great circle is described by stating the angle it subtends at the centre of the sphere. The spherical distance along a complete great circle is 360°. That along a semi-great circle is 180°, and the spherical distance along a quadrant of a great circle is 90°. Two points on any great circle which are diametrically opposed to one another, that is to say two points the spherical distance between which is 180°, are known as *antipodal points*, each being the *antipodes* of the other.

Two points on the surface of a sphere whose spherical distances from every point on a particular great circle are 90°, are known as the *poles* of the great circle. The diameter of the sphere connecting the poles of a great circle is known as the *axis* of the great circle.

Any great circle on which lies the poles of a given great circle

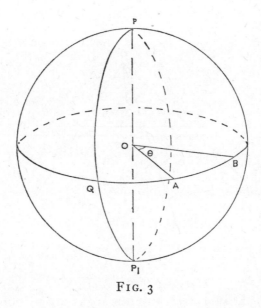

FIG. 3

is known as a *secondary great circle* in respect of the given great circle which is known as a *primary great circle*. Meridians on the Earth are secondary to the equator; and vertical circles on the celestial sphere are secondary to the celestial horizon of an observer, the equator and the horizon, in these cases, being primary great circles.

In Fig. 3, O is the centre of the sphere illustrated. A and B are two points lying on a great circle whose poles are at P and P_1; the axis of this great circle is the diameter PP_1. Arc PQ is a quadrant of a great circle which is secondary to the primary great circle of which arc AB forms a part. The angular measure, or spherical distance between A and B is $\theta°$ which is the angle between the radii AO and BO.

The planes of any two great circles must intersect along a diameter which forms a common axis of both great circles, for the points of intersection of any two great circles on the sphere's surface are antipodal points.

The angles at which great circles intersect on the sphere's surface are known as *spherical angles*. A spherical angle is measured by the plane angle between the tangents to the great circles at either point of intersection. The tangents of two great circles lie respectively in the planes of the great circles, and they are perpendicular to the line which forms the common axis of the two great circles. Therefore the angle between the tangents at a point of intersection is a measure of the dihedral angle between the planes of the two great circles.

The linear length of the circumference of any circle is a constant number of times the diameter of the circle. This constant number is an incommensurable quantity known as π (pi). Thus, if the diameter of a circle is $2R$, where R is the radius, the circumference is $2\pi R$. π is $3.1415926\ldots$ to seven places of decimals. It is often taken as $3\frac{1}{7}$ or 3.1428. This value is too great but is correct to two places of decimals. The value of π may readily be verified by direct measurement to an accuracy of two places of decimals.

The area of a circle is πr^2 where r is the radius. This may be proved by considering a circle as being the limiting case of a polygon.

The area A of a regular n-sided polygon such as the one illustrated in Fig. 4 and which is enclosed by the circle of radius R as illustrated, may be expressed as follows:

$$A = n \times \text{area AOB} = n \times \tfrac{1}{2}\text{AB} \times \text{DO}$$

$$= \frac{n}{2} \times \text{AB} \times \text{DO} = \tfrac{1}{2} \text{ perimeter of polygon} \times \text{DO}.$$

This is true regardless of the value of n. If n is increased infinitely, the polygon becomes a circle, of radius DO and perimeter $2\pi R$.

Thus:

Area of circle, $A = \frac{1}{2} \times 2\pi R \times R$
$= \pi R^2$, where R is the radius.

If a sphere is enveloped in a circumscribing cylinder, any two planes which are perpendicular to the axis of the cylinder, cut off belts of equal surface area from both sphere and cylinder. It follows from this that the surface area of a sphere is equal to the area of the curved part of a circumscribing cylinder which has the same external dimensions as those of the sphere.

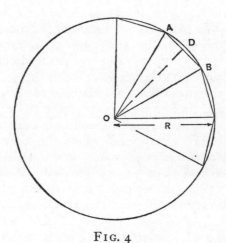

FIG. 4

If R is the radius of the sphere and the cylinder, and the height of the cylinder is equal to the diameter of the sphere, then:

Area of sphere $=$ Area of curved part of cylinder
$= 2R \times 2\pi R$
$= 4\pi R^2$

This is proved with reference to Fig. 5.
To prove:

Area of belt of sphere of thickness a

$=$ Area of belt of cylinder of thickness a
$= 2\pi R a.$

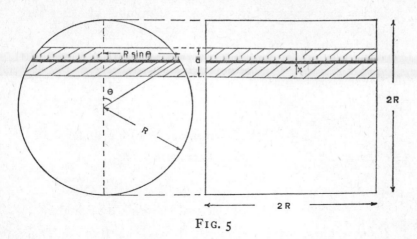

FIG. 5

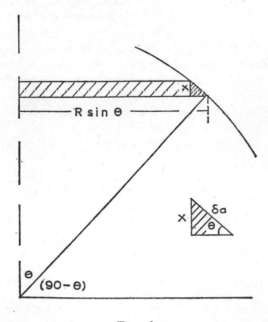

FIG. 6

4

Divide the belt of sphere into a large number of elementary belts of thickness x such as the one whose radius is $R \sin \theta$. Referring to Fig. 6,

Area of elementary belt on sphere

$= $ Circumference of small circle $\times \delta a$

$= 2\pi R \sin \theta \times x \cosec \theta$

$= 2\pi R \, x$

$= $ Area of elementary belt on cylinder

Area of belt of thickness a on sphere

$= 2\pi R \sum x$

$= 2\pi R \, a$

$= $ Area of belt of thickness a on cylinder

If the whole sphere is considered, then a is equal to $2R$. Thus:

Area of sphere $= 2\pi R \times 2R$

$= 4\pi R^2$

In other words, the surface area of a sphere is equal to four times the area of a circle which has the same radius as that of the sphere.

The expression for the volume of a sphere may be deduced by considering the surface of the sphere to be divided into an infinite number of small elements. In the limit, each of these elements has a plane surface and may be regarded as forming the base of a pyramid whose vertex is at the centre of the sphere, and whose vertical height is equal to the radius of the sphere. If the radius of the sphere is R and the base area of the elementary pyramid is a, then:

$$\text{Volume of elementary pyramid} = \frac{aR}{3}$$

Now the sum of the base areas of all the elementary pyramids is equal to the area A of the surface of the sphere, and the sum of their volumes is equal to the volume of the sphere. Thus:

$$\text{Volume of sphere} = \frac{A}{3}(R) = \frac{4\pi R^2}{3}(R) = \tfrac{4}{3}\pi R^3$$

That part of a sphere's surface which is cut off by two semi-great circles is known as a *lune*. The spherical angle between the two great circles is known as the *angle of the lune*. The whole surface of a sphere may be regarded as being a lune whose lunar angle is 360°. The areas of lunes of a sphere are clearly proportional to their lunar angles. Thus, if the lunar angle is θ° and the radius of the sphere is R:

$$\text{Area of lune} = \frac{\theta}{360} (4\pi R^2) = \frac{\theta}{90} \times \pi R^2$$

A triangle on the surface of a sphere, the sides of which are arcs of great circles, is a *spherical triangle*.

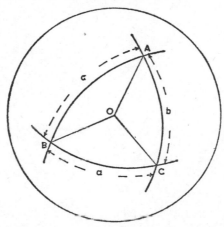

FIG. 7

Whereas the sum of the angles of a plane triangle is always 180°, the sum of the three spherical angles of a spherical triangle is always more than 180°. The maximum value of a spherical angle in a spherical triangle is 180°, so that the sum of the three angles must be less than 540°. The limiting case of a spherical triangle is a hemisphere, and the sum of the three spherical distances forming the three sides of a spherical triangle must be less than 360°.

It must be emphasized that a spherical triangle is formed by arcs of great circles only: arcs of small circles do not form the sides of spherical triangles.

Fig. 7 depicts a typical spherical triangle. If the corners of the spherical triangle ABC depicted in Fig. 7 are joined to the centre

O of the sphere, the three planes AOB, BOC and COA, form a trihedral angle at O. The sides a, b and c of the spherical triangle ABC may be considered as either spherical distances a, b and c respectively, or face angles COB, AOC and AOB respectively. Thus, the sides of a spherical triangle may be expressed in degrees. Moreover, the spherical angles A, B and C, have the same measures as the dihedral angles of the solid angle (O, ABC); and, as we have already proved (p. 35), the sum of any two face angles of a solid angle is greater than the third face angle, it follows that the sum of any two sides of a spherical triangle is greater than the third side.

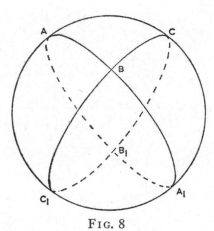

FIG. 8

An extension of this proposition is that any side of a spherical polygon is less than the sum of the remaining sides; and accordingly, the shortest line on the sphere's surface between two points on its surface is the minor arc of the great circle on which both points lie; because any other line between the two points may be regarded as the sum of minute arcs of great circles in the limit when each minute arc is diminished indefinitely.

To find the area of a spherical triangle. Let Δ be the area of the spherical triangle ABC depicted in Fig. 8.

$$\text{Area of lune A} = \Delta + A_1BC$$
$$\text{Area of lune B} = \Delta + AB_1C$$
$$\text{Area of lune C} = \Delta + ABC_1$$

By addition:

Lune A + lune B + lune C $= 2\varDelta + (\varDelta + A_1BC + AB_1C + ABC_1)$

That is:

$$\frac{A}{90}\pi R^2 + \frac{B}{90}\pi R^2 + \frac{C}{90}\pi R^2 = 2\varDelta + 2\pi R^2$$

$$\frac{\pi R^2}{90}(A° + B° + C°) = 2\varDelta + 2\pi R^2$$

$$\frac{\pi R^2}{180}(A° + B° + C°) = \varDelta + \pi R^2$$

$$\varDelta = \frac{\pi R^2}{180}\overline{(A° + B° + C°)} - \pi R^2$$

i.e. $\quad \varDelta = \frac{\pi R^2}{180}\overline{(A° + B° + C°} - 180)$

Since $\varDelta$ is a positive quantity it follows that $(A° + B° + C°)$ must be greater than 180°. The amount by which $(A° + B° + C°)$ exceeds 180° is known as the *spherical excess*. If the spherical excess—denoted by E—is given in degrees:

$$\varDelta = \frac{\pi R^2}{180} \times E$$

If E is given in radians, where $1° = 180/\pi°$ then:

$$\varDelta = ER^2$$

2. *The ellipsoid and its formulae*

The Earth's shape is that of an ellipsoid of rotation. To understand certain problems related to navigation and mapping it is necessary, therefore, to have some knowledge of the geometry of the ellipse. An *ellipse* is a conic section; that is to say, it is a curve which forms the boundary of a particular plane section of a cone. The ellipse is a curve which is described as the locus of a point which moves so that the ratio between the distance from any point on the curve to a fixed point called the *focus* of the ellipse, and the perpendicular distance from the point to a fixed straight line called the *directrix* of the ellipse, is constant and less than unity. The ratio, which is denoted by e, is called the *eccentricity* of the ellipse.

In Fig. 9 if F is the focus and RR_1 is the directrix, the curve through the point P is an ellipse if FP/PM is constant (e) and less than 1, for all positions of P on the curve. That is:

$$\frac{FP}{PM} = e \quad \text{or} \quad FP = e \times PM$$

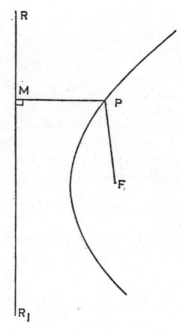

FIG. 9

THE EQUATION OF THE ELLIPSE

The equation of an ellipse is usually given in the form:

$$\frac{x^2}{a^2} + \frac{y^2}{a^2} = 1$$

This may be proved as follows:

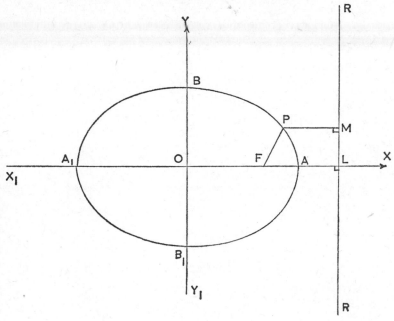

FIG. 10

Referring to Fig. 10:

F is the focus of an ellipse and RR_1 the directrix. The straight line XX_1 is perpendicular to the directrix and passes through F. There are two points on XX_1 through which the ellipse passes: one at A such that $FA = eAL$, and the other at A_1 such that $FA_1 = eA_1L$. The point O on XX_1, lies midway between A and A_1; and YY_1 is a straight line through O parallel to RR_1.

Let the lines XX_1 and YY_1 be the axes of reference for rectangular cartesian coordinates, and let OA be denoted by a.

Now $$FA + FA_1 = e(AL + A_1L)$$

Thus, $$2a = e \times 2OL$$

so that $$OL = a/e$$

It follows, therefore, that the point L has coordinates $(a/e, O)$, and the directrix is the straight line $x = a/e$

Also $$FA_1 - FA = e(A_1L - AL)$$

Thus, $$2OF = e \times 2a$$

so that, $$OF = ea$$

It follows that the coordinates of F are (ae, O).

If P is any point on the ellipse having coordinates (x, y) we have:

$$FP = ePM \quad \text{and} \quad FP^2 = e^2PM^2$$

where PM is perpendicular to RR_1.

Therefore:

$$(x - ae)^2 + y^2 = e^2(a/e - x)^2$$

and $$x^2 - 2aex + a^2e^2 + y^2 = a^2 - 2aex + e^2x^2$$

From which:

$$x^2(1 - e^2) + y^2 = a^2(1 - e^2) \tag{1}$$

Let OB in Fig. 10 be denoted by b.

Because $$OF = ae$$

and $$BF = a$$

therefore $$b^2 = a^2(1 - e^2)$$

By dividing equation (1) throughout by b^2 we get the general form of the equation of the ellipse, which is:

$$\frac{x^2}{a^2} + \frac{y^2}{b^2} = 1$$

For any value of x, y has two values of equal magnitude but opposite signs, and for any value of y, x has two values of equal magnitude but opposite signs. The ellipse is, therefore, symmetrical about both axes of reference XX_1 and YY_1. The point O is called the *centre of the ellipse* and the length AA_1, or $2a$, is known as the *major axis* of the ellipse. A straight line cutting the major axis through the centre of the ellipse of length BB_1 or $2b$, is known as the *minor axis* of the ellipse.

The ratio between the difference between the semi-major and semi-minor axes of an ellipse, and the semi-major axis, is known as the *compression* or *ellipticity* of the ellipse, usually denoted by c. Referring to Fig. 11,

$$c = \frac{a-b}{a} \quad \text{or} \quad b = a(1-c)$$

Consider the ellipse illustrated in Fig. 12, and whose centre is at O and whose semi-major axis and semi-minor axis are OA and OB respectively. Let these semi-axes be denoted by a and b respectively.

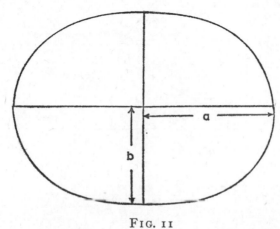

FIG. 11

The straight line TL is a tangent to the ellipse at T and this meets the line OA produced at L. Let the coordinates of T be (x, y). Let the line joining T to the centre of the ellipse make an angle θ with OX, and let the normal TN to the tangent at T make an angle of ϕ with OX. Let the angle at T between TO and TN be r. Then, $r = \phi - \theta$.

The angle r can be expressed in terms of the ellipticity c and the angle ϕ. The relationship between these quantities is of some importance to our purpose. The relationship is:

$$\tan(\phi - r) = (1 - c)^2 \tan \phi$$

For those readers having a knowledge of the differential calculus, the following proof of this important relationship is given.

The equation of the ellipse through T (x, y) is:

$$\frac{x^2}{a^2}+\frac{y^2}{b^2} = 1$$

that is,

$$y^2 = b^2 - \frac{b^2 x^2}{a^2}$$

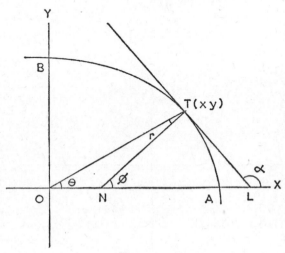

FIG. 12

Differentiating y with respect to x, we have:

$$2y\left(\frac{dy}{dx}\right) = -2\frac{b^2}{a^2}(x)$$

that is,

$$\frac{dy}{dx} = -\frac{b^2}{a^2}\left(\frac{x}{y}\right)$$

Let the angle between the tangent at T and the line OX be α. Then,

$$\tan \alpha = \frac{dy}{dx} = -\frac{b^2 x}{a^2 y}$$

now

$$\alpha = (90 - \phi)$$

and

$$\tan \alpha = -\cot \phi$$

Therefore, $\cot \phi = \dfrac{b^2}{a^2}\dfrac{x}{y}$

but, $\dfrac{x}{y} = \cot \theta$

therefore, $\cot \phi = \dfrac{b^2}{a^2} \cot \theta$

now, $b = a(1 - c)$

and $b^2 = a^2(1 - c)^2$

therefore, $\cot \phi = (1 - c)^2 \cot \theta$

now, $\theta = (\phi - r)$

therefore, $\cot \phi = (1 - c)^2 \cot (\phi - r)$

and $\tan (\phi - r) = (1 - c)^2 \tan \phi$

But $\phi - r = \theta$

therefore $\tan \theta = (1 - c)^2 \tan \phi$

To find the radius for any given value of θ, where θ is the angle between the major axis and the radius itself.

Referring to Fig. 13, let P be any point on the ellipse whose centre is at O. Let the angle between the radius OP and the major axis be θ. Let the length of the radius OP be R and the coordinates of P be (x, y)

$$x = R \cos \theta \quad \text{and} \quad y = R \sin \theta$$

Substituting these values for x and y in the general equation for the ellipse, we have:

$$\frac{R^2 \cos^2 \theta}{a^2} + \frac{R^2 \sin^2 \theta}{b^2} = 1$$

now, $b = a(1 - c)$

therefore, $\dfrac{R^2 \cos^2 \theta}{a^2} + \dfrac{R^2 \sin^2\theta}{a^2(1 - c)^2} = 1$

From which:

$$R^2 \cos^2 \theta (1-c)^2 + R^2 \sin^2 \theta = a^2(1-c)^2$$

thus,

$$R^2[\cos^2 \theta (1-c)^2 + \sin^2 \theta] = a^2(1-c)^2$$

and

$$R^2 = \frac{a^2(1-c)^2}{\cos^2 \theta (1-c)^2 + \sin^2 \theta}$$

and

$$R = \frac{a(1-c)}{[\cos^2 \theta (1-c)^2 + \sin^2 \theta]^{1/2}}$$

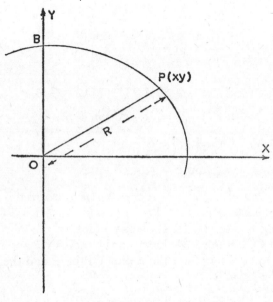

FIG. 13

If the ellipse illustrated in Fig. 13 is rotated about its minor axis, an ellipsoid will be traced out. Every point such as P on the ellipse will trace out a circle the radius of which is $R \cos \theta$.

The radius of any circle on an ellipsoid is equal to $R \cos \theta$ and the circumference of this circle is $2\pi R \cos \theta$, and this is equal to:

$$\frac{2\pi \cos \theta \, a(1-c)}{[\cos^2 \theta (1-c)^2 + \sin^2 \theta]^{1/2}}$$

CHAPTER THREE

The Triangle

1. *The geometry of the triangle*

Trigonometry—a fearsome name to the uninitiated, and meaning simply 'triangle measurement'—is a branch of geometry. Geometry is concerned with the mathematics of magnitudes, whether linear, superficial or solid, and their properties and relations in space. The beginnings of geometry stemmed from the necessity of measuring land—man's principal form of earthly wealth—and this is reflected in the very name of the subject, geometry or 'earth-measurement'.

The simplest geometrical figure having rectilinear boundaries, or sides, is a triangle; and the major part of elementary geometry is related to the study of triangles. The triangles with which we shall be concerned are of two types, named respectively *plane* and *spherical*. A plane triangle is one whose three sides lie in the same plane: a spherical triangle is one formed on the surface of a sphere by the intersection of three great circles.

Whereas practical geometry is essentially a matter for measuring, trigonometry is essentially a matter for calculation. Every triangle has six parts, three of which are sides and three of which are angles. If three parts of a plane triangle are known, provided that one at least of the known parts is a side, it is possible by geometrical construction to form the triangle either full size; or, more generally, to scale. Having formed the triangle it is possible to measure the unknown parts. Alternatively, the unknown parts of a triangle may be found by trigonometrical calculation.

To facilitate the calculation of the unknown parts of a triangle, devices called *trigonometrical functions* are employed. The six principal trigonometrical functions are the six ratios of the lengths of the six unique pairs which may be formed from the three sides of a right-angled triangle. A ratio is simply a numerical comparison between quantities; and the ratios of the lengths of the sides of a right-angled triangle are known as *trigonometrical ratios*. Before discussing the trigonometrical ratios and their use, let us first consider, by way of revision, the properties of triangles which are relevant to our purpose.

A plane triangle is a three-sided figure, the sides being straight lines which intersect to form three angles. A plane angle is formed when a straight line is rotated about a fixed point. If any straight line is rotated in a fixed plane about a point in a clockwise or anticlockwise direction, and is brought back to its original position after one complete rotation, the end of the straight line which moves, and indeed any fixed point on the line, describes a circle. The angle swept out at the fixed point (which lies at the centre of the circle) is divided arbitrarily into 360 parts, each of which is called a degree. Each degree is subdivided into 60 minutes of arc ('), and each minute of arc is subdivided into 60 seconds of arc (").

Degrees, minutes and seconds of arc provide only one system of measuring angles. Angles may be measured in hours, minutes and seconds of time, in which case, 24 hours are equivalent to 360 degrees, and:

$$1 \quad \text{hr} = 15°$$
$$1 \text{ min} = 15'$$
$$1 \quad \text{sec} = 15''$$
$$1° \quad = 4 \text{ min}$$
$$1' \quad = 4 \text{ sec}$$

Another angular unit which is of great importance mathematically, is the *radian*. This is an angle at the centre of a circle contained between two radii, the arc length between them being equivalent to the radius of the circle. The circumference of any circle is a constant number of times the diameter of the circle. The constant is π (pi) (see p. 37), and the circumference is π times the diameter or 2π times the radius of the circle. It follows, therefore, that 360° is equivalent to 2π radians (°). Thus:

$$1° \text{ is equivalent to } 360/2\pi°$$
$$1° \qquad \text{,,} \qquad 2\pi/360°$$

For practical purposes, 1° is taken as being equivalent to 57·3° or 3,438′.

A plane angle is, for our purposes, described as being acute, right-angled or obtuse. A right angle is formed when a straight line is swept through a quarter of a circle or quadrant. Angles that are less than a right angle—which is 90°, 6 hr or $(\pi/2)°$—are known as acute angles. Angles greater than a right angle are described as *obtuse*. All angles other than right angles are called *oblique* angles.

The three angles of any plane triangle add up to 180° or two right angles. This is easily proved as follows:

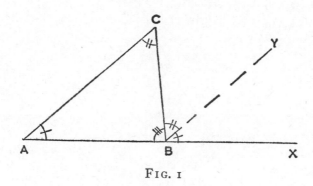

FIG. 1

In Fig. 1, the side of the triangle ABC is produced from B to X as shown. A straight line BY is drawn parallel to the side AC.

Now,   angle YBX = angle CAB

and,   angle CBY = angle ACB

therefore   angles YBX + CBY = angles CAB + ACB

Add to each side the angle ABC and we have,

     angles YBX + CBY + ABC = angles CAB + ACB + ABC

But

     angles YBX + CBY + ABC = 180° (straight angle)

therefore,

     angles CAB + ACB + ABC = 180°

and   angles A + B + C = two right angles

Because the sum of the three plane angles in any plane triangle is 180°, any one of the angles must be less than 180°. For our purposes—which are concerned essentially with the solving of triangles—we need not consider angles over 180°.

Triangles which are identical with one another in respect of the magnitudes of their sides and angles, are known as *congruent* triangles. Triangles which are equiangular, but whose corresponding sides have different lengths, are known as *similar* triangles. Triangles which have three unequal sides are known as *scalene* triangles: those which have three equal sides are known as *equilateral* triangles; and those which contain a right angle are known as *right-angled triangles*.

It is easy to prove that the angles of an equilateral triangle are each equal to 60°.

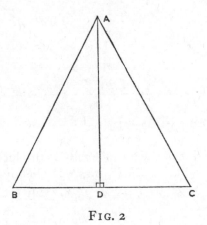

FIG. 2

Referring to Fig. 2, which illustrates an equilateral triangle ABC, AD is a perpendicular from A on to the opposite side BC. (A perpendicular is a straight line which meets another straight line at right angles.)

The triangles ABD and ACD are congruent and, therefore, angle B = angle C. By dropping a perpendicular from B or C on to the opposite side, it may be proved that angle A = angle C (or angle A = angle B), from which we deduce that angle A = angle B = angle C, and that each is equal to a third of 180°, that is 60°.

An important property of similar triangles is that the ratios between the lengths of corresponding sides are equal.

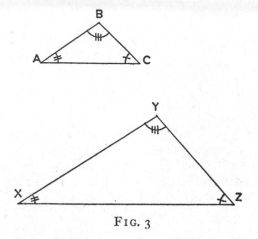

FIG. 3

In Fig. 3, the triangles ABC and ZYX are similar, the corresponding angles being angle A and angle X, angle B and angle Y and angle C and angle Z, and the corresponding sides being AB, XY; BC, YZ and AC, XZ. It can be proved geometrically and verified by direct measurement that:

$$\frac{AB}{XY} = \frac{BC}{YZ} = \frac{AC}{XZ}$$

Thus, if AB is 2 units and XY 4 units, the ratio between AB and XY is 2:1, therefore, XZ = 2AC, and YZ = 2BC.

2. *Trigonometrical ratios*

The principal trigonometrical function is called the *sine*. Referring to Fig. 4, suppose a straight line initially occupying the position OA is rotated in the direction indicated so that an angle of 180° is swept out, after which the line will occupy the position OD. It should be clear that as the angle increases from 0° to 180°, the perpendicular from the moving end of the straight line on to

5

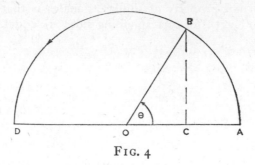

FIG. 4

OA or OA produced, will change its length, reaching a maximum (which is equal to the length of OA) when the angle at O is 90°; and, for increasing angles over 90°, the length will diminish to zero when the angle is 180°. The length of this perpendicular graphed against angle would produce the curve depicted in Fig. 5.

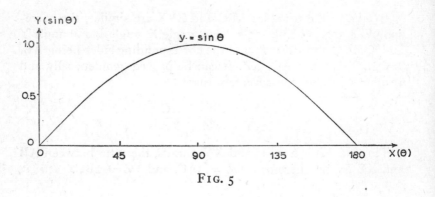

FIG. 5

The curve illustrated in Fig. 5 is known as a *sine curve*. The length of the perpendicular discussed in relation to Fig. 4, expressed as a ratio of the length OA, for any given angle θ, is known as the sine of θ, abbreviated to sin θ. It should be clear that sin θ is quite independent of the length of OA.

In Fig. 6, the sine of angle θ may be expressed in terms of the length of either perpendicular B_1A_1 or B_2A_2. The triangles

OA_1B_1 and OA_2B_2 are similar triangles and, therefore, ratios of corresponding sides are equal. Thus:

$$\frac{A_1B_1}{OB_1} = \frac{A_2D_2}{OB_2} = \sin \theta$$

It is for this reason that the somewhat unsatisfactory parrot-fashion definition of the sine of an angle is: 'the ratio of the lengths of the side opposite to the angle which is contained in any right-angled triangle, and the hypotenuse of the triangle'; and every schoolboy learns that the sine of an angle equals opposite over hypotenuse.

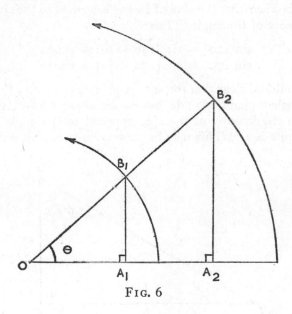

FIG. 6

This is unsatisfactory as it clearly applies only to angles of less than 90°. It is, therefore, not general in its application. The sine of an angle may be found by direct measurement in a right-angled triangle or from a sine curve; or it may be computed to any degree of accuracy by mathematical methods. The sines of all angles from 0° to 90° are tabulated and sine tables are normally used when the sine of a particular angle is required.

It should be clear from the graph illustrated in Fig. 5 that the part of the sine curve shown is symmetrical about an ordinate at 90°, so that it is unnecessary to tabulate sines of angles greater than 90°.

Two angles which add together to make 90° are known as *complementary angles*, each being the *complement* of the other. The two non-90° angles in any right-angled triangle are clearly complementary because the sum of the three angles in any plane triangle is 180°.

Two angles whose sum is 180° are known as *supplementary* angles, each being the *supplement* of the other. 60° and 120° are supplementary angles and so are 10° and 170°. From Fig. 5 it should be clear that the sine of an angle is equal to the sine of the supplement of the angle. Thus:

$$\sin 120° = \sin (180 - 120) = \sin 60°$$
and $\qquad \sin 170° = \sin (180 - 170) = \sin 10°$

It should be clear that the sine of 30° is 0·5 exactly; for, in any right-angled plane triangle having an angle of 30°, the ratio between the lengths of the side opposite to the angle and the hypotenuse is 1/2. This may be proved easily as follows:

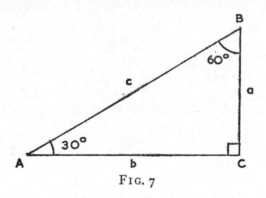

FIG. 7

Fig. 7 is a diagram of a right-angled triangle having one angle, A, equal to 30° and another, B, equal to 60°. The sides of a triangle are usually denoted by small letters corresponding to the opposite angles. Let, therefore, BC be denoted by a; AC by b and AB by c.

Now, $a = c/2$

and $\sin A = a/c$

therefore $\sin A = 1/2$

Pythagoras' theorem, states that 'In any right-angled plane triangle, the square on the hypotenuse is equal to the sum of the squares on the other two sides,' and thus in triangle ABC (Fig. 7):

$$c^2 = a^2 + b^2$$

i.e. $c^2 = (c/2)^2 + b^2$

i.e. $b^2 = c^2 - (c/2)^2$

i.e. $b^2 = \tfrac{3}{4}c^2$

and $b = c\sqrt{3}/2$

Now $\sin 60° = b/c$

therefore: $\sin 60 = \sqrt{3}/2$

The sine of the complement of an angle is a trigonometrical ratio known as the *cosine* of the angle (abbreviated to cos). As we have seen:

$$\sin 30° - 1/2 \quad \text{and} \quad \sin 60° - \sqrt{3}/2$$

Now 30° and 60° being complementary angles, it follows that:

$$\cos 30° = \sqrt{3}/2 \quad \text{and} \quad \cos 60° = 1/2$$

The word cosine is derived from *sine complement*. The graph of the cosine of θ from 0° to 180° against θ, is illustrated in Fig. 8.

Whereas the whole of that part of the sine curve for angles between 0° and 180° lies above the X axis, and the sines of all angles between 0° and 180° are positive, that part of the cosine curve applicable to angles between 0° and 180° lies partly above and partly below the X axis. The cosines of angles in the first quadrant, that is from 0° to 90°, are positive; and those of angles in the second quadrant, that is from 90° to 180°, are negative. The part of the cosine curve depicted in Fig. 8 is symmetrical about the X axis; and, clearly, the magnitude of the cosine of an angle in the second quadrant is equal to the cosine of its supplement but it is opposite in sign.

$$\cos 120° = \cos (180° - 60°) = -\cos 60°$$
$$\cos 170° = \cos (180° - 10°) = -\cos 10°$$

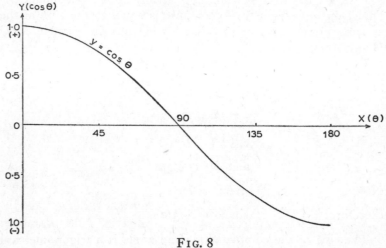

FIG. 8

The cosine of an angle is often defined in a similar way to that of the sine, viz., as the ratio between two sides of a right-angled triangle which contains the angle. 'Cosine of an angle is adjacent over hypotenuse', as the schoolboy learns.

The trigonometrical ratios other than the sine and the cosine, are named *tangent, cotangent, secant* and *cosecant*.

Let the straight line OA depicted in Fig. 9, be rotated about the end marked O in the direction indicated. The line AT is tangential to the circle described by A and the length cut off this tangent by the rotating line produced, for any angle θ, expressed by the same units of which the length of OA is one, is known as the *tangent* of the angle θ, abbreviated to tan θ. For an angle less than 90°, the tangent of the angle may be defined as the ratio between the lengths opposite and adjacent to the angle which is contained in any right-angled triangle. It should be clear that the tangent of 0° is 0; the tangent of 45° is 1, and the tangent of 90° is ∞.

The tangent of the complement of any angle is known as the *cotangent* of the angle, abbreviated to cot. Thus:

$$\tan \theta = \cot (90° - \theta)$$

and $$\cot \theta = \tan (90° - \theta)$$

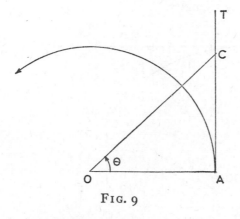

FIG. 9

Geometrically, any line which cuts a circle is known as a *secant*. The line which cuts the circle described by the rotating arm OA in Fig. 9, that is the line OC, is, if its length is expressed in units of OA, called the *secant* of θ, abbreviated to sec θ.

The secant of the complement of any angle is a ratio known as the *cosecant* of the angle, abbreviated to cosec. Thus:

$$\sec \theta = \operatorname{cosec} (90° - \theta)$$

and $$\operatorname{cosec} \theta = \sec (90° - \theta)$$

In Fig. 10 the trigonometrical ratios of θ are shown as lengths of particular lines.

In Fig. 10, the length OA is any unit.

$$BD = \sin \theta$$
$$OD = \cos \theta$$
$$AT_1 = \tan \theta$$
$$ET_2 = \cot \theta$$
$$OT_1 = \sec \theta$$
$$OT_2 = \operatorname{cosec} \theta$$

provided that the lengths are expressed in the units of OA.

By considering the variation in these lengths as θ changes the graphs of the trigonometrical ratios of all angles may be drawn, and the trigonometrical ratio of any angle may be found by scale drawing. The values of the trigonometrical ratios are computed and tabulated, and these so-called *trig. tables* are of great assistance in solving triangles.

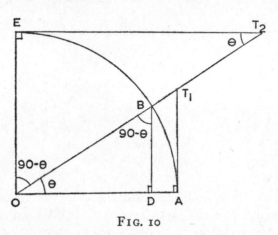

FIG. 10

Examination of Fig. 10 will reveal the presence of three similar triangles, OBD; OT$_1$A, and ET$_2$O. Using the property of similar triangles stated above, we have:

$$\frac{BD}{OB} = \frac{AT_1}{OT_1} = \frac{OE}{OT_2}$$

thus,
$$\frac{\sin \theta}{1} = \frac{\tan \theta}{\sec \theta} = \frac{1}{\operatorname{cosec} \theta}$$

Also,
$$\frac{OD}{OB} = \frac{OA}{OT_1} = \frac{ET_2}{OT_2}$$

thus,
$$\frac{\cos \theta}{1} = \frac{1}{\sec \theta} = \frac{\cot \theta}{\operatorname{cosec} \theta}$$

Also,
$$\frac{BD}{OD} = \frac{AT_1}{OA} = \frac{OE}{ET_2}$$

thus,
$$\frac{\sin \theta}{\cos \theta} = \frac{\tan \theta}{1} = \frac{1}{\cot \theta}$$

The sine and cosine, the tangent and cotangent and the secant and cosecant, are known as *complementary* ratios; the sine and cosecant, the tangent and cotangent, and the cosine and secant, are pairs of *reciprocal* ratios. By Pythagoras' theorem, we have, from Fig. 10:

$$OD^2 + BD^2 = OB^2$$

$$\sin^2\theta + \cos^2\theta = 1 \qquad (1)$$

also, $$AO^2 + AT_1^2 = OT_1^2$$

$$1 + \tan^2\theta = \sec^2\theta \qquad (2)$$

also, $$OE^2 + ET_2^2 = OT_2^2$$

$$1 + \cot^2\theta = \operatorname{cosec}^2\theta \qquad (3)$$

The relationships (1), (2) and (3), which hold good for all values of θ, are known as the *standard identities*.

3. *Plane trigonometry*

The trigonometrical ratios facilitate, as we have stated, the solution of plane triangles. This applies particularly if the triangles are right-angled. Any triangle which is not right-angled, that is to say, any oblique triangle, may be divided into two right-angled triangles simply by dropping a perpendicular from any vertex on to the opposite side, or opposite side produced. Therefore any plane triangle can be solved with the same ease as the solution of a right angled triangle, provided that at least three parts (one or more of which must be a side), are known, and that trig. tables are at hand. The following examples will make this clear.

Example 1 In triangle ABC

angle A = 20°   angle C = 90° $a = 10$ in

Find the unknown parts.

Refer to diagram (i) in Fig. 11:

angle B = 180° − (90° + 20°)

= 70°

$b = a \cot 20°$ (or $a \tan 70°$)
$= 10 \times 2·75 \ldots$
$= 27·50$ inches   to two decimal places

$c = a \operatorname{cosec} 20°$ (or $a \sec 70°$)
$= 10 \times 2·92 \ldots$
$= 29·2$ inches   to one place of decimals

Example 2 In triangle ABC

angle A $= 50°$ angle C $= 90°$ $b = 6$ miles

Find the unknown parts.
  Refer to diagram (ii) in Fig. 11:

angle B $= 180° - (90° + 50°)$
$= 40°$

$a = b \tan 50°$ (or $b \cot 40°$)
$= 6 \times \tan 50°$
$= 6 \times 1·19 \ldots$
$= 7·14$ miles   to two decimal places

$c = b \sec 50°$ (or $b \operatorname{cosec} 40°$)
$= 6 \times \sec 50°$
$= 6 \times 1·55572 \ldots$
$= 9·33432$ miles   to five places of decimals

Example 3 In triangle ABC,

angle B $= 60°$ angle C $= 90°$ $c = 26$ yards

Refer to diagram (iii) in Fig. 11:

angle $A = 180° - (90° + 60°)$
$= 30°$

$a = c \cos 60°$ (or $c \sin 30°$)
$= 26 \times 1/2$
$= 13$ yards exactly

$b = c \sin 60°$ (or $c \cos 30°$)
$= 26 \times \sqrt{3}/2$
$= 13\sqrt{3}$ exactly   or
    22·517, to three decimal places

The solution of right-angled triangles is of such importance in surveying and navigation that tables for the solutions of right-angled triangles, known as *traverse tables*, are available. From traverse tables right-angled triangles may be solved with little or no computation and without having to resort to geometrical methods.

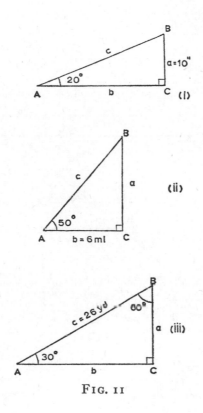

Fig. 11

Plane triangles which do not contain an angle of 90°, that is to say, oblique triangles, may be solved by means of the fundamental *plane sine* and/or *cosine formulae*. The plane sine formula is usually expressed thus:

The ratio between any two sides of a plane triangle is equal to the ratio between the sines of the opposite angles.

In Fig. 12, ABC is any plane triangle. The sine formula applied to this triangle is:

$$\frac{a}{\sin A} = \frac{b}{\sin B} = \frac{c}{\sin C}$$

This may be proved as follows:

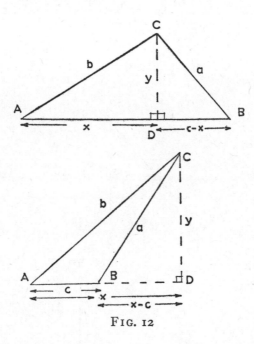

FIG. 12

Referring to Fig. 12:

CD is a perpendicular from C on to AB or AB produced.
$y = b \sin A = a \sin B$, in both cases,
remembering that $\sin B = \sin (180 - B)$.

Therefore:

$$b \sin A = a \sin B \quad \text{or} \quad \frac{a}{\sin A} = \frac{b}{\sin B}$$

Similarly it may be proved, by dropping a perpendicular from

B on to AC or AC produced, or from A on to BC or BC produced, that:

$$\frac{b}{\sin B} = \frac{c}{\sin C} \quad \text{and} \quad \frac{a}{\sin A} = \frac{c}{\sin C}$$

Therefore:

$$\frac{a}{\sin A} = \frac{b}{\sin B} = \frac{c}{\sin C}$$

The cosine formula may be used to find an angle when the three sides of any triangle are given; or to find a side when the other two sides and the included angle are given. The cosine formula finds its greatest use when the lengths of the sides of the triangle used in the calculation are numbers that are easily squared. When this is not the case, a formula derived from the cosine formula may be used.

In any plane triangle ABC:

$$\cos A = \frac{b^2 + c^2 - a^2}{2bc}$$

or $$a^2 = b^2 + c^2 - 2bc \cos A$$

This may be proved as follows.

Referring again to Fig. 12, by applying Pythagoras' theorem to the two right-angled triangles ACD and CBD we have:

$$b^2 = y^2 + x^2 \tag{1}$$

$$a^2 = y^2 + (c - x)^2 \tag{2}$$

Subtract (2) from (1):

$$b^2 - a^2 = x^2 - (c - x)^2$$

i.e. $$b^2 - a^2 = x^2 - (c^2 + x^2 - 2cx)$$

i.e. $$b^2 - a^2 = x^2 - c^2 - x^2 + 2cx$$

i.e. $$b^2 - a^2 = -c^2 + 2cx$$

i.e. $$a^2 = b^2 + c^2 - 2cx$$

but, $$x = b \cos A$$

Therefore:

$$a^2 = b^2 + c^2 - 2bc \cos A$$

and $$\cos A = \frac{b^2 + c^2 - a^2}{2bc}$$

Important trigonometrical identities are those which follow, and which are related to compound angles.

$$\sin (A+B) = \sin A \cos B + \cos A \sin B$$
$$\cos (A+B) = \cos A \cos B - \sin A \sin B$$
$$\sin (A-B) = \sin A \cos B - \cos A \sin B$$
$$\cos (A-B) = \cos A \cos B + \sin A \sin B$$

These relationships may be proved as follows:

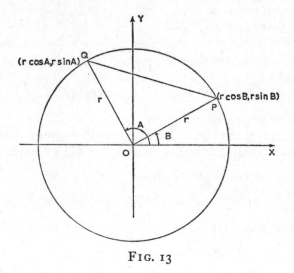

FIG. 13

In Fig. 13, the points P and Q, relative to the cartesian axes of reference OX and OY have coordinates ($r \cos B$, $r \sin B$) and ($r \cos A$, $r \sin A$) respectively.

By Pythagoras' theorem:

$$PQ^2 = (r \cos A - r \cos B)^2 + (r \sin A - r \sin B)^2$$

By plane cosine formula:

$$PQ^2 = r^2 + r^2 - 2rr \cos (A - B)$$

Equating these two we have

$$2r^2 - 2r^2 \cos (A - B)$$
$$= r^2 \cos^2 A + r^2 \cos^2 B - 2r^2 \cos A \cos B +$$
$$r^2 \sin^2 A + r^2 \sin^2 B - 2r^2 \sin A \sin B$$

From which

$$2\{1 - \cos (A - B)\} = 2(1 - \cos A \cos B - \sin A \sin B)$$

Therefore

$$\cos (A - B) = \cos A \cos B + \sin A \sin B \qquad (1)$$

Put B = − B in (1) and,

$$\cos (A + B) = \cos A \cos B - \sin A \sin B \qquad (2)$$

Put A = (90 − A) in (1)

$$\cos (90 - A) - B) = \cos (90 - (A + B)$$
$$= \sin (A + B)$$

therefore

$$\sin (A + B) = \cos (90 - A) \cos B + \sin (90 - A) \sin B$$

and $$\sin (A + B) = \sin A \cos B + \cos A \sin B \qquad (3)$$

Put B = − B in (3) and

$$\sin (A - B) = \sin A \cos (-B) - \cos A \sin (-B)$$

and $$\sin (A - B) = \sin A \cos B - \cos A \sin B \qquad (4)$$

The tangents of the sum and difference of two angles A and B are sometimes useful. They are

$$\tan (A + B) = \frac{\sin (A + B)}{\cos (A + B)} = \frac{1 - \tan A \tan B}{\tan A + \tan B}$$

$$\tan (A - B) = \frac{1 + \tan A \tan B}{\tan A - \tan B}$$

If A = B, then,

$$\sin (A+B) = \sin 2A$$
$$= 2 \sin A \cos A$$

$$\cos (A+B) = \cos^2 A - \sin^2 A$$
$$= 1 - 2 \sin^2 A$$
$$= 2 \cos^2 A - 1$$

$$\tan (A+B) = \tan 2A$$
$$= \frac{2 \tan A}{1 - \tan^2 A}$$

If B = 2A:

$$\sin 3A = \sin (A+2A)$$
$$= 3 \sin A - 4 \sin^3 A$$

$$\cos 3A = \cos (A+2A)$$
$$= 4 \cos^3 A - 3 \cos A$$

$$\tan 3A = \tan (A+2A)$$
$$= \frac{3 \tan A - \tan^3 A}{1 - 3 \tan^2 A}$$

FUNCTIONS OF SMALL ANGLES

Remembering that the area of a plane triangle is equal to half the product of the base and the perpendicular height measured from the base; and that the area of a sector is equal to half the product of the radius squared and the angle in radians: referring to Fig. 14, we have:

Area $\triangle$OAB > Area sector OAC > Area $\triangle$OAC

Therefore:

$$\tfrac{1}{2}r^2 \tan \theta > \tfrac{1}{2}r^2 \theta > \tfrac{1}{2}r^2 \sin \theta$$

and

$$\tan \theta > \theta^c > \sin \theta$$

and

$$\frac{\tan \theta}{\theta} > 1 > \frac{\sin \theta}{\theta}$$

As θ tends to zero,

$$\frac{\tan \theta}{\theta} \text{ tends to } 1 \quad \text{and} \quad \frac{\sin \theta}{\theta} \text{ tends to } 1$$

For small angles, therefore, we may write θ° for either $\sin \theta$ or $\tan \theta$.

Now
$$\cos \theta = \cos \left(\tfrac{1}{2}\theta + \tfrac{1}{2}\theta\right)$$
$$= 1 - 2 \sin^2 \tfrac{1}{2}\theta$$

Thus, when θ is small, we may write $\left(1 - \dfrac{\theta^2}{2}\right)$ for $\cos \theta$.

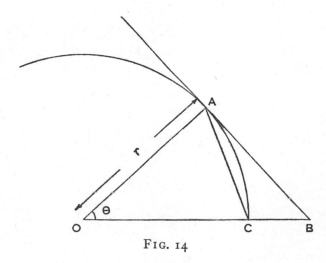

FIG. 14

4. Spherical trigonometry

Spherical trigonometry is concerned with the solution of spherical triangles. A spherical triangle, as explained in Chapter Two, is formed by arcs of three intersecting great circles. The sum of the three angles of any spherical triangle is less than four right angles, or 360°. This follows because the maximum spherical distance of any of the sides of a spherical triangle is two right angles; and, in the limiting case, a spherical triangle is a hemisphere. For the same reason the sum of the three spherical angles of a spherical triangle must be less than six right angles or 540°.

6

If any three parts of a spherical triangle are known (even if the three parts are angles), it is possible to calculate the unknown parts by using the spherical sine and/or cosine formula. These two formulae together with one other are referred to as the *fundamental spherical formulae*. In addition to these fundamental formulae there are several derived formulae, designed mainly for logarithmic computations.

THE SPHERICAL SINE FORMULA

In any spherical triangle:

$$\frac{\sin a}{\sin A} = \frac{\sin b}{\sin B} = \frac{\sin c}{\sin C}$$

where angles A, B and C are the spherical angles and *a*, *b* and *c* are the sides.

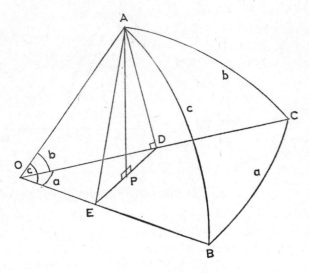

FIG. 15

Fig. 15 represents part of a sphere whose centre is at O. Let AB, AC and BC be arcs of great circles which intersect to form the spherical triangle ABC. Let the spherical distances AB, AC

and BC, be *c*, *b* and *a*, respectively. These angles are equivalent
to the face angles AOB, AOC and BOC respectively, of the solid
angle (O, ABC).

From any vertex, drop a perpendicular on to the opposite face
of the trihedral angle formed by the spherical triangle. In Fig. 15,
a perpendicular is dropped from A on to the plane OBC at P.
From P drop perpendiculars on to the radii OB and OC at E and
D respectively, and join AE and AD.

$$\frac{\sin b}{\sin B} = \frac{\frac{AD}{OA}}{\frac{AP}{AE}} = \frac{AD.AE}{OA.AP}$$

$$\frac{\sin c}{\sin C} = \frac{\frac{AE}{OA}}{\frac{AP}{AD}} = \frac{AE.AD}{OA.AP}$$

Therefore

$$\frac{\sin b}{\sin B} = \frac{\sin c}{\sin C}$$

By dropping a perpendicular from B on to the plane OAC (or
from C on to the plane OAB) it may be proved that:

$$\frac{\sin a}{\sin A} = \frac{\sin b}{\sin B} = \frac{\sin c}{\sin C}$$

THE SPHERICAL COSINE FORMULA

In any spherical triangle ABC:

$$\cos A = \frac{\cos a - \cos b \cos c}{\sin b \sin c}$$

$$\cos a = \cos A \sin b \sin c + \cos b \cos c$$

Fig. 16 represents part of a sphere whose centre is at O. The
spherical triangle ABC is delineated on the surface of this sphere.
Let the sides of the triangle ABC be a, b and c respectively. These
spherical distances are equivalent to the corresponding face
angles in the trihedral angle (O, ABC).

AE and AD are tangents at A lying in the planes of the great circles through B and C respectively. Let these tangents meet the plane of OBC at E and D. Extend OC to E and OB to D and join DE.

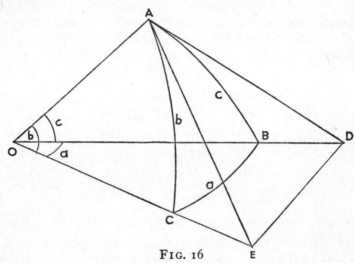

FIG. 16

By the plane cosine formula,

$$DE^2 = OD^2 + OE^2 - 2OD \cdot OE \cos a \qquad (1)$$

Also:

$$DE^2 = AD^2 + AE^2 - 2AD \cdot AE \cos A \qquad (2)$$

Subtract (2) from (1):

$$0 = OD^2 + OE^2 - 2OD \cdot OE \cos a - AD^2 - AE^2 + 2AD \cdot AE \cos A$$

i.e. $0 = (OD^2 - AD^2) + (OE^2 - AE^2) - 2OD \cdot OE \cos a$
$$+ 2AD \cdot AE \cos A$$

i.e. $2AD \cdot AE \cos A = -2OA^2 + 2\, OD \cdot OE \cos a$

$$\cos A = \frac{OD \cdot OE \cos a - OA^2}{AD \cdot AE}$$

Divide throughout by OD . OE, and:

$$\cos A = \frac{\cos a - \cos b \cos c}{\sin b \sin c}$$

or, $\cos a = \cos A \sin b \sin c + \cos b \cos c$

NAPIER'S RULES FOR RIGHT-ANGLED SPHERICAL TRIANGLES

If a spherical triangle contains an angle of 90°, its solution is facilitated by employing *Napier's Rules of Circular Parts*. These rules were invented by the illustrious Baron Napier, the 16th-century mathematician who is credited with the invention of logarithms. The rules are derived from the fundamental spherical formulae, viz. the *sine, cosine* and *four parts formulae*: the last named we have not discussed.

It is possible to derive ten relatively simple formulae that provide the means of solving every case of a right-angled spherical triangle. Napier's Rules are simple devices for deriving the appropriate formula for the solution of a particular case. The devices are in the form of mnemonics. The parts, excluding the right angle, of a right-angled spherical triangle which is to be solved, are written in order in the five sectors of a circle as illustrated in Fig. 17.

The two parts adjacent to the right angle—the sides *a* and *b* in our example illustrated in Fig. 17—stand as they are in the sectors adjacent to the radius which represents the right angle and which is marked C = 90°, in the diagrams. The remaining three parts are written in their respective sectors—each preceded by the prefix 'co' meaning complement.

Of any three parts shown in the sector, two are always opposite or adjacent with respect to the other one. For example, of the parts b, A and c, A is the middle part and the other two parts are adjacent parts. Of the parts B, A and b, B is the middle part and A and b are opposites etc.

Napier's Rules are:

sin middle part = product cosines of opposites

sin middle part = product tangents of adjacents

Thus of the three parts B, A and *b* in our example:

$$\sin \text{co } A = \tan b \tan \text{co } c$$

which reduces to:

$$\cos A = \tan b \cot c$$

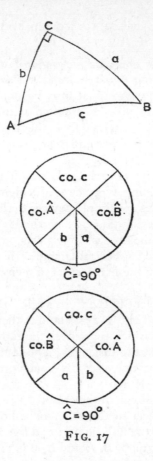

FIG. 17

Of the three parts B, A and b in our example:

$$\sin \text{co } B = \cos \text{co } A \cos b$$

which reduces to:

$$\cos B = \sin A \cos b$$

Because any oblique spherical triangle may be divided into two right-angled spherical triangles, Napier's rules provide a powerful means of solving spherical triangles.

CHAPTER FOUR

Problems of Sailing on the Earth

This chapter is concerned with the problems connected with sailing, in the most expeditious manner, from one place to another on the Earth's surface. The principal problems are involved in finding courses and distances between places on the globe. Consideration will be given to both *rhumb-line* and *great-circle sailing*. The main distinction between these two methods of sailing is that in the former the course angle between the two places is constant at all points on the track; whereas in the latter method, unless the places of departure and destination are on the same meridian, or on the equator, the course angle changes continually along the track.

The *course* of a ship or aircraft when making headway is the horizontal angle between the directions of the north point of the horizon and the fore and aft line of the ship or aircraft. The course is usually expressed in three-figure notation: north being denoted by 000°; east by 090°; south by 180°, west by 270°, etc.

The distance between two places on the Earth is given in *statute* or *nautical miles*, and is designated as either a *rhumb-line distance* or a *great-circle distance*. The rhumb-line distance between two places is the distance along the line of constant course between the places, whereas the great-circle distance is the distance along the shortest route between the two places along the Earth's surface. The shortest route between two places on the surface of a sphere is along the minor arc of the great circle on which both the places lie. This may readily be verified by means of a length of cord and a model globe.

1. *The nautical mile and its derivation*

Let us investigate the units of distance used in sailing problems. The *statute mile* is an arbitrary measure and was evolved from early makeshift units such as the length of a grain of corn, or the length of a man's forearm or foot. It is described as a length containing 1,760 yards, the statute yard being defined by a length of a bar of platinum which is preserved in the Standards Department of the Board of Trade. The statute mile of eight furlongs is invariably used by travellers ashore and sometimes by airmen and yachtsmen, but never by professional seamen.

The unit of distance used in navigation is the *nautical mile*, the tenth part of which is the *cable*. The nautical mile is related closely to the magnitude of the Earth, whereas the statute mile is an arbitrary measure not related to the Earth's size in any way. Were the Earth a perfect sphere, the length of a minute of arc of the Earth's surface would everywhere be the same. This length would provide a useful unit of distance for navigational purposes, because it would be equivalent, not only to the length of a minute of longitude at the equator but, more important, it would be equivalent to the length of a minute of the meridian at any place on Earth so that, when sailing northwards or southwards, each minute-of-arc change in the latitude will correspond to a northing or southing of one unit of distance. Although the Earth is not a sphere, this ideal unit of distance does however form the basis of measuring distance for navigational purposes.

The length of the circumference of any circle is 2π times the radius of the circle. In other words the radius of a circle will fit 2π times into the circumference of the circle. The angle at the centre of a circle subtended by an arc whose length is equal to the radius of the circle, is an angular unit known as a radian (°), and clearly:

$$360° = (360 \times 60)' = 2\pi°$$

and $$1° = (60 \times 360)/2\pi'$$

The constant π is an incommensurable quantity; but, for practical purposes, one radian is taken as being equivalent to 3,438 minutes of arc. It follows, therefore, that the radius of a sphere in units of an arc length of one minute on its surface is 3,438 units.

The shape of the Earth is that of an ellipsoid. Every meridian is elliptical in form, and the only great circle of the Earth, which is in fact a circle, is the equator. The length of a minute of arc of the equator is a unit known as a *geographical mile*. The length of a geographical mile in English feet is 6,087·2.

In Great Britain, the nautical mile is defined as the length of a minute of arc of a meridian. Two points on the same meridian whose astronomical latitudes differ by one minute of arc are one nautical mile apart.

Astronomical latitude, which is sometimes called *geographical latitude*, is defined as the angle at a place between the horizon and the celestial pole measured in the plane of the meridian of the place. Thus, two points on the same meridian are one nautical mile apart if the horizons or verticals at the two points are inclined to one another at an angle of one minute of arc.

In Fig. 1, V_A and V_B are the verticals, and H_A and H_B are the horizons, of two places on the same meridian, A and B respectively. The geographical latitudes of A and B are β and α respectively.

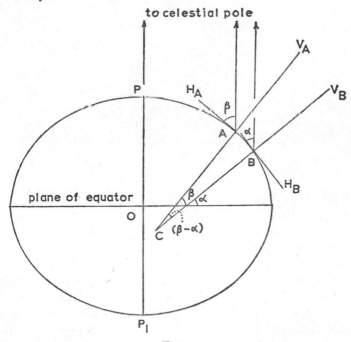

FIG. 1

If the difference between the geographical latitudes of A and B is 1′, that is to say, if $\beta - \alpha = 1′$, then, the arc length AB is one nautical mile. What amounts to the same thing is that arc AB is one nautical mile if the verticals at A and B are inclined to one another by one minute. For this reason, the nautical mile is often defined as the length of an arc of a meridian subtending an angle of one minute at the centre of curvature.

The centre of curvature of any part of a meridian is not located at the Earth's centre, as will be evident from Fig. 1. The radius

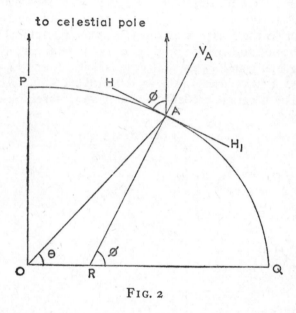

FIG. 2

of curvature varies with latitude, it being greatest at the poles and least at the equator. The curvature of the meridians being greatest at the equator—where the radius of curvature is least—results in the length of the nautical mile, as defined above, being least at the equator, its length increasing polewards.

Referring to Fig. 2, in which PQ is a quadrant of a meridian, O being the centre of the Earth; the geographical latitude of A is ϕ. This is equivalent to the angle at R, between the vertical at A and the plane of the equator measured in the plane of the meridian of A.

The angle at the Earth's centre O, between the radius AO and the plane of the equator (θ in Fig. 2), is an angle known as the *geocentric latitude* of A. Because the geocentric latitude is never greater than the geographical latitude of the same point, it is often called *reduced latitude*, and the angular difference between geographical and reduced latitudes of any place on the Earth's surface is known as the *reduction of the latitude*.

The reduction of the latitude is nil for latitudes 0° and 90°, and has its greatest value when the geographical latitude is 45°.

We have shown in Chapter Two, which deals with the geometry of the ellipse, that:

$$\tan (\phi - r) = (1 - c)^2 \tan \phi \qquad (1)$$

applying this formula to the Earth's meridians where:

ϕ = geographical latitude

$r = (\phi - \theta)$

θ = geocentric latitude

c = the ellipticity of the meridian

In this case:

$$\phi - r = \theta$$

therefore:

$$\tan \theta = (1 - c)^2 \tan \phi \qquad (2)$$

Expanding formula (1) we have:

$$\frac{\tan \phi - \tan r}{1 + \tan \phi \tan r} = \tan \phi \, (1 + c^2 - 2c)$$

i.e. $\qquad \tan \phi - \tan r = \tan \phi \, (1 + \tan \phi \tan r)(1 + c^2 - 2c)$

i.e. $\qquad \tan \phi - \tan r = (\tan \phi + \tan^2 \phi \tan r)(1 + c^2 - 2c)$

i.e. $\qquad \tan \phi - \tan r = \tan \phi + \tan \phi \, c^2 - 2c \tan \phi$

$$+ \tan^2 \phi \tan r + \tan^2 \phi \tan r \, c^2$$

$$- \tan^2 \phi \tan r \, 2c \qquad (3)$$

Now the quantities c and r are small compared with ϕ, so that $\tan r$ may be expressed as r radians, and terms containing c^2 and products of c and r may be ignored. Therefore equation (3) reduces to:

$$-r = -2c \tan \phi + r \tan^2 \phi$$

and

$$2c \tan \phi = r(1 + \tan^2 \phi)$$

i.e.

$$r = \frac{2c \tan \phi}{1 + \tan^2 \phi}$$

i.e.

$$r = \frac{2c \tan \phi}{\sec^2 \phi}$$

i.e.

$$r = 2c \sin \phi \cos \phi$$

Therefore:

$$r = c \sin 2\phi \qquad (4)$$

From formula (4) the reduction of the latitude can be found for any value of geographical latitude for any terrestrial spheroid.

If c is $1/300$, then r is $1/300$ radians when ϕ is $45°$. Assuming that one radian is equivalent to $3,438$ minutes, then the maximum value of r for a terrestrial spheroid in which c is $1/300$ is ($1/300 \times 3,438$), that is $11 \cdot 46$.

2. Length of a nautical mile in any latitude

Referring to Fig. 3: A and A_1 are two points on the meridian PQ. Let ϕ be the geographical latitude of A and let $(\phi - \delta\phi)$ be the geographical latitude of A_1, where $\delta\phi$ is a small increment. Let θ be the geocentric latitude of A.

Let the coordinates of A be (x, y) and those of A_1 be $(x - \delta x, y + \delta y)$ the axes of reference being OX and OY through O the Earth's centre. Since AA_1 is a small arc of the meridian through A, the triangle AA_1B may be regarded as a plane triangle right-angled at B. Let the distance AA_1 be denoted by δs, thus:

$$\sec \phi = \frac{\delta s}{\delta y} \text{ approximately}$$

In the limit as

$$\delta s \to O, \quad \frac{\delta s}{\delta y} \to \frac{ds}{dy}$$

and so

$$\frac{ds}{dy} = \sec \phi \text{ exactly}$$

This gives the limiting ratio between the length of an arc of a meridian and the length of the piece of the ordinate through A_1 Now the limiting ratio between δs and $\delta\phi$, which is what we require, may be expressed in the form:

$$\frac{ds}{d\phi} = \frac{ds}{dy}\frac{dy}{d\phi}$$

i.e.
$$\frac{ds}{d\phi} = \sec\phi \frac{dy}{d\phi} \qquad\qquad (A)$$

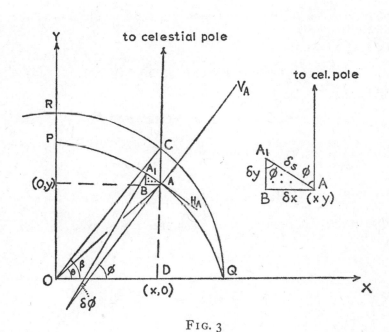

FIG. 3

Consider the circle which lies in the plane of the meridian PQ, and whose radius is OQ. Let the ordinate through A cut the circle at C, and let the radius through C make an angle of β at O with the X axis.

In triangle OCD: $x = a \cos\beta$

From the general equation of the ellipse:

$$\frac{x^2}{a^2} + \frac{y^2}{b^2} = 1$$

$$\frac{y^2}{b^2} = 1 - \frac{x^2}{a^2}$$

$$= 1 - \cos^2 \beta$$

$$= \sin^2 \beta$$

and
$$y = b \sin \beta$$

where a and b are the semi-major and semi-minor axes of the elliptical meridian.

We have shown that:

$$\tan(\phi - r) = (1 - c)^2 \tan \phi \text{ (p. 49)} \qquad (1)$$

and because
$$\phi - r = \theta$$

therefore
$$\tan \theta = (1 - c)^2 \tan \phi \qquad (2)$$

Now
$$\tan \theta = \frac{y}{x}$$

therefore
$$\frac{y}{x} = (1 - c)^2 \tan \phi$$

Substituting values for x and y given above, we have:

$$\frac{b \sin \beta}{a \cos \beta} = (1 - c)^2 \tan \phi$$

Now
$$\frac{b}{a} = (1 - c)$$

therefore
$$\tan \beta = (1 - c) \tan \phi \qquad (3)$$

Differentiating (3) with respect to ϕ, we have:

$$\sec^2 \beta \frac{d\beta}{d\phi} = (1 - c) \sec^2 \phi$$

$$\frac{d\beta}{d\phi} = (1 - c) \sec^2 \phi \cos^2 \beta \qquad (4)$$

Now
$$y = b \sin \beta$$

therefore
$$\frac{dy}{d\beta} = b \cos \beta \qquad (5)$$

Now
$$\frac{dy}{d\phi} = \frac{dy}{d\beta} \frac{d\beta}{d\phi}$$

Substituting values for $dy/d\beta$ and $d\beta/d\phi$ from equations (4) and (5), we have:

$$\frac{dy}{d\phi} = b \cos \beta (1-c) \sec^2 \phi \cos^2 \beta$$

that is
$$\frac{dy}{d\phi} = b(1-c) \sec^2 \phi \cos^3 \beta$$

i.e.
$$\frac{dy}{d\phi} = \frac{a(1-c)^2 \sec^2 \phi}{\sec^3 \beta}$$

i.e.
$$\frac{dy}{d\phi} = \frac{a(1-c)^2 \sec^2 \phi}{(1+\tan^2 \beta)^{3/2}}$$

Substituting the value for $\tan \beta$ from equation (3) we have:

$$\frac{dy}{d\phi} = \frac{a(1-c)^2 \sec^2 \phi}{[1+(1-c)^2 \tan^2 \phi]^{3/2}}$$

i.e.
$$\frac{dy}{d\phi} = \frac{a(1-c)^2 \cos \phi}{[\cos^2 \phi + (1-c)^2 \sin^2 \phi]^{3/2}}$$

i.e.
$$\frac{dy}{d\phi} = a(1-c)^2 \cos \phi [\cos^2 \phi + (1-c)^2 \sin^2 \phi]^{-3/2}$$

Expanding the right-hand side of this expression and neglecting powers of c higher than one, we have:

$$\frac{dy}{d\phi} = a(1-2c) \cos \phi [1 + 3c \sin^2 \phi]$$

i.e.
$$\frac{dy}{d\phi} = a \cos \phi [1 - 2c + 3c \sin^2 \phi]$$

i.e.
$$\frac{dy}{d\phi} = a \cos \phi [1 - c(2 - 3 \sin^2 \phi)]$$

i.e. $$\frac{dy}{d\phi} = a \cos \phi [1 - c/2(4 - 6 \sin^2 \phi)]$$

i.e. $$\frac{dy}{d\phi} = a \cos \phi [1 - c/2(1 + 3 \cos 2\phi)]$$

Substituting this value for $dy/d\phi$ in equation (A) we get:

$$\frac{ds}{d\phi} = \sec \phi \, a \cos \phi [1 - c/2(1 + 3 \cos 2\phi)]$$

i.e. $$\frac{ds}{d\phi} = a[1 - c/2(1 + 3 \cos 2\phi)]$$

and $$ds = a[1 - c/2(1 + 3 \cos 2\phi)] \, d\phi$$

also $$\delta s = a[1 - c/2(1 + 3 \cos 2\phi)] \, \delta\phi$$

provided that δs and $\delta \phi$ are small quantities.

If ϕ is one minute of arc, i.e. $1/3438$ radians, then δs is equivalent to one nautical mile. Thus:

In latitude ϕ

$$\text{Length of a nautical mile} = \frac{a}{3,438} [1 - c/2(1 + 3 \cos 2\phi)]$$

In latitude $0°$

$$\text{Length of nautical mile} = \frac{a}{3,438} (1 - 2c)$$

In latitude $90°$

$$\text{Length of nautical mile} = \frac{a}{3,438} (1 + c)$$

If c is taken as $1/300$, the difference between the maximum and minimum lengths of the nautical mile is:

$$= \frac{a}{3,438} (1 + c) - \frac{a}{3,438} (1 - 2c)$$

$$= \frac{a}{3,438} 3c$$

$$= \frac{a}{3,438} \, 3\left(\frac{1}{300}\right)$$

$$= \frac{u}{343,800}$$

where a is the equatorial radius of the spheroid. The value of this difference is approximately 60 feet.

To define the length of a nautical mile—which, as we have seen, is a unit the length of which varies with the latitude—the figure of the Earth for a particular ellipsoid must be used. Ideally the nautical mile should be related to the spheroid used as a basis for navigational charts. But several spheroids have been used for this purpose, there being no measure of uniformity amongst chartmakers of different nations in this respect. British Admiralty charts are based on the Clarke spheroid of 1880 which has an ellipticity of $1/293 \cdot 5$ and an equatorial radius of 20,925,972 feet. On this spheroid, the length of the nautical mile at latitude $0°$ is 6,046 feet, and at latitude $90°$, it is 6,108 feet. The average length of a nautical mile on the Clarke (1880) ellipsoid is 6,077 feet, this being the length in latitude $45°$. The general expression for finding the length of a nautical mile in any latitude ϕ is:

$$(6,077 - 31 \cos 2\phi) \text{ feet}$$

The standard nautical mile adopted in Great Britain is 6,080 feet, which is the length of a nautical mile in latitude $48°$. This is the nearest round figure to the length of the average nautical mile.

The standard nautical mile is used as a basis for calibrating patent logs which register the distance run by a ship through the water. No material error is introduced into normal navigational problems by using the standard nautical mile for all latitudes. The greatest error occurs in equatorial latitudes; but, even here, the error amounts to no more than about one mile in fifty. That is to say, the maximum percentage error is about 2%. Since errors in the estimated effects of wind and current normally exceed this, the discrepancy due to the standard nautical mile being different in length from that of the actual nautical mile escapes notice in practical navigation.

7

In the U.S.A., the nautical mile is defined as the length of a minute of arc of a great circle on a sphere, the surface area of which is equal to that of the Clarke spheroid of 1866. The figure of the Earth for this spheroid ($c = 1/295$, $a = 20,925,832$ feet) forms the basis of the navigational charts published by the U.S.A. Hydrographic Office. In English feet, the nautical mile, as defined in the U.S.A., is 6,080·2 feet. It is coincidental that this figure is almost identical with the length of the standard nautical mile of Great Britain.

3. *Rhumb-line sailing. Parallel and plane sailing formulae*

Treating the Earth as a sphere it is an easy matter to prove that the length of any parallel of latitude is proportional to the cosine of the latitude. If we regard a mile as a unit the length of which is equivalent to an arc length of one minute of a spherical Earth, then the distance in miles between any two points on the same parallel of latitude is equal to the product of the difference of longitude (d.long.) between the two points in minutes of arc, and the cosine of the latitude. In other words:

$$d = D \cos \theta$$

where d is distance between two points along parallel of latitude θ,
    D is d.long. between points.

This formula is known to seamen as the *parallel sailing formula*. A simple proof of its validity follows.

In Fig. 4, C and D are two points on the same parallel of latitude θ North. PA and PB are the meridians of these points, and O is the spherical Earth's centre.

$$\frac{CD}{AB} = \frac{d}{D}$$

$$= \frac{CE}{AO} \quad \text{(radii} \propto \text{arcs)}$$

$$= \frac{CE}{OC} \quad \text{(AO = OC, radius of sphere)}$$

$$= \cos \text{ angle ECO}$$

$$= \cos \theta \quad \text{(ECO = CAO alternate angles)}$$

Therefore:

$$d = D \cos \theta$$

The distance in miles that one terrestrial position is east or west of another is known as the *departure* between the two positions. The departure between two positions on the same parallel of latitude θ may be found from the parallel sailing formula, that is:

departure along parallel = d.long. × cos latitude θ

It follows from the parallel sailing formula that the length of any parallel of latitude is equal to the product of the length of the equator and the cosine of the latitude of the parallel.

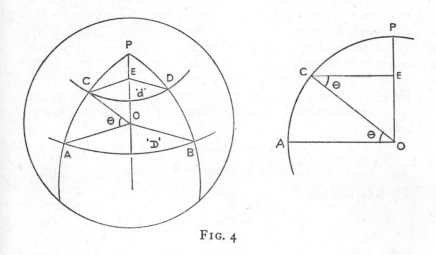

Fig. 4

The length of the equator is (360 × 60), that is 216,000 miles, so that the length of any parallel in miles is 216,000 cos lat. The length of parallel 60°, is 108,000 miles because the cosine of 60° is 0·5, etc.

The horizontal angle between the plane of the meridian and the direction of a ship's fore and aft line is known as the *ship's course*. Now the most convenient method of sailing from one position to another, is one in which the course is constant. A line of constant course cuts all the meridians it intersects at the same angle. Any such line, which cuts meridians obliquely, is known as a *loxodrome*, a word derived from the Greek *loxos* meaning oblique and *dromos* meaning running.

On a ship sailing along a loxodrome it is easy to see that a horizontal straight line extending from the centre of the compass through the point of the compass card which is coincident with the lubber's line marking the ship's course, is in line with the loxodrome along which the ship is sailing. The radial lines on a mariner's compass are called *rhumb lines*. Therefore, a line of constant course is called a rhumb line, this homely name being used by seamen instead of the more sophisticated name loxodrome.

When a vessel steams along a meridian, the distance she makes, assuming that there is no wind or current, is equal in miles to the angular difference in minutes of arc between the latitudes left and arrived at—a quantity known as *d.lat.* When a vessel steams along a parallel of latitude, the distance she makes, as we have noted, is equal to the departure (dep.) between the points left and arrived at. When a vessel steams along any rhumb line which is oblique to the meridians she crosses, the d.lat. and dep. she makes can be found by means of the *plane sailing formulae*:

$$\text{Departure} = \text{Distance} \times \sin \text{course} \qquad (1)$$

$$\text{d.lat.} = \text{Distance} \times \cos \text{course} \qquad (2)$$

From (1) and (2),

$$\frac{\text{dep.}}{\text{d.lat.}} = \tan \text{course} \qquad (3)$$

The plane sailing formulae are so-called because plane trigonometry is used when solving problems by their means. In other words, the arguments used can be represented as forming parts of a plane right-angled triangle. The hypotenuse of this triangle, a typical one of which is illustrated in Fig. 5, represents the rhumbline distance. One of the non-90° angles is the course angle, and the sides opposite to and adjacent to the course angle are the departure and d.lat. respectively.

Fig. 6 illustrates a typical rhumb line extending from a point A on the equator, the course angle being θ.

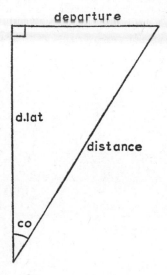

FIG. 5

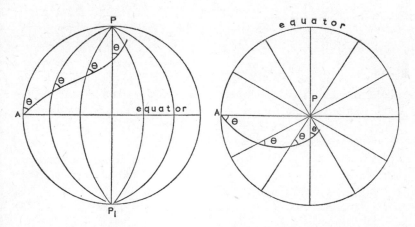

FIG. 6

It will be noticed from the diagrams of Fig. 6, that a ship following a rhumb line which crosses the meridians obliquely, will trace out an equi-angular spiral curve which, assuming that the ship is sailing polewards, will continually get closer to the pole of the hemisphere in which the ship is sailing. The spiral form of an oblique rhumb line is due to the *convergence of the meridians* towards the pole.

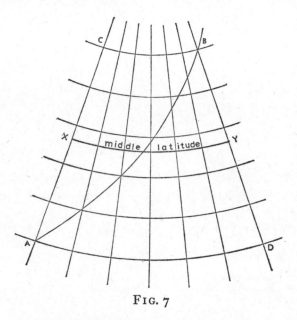

FIG. 7

The angle between the tangents to the meridians of any two places on the globe is known as the *angle of convergency*. The angle of convergency for any two points on the equator is zero, because all meridians are parallel to one another at the equator. As the latitude increases, the angle of convergency between points on different meridians increases until a maximum is reached in latitude 90° where the angle of convergency is equal to the d.long. between the meridians. Convergency, therefore, varies as the sine of the latitude. The general formula for convergency is:

Convergency = d.long. sin lat.

Fig. 7 illustrates a part of the northern hemisphere of the

Earth with the graticule of parallels of latitude and meridians. The curved line AB is a rhumb line.

The number of miles that B is north of A is equal to the number of minutes of arc of any meridian between the parallels of latitude through A and B. Thus,

Distance AC = Distance DB = d.lat. AB

The number of miles that B is east of A, that is to say, the departure between A and B, is greater than the distance CB and less than the distance AD.

If the Earth is considered to be perfectly spherical the departure between A and B may be considered to be the departure between two points X and Y on the meridians through A and B respectively, along a parallel of latitude between those through A and B. The latitude of this parallel is an angle known as the *middle latitude*—an unfortunate name because it is not, as might at first be thought, the arithmetical mean of the latitudes of the parallels through A and B—an angle known as *mean latitude*.

For short distances, it is generally sufficiently accurate to assume that the departure between A and B is the east–west distance in miles along the parallel of the mean latitude; but, for long-distance sailing, a correction should be applied to the mean latitude to obtain the middle latitude if it is necessary to convert d.long. between two positions into departure, or vice versa, using the parallel sailing principle. Before discussing this problem further, let us first prove the plane sailing formulae.

Fig. 8 represents a portion of the Earth's surface on which the rhumb line AB is drawn. AD and BC are portions of parallels of latitude through A and B respectively, and AC and BD are portions of meridians through A and B respectively.

Let the rhumb-line course be θ; the distance between A and B be S; and the d.lat. and dep L and P respectively. Consider a small element of the track δS between points a and c on the track. The sides of the small triangle abc formed by δS and the meridian through a and the parallel through b, may be regarded as a plane right-angled triangle in which δL is an element of d.lat. between a and b, and δP is an element of departure between a and b. In triangle abc:

$$\delta L = \delta S \cos \theta \quad \text{and} \quad \delta P = \delta S \sin \theta$$

Now
$$L = \sum_{\text{lat A}}^{\text{lat B}} \delta L \quad \text{and} \quad P = \sum_{\text{lat A}}^{\text{lat B}} \delta P$$

Therefore,

$$L = \sum_{\text{lat A}}^{\text{lat B}} \delta S \cos \theta \quad \text{and} \quad P = \sum_{\text{lat A}}^{\text{lat B}} \delta S \sin \theta$$

Therefore
$$L = S \cos \theta$$
$$P = S \sin \theta$$

or,
$$\text{d.lat.} = \text{distance} \times \text{sine course}$$
$$\text{dep.} = \text{distance} \times \text{cosine course}$$

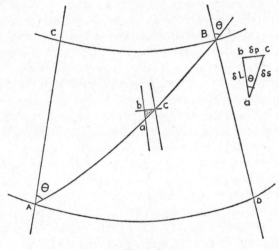

Fig. 8

It should be noted that the canons of plane sailing hold good for all distances on a spherical Earth. It should also be noted that the plane sailing formulae cannot alone provide a solution to either of the practical sailing problems, viz:

(1) To find the rhumb-line course and distance between two given positions.

(2) To find the position of arrival after sailing a given distance on a given rhumb-line course from a given position.

The reason for this is that the argument d.long. does not appear in the plane sailing formulae.

4. The Mercator chart

To solve a rhumb-line sailing problem, the navigator uses the *Mercator principle*, named after the Flemish cartographer and geographer who was first to devise a chart for seamen which took into account the convergency of the meridians, and which allowed for the diminishing distance polewards between any two given meridians along parallels of latitude. There is little or no doubt that Mercator did not fully understand the mathematical principle of the chart which bears his name, and the discovery of this principle and its explanation was left to our compatriot Edward Wright—a scholar foremost amongst the many mathematical navigators of Elizabethan times, an era in which many of Britain's illustrious philosophers devoted their talents to the advancement of the science of navigation.

The great need that a navigator has in respect of his chart is that it should be *orthomorphic*. That is to say, angles—essentially course and bearing angles—should be represented truly. On the Mercator chart all rhumb lines are projected as straight lines; and, being based on an orthomorphic principle, angles at all points on the chart are truly represented. In particular, the angles between parallels of latitude and meridians, which are everywhere on the globe equal to 90°, are represented as right angles on the chart. In other words, the *graticule* of the chart, that is to say the network of projected parallels and meridians, has a rectangular pattern, meridians and parallels of latitude being represented by parallel straight lines intersecting at right angles.

Because meridians are projected on a Mercator chart as parallel straight lines, the exaggeration of the spacing of the meridians increases polewards; and because on the globe all meridians converge to a point, whereas on the chart they appear as parallel straight lines, the east–west exaggeration of any part of the chart is proportional to the secant of the latitude. To achieve the property of orthomorphism, the spacing of the projected parallels of latitude increases polewards, the north–south exaggeration of any part of the chart being proportional to the secant of the latitude. Because the spacing of the projected parallels of latitude is not uniform, the latitude scale, which is also the scale of distance, is variable. This is the principal defect of the Mercator chart for navigational purposes.

Although areas are exaggerated on a Mercator chart, and polar regions cannot be represented (and seamen are not the least bit concerned with either of these considerations), the map is orthomorphic and rhumb lines are projected as straight lines. These two factors make the Mercator chart ideally suited to the needs of the navigator.

In order to find the rhumb-line course from one point to another, the projected positions of the points are connected with a straight line. The inclination of this straight line with any of the projected meridians which it crosses is the rhumb-line course angle. This is measured by means of a pair of parallel rulers. Although, in general, distances on a Mercator chart cannot be measured accurately, they can, nevertheless, be measured with a degree of accuracy sufficient for the needs of navigation by using the variable latitude scale in the vicinity of the middle latitude of the rhumb-line track.

Finding the rhumb-line course and distance between two places by means of a Mercator chart is only one of two practical sailing problems: the other is related to finding the position of arrival after sailing on a given course for a given distance. This problem can be solved by means of a Mercator chart just as easily as the problem of finding a rhumb-line course and distance.

To facilitate the calculation of either of the practical rhumb-line sailing problems (and this may be necessary when a large-scale chart is not available), the Mercator principle is employed through the agency of meridional parts.

MERIDIONAL PARTS

The scale of longitude on a Mercator chart is constant, and the length of a minute of longitude on a Mercator chart provides a convenient unit, therefore, for constructing Mercator charts, and also for calculating rhumb-line sailing problems.

The number of units of the longitude scale contained in any piece of a projected meridian between the projected equator and any projected parallel of latitude is known as the *meridional parts* for that latitude. Meridional parts (m.pts) for all latitudes have been calculated and tabulated, and the navigator arms himself with a table of m.pts, by means of which he may solve his sailing problems accurately by calculation.

Fig. 9 illustrates a portion of a Mercator chart. It will be noticed that the spacing of the meridians is constant, but that of the parallels of latitude which are projected increases polewards.

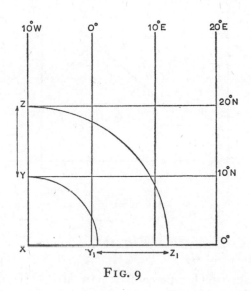

FIG. 9

The number of minutes of the longitude scale contained in any piece of a meridian may readily be found by means of a pair of drawing compasses or dividers.

Referring to Fig. 9: with centre X and radius XY, an arc cutting the projected equator will cut off, between X and Y_1, the number of m.pts for latitude 10°. Similarly, with centre X and radius XZ, an arc cutting the projected equator will cut off, between X and Z_1, the number of m.pts for latitude 20°. The difference between the m.pts for any two latitudes, is equal to the number of m.pts contained in the piece of any meridian between the projected parallels of latitude. This difference is known as the *difference of meridional parts*—abbreviated to D.M.P.

If tables of m.pts are available, the D.M.P. between any two places may be found if the latitudes of the places are known. If the longitudes of the two places are also known, the rhumb-line course from either to the other may readily be found.

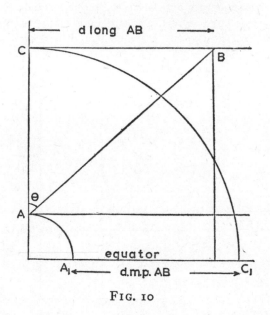

FIG. 10

In Fig. 10, which represents a part of a Mercator chart on which the rhumb line joining A to B is projected, the rhumb-line course is $\theta°$ as shown. In the right-angled triangle ABC, the sides AC and BC, if measured on the scale of longitude in minutes, will give the D.M.P. and d.long. respectively between A and B.

Now, $$\tan \theta = \frac{BC}{AC}$$

therefore $$\tan \text{course} = \frac{\text{d.long.}}{\text{D.M.P.}}$$

or $$\cot \text{course} = \frac{\text{D.M.P.}}{\text{d.long.}}$$

Having found the course by the Mercator principle, the distance may be found by the plane sailing formula which connects distance, d.lat., and course angle.

viz.   distance = d.lat. secant course

5. *Middle-latitude sailing*

A method alternative to the Mercator method, described above, for solving practical rhumb-line sailing problems, is known as *Middle-Latitude Sailing*.

We have shown that:

$$\frac{\text{dep}}{\text{d.lat.}} = \text{tan course} \qquad (1)$$

$$\frac{\text{d.long.}}{\text{D.M.P.}} = \text{tan course} \qquad (2)$$

$$\frac{\text{dep}}{\text{d.long.}} = \text{cos middle latitude} \qquad (3)$$

From (1) and (2), we get:

$$\frac{\text{dep}}{\text{d.lat.}} = \frac{\text{d.long.}}{\text{D.M.P.}}$$

therefore: $$\frac{\text{dep.}}{\text{d.long.}} = \frac{\text{d.lat.}}{\text{D.M.P.}}$$

But, $$\frac{\text{dep.}}{\text{d.long.}} = \text{cos middle latitude}$$

therefore: $$\frac{\text{d.lat.}}{\text{D.M.P.}} = \text{cos middle latitude}$$

The angular difference between the mean and middle latitudes of any rhumb-line track may be found by using the Mercator principle. This angular difference is usually described as the *correction to apply to the mean latitude to give the middle latitude*. The middle latitude is the name given to the angle whose cosine is equal to the ratio between departure in miles and d.long. in minutes of arc, between any two terrestrial positions.

A table of these corrections for all practical values of mean latitude and d.lat. was first drawn up by Workman in the early years of the 19th century. When Workman introduced his mean-to middle-latitude correction table, a second method of solving rhumb-line sailing problems became available. This alternative method, in effect, was Mercator sailing by Workman's method, as distinct from Mercator sailing by Wright's method—the latter method requiring the use of a table of meridional parts.

The following example should make it clear how Workman's correction is found for any particular values of mean latitude and d.lat.

Example. Using a table of m.pts for sphere, find the middle latitude between A in latitude 20°N., and B in latitude 30°N., and hence find Workman's correction.

$$\text{Lat. A} = 20° \ 00'\text{N.} \qquad \text{m.pts lat. } 20° = 1225\cdot14$$

$$\text{Lat. B} = 30° \ 00'\text{N.} \qquad \text{m.pts lat. } 30° = 1888\cdot38$$

$$\text{d.lat.} = 10° \ 00 \qquad\qquad\quad \text{D.M.P.} = \ 663\cdot24$$

$$= 600'\text{N.}$$

Now, $\qquad\qquad$ Sec Mid. Lat. $= \dfrac{\text{D.M.P.}}{\text{d.lat.}}$

$$= \frac{663\cdot24}{600}$$

$$= 1\cdot1054$$

$$\text{Middle latitude} = 25° \ 14'\text{N.}$$

$$\text{Mean latitude} = 25° \ 00'\text{N.}$$

$$\text{Workman's corr.} = \qquad 14'.$$

6. *Great-circle sailing*

The principal disadvantage of rhumb-line sailing is that a rhumb-line track between two places is not the line of least distance unless the track lies along the equator or along any meridian. The shortest route between two points on the surface of a sphere is along the minor arc of the great circle on which the two points lie.

The difference between the rhumb-line and great-circle distances between two places is dependent upon:

(a) the distance between the two places
(b) the latitudes of the two places
(c) the difference of longitude between the two places.

When the distance and d.long. are large, and the latitudes of the places are high, the difference between the rhumb-line and great-circle distances between the places is considerable. For long-distance sailing, therefore, especially in high latitudes, great-circle routes should be followed when safe and practicable, for reasons of economy.

Great-circle sailing has two principal disadvantages viz.:

(a) the course is different at every point on the track.
(b) the ship is carried into latitudes higher than those into which she would be carried were the single rhumb-line track between the places followed. Consequently there may be delays because of foul weather which is usually associated with high latitudes, despite the shorter distance.

A third disadvantage of great-circle sailing is due to the relative difficulty of drawing a great-circle track on a Mercator chart.

The main problems of great-circle sailing are those involved in finding: the initial course; the spherical distance; and positions of points on the track to facilitate the plotting of the track on a Mercator chart. These problems are simplified by means of a gnomonic chart or, in the absence of such a chart, by means of great-circle tables, which contain solutions of numerous spherical triangles, laid down in an orderly tabular arrangement.

A gnomonic chart is one based on the gnomonic projection, which is a geometrical or perspective projection described in Chapter Eight. The principal property of a gnomonic chart is that all great circles are projected as straight lines. Angles are distorted on a gnomonic chart but positions (latitudes and longitudes) may be lifted or plotted with ease. If it is intended to navigate along a great-circle track between two positions, the positions are first plotted on a gnomonic chart, and a straight line is drawn between them. This straight line represents the great circle track. The positions of several points on the track are lifted and transferred to the Mercator chart. A fair curve is then drawn through these plotted positions, this representing the great-circle track on the navigational chart. The ship is then navigated along this track by means of a series of short rhumb-lines. Each time the ship's position is found during the passage, the procedure is repeated if necessary and the new great-circle track connecting the ship's position to the destination is determined.

If a gnomonic chart is not at hand the same problems may be solved by means of tables. The following mathematical treatment of a great-circle sailing problem forms the basis of the construction of great-circle tables.

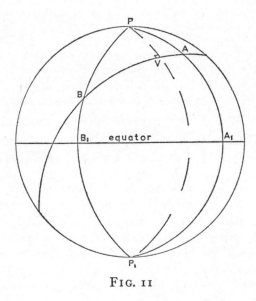

FIG. 11

Fig. 11 illustrates the spherical Earth with the great-circle track between A and B drawn. PAP_1 and PBP_1 are the meridians respectively of A and B. The arcs AA_1 and BB_1 are respectively the latitudes of A and B.

In the spherical triangle APB:

$$\text{Arc AP} = (90° - \text{lat A})$$

$$\text{Arc BP} = (90° - \text{lat B})$$

Given two sides and the included angle of the spherical triangle APB, the third side, arc AB, which is the spherical distance between A and B, may be found by means of spherical trigonometry.

The fundamental spherical cosine formula, viz.:

$$\cos AB = \cos P \sin PA \sin BP + \cos PA \cos BP$$

may be used for this purpose, although practical navigators use a formula derived from this.

Having found the spherical distance AB, the initial course, which is found from PAB, may then be computed. Using the fundamental cosine formula to find this angle given the three sides, we have:

$$\cos A = \frac{\cos PB - \cos PA \cos AB}{\sin PA \sin AB}$$

Alternatively, the fundamental spherical sine formula may be used for finding angle A, care being taken to give A its correct value, remembering that $\sin A = \sin (180° - A)$.

$$\sin A = \frac{\sin PB \sin P}{\sin AB}$$

It is evident, from Fig. 11, that the course angle changes along the track AB. There are two points on every great circle where the course angle, that is the angle between the great circle and the meridian, is a right angle. These two points are called the *vertices* of the great circle. One vertex lies in the northern hemisphere and the other lies in the southern hemisphere occupying an antipodal position to the northern vertex.

The vertex lying within the hemisphere in which a great circle track lies, may be within or outside the track. If the angles A and B are both less than 90° the vertex lies within the track, but if one of the two angles is greater and the other one less than 90°, the vertex lies outside the track on the side of the greater angle.

If the vertex of a great-circle track lies between the position left and the destination, the course of the ship changes from northerly to southerly (or vice versa) at the vertex where the course is 090° or 270°. The vertex, therefore, is the point of highest latitude of a great circle.

8

The meridian through the vertex of a great circle cuts the great circle at a right angle; and, by means of Napier's *Rules for Circular Parts*, the position of the vertex of a great circle may readily be found if the initial (or final) course is known.

Having found the position of the vertex of a great circle, it is an easy matter—again using Napier's *Rules*—to calculate the longitudes of points whose latitudes are given, and which lie on the track. These positions are plotted on a Mercator chart so that the great-circle track may be drawn.

CHAPTER FIVE
The Earth's Orbit

1. *Equinox and solstice*

The Earth, in common with all spinning bodies, possesses the property of *gyroscopic inertia*. Gyroscopic inertia, which is sometimes called *rigidity in space*, is the property of a spinning body by virtue of which it tends to maintain its plane of rotation. In other words, the axis of rotation of a spinning body tends to remain pointing rigidly to a fixed point in space. This it will do if no external couples act on the body. An external couple acting on a rotating mass tends to cause the axis of rotation of the mass to describe a conical rotation which is slow compared with the rotation of the mass about its spin axis. This relatively slow motion is known as *precession*.

The Earth's axis precesses in response to the external couples due to gravitational forces acting between the Earth and the Sun and between the Earth and the Moon. The rate of precession of the Earth's axis is extremely slow: one complete circle, having a spherical radius of $23\frac{1}{2}°$, is described in about 26,000 years. The effects of the precession of the Earth's axis are of prime importance to astronomers, but are of little or no concern of the geographer.

In contrast to precession, the other property of the spinning Earth, viz., her tendency to maintain her plane of spin because of her gyroscopic inertia, is, as we shall see presently, of great importance to geographers. For practical purposes we may regard the spin axis of the Earth as pointing to two fixed points on the celestial concave known respectively as the *north* and *south celestial poles*. The great circle on the Earth which lies in the plane of the Earth's rotation is the equator, and the projection of the equator from the Earth's centre on to the celestial sphere is the *equinoctial*.

The Earth not only rotates about her axis; she also revolves around the Sun, describing one circuit of an elliptical orbit in a natural unit of time known as a *year*. The revolution of the Earth around the Sun is manifested by an apparent revolution of the Sun around the celestial concave, against the background of the fixed stars, once in a year. The circular path which the Sun appears to trace out on the celestial concave, during his annual apparent revolution, is known as the *ecliptic*. Fig. 1 serves to illustrate the Sun's apparent annual circuit of the heavens across the background of the fixed stars.

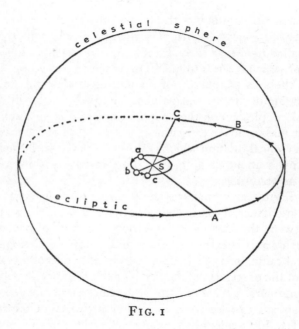

FIG. 1

In Fig. 1 the large circle represents the celestial concave with the Sun, denoted by S, occupying the central position. The small ellipse represents the Earth's orbit. When the Earth is at a, b and c, in her orbit, the Sun appears to be at A, B and C respectively on the celestial sphere. As the Earth moves in her orbit from a to c, the Sun appears to move across the surface of the celestial sphere from A through B to C. The great circle on the celestial sphere on which these points lie is the ecliptic.

2. *The seasons*

The planes of the Earth's rotation about her spin axis, and her revolution around the Sun, are inclined to one another at an angle of 23½° approximately. This angle is known as the *obliquity of the ecliptic,* and it is clearly equal to the angle between the planes of the equinoctial and the ecliptic, or the maximum declination of the Sun.

The Earth's spin axis is inclined at an angle of 66½° approximately to the plane of her orbit around the Sun; and, because of

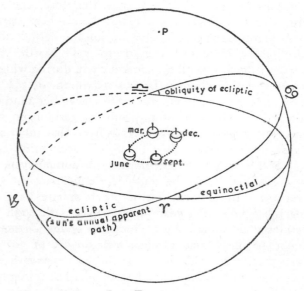

FIG. 2

the Earth's gyroscopic inertia, this angle is constant. It follows, therefore, that for half the year the Earth's North Pole is directed towards the Sun, and for the remaining half year it is directed away from the Sun. As a consequence of this, the year is naturally divided into four *seasons.* Moreover, the lengths of daylight and darkness during any 24-hour period between successive sunrises or sunsets are not generally equal to one another.

Fig. 2 serves to illustrate the ecliptic, or Sun's annual apparent path, in relation to the equinoctial.

On March 21st the Sun appears to occupy a point on the celestial sphere which is on the equinoctial. At this time of the year, the Sun moves from the southern into the northern celestial hemisphere. In other words, his declination changes from southerly to northerly. For the following three months the declination of the Sun increases from $0°$ until it reaches a maximum of $23\frac{1}{2}°$ approximately on June 21st, after which the declination decreases until it is $0°$ again on September 23rd. Between September 23rd and the following March 21st, the Sun's declination is southerly, reaching a maximum of $23\frac{1}{2}°$ approximately on December 22nd. The year is, therefore, divided into four periods or seasons. In the northern hemisphere, *spring* extends from March 21st to June 21st, during the period when the Sun's declination increases from $0°$ to $23\frac{1}{2}°$ North. *Summer* extends from June 21st until September 23rd, during which time the Sun's declination changes from a maximum of $23\frac{1}{2}°$ to $0°$. *Autumn* extends from September 23rd to December 22nd during which time the declination of the Sun increases from $0°$ to a maximum of $23\frac{1}{2}°$ South. *Winter* extends from December 22nd to March 21st during which time the Sun's declination changes from $23\frac{1}{2}°$ South back to $0°$ to complete his annual cycle of the changes in declination. In the southern hemisphere the seasons are the reverse of those in the northern hemisphere.

During the course of a year the Sun passes through twelve constellations which form the twelve *signs of the Zodiac*. Each constellation of the zodiac extends over an arc of $30°$ of the ecliptic, so that at monthly intervals the Sun moves from one zodiacal constellation to the next adjacent one. For this reason we say that on March 21st, the Sun enters the constellation of Aries the Ram. A month later he enters the constellation of Taurus the Bull, and so on. The constellations of the zodiac are given in order in the following well-known rhyme:

> The ram, the bull, the heavenly twins,
> The next the crab, the lion shines,
> The virgin and the scales;
> The scorpion, archer and he-goat,
> The man that holds the watering pot,
> And fish with glittering tails.

On March 21st the Sun is said to be at the *first point of Aries*, and on September 23rd he is said to be at the *first point of Libra.* These points on the celestial sphere are denoted by ♈ and ♎ respectively. They are also known as the *spring* or *vernal* and the *autumnal equinoxes* respectively. The name *equinox* signifies that on these days there is equal daylight and darkness for every place on Earth.

On June the 21st the Sun is said to be at the *first point of Cancer,*

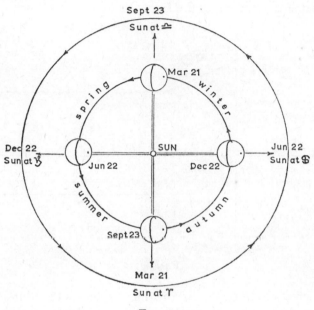

FIG. 3

and on December 22nd he is said to be at the *first point of Capricorn.* On these days, when the Sun's declination is maximum, he appears to stand still in the sky; that is to say, he ceases to increase his declination. For this reason the first points of Cancer and Capricorn are known as the *solstitial points,* the *summer* and *winter solstices* respectively.

Fig. 3 illustrates the seasons.

Fig. 3 illustrates the Earth's orbit drawn on the plane of the ecliptic. The position of the Earth in her orbit is shown for each of the four principal points of the orbit, namely the points occupied by the Earth on the days of the equinoxes and solstices. It will be noticed from Fig. 3 that the north extremity of the Earth's axis which is pointing in a fixed direction in the celestial sphere, is directed towards the Sun during the half year between March 21st and September 23rd, and away from the Sun during the remaining half year.

Fig. 4 illustrates the Earth on the day of the summer solstice (June 21st), when the Earth's spin axis lies on the plane of the line joining the Earth and the Sun.

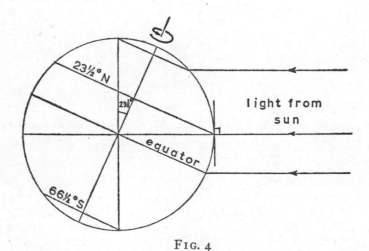

FIG. 4

The great circle on the Earth which separates the illuminated from the dark hemisphere of the Earth, is known as the *circle of illumination*. It will be seen from Fig. 4 that on the day of the summer solstice, every point on the Earth's northern hemisphere will be on the illuminated side of the circle of illumination for longer than twelve hours and that the length of daylight increases as the latitude increases. The polar cap, north of the parallel of $66\frac{1}{2}°$N., will have 24 hours of daylight. In the southern hemisphere on the day of the summer solstice the length of daylight will everywhere be less than twelve hours, and south of the parallel of $66\frac{1}{2}°$S., 24 hours of darkness will be experienced. In the northern hemisphere on the day of the summer solstice, because the length of daylight exceed twelve hours, the Sun will rise before 6 a.m. and sunset will occur after 6 p.m.

Fig. 5 illustrates the unequal lengths of daylight and darkness of two places, one in latitude 50°N., and the other in latitude 50°S., on the day of the summer solstice.

The diagrams of Fig. 5 are drawn on the planes of the horizons of observers whose zeniths are located at Z in each of the diagrams. P is the celestial pole and WQE is the equinoctial. N, E, S and W, are the north, east, south and west points of the observer's horizon. The arcs PX and PX₁ are the celestial meridians of the

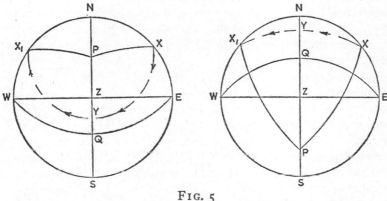

FIG. 5

Sun at the times of sunrise and sunset respectively. Y is the position of the Sun (whose declination is $23\frac{1}{2}$°N., and which is equivalent to the arc QY), when he is at meridian passage. In both diagrams of Fig. 5 the spherical angle ZPX₁ is a measure of the interval of time between meridian passage of the Sun and sunset. If the Sun's declination is regarded as being constant throughout the day, the diurnal circle XYX₁ will be parallel to the equinoctial EQW.

In latitude 50°N., as will be evident from Fig. 5, angle XPY is greater than 6 hours, whereas in latitude 50°S., angle XPY is less than 6 hours. Hence sunrise occurs before 6 a.m. on the day of the summer solstice in latitude 50°N. and in every other parallel of north latitude, and indeed during the whole of the six-month period when the declination of the Sun is northerly. Likewise, sunrise in latitude 50°S., will occur after 6 a.m. and sunset will occur before 6 p.m., because each of the angles XPY and YPX_1 is less than 90° or 6 hours. This will apply for every day during the period between March 21st and September 23rd, when the Sun has north declination.

Another consequence of the changing declination of the Sun during the course of the year, is the varying meridian altitude of the Sun. On the day of the summer solstice the noon altitude of the Sun is 90°, that is to say, the Sun transits at the zenith at every point located on the parallel of latitude of $23\frac{1}{2}$°N. This will be clear from Fig. 4. On this day the Sun will transit bearing south of every observer situated north of $23\frac{1}{2}$°N., and he will transit north of every observer located south of this parallel. On the parallel of $66\frac{1}{2}$°N., the Sun's meridian altitude will be $47\frac{1}{2}$° bearing south. On the equator the Sun's meridian altitude will be $66\frac{1}{2}$° bearing north, etc.

On the day of the winter solstice (December 22nd) all places in the northern hemisphere will experience a period of daylight of less than twelve hours. The Sun will rise after 6 a.m., and set before 6 p.m. In the southern hemisphere, on the same day, the period of daylight will be longer than twelve hours: the Sun rising before 6 a.m. and setting after 6 p.m. On the day of the winter solstice the Sun will transit at the zenith of every place on the parallel of $23\frac{1}{2}$°S. The polar cap north of $66\frac{1}{2}$°N. will experience darkness, and the polar cap south of $66\frac{1}{2}$°S. will experience daylight, for 24 hours.

On the days of the equinoxes, the Earth's axis lies in the plane of the circle of illumination and, therefore, every place on Earth will experience twelve hours daylight and twelve hours darkness. The Sun will rise at 6 a.m. at all places on Earth, and he will set at 6 p.m. The Sun will transit at the zenith of every point on the equator on the days of the equinoxes, and will bear south at meridian passage at all places north of the equator, and north at all places south of the equator.

3. *Climatic zones*

As a result of the changing declination of the Sun during the course of a year, the Earth's surface is divided into climatic zones by the parallels of latitude $23\frac{1}{2}$° and $66\frac{1}{2}$°N. and S.

The zone between the parallels of 23½°N. and S., is known as the *tropical* or *torrid zone*. Within these parallels, which are known as the *tropics of Cancer* and *Capricorn* for the northern and southern parallels respectively, the Sun on two days of the year will be at the zenith at the time of his meridian passage. The parallel of latitude 66½°N., is known as the *Arctic Circle*, and that of 66½°S. as the *Antarctic Circle*. These circles form the boundaries of spherical or polar caps, within which, on at least one day

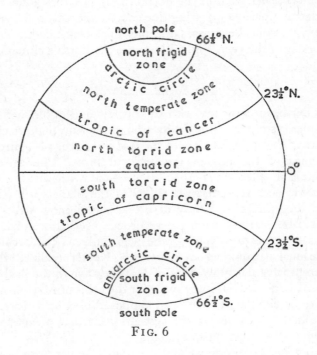

FIG. 6

of each year, there is darkness during the 24-hour period of the day, and on at least one day of the year there is 24 hours of daylight. The actual number of days of complete daylight or darkness within the polar caps increases with the latitude so that, at either pole, there is a six-month period when the Sun never rises out of the horizon followed by a six-month period when he never sets below the horizon. During the winter the northern hemisphere experiences a longer period of darkness than daylight during the day, the difference between these periods increasing polewards. During the summer the reverse is the case.

Lands such as parts of Norway, Canada and the U.S.S.R., that lie polewards of the Arctic or Antarctic circles, can claim the title *land of the midnight sun* because, on at least one day of the year, the Sun is above the horizon for the whole day and he is, therefore, visible at lower meridian passage at midnight. The zones which lie between the polar caps and the tropics are known as the *temperate zones.* Within the northern temperature zone, the Sun crosses the meridian bearing due south, whereas in the southern temperate zone he crosses the meridian bearing due north on every day of the year. Fig. 6 illustrates the Earth's climatic zones.

4. The Earth's elliptical orbit

The Earth, in company with the planets and other members of the solar system describe orbits around the Sun that are elliptical in form. The elliptical form of the planetary orbits is a direct consequence of the law of gravitational force. The astronomer Johannes Kepler (1571–1630) is credited with making the remarkable discovery that the orbits of the planets are elliptical. After long and close study of the apparent movements of the planet Mars, largely from the recorded observations of his illustrious predecessor Tycho Brahe who ranks as the greatest observational astronomer of all times, Kepler realized that the apparent irregular movement of Mars relative to the background of fixed stars, made it impossible for the orbit of Mars around the Sun to be circular, as had been supposed by Copernicus, whose name had been given to the system of circular planetary orbits known as the Copernican system.

From his observations and analyses, Kepler formulated his well-known laws of planetary motion:

(1) Every planet revolves around the Sun in an elliptical orbit having the Sun at one focus of the ellipse.

(2) The line joining any planet to the Sun sweeps out equal areas in equal time intervals.

A third law gives the relationship between the *period* of a planet, that is, the time given for the planet to describe one revolution of its orbit, and the distance between the planet and the Sun.

As the Earth describes her orbit around the Sun, the Sun, as we have seen, describes an apparent path across the celestial concave. Because of this, the aspect of the heavens changes during the year, the star-groups or constellations which transit at midnight being those which occupy the vicinity of the celestial meridian which is diametrically opposite to that occupied by the Sun. In other words, a star whose right ascension is 12 hours different from that of the Sun at any time, will transit at midnight. The R.A's of stars are practically constant whereas that of the Sun changes because of his apparent annual motion of 360° or 24 hours in a year. On the day of the spring equinox the Sun's R.A. is oo hours oo minutes. 24 hours later it is oo hours 04 minutes. It increases, therefore, at an average rate of 4 minutes per day throughout the year. On the day of the winter solstice the Sun's R.A. is about 6 hours; so that on this day, stars whose R.A's are about 18 hours will transit at midnight. On the day of the autumnal equinox, the Sun's R.A. is about 12 hours, so that on September 23rd stars whose R.A's are about oo hours will transit at midnight. On the day of the summer solstice the Sun's R.A. is about 18 hours, so that on June 22nd stars whose R.A's are about 6 hours will transit at midnight.

By studying, during a year, the position of the Sun on the celestial sphere relative to the stars, it was discovered that the Sun's apparent annual path is an ellipse with the earth at one of its foci. These observations provide conclusive proof that the Earth is a planet, the Sun's apparent motion being a reflection of the Earth's true motion.

It is interesting to note that Kepler formulated his famous laws from the results of observations only, and the explanation of the elliptical orbits of the planets around the Sun and the Moon around the Earth was due to Sir Isaac Newton (1642–1727). Newton's explanation, which is based on the *Law of Universal Gravitation*, was advanced after Kepler's death.

Universal Gravitation is an expression of the fact that every two masses in the universe (not only the Earth and objects on its surface), attract each other with a force which is proportional to the product of the masses and inversely proportional to the square of the distance between them. If m and M are the masses, and the distance between them is d, then the force of attraction F between the masses is,

$$F \propto \frac{mM}{d^2}$$

The attraction between the Sun and the Earth is known as the *solar attraction*. Because the Earth is a moving body, she has a tendency to continue moving in a fixed direction along a straight path in space, due to her inertia. But, because the Earth is affected by solar attraction, her path through space around the Sun is curved in such a way that she continually falls towards the Sun, the solar attraction being balanced by a so-called *centrifugal force*.

The distance between the Earth and the Sun varies because the orbit of the Earth is elliptical. The point in the Earth's orbit which is nearest to the Sun is known as *perihelion*, and the point in her orbit which is farthest removed from the Sun is known as *aphelion*. When the distance between the Earth and the Sun is least, that is to say, when the Earth is at perihelion, the solar attraction is greatest; when the Earth is at aphelion, the solar attraction is least, the attraction force varying inversely as the square of the distance between the Earth and the Sun. It follows, therefore, that the motion of the Earth in her orbit is greatest when she is at perihelion and least when she is at aphelion, because the centrifugal force varies as the solar attraction; and when centrifugal force is greatest the Earth moves most rapidly in her orbit.

The Earth is at perihelion on January 3rd approximately each year. She is at aphelion six months later: that is, at approximately July 3rd. It is the varying speed of the Earth in her orbit that gives rise to Kepler's second law, namely, areas swept out by the radius vector of the elliptical orbit are equal for equal time intervals.

The average distance between the Sun and the Earth is about 93,005,000 miles. When the Earth is at perihelion the distance is about 91 million miles and when she is at aphelion the distance is about 94·5 million miles.

Because the Earth's orbit is elliptical—the ellipticity being very small and in the order of 1/7200—the lengths of the seasons are slightly unequal. The Earth is at perihelion on January 3rd approximately, this date being about a fortnight after the time of the winter solstice (December 22nd). Because the Earth's orbital movement (and the Sun's apparent orbital movement), is greatest when the distance between the Sun and the Earth is least, the first day of spring—March 21st—is brought forward, because it is in the quarter period of the year following the time of the winter solstice that the Earth moves fastest and farthest.

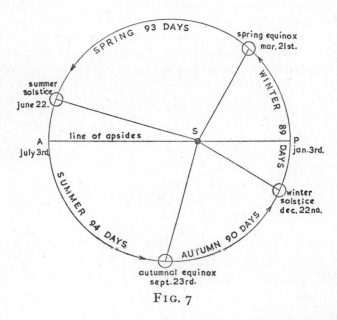

FIG. 7

The time of the summer solstice is about a fortnight before the time of aphelion. The Earth travels relatively slowly at this time, so that the first day of autumn is delayed. The seasons, therefore, are of unequal length. For the northern hemisphere the approximate lengths of the seasons are:

Spring   — 93 days
Summer — 94 days
Autumn — 90 days
Winter   — 89 days

Fig. 7 serves to illustrate the unequal lengths of the seasons.

The date of perihelion decides the lengths of the seasons. The line joining the points of perihelion and aphelion, a line which is known as the *apse line* or *line of apsides*, swings slowly around the Earth's orbit in the same direction as the orbital movement of the Earth. This results in the dates of perihelion and aphelion occurring later as time advances. The rate of movement of the apse line is very slow, it being about $11\frac{1}{4}$ seconds of arc per year.

At the present time, northern winter and autumn occur when the Earth is comparatively near to the Sun, so that the severity of northern winter and autumn is mitigated. For the same reason the severity of southern winter is increased. By similar arguments southern summer is warmer than it would be were the seasons of equal duration, or the dates of perihelion and aphelion reversed.

CHAPTER SIX

The Earth's Rotation and Problems of Finding Latitude and Longitude

1. *The measurement of time*

We have seen, in Chapter One, how the latitude of a terrestrial position may be found by astronomical means. If the meridian altitude of a celestial body of known declination is measured, the latitude of the observer—which is a combination of the body's declination and its meridian zenith distance—may readily be ascertained. Alternatively the maximum and minimum altitudes of a circumpolar star, which is visible at both upper and lower transits, may be used to find latitude: the latitude of the observer, in this case, being the mean of the meridian altitudes at upper and lower transits, measured from the horizon vertically below the elevated pole.

The latitude of an observer is equal to the altitude of the celestial pole at the observer's position. Hence a third method of finding latitude astronomically is available. This method, which is applicable to the northern hemisphere only, involves applying a correction to the measured altitude of the Pole Star. The correction, which depends upon the time of the observation, is obtained from specially designed Pole Star tables.

The problems of finding latitude are relatively simple of solution, and the general methods used at the present time have been used for many centuries. The problem of finding longitude, however, demands knowledge of the time at both the local meridian and at a datum or standard meridian from which longitude is measured.

Before the days of accurate mechanical timepieces, longitudes of places were found astronomically by comparing the local time

9

of an astronomical event, such as an eclipse of the Sun or Moon, or the occultation of a star or planet by the Moon, with the predicted time for some standard meridian. Before the necessary predictions could be made considerable knowledge of the movements of the celestial bodies was essential. So also was an accurate chart of the heavens on which the declinations and right ascensions of the stars were plotted. The body of observations necessary to make this possible required accurate observations made over a long period of time. It is not surprising, therefore, that the longitudes of very few places were known with a high degree of accuracy before the advent of accurate timekeepers. Let us investigate the close relationship that exists between time and longitude.

In an astronomical sense time is defined as that which persists while events take place. The events in which astronomers are interested, in this respect, are events such as meridian passages of celestial bodies.

The measurement of time is closely related to the movements of the Earth. The period of the Earth's rotation about her spin axis is a natural unit of time known as the day; and the period of the Earth's revolution around the Sun is another natural unit of time known as the year. The Earth spins at a slow but uniform rate; making one complete rotation in the time it takes for the hour hand of an accurate clock to make two circuits of the dial. The Earth's rotation is manifested by the apparent diurnal movements of the celestial bodies around the Earth.

The time taken for the Earth to make one rotation of exactly 360° is known as a *sidereal-* or *star-day*. This constant time unit is so called because it is equivalent to the interval of time that elapses between successive instants when a fixed star transits the celestial meridian of a stationary observer.

The fixed point on the heavens which has been chosen to mark the passage of sidereal time is the First Point of Aries (♈). When ♈ is at meridian passage, the sidereal day for the meridian it transits commences. That is to say, the local sidereal time (L.S.T.) of this event is oo hr oo min oo sec. A mechanical timepiece which is regulated and set to keep sidereal time would keep step with the apparent diurnal movement of ♈ (or any other fixed point on the heavens), and it would register 24 hr oo min oo sec at the end of each sidereal day when ♈ is at meridian passage, so marking the end of the latest sidereal day and the beginning of the next. Sidereal time is of use to astronomers, but serves little or no purpose in general everyday affairs.

For general purposes the Sun regulates the lives of human beings. For this reason the apparent diurnal revolution of the Sun around the Earth is used as a basis for timekeeping. A *solar day* is defined as the interval of time between two successive transits of the Sun across the celestial meridian of a stationary observer. It is convenient to regard the commencement of the solar day as the instant when the Sun (often called the *apparent Sun* for this purpose because we are interested in his apparent diurnal motion) crosses the lower celestial meridian of an observer; so that the instant when the Sun is at upper meridian passage marks the middle of the solar day, known as *midday* or *noon*.

The day is subdivided into 24 equal parts each known as an hour. Each hour is further subdivided into minutes and seconds. Time is essentially angular measurement—24 hours corresponding to 360°.

$$24 \text{ hours} \quad = 360°$$
$$1 \text{ hr} \quad = 15°$$
$$1 \text{ min of time} = 15'$$
$$1 \text{ sec of time} = 15''$$

We may regard the celestial meridian on which the Sun is located as sweeping out angles at the celestial pole. The celestial meridian of the Sun is usually called the *Sun's hour circle*, because the position of this circle relative to the observer's lower celestial meridian is a function of the solar time of day.

In Fig. 1 the small circle represents the Earth drawn on the plane of the equator. The large circle represents the equinoctial, and PL and PU are respectively the lower and upper celestial meridians of an observer. The apparent diurnal revolution of the heavens is westwards; and when the Sun, in describing his diurnal circle, crosses the observer's lower celestial meridian the solar time at the observer's position (and at every point on his meridian) is 00 hr 00 min 00 sec. As the Earth rotates towards the east the hour circle of the Sun sweeps westwards; and when it occupies the position illustrated in Fig. 1, the angle at P, between PL

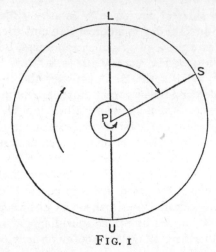

FIG. I

and PS is a measure of the time that has elapsed since the solar day commenced. It is, therefore, a measure of the local solar time for which Fig. 1 applies.

The semi-great circle which extends from the celestial pole through the Sun may be regarded as the hour hand of a solar sky clock, which is illustrated in Fig. 2.

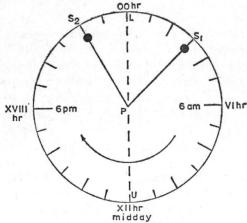

Arrow indicates the direction of the apparent diurnal motion of the celestial sphere.

FIG. 2

It should be obvious, from an examination of Fig. 2, why the semi-great circle extending from the celestial pole through the Sun is called an hour circle. When the Sun is at S_1, the local solar time at every place on the meridian of an observer whose upper celestial meridian is PU, is equivalent to the arc LS_1, which is 45°, the time being 3 a.m. When the Sun is at S_2, the time is 22 hours or 10 p.m.

The *local solar time* at any instant is defined as the angle at the celestial pole, or the arc of the equinoctial, contained between the local lower celestial meridian and the hour circle of the Sun at the instant, measured westwards from the local lower celestial meridian.

The *local hour angle* (L.H.A.), of the Sun (or any other celestial body), is measured westwards from the upper celestial meridian. It follows, therefore, that the local solar time and the Sun's local hour angle differ by 12 hours.

When the Sun is east of the meridian of any observer, the observer's local time is less than 12 hours, and is designated *a.m.* (*ante meridiem*) to indicate that the time is before that of meridian passage. The local hour angle of the Sun, when the Sun is east of the meridian, is more than 12 hours.

When the Sun is west of the meridian of any observer, the L.H.A.—which is often regarded as solar time *p.m.* (*or post meridiem*)—is less than 12 hours; and the local solar time, measured from the observer's lower celestial meridian, is more than 12 hours. In general:

L.H.A. of Sun = Local Solar Time ± 12 hours

The principal disadvantage of using solar time is that the length of the solar day is not uniform throughout the year. This is due to the combination of the effects due to the elliptical form of the Earth's orbit, and the obliquity of the ecliptic.

To overcome the disadvantage of keeping *apparent solar time* (A.T.)—as registered by a sundial during the daytime—and yet employing the Sun as a basis of timekeeping, an artificial point on the celestial sphere known as the *mean Sun*, is used for measuring mean solar time (M.T.)

The mean Sun moves uniformly in the equinoctial, whereas the apparent (or true) Sun moves irregularly in the ecliptic.

The *astronomical mean Sun* (more commonly called the mean Sun), moves uniformly in the equinoctial at such a rate that its R.A. increases at the same rate as the angular motion of a point known as the *dynamical mean Sun*. The dynamical mean Sun is an artificial point which moves uniformly in the ecliptic at the average rate of the true Sun in the ecliptic.

The *mean solar day* is defined as the interval of time which elapses between two successive transits of the mean Sun across the lower celestial meridian of a stationary observer.

The *local mean time* (L.M.T.) at any instant is the angle at the celestial pole, or the arc of the equinoctial, contained between the local lower celestial meridian and the hour circle of the mean Sun at the instant, measured westwards from the local lower celestial meridian.

Because the mean Sun moves at the average rate of the true Sun, it should be clear that during some parts of the year, the L.M.T. at any instant is in advance of the L.A.T. At other periods, L.M.T. is behind L.A.T.

The difference between L.M.T. and L.A.T. at any instant is known as the *equation of time* (e).

The equation of time is oo hr oo min oo sec on four occasions during the year. A graph of the equation of time is illustrated in Fig. 3.

The sign of the equation of time, as illustrated in Fig. 3, is +ve when L.M.T. is greater than L.A.T.; and −ve when L.M.T. is less than L.A.T. This is the sign convention used by navigators and is the reverse from that used by professional astronomers. For our purposes, we shall regard the relationship between L.M.T., L.A.T. and e, to be: L.M.T. − L.A.T. = e.

That is to say, the equation of time is the excess of mean time over apparent time at any instant. If the L.M.T. is greater than L.A.T. the equation of time is +ve. If L.M.T. is less than L.A.T. the equation of time is −ve.

The difference between the local times (sidereal, mean or apparent), at two different meridians is equal to the difference between the longitudes of the meridians reckoning 15° of difference of longitude as one hour. This should be clear from Fig. 4.

Fig. 4 represents the celestial sphere drawn on the plane of the

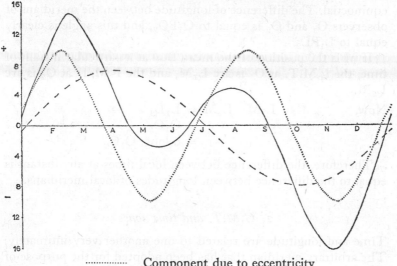

.... Component due to eccentricity
- - - - - Component due to obliquity
——— Equation of Time

FIG. 3

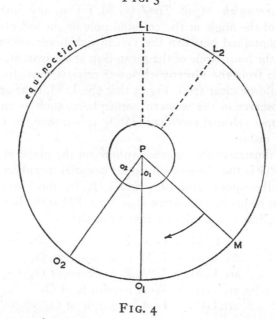

FIG. 4

equinoctial. The difference of longitude between the meridians of observers O_1 and O_2 is equal to O_1PO_2, and this angle is clearly equal to L_1PL_2.

If M is the position of the mean Sun at a particular instant of time, the L.M.T. at O_1 is arc L_1M, and the L.M.T. at O_2 is arc L_2M.

Now,
$$L_1M - L_2M = L_1L_2$$
$$= O_1O_2$$
$$= \text{d.long. } O_1O_2$$

Therefore, the difference between local times at any instant is equal to the difference between longitudes of local meridians.

2. G.M.T. and time zones

Time and longitude are related to one another very intimately. The arbitrary meridian that has been adopted for the purpose of measuring longitude is the Greenwich meridian. The prime meridian and its antipodal meridian divide the Earth into the eastern and western hemispheres.

The *Greenwich Mean Time* (G.M.T.) at any instant, is a measure of the angle at the celestial pole or the arc of the equinoctial, contained between the Greenwich lower celestial meridian and the hour circle of the mean Sun at the instant, measured westwards from the Greenwich lower celestial meridian.

It should be clear from Fig. 5 that the L.M.T. at any instant for an observer in the western hemisphere, such as an observer whose upper celestial meridian is PO_1, is less than the G.M.T. at the same instant.

Fig. 5 illustrates the celestial sphere on the plane of the equinoctial. PG is the Greenwich upper celestial meridian. PO_1 and PO_2 are the upper, and LO_1 and LO_2 are the lower, celestial meridians respectively, of two observers. PM is the hour circle of the mean Sun at a particular instant of time.

$$\text{arc } L_GM = \text{G.M.T.}$$
$$\text{arc } L_1M = \text{L.M.T. at observer } O_1$$
$$\text{arc } L_2M = \text{L.M.T. at observer } O_2$$
$$\text{arc } GO_1 = \text{West longitude of } O_1$$
$$\text{arc } GO_2 = \text{East longitude of } O_2$$

Considering observer O_1:

$$L_GM - L_1M = L_GL_1$$
$$= GO_1$$

Therefore:

G.M.T. – L.M.T. = West longitude of observer

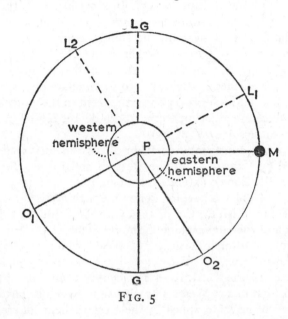

Fig. 5

Considering observer O_2:

$$L_2M - L_GM = L_2L_G$$
$$= GO_2$$

Therefore: L.M.T. – G.M.T. = East longitude of observer. Hence the well-known rule, 'Longitude West, Greenwich time best; Longitude East, Greenwich time least'.

Considering the high speeds of modern methods of transport the variation in local mean time for different meridians is of great importance. It would be chaotic if L.M.T's were everywhere kept: for such purposes as drawing up time-tables for transport services and other schedules, there is a need for a uniform system of time-keeping.

A system of *standard times* has been adopted in which the whole of a small country, such as Holland or Great Britain, or part of a large country such as U.S.A. or U.S.S.R., keeps the local time of a particular standard meridian which, ideally, lies approximately midway between the east and west extremities of the country, and the longitude of which differs from that of Greenwich by a multiple of $15°$. In most instances the standard time adopted corresponds to *zone time*.

In the zone-time system, the standard time everywhere is an integral number of hours different from G.M.T. To facilitate the keeping of zone time on moving ships or other means of transport, the Earth's surface is divided into 24 time-zones, each bounded by meridians which are $15°$ apart (except in the cases of the two zones which are adjacent to the 180th degree meridian for which the boundaries are $7\frac{1}{2}°$ apart).

The zones are numbered from 0 to 12 inclusive, and are designated ($+$) and ($-$) in the western and eastern hemispheres respectively. Zone 0 extends from longitude $7\frac{1}{2}°$ East to longitude $7\frac{1}{2}°$ West. All places keeping zone time within this zone have their clocks set to G.M.T., that is to say, to the L.M.T. of the central meridian of the zone, which is the meridian of Greenwich. Zone $+1$ extends from longitude $7\frac{1}{2}°$ West to longitude $22\frac{1}{2}°$ West. Within this zone, all places keeping zone time will have their clocks set to the L.M.T. of the central meridian of the zone, which is that of $15°$ West. The plus sign, which is part of the designation of all time zones in the western hemisphere, signifies that if a number of hours corresponding to the zone number is added to the zone time, the result will be the G.M.T. Zone -1 extends from longitude $7\frac{1}{2}°$ East to longitude $22\frac{1}{2}°$ East; Zone -2 from $22\frac{1}{2}°$ East to $37\frac{1}{2}°$ East; etc.

The navigator of a ship on which the system of zone time is used alters his clock one hour abruptly as each boundary of a time zone is crossed. When travelling westwards, the clocks are put back an hour on crossing the boundary of a time zone; when travelling eastwards they are advanced. On crossing the meridian of $172\frac{1}{2}°$ West, and travelling westwards, the ship will move from Zone $+11$ to Zone $+12$, and the clock is retarded one hour. On crossing the meridian of $172\frac{1}{2}°$ East, and travelling eastwards, the ship will move from Zone -11 to Zone -12, and the clocks will

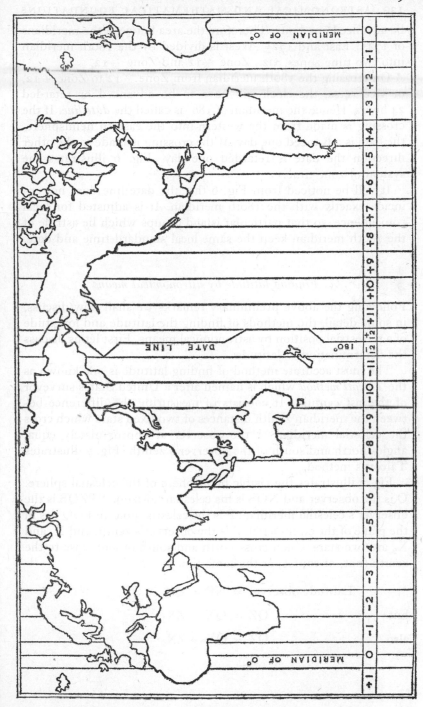

FIG. 6

be advanced one hour. Therefore the area between the meridians of $172\frac{1}{2}°$ East and $172\frac{1}{2}°$ West is divided by the 180th meridian into two time zones, viz., Zone $+12$ and Zone -12.

On crossing the 180th meridian from Zone -12 to Zone $+12$, or vice versa, the clock will have to be advanced or retarded 24 hours. Hence the meridian of 180° is called the *date line*. If the crossing is made from the western into the eastern hemisphere, the date is advanced one day. If the crossing is made in the other direction the date is retarded one day. Fig. 6 illustrates the system of zone time.

It will be noticed from Fig. 6 that the date line does not co-incide exactly with the 180th meridian. It is adjusted for local convenience, so that particular island groups which lie astride of the 180th meridian keep the same local standard time and date.

3. *Finding latitude by astronomical means*

Following the above preliminary remarks we shall now discuss, in some detail, the methods of finding the latitude and longitude of a terrestrial position by astronomical means. First let us discuss the determination of latitude.

The most accurate method of finding latitude is one known as the *Talcott method* which is named after a United States surveyor of the last century. It consists of measuring the difference be-tween the meridian zenith distances of two fixed stars which cross the celestial meridian of the observer at approximately equal angles north and south of the observer's zenith. Fig. 7 illustrates Talcott's method.

Fig. 7 illustrates the visible hemisphere of the celestial sphere. O is the observer and NOS is his celestial horizon. NPZQS is the observer's celestial meridian. P is the celestial pole and OQ lies in the plane of the equinoctial. Z is the observer's zenith and X_1 and X_2 are two stars which cross north and south of and close to the zenith (not, of course, at the same time).

$$\text{Latitude observer} = NP = QZ$$

but
$$QZ = QX_1 - ZX_1$$

also
$$QZ = QX_2 + ZX_2$$

therefore, $\qquad 2QZ = QX_1 - ZX_1 + QX_2 + ZX_2$

that is, $\qquad 2QZ - (QX_1 + QX_2) + (ZX_2 - ZX_1)$

and, $\qquad QZ = \frac{1}{2}\left[(QX_1 + QX_2) + (ZX_2 - ZX_1)\right]$

Hence,

Latitude $= \frac{1}{2}$ sum declinations of X_1 and X_2
$+\frac{1}{2}$ difference between zenith distances of X_1 and X_2

The difference between the zenith distances of the two stars X_1 and X_2 is measured to a high degree of accuracy by means of a *zenith sector*. This is a telescope the axis of which is set, when used, in the plane of the meridian. The angle of the axis of the telescope is set so that the telescope is directed to a point in the

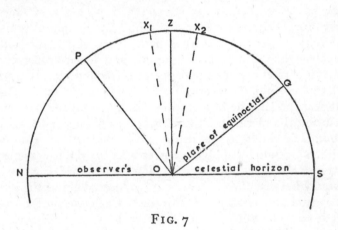

FIG. 7

heavens which has a zenith distance equal to the mean of the zenith distances of the two stars. The angles between the stars when at their meridian passages, and the horizontal cross-wire in the field of view of the telescope, are measured by means of a micrometer, the telescope being reversed after the first star to cross the meridian has been observed, in readiness for the observation of the second star. From the two measurements the difference between the zenith distances of the two stars at meridian passages is obtained. If the declinations of the two stars are known, the latitude of the observer may readily be found.

The value of the Talcott method arises from the fact that because the stars are near to the zenith at the times of their observations, errors due to atmospheric refraction, which is zero when the altitude is 90°, are avoided.

To find the latitude by observations of a circumpolar star, a *meridian-* or *transit-circle* is used. This is a telescope, the axis of which is set in the plane of the meridian, and which is capable of being turned about a horizontal east–west axis. Fitted to the telescope and lying parallel to it is a large circular scale which is graduated in degrees, minutes and seconds of arc. When the axis of the telescope is directed to a star at meridian passage, the observed meridian altitude of the star may be read off the graduated scale with great accuracy.

The circumpolar stars used for determining latitude are described as *close* circumpolar stars; that is to say they are stars whose diurnal circles have small radii, and their azimuths are the same (either north or south) at both upper and lower transits. The mean of the altitudes at upper and lower transits, after applying corrections for atmospheric refraction etc., is equal to the latitude of the observer.

At sea, the latitude of a ship is found during the daytime by measuring the meridian altitude of the Sun's lower limb with a *sextant*. The Sun's true altitude is obtained from the observed meridian altitude by applying corrections for semi-diameter, refraction, solar parallax and dip. The last-named correction is necessary because the observer's eye is located above the level of the sea, and the measured angle is the angle between the apparent directions of the Sun's lower limb and the visible horizon which is depressed below the celestial horizon by an angle which increases as the height of eye increases. The Sun's true meridian altitude is subtracted from 90° to give the Sun's meridian zenith distance. This, when combined with the Sun's declination at the time of its meridian passage, gives the latitude of the observer.

The Sun's declination is obtained from the *Nautical Almanac* —the seaman's handbook, published annually, which contains the necessary astronomical data by means of which the mariner is assisted in fixing his ship, when out of sight of land, by astronomical methods. If the latitude of an observer is known, the local time at any instant may be calculated by spherical trigonometry after making the necessary astronomical observation: namely, the measuring of the altitude of a heavenly body at the instant for which the local time is required. The spherical triangle which is solved for this purpose is known as the *astronomical* or *PZX triangle*. Fig. 8 illustrates a typical PZX triangle applicable to an observer located in the northern hemisphere.

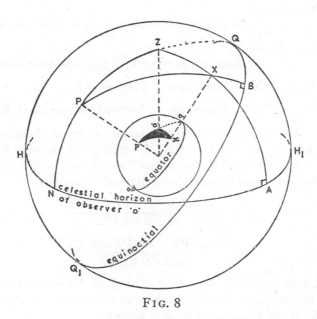

FIG. 8

In Fig. 8 the small circle represents the Earth and the large circle the celestial sphere. O is an observer situated in the northern hemisphere: Z is his zenith, and HH_1 is his celestial horizon. QQ_1 is the equinoctial and P is the elevated celestial pole. qq_1 is the equator, and x is the position on the Earth at which the celestial body X at the time of the observation would be in the zenith of x. The position x is known as the *geographical position* of X.

It should be clear that the spherical triangles PZX on the concave and pox on the Earth are similar.

$$\text{Arc NP} = \text{Altitude of celestial pole} = \text{ZQ} = \text{qo}$$
$$= \text{Latitude of observer o}$$
$$\text{Arc XB} = \text{Declination of X}$$
$$\text{Arc XA} = \text{Altitude of X}$$

In the spherical triangles PZX and pox:

$$\text{Arc PZ} = \text{Arc po}$$
$$= \text{Co-latitude observer}$$

$$\text{Arc ZX} = \text{Arc ox}$$
$$= \text{Zenith distance of X} = (90° - \text{altitude of X})$$

$$\text{Arc PX} = \text{Arc px}$$
$$= \text{Polar distance of X} = (90 - \text{declination of X})$$

$$\text{Angle ZPX} = \text{Angle opx} = \text{L.H.A. of X}$$

$$\text{Angle PZX} = \text{Angle pox} = \text{Azimuth or bearing of X}$$

If the three sides of a spherical triangle are given, the spherical angles may be calculated. In the PZX triangle depicted in Fig. 8:
Given PZ, PX and ZX, the angles P and Z may be found using the spherical cosine formula (or a derived formula).

$$\cos P = \frac{\cos ZX - \cos PZ \cos PX}{\sin PZ \sin PX}$$

$$\cos Z = \frac{\cos PX - \cos PZ \cos ZX}{\sin PZ \sin ZX}$$

If X is the Sun, the calculation of his L.H.A. (which is angle P in the astronomical triangle) enables an observer to ascertain his L.M.T., if the equation of time is known.

$$\text{L.M.T.} = \text{L.A.T.} - e$$

and $$\text{L.A.T.} = \text{L.H.A. Sun} \pm 12 \text{ hours}$$

therefore $$\text{L.M.T.} = \text{L.H.A. Sun} \pm 12 \text{ hours} - e$$

4. *Finding longitude by astronomical means*

If the G.M.T. of the instant of observation is known, the longitude of the observer may be found: because, as we have seen,

$$\text{G.M.T.} \sim \text{L.M.T.} = \text{longitude}$$

If the X is the Moon or a planet, the longitude may be found from the observation by taking the difference between the L.H.A. of the object and the G.H.A. of the object at the time of the observation, the G.H.A. being lifted from the *Nautical Almanac*, in which it is tabulated (as indeed is that for the Sun) against G.M.T.

$$\text{G.H.A.} * \sim \text{L.H.A.} * = \text{longitude}$$

where * is any celestial object.

The principal problem of finding longitude is related to finding the G.M.T. of the observation. The common method used at the present time is the employment of a radio or telegraphic link between the observer and a station at which G.M.T. is known (it being kept by means of an accurate timekeeper.

Radio time-signals are transmitted frequently by radio telegraphy and radio telephony on specified frequencies. If an observer is able to compare a radio time-signal with the time shown by his clock at the instant of the observed time-signal, and if the error of his clock is known from the calculation of the astronomical triangle, the longitude of the observer's position may be found.

The problem of finding longitude at sea is rather more difficult than is the same problem on land. The reason for this is that generally, at the time of an astronomical observation for longitude, the latitude of the ship is not known to the required degree of accuracy.

During the daytime the latitude of the ship may be found from a meridian altitude observation of the Sun (or perhaps the Moon or a planet if these objects are suitably placed for observation). This will enable the observer to find his latitude. Because the local time of meridian passage cannot be found at sea with a high degree of accuracy (as it can on land by means of a transit instrument), the longitude cannot be found from a meridian altitude observation.

For about a century and a half after the introduction of the chronometer—which is simply an accurate timepiece having a small and uniform rate of gaining or losing—there was no systematic method for finding longitude at sea by its use. Finding the longitude by chronometer depended upon knowledge of the

10

latitude. If the latitude is known the problem is simple and no different from what it is ashore. If, however, the latitude is not known, an estimate has to be made; and, in general (unless the Sun bears due east or west) an error in the estimated latitude used in the calculation of the PZX triangle produces an error in the longitude by chronometer.

The American navigator Thomas Sumner is credited with being the first to systematize the longitude-by-chronometer problem of astronomical navigation; and it is to the ingenuity of this American sea-captain that seamen owe a debt of gratitude for the introduction of the concept of *astronomical position-line navigation*. Sumner argued that at any instant of time any particular celestial object is in the zenith of a particular spot on the Earth's surface. This spot is the geographical position of the celestial object. If the object is the Sun, the geographical position is often referred to as the *sub-solar point*; and if it is a star it is sometimes called the *sub-stellar point*.

Fig. 9 serves to illustrate that the latitude and west longitude of the geographical position of a heavenly body at any instant are equal, respectively, to the declination and the Greenwich Hour Angle (G.H.A.) of the body at the instant.

In Fig. 9, the small circle represents the Earth, and the large circle the celestial sphere. pg is the meridian of Greenwich and PG is the Greenwich upper celestial meridian. X is any celestial body whose geographical position is at x. PQ is the celestial meridian of X and pq is the meridian through the geographical position of X. From the figure:

$$\text{Arc xq} = \text{Arc XQ}$$

Therefore:

$$\text{Latitude of G.P. of X} = \text{Declination of X}$$

Also,

$$\text{Arc gq} = \text{Arc GQ}$$

or

$$\text{Angle qpg} = \text{Angle QPG}$$

Therefore:

$$\text{Longitude of G.P. of X} = \text{G.H.A. of X}$$

Any small circle on the Earth, which has its centre at the geographical position of a heavenly body, is one on which the altitude of the heavenly body at any instant of time will be the same at every point on it. Such a circle is called a *circle of equal altitude*. Captain Sumner argued that if a navigator knows that his ship is located on a particular circle of equal altitude the information is just as valuable to him as knowledge that his ship is on a particular parallel of latitude or a particular meridian.

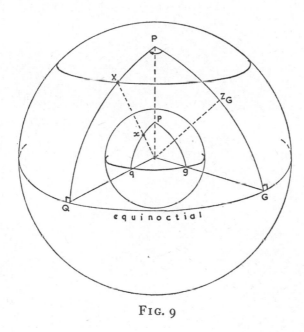

FIG. 9

The modern concept of Sumner's method of finding longitude is illustrated in Fig. 10.

In Fig. 10 the small circle represents the Earth. p is the Earth's North Pole and P is the elevated celestial pole of an observer whose position is not known within several miles of the truth. X is a celestial body whose geographical position is at x. c is a point lying on a chosen parallel of latitude, the latitude of which approximates to the observer's latitude. Z_c is the zenith of c, which is located not only on the chosen parallel but also on a circle of equal altitude the radius of which, in nautical miles, is equal to the zenith distance of X at the time of the observation, in minutes of arc.

The spherical triangles PZ_cX and pxc are similar.

In spherical triangle PZ_cX:

Arc PX = Polar distance of X

Arc PZ_c = Co-latitude of c

Arc Z_cX = Zenith distance of X at any point on the circle of equal altitude through c

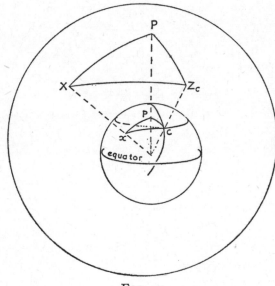

FIG. 10

Given these three spherical distances, the spherical angles P and Z may be calculated. The spherical angle P is equal to the spherical angle p. Therefore, the L.H.A. of X at the position c is equal to the difference of longitude between x and c.

The longitude of x at the time of the observation may be found if the G.M.T. of the observation is known (and this is obtained from a chronometer, the error of which is known from radio time-signal observations), and if a *Nautical Almanac* is available. Thus the longitude of c may be found.

The angle PZ_cX is equal to the angle pcx, and either of these is equal to the bearing of X at the time of the observation at the position c.

The angles P and Z which are calculated are those which apply to position c. We must remember that the observer's position, which is unknown to him, is unlikely to be at position c. Let us suppose that the observer is at position c_1, which is slightly to the

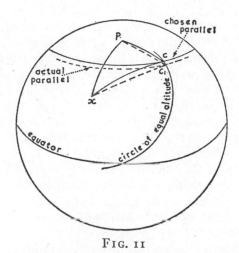

FIG. 11

south of c. Point c_1 must lie on the circle of equal altitude through c, and if the distance cc_1 is small (and in practice it is seldom more than twenty miles or so), the bearings of x from both c and c_1, may be regarded as being the same, because the radius of the circle of equal altitude is usually in the order of thousands of miles.

Fig. 11 depicts the Earth. p is the Earth's North Pole; x is the geographical position of the observed celestial object; c is the point at the intersection of the chosen parallel of latitude and the circle of equal altitude. The triangle pcx is similar to the astronomical triangle PZ_cX which has been calculated in order to find the longitude of c. c_1 lies on the actual but unknown parallel of latitude of the observer. If cc_1 is small compared with the radius xc (or xc_1) of the circle of equal altitude, the angle pc_1x is not materially different from angle pcx. If the bearing of the geographical position of the observed object is known, the direction of the circle of equal altitude in the vicinity of the ship is also known, because the direction of the circumference of a circle at any point on it is always at right angles to the radius terminating at the point.

The navigator, therefore, plots the position c on his chart or plotting sheet, and projects a part of the circle of equal altitude through this position in a direction at right angles to the azimuth of the observed object at the time of the observation. The arc of the circle of equal altitude is projected as a straight line with justification, for the navigator is concerned with only a small fragment of it, and the curvature of the circle over a small arc-length may normally be ignored, no error being introduced by so doing.

The projection of the arc of the circle of equal altitude is called a *position line*, because the ship's position lies somewhere on it. It should be noted that the ship's position will be at c only if the chosen latitude happens to be the actual latitude, and this is not to be expected. If the latitude of the ship at the time of the observation is known, and if it is used to calculate the angle P of the astronomical triangle, the longitude found will of course be the ship's actual longitude, and there will be no need to find the angle Z.

Fig. 12 illustrates the normal procedure, following the solving of the PZX triangle using Sumner's method for obtaining a position line.

In Fig. 12, c is the point on the chosen parallel of latitude and the meridian of the calculated longitude. θ is the azimuth of the celestial object, at the time of observation. PL is the position line obtained. Had the observer been in lat. α his position at the time of the observation would have been at F_n which is a' west of c. Had he been in lat. β, his position would have been at F_s, which is b' east of c.

A publication essential to navigation is the *Nautical Almanac*. This, as we have already noted, is a publication in which the astronomical data necessary for finding position at sea are tabulated.

The longitude of the point c, when using the Sumner method for determining a position line, is found by taking the difference between the L.H.A. of the observed object and its G.H.A. at the time of the observation. The G.H.A's of the Sun, Moon and the four navigational planets (Venus, Mars, Jupiter and Saturn), are

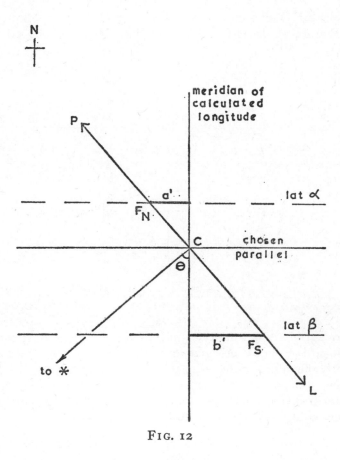

FIG. 12

tabulated for every hour of G.M.T. for the year for which the *Nautical Almanac* applies. Specially designed interpolation tables are provided for finding the G.H.A. of any of these celestial objects should the G.M.T. of the observation be other than an integral number of hours G.M.T.

In addition to the tabulation of the G.H.A. of the Sun, Moon and planets, that of the First Point of Aries (♈) is also tabulated for every integral hour of G.M.T. for the whole year. The G.H.A. ♈ at any instant, combined with a quantity known as the *sidereal hour angle* (S.H.A.) of any star, gives the G.H.A. of the star.

The S.H.A. of a star is defined as the angle at the celestial pole, or the arc of the equinoctial, contained between the celestial

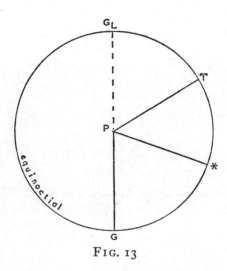

FIG. 13

meridian of ♈ and the celestial meridian of the star measured westwards from the celestial meridian of ♈. S.H.A. of a star is clearly the difference between the star's R.A. (which is measured eastwards from ♈), and 360° or 24 hours. Whereas R.A. is usually given in hours, minutes and seconds of time S.H.A. is always given in degrees, minutes and seconds of arc.

S.H.A. ＊ = 360° − R.A. ＊ expressed in degrees, etc.

Fig. 13 illustrates the relationship between G.H.A. ♈, S.H.A. ＊ and G.H.A. ＊.

In Fig. 13, P represents the celestial pole and the circle represents the equinoctial. PG, P♈ and P＊, are respectively the celestial meridians of Greenwich, Aries and any star.

$$\text{Arc GG}_L \, \Upsilon = \text{G.H.A.} \, \Upsilon$$

$$\text{Arc GG}_L * = \text{G.H.A.} *$$

$$\text{Arc} \, \Upsilon * = \text{S.H.A.} *$$

Now, $\text{Arc GG}_L * = \text{Arc GG}_L \, \Upsilon + \text{arc} \, \Upsilon *$

therefore: $\text{G.H.A.} * = \text{G.H.A.} \, \Upsilon + \text{S.H.A.} *$

In computing the angle P of the astronomical triangle, for the purpose of finding the L.H.A. of a celestial body, it is necessary to work to a high degree of accuracy, because the calculated longitude is required normally to the nearest minute of arc. In practice at sea, five- or six-figure logarithms are used in order to attain the required degree of accuracy. On the other hand, the direction of the position line—which is obtained from the angle Z in the astronomical triangle, is required to a relatively coarse degree of accuracy: the nearest half degree is generally good enough. It is customary, therefore, to lift the azimuth from *azimuth tables* instead of calculating the triangle for angle Z.

There are many astronomical navigation tables, by means of which the solution of the PZX triangle may be obtained quickly and accurately. These tables find their greatest use in air navigation: the great speed of aircraft compared with that of ships demands the use of rapid methods of navigation.

A method for determining a position line, alternative to that invented by Captain Sumner, was introduced by the French navigator Marcq Saint Hilaire, in 1875.

The *Marcq Saint Hilaire method*, which is usually called the *intercept method*, involves finding the zenith distance of an observed object—this angle in minutes of arc being equivalent to the radius of the circle of equal altitude in nautical miles—at a chosen position which is near to the actual—but unknown—position of the ship at the time of the observation.

Fig. 14 illustrates the intercept method of finding a position line.

In Fig. 14 p is the Earth's North Pole and P is the elevated celestial pole. X is a celestial body whose geographical position at the time of the observation is x. c is a chosen position which is near to the ship's actual but unknown position depicted at o. The zenith at c is Z_c and that at the observer is Z_o.

The circle through c is a circle of equal altitude. The parallel circle through o is likewise a circle of equal altitude. The radii of these circles in nautical miles are the zenith distances of X, namely Z_cX and Z_oX in minutes of arc respectively. The perpendicular distance between these is known as the *intercept*.

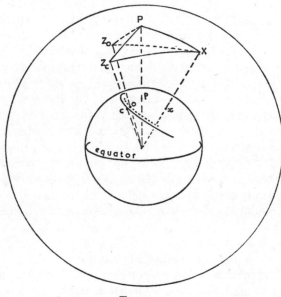

FIG. 14

The zenith distance of X at the chosen position may be calculated. In the spherical triangle PZ_cX:

Arc PZ_c = co lat. of c   (given)

Arc PX = $90° \pm$ dec ∗   (from *Nautical Almanac*)

Angle Z_cPX = L.H.A. of star at c's meridian
(L.H.A. ∗ = G.H.A. $\pm$ longitude of c)

By the spherical cosine formula:

$$\cos Z_cX = \cos P \sin PZ_c \sin PX + \cos PZ_c \cos PX$$

The azimuth of X at the time of observation—which is angle PZ_oX—is very nearly equal to PZ_cX. This may be found by spherical trigonometry or by means of azimuth tables. The difference between Z_cX, which is known as the *calculated zenith distance* (C.Z.D.), and Z_oX, which is known as the *observed zenith distance* (O.Z.D.) obtained from a sextant observation, is

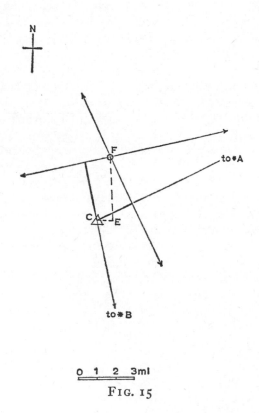

FIG. 15

the intercept. The intercept is named *away* or *towards*, according to whether the O.Z.D. is greater than or less than the C.Z.D. In Fig. 14, the intercept is named *towards*, because the radius of the circle of altitude through o is less than that of the circle of equal altitude through c.

The position line, somewhere on which the observer is located, is drawn through the end of the intercept which is drawn from the plotted chosen position. The direction of the position line is at right angles to the bearing of the observed object X at the time of the observation, this bearing having been found as explained above.

To exemplify the above description, suppose an observer in the Atlantic observed the altitudes of two stars A and B, and found the observed zenith distances (corrected for refraction and height of observer's eye above sea level) to be 36° 40′ and 47° 32′ respectively. Using position latitude 49° 00′N. longitude 35° 16′W., which he knows from his reckoning to approximate to the ship's actual position, he determines the calculated zenith distances of A and B, and finds them to be 36° 42′ for A which bore 065°, and 47° 29′ for B which bore 170°. He would find the position of his ship at the time of the observations in the following way.

Using a plotting sheet (which, in its simplest form, is merely a sheet of paper), because the scale of his navigational chart is too small for plotting, he would mark a spot to represent the chosen position (lat 49° 00′N. long 35° 16′W.). He would then draw lines to represent the intercepts (having chosen a suitable scale of distance) either away or towards. The position lines would then be drawn at right angles to and through the ends of the intercepts. The point of intersection of the position lines represents the ship's position at the time of the observation.

Fig. 15 illustrates this example.

In Fig. 15:

Az * A = 065°	Az * B = 170°
C.Z.D. * A = 36° 42′	C.Z.D. * B = 47° 29′
O.Z.D. * A = 36° 40′	O.Z.D. * B = 47° 32′
Intercept = 2′ towards	= 3′ away

F represents the ship's position at the time of the observation. By measurement F is ½ mile east of c (represented by CE) and 3 ml north of c (represented by EF).

The distance CE is the departure between c and F. In order to find the longitude of F it will be necessary to convert this departure into minutes of longitude.

d.long. CE = departure CE cos lat. c

   dep CE = 0·5 miles

   d long. =   1'E.   lat. c = 49° 00'N.

   long. c = 35° 16'W.   d.lat. =   3'N.

   long. o = 35° 15'W.   lat. o = 49° 03'N.

      Position of observer: Lat. 49° 03'N.
                        Long. 35° 15'W.

CHAPTER SEVEN

The Elements of Surveying

1. General principles

A map represents the whole or part of the Earth's surface on a reduced scale. For convenience a map is drawn on a flat piece of paper and the mapmaker is faced with the problem of representing a curved surface on a flat plane. For small areas of the Earth—up to about eight miles square—the error introduced by assuming the Earth to be perfectly flat (apart from relief features) is negligible. For larger areas, the cartographer uses one of a variety of *map projections*, some of which are discussed in Chapter Eight.

Before a map can be produced the area which is to be portrayed must be surveyed. The framework of a survey is formed by straight lines which link conspicuous marks—natural or artificial—the relative positions of which are known with accuracy. These marks on the ground, which provide 'points of control' for the operation, are plotted, after a choice has been made of a suitable scale of distance for drawing. If it is necessary to link the results of a survey with those of adjacent territories, it will be necessary to determine, by astronomical observations, the geographical position (latitude and longitude) of at least one of the control points of the survey.

The surveys on which maps such as those published by the Ordnance Survey of Great Britain are based, are conducted most meticulously using surveying instruments of the highest attainable degree of accuracy.

The principal instrument used by the professional surveyor is the *theodolite*. The theodolite is an instrument by means of which angles in the horizontal or vertical plane may be measured with an extremely high degree of accuracy—often to an accuracy in the order of a second of arc. The principle of the theodolite is simple although its setting up and use require considerable skill. The instrument consists of a telescope which is mounted on a tripod so that it may be rotated, after the instrument has been properly levelled, in either a vertical or horizontal plane. Measured angles are read off horizontal and vertical scales. Although, as we shall see presently, the measuring of angles plays the major rôle in most surveying operations, the fundamental process in all surveys is the measurement of a distance along the ground.

The so-called geodetic survey, the purpose of which may be to improve knowledge of the figure of the Earth, or to provide the necessary data for a very accurate graphic representation of the area surveyed, is the most important method of surveying used at the present time, although photographic surveying, employing aircraft, is becoming increasingly important.

2. *Triangulation*

A *geodetic survey* involves, in the early stages of the work, the setting up of a sufficient number of control points known as *trigonometrical stations*. These are usually thirty to fifty miles apart and occupy sites which are conspicuous from the greater part of the area to be surveyed. The straight lines joining the trigonometrical stations form a series of triangles and polygons known as the *triangulation*. This forms the framework to which the topographical features of the area are subsequently related. At each trigonometrical station, the theodolite is used to measure horizontal angles between visible pairs of other trig stations. If the stations are not at the same altitude—and this will generally be the case—vertical angles of depression or elevation are also measured with the theodolite.

One of the triangles of the triangulation is connected with a measured length which forms the *base line* of the survey. The accuracy with which the base line is measured plays the most important part in the accuracy of the survey as a whole.

The base line of a geodetic survey is usually in the order of a mile in length. It is generally measured with a tape of *invar*— which is an alloy whose coefficient of expansion is negligible. The site for the base line should be level and clear for measuring. The accuracy with which the base line is measured is in the order of about an inch in 2,000 feet, but the probable error may be as little as one in a million in the case of base lines which are measured with very great refinement.

The stations of the main triangulation are chosen in relation to one another, and their positions are found precisely from astronomical observations. In addition to the main trigonometrical stations—the number of which is kept to a minimum—there is a number of *secondary trig stations* which provide for an increased measure of control of the survey. Secondary trig stations are usually about five to ten miles apart.

The number of control points of a survey is dependent upon the required scale of the map for which the survey is conducted. Trig stations which are five to ten miles apart are considered suitable for maps having a *Natural Scale* or *Representative Fraction* (R.F.) of about 1:100,000. This corresponds to a scale a little smaller than one inch to the mile, the R.F. for which is 1:63,360. If it is required to produce an accurate map having a scale larger than this, a system of *tertiary trig stations* will be set up, these being located not more than a mile or so apart.

It must be remembered that a map is a representation of a level plane. Heights above and depths below a datum level—usually that of mean high water level—are represented by cartographical devices such as contours, layer colouring, hachuring or other means.

The sum of the three angles of any of the triangles of a triangulation will be more than 180°, because the lines of sight between adjacent trig stations are arcs of great circles. The triangles are, therefore, spherical and not plane. The difference between the sum of the three angles of a spherical triangle and 180° is known as the *spherical excess* (see Chapter Two). It can be shown that if the measured angles of a small spherical triangle are adjusted by apportioning the spherical excess in proportion to the angles, so that the sum of the adjusted angles is exactly 180°, the triangle may be treated as a plane triangle, and the plane trig formulae may be used for computing the lengths of the unknown sides.

The most elementary form of a triangulation is a system of triangles, each having a side common to a neighbouring triangle. Fig. 1 illustrates this simple form.

In Fig. 1, if the length AB is known and all the angles measured, the points C, D, E, F and G, are determined relative to one another. This triangulation is described as being *weak*, because no check is provided for fixing points subsequent to its formation: each point in the triangulation being fixed from the measurement of two angles only. In other words each point is dependent upon one triangle only.

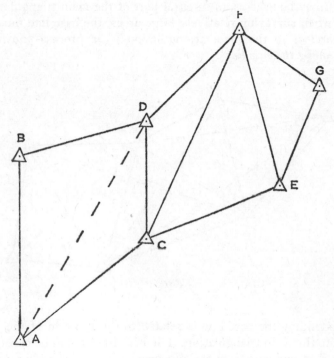

FIG. 1

The lines of sight in a triangulation are referred to as *rays*. Whenever possible, more than one ray (which applies to weak triangulations) should be observed from each trig station.

Referring to Fig. 1, had the angle BAD been measured when the theodolite was set up at station A, then the position of D could be checked from triangle BAD as well as from triangle ACD. Any such point, the position of which may be checked

11

through having three or more rays passing through it, is said to be *strengthened*.

In a weak triangulation any error in one triangle will affect all subsequent triangles. It is important, therefore, that the position of every trig station should be capable of being strengthened. This will be the case if the triangulation consists of a series of quadrilaterals or polygons as illustrated in Fig. 2.

When a relatively small area is to be surveyed, the base line itself may be used as an integral part of the main triangulation; but when surveying relatively large areas, the base line must be *'connected'* to the main triangulation by a process known as *'extending the base line'*.

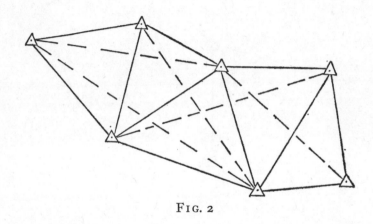

FIG. 2

Extending the base line is related to the tying in of the base line to the main triangulation. The base line should be chosen so that its terminal points are nicely positioned for building up a system of triangles between the base line and one side of the triangulation. The marks used in the process of extending the base line (and this applies to the main triangulation as well), should be located in such positions that *well-conditioned triangles* are formed. The term 'well-conditioned', in this context, means simply that the shapes of the triangles should be such that any error in angular measurement will result in a minimum error in fixing the corners of the triangles. All triangles in a triangulation should, therefore, be well-conditioned; ill-conditioned triangles should be avoided.

Fig. 3 illustrates the process of extending the base line.

In Fig. 3 the line AB is the base line, and the peck lines AC, AD, CX, etc., build up the triangulation from the base line to the side XY of the main triangulation.

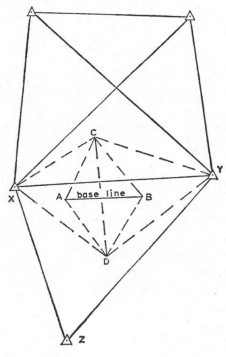

FIG. 3

Triangulation may be in the form of either a *chain of triangles* or a *network*. When surveying a large territory of continental size, chains extending north–south or east–west form the basis of the survey. For small territories, the area may be covered conveniently with a network of lines as illustrated in Fig. 4.

When the area to be mapped is provided with a framework of triangulation, the process of plotting the topographic detail of the area is commenced. This detail is 'filled in' in relation to the triangulation.

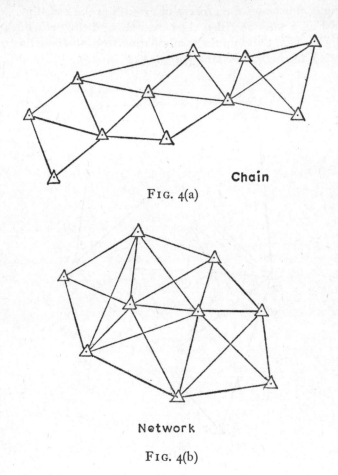

Chain

FIG. 4(a)

Network

FIG. 4(b)

3. *Chain surveying*

Following the brief discussion on surveying given above, let us now consider the principles as they apply to the surveying of small areas. Now that it is possible to measure angles with a high degree of accuracy by means of a theodolite, linear measurement in surveying is not of such great importance as it was formerly.

Yet, for making a simple survey of a small area, a chain survey involving the measuring of distances along the ground is often employed.

The gear required for chain surveying consists of a *surveyor's chain* or *tape measure*; a *set of pegs* or *markers* to assist in the measuring of distances; and a short staff to aid in measuring short distances. A note book—or *field book* as it is usually called—and a pencil are also required.

The area to be surveyed is regarded as being made up of a series of well-conditioned triangles, the apices of which are marked by natural or artificial features. After the survey has been planned, a rough sketch is made of the area and the sides of the triangles are depicted on it. The sides of the triangles are lettered or numbered in accordance with a proposed route which will take in all the sides of the triangles. The route is planned as carefully as possible to minimize walking. The chain survey is then started, commencing at one end of the first chain line, and measuring or chaining its length as accurately as possible using the pegs or markers to assist.

A surveyor's chain—*Gunter's chain* as it is commonly called—is made up of 100 *links* each 7·92 inches long, designed to facilitate folding, and is 22 yards long (22 yards = 1 chain). As the measuring of each chain line proceeds, an assistant measures the distances from the chain line, and if possible at right angles to it, to important features including roadways, buildings, streams, hedges, trees, etc. These distances, or *offsets*, are recorded in the field book. All measurements are recorded in the field book in a convenient and unambiguous way. It is customary to make entries starting at the bottom of the last page of the book and to work forwards. Fig. 5 serves to illustrate a simple chain survey and part of the field book record.

For an accurate chain survey all offsets should be short. This may involve having a large number of triangles making, therefore, a relatively complex triangulation. This in turn will involve considerable walking and measuring. The recording of all measurements must be done with the greatest of care. The map of the area is drawn from the record; and it is important, therefore, that no blunders are made in making the record.

A chain survey is suitable for a small area of simple shape with

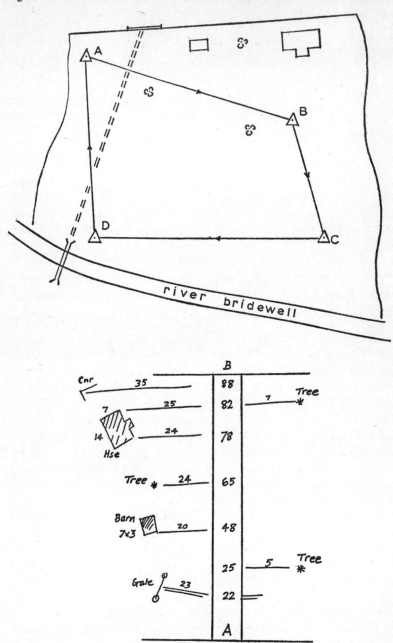

FIG. 5

little or no relief, so that few triangles are needed and long lines may be chained. This method of survey is sometimes used to survey a route—natural or artificial—but it suffers the grave disadvantage in that the map is drawn always from the field record; so that if the record is in error the map also will be in error and, moreover, there is no way of checking apart from making a fresh survey.

In the above brief description of a chain survey, an important principle—which is applicable to all surveys—is to be noted. This principle is that a survey always proceeds from the whole to the part: this applies to surveying a continent as well as to surveying a field.

4. The traverse

We shall now describe briefly a method of surveying a small area or a route between two points whose positions relative to one another are known: a method known as a *traverse*. The traverse consists of a series of measured lines which is described as either '*open*' or '*closed*', the former applying to a route survey, and the latter to the survey of a small area.

The record of a traverse survey is kept in a way similar to that of a chain survey, and the map is drawn from the field record in the same way as it is in the case of a chain survey. In a simple traverse survey a prismatic compass is used to measure the directions of the lines forming the traverse.

There are two methods of plotting the results of a compass traverse:

(1) Direct plotting using scale and protractor.
(2) Indirect plotting using rectangular coordinates.

In the direct plotting method, a trial plot is first made from the field record, the end points of the route, in the case of a route survey, having first been plotted. Any errors in the field record will likely result in the end of the plotted traverse not coinciding with the initial point in the case of the areal survey, or the end point of a route survey. Should this be the case, an *error of closure* is said to exist, and the legs of the traverse must be adjusted to eliminate, as far as possible, the errors of the survey.

When an error of closure exists, the errors of the survey are distributed in such a way that each leg is adjusted by an amount which is proportional to its length. This is justifiable because the error of the survey is generally due to inaccurate measurement of the lengths of the legs. Errors in measuring lengths are usually cumulative so that, in general, the longer the leg the greater the possible error.

Fig. 6 illustrates how an error of closure is distributed, in order to adjust a traverse, when the direct plotting method is used.

Diagram (a) in Fig. 6 illustrates the method of dealing with an error of closure in an open traverse. Diagram (b) illustrates how an error of closure is dealt with in a closed traverse.

Lines are drawn parallel to the error of closure at the ends of each leg of the traverse. The total length of the traverse is then drawn to the same scale as the plot, and the legs of the traverse are marked off on this line. A line is then drawn at the end of this line and perpendicular to it, the length of which is equal to the error of closure. The hypotenuse of the triangle, of which the sides are the error of closure and the total traverse, is then drawn; and perpendiculars are erected at the ends of the traverse legs. The lengths of these perpendiculars cut off by the hypotenuse are the proportions of the total error of closure corresponding to the respective traverse legs. These proportionate lengths are laid off at the ends of the legs on the trial plot and the plot adjusted as illustrated in Fig. 6.

The method of plotting by rectangular coordinates involves treating each leg of the traverse as the hypotenuse of a right-angled triangle, the other two sides of which are the d.lat. and departure respectively between the end points of the leg. In the case of the closed traverse the sum of both the d.lats and departures of all the right-angled triangles formed should be zero. If this is not so there is an error of closure; and the resultant d.lat. and departure must be divided between the triangles in proportion to the lengths of the legs which form their hypotenuses.

When using the method of *rectangular coordinates* to plot a route which has been surveyed by the method of compass traverse the sum of the d.lats and departures should be equal to the d.lat. and departure between the end points of the route.

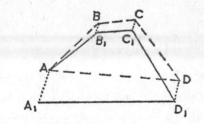

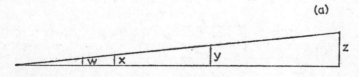

(a)

AB$_1$C$_1$D$_1$A$_1$ – trial plot
AA$_1$ – error of closure
ABCDA   – corrected plot

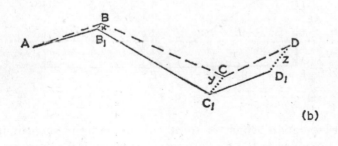

(b)

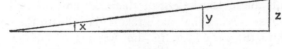

AB$_1$C$_1$D$_1$ – trial plot
DD$_1$ – error of closure
ABCD   – corrected plot

FIG. 6

Fig. 7 illustrates the method of plotting by the use of rectangular coordinates.

Referring to Fig. 7, the total d.lat. obtained from the traverse

$$= d_1 \cos \alpha + d_2 \cos \beta + d_3 \cos \gamma + \cdots$$

Total departure $= d_1 \sin \alpha + d_2 \sin \beta + d_3 \sin \gamma + \cdots$

These parts of the d.lat. and departure are normally obtained from traverse tables. If these totals are equal to d.lat. AE and departure AE, there is no error of closure.

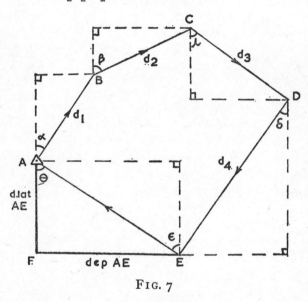

FIG. 7

The operation which is most tedious and time-consuming when surveying is the measuring of distances. All survey work demands the measurement of distances and the major improvements in surveying that have taken place down the centuries are related to the reduction in the amount of labour involved in measuring distances along the ground.

In the history of surveying it was early realized that a point could be fixed by measuring angles at each of two points of known position, so forming a triangle, one side and the two adjacent angles of which being known. Knowledge of these three parts of a triangle facilitates the calculation of the lengths of the remaining sides.

In Fig. 8, if A and B are two points whose positions and distance apart are known, the angles α and β together with distance d may be used to compute the sides AC and BC of the triangle ABC. Hence the fixing of C relative to A or B is possible without having to measure AC and BC. Moreover, if the angles α and β are measured accurately the computed values of AC and BC will likely be nearer to the truth than the measured values.

In modern surveying the measuring of angles can, by theodolite, be performed with a very high degree of accuracy, and hence angle-measuring plays a predominant part in modern surveying.

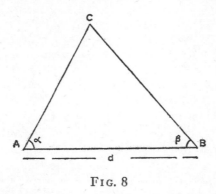

FIG. 8

The mathematician and surveyor Willebrord Snell (Snellius), is credited with being the first to use the method of triangulation for surveying purposes. We have had occasion, in Chapter One, to describe Snell's attempt at measuring the Earth's dimension by means of a chain of triangles extending from Alkmaar to Bergen-op-Zoom through Leiden.

5. *The plane table*

We have discussed, in brief detail, the principles of triangulation in relation to theodolite surveying. A method of surveying using the same principles is known as *plane tabling*. A *plane table* is an instrument consisting of a flat board about 30 inches square which is mounted on a tripod in such a way that it may be levelled (using a spirit level for doing so), and turned about a vertical axis through its centre.

The equipment normally used in conjunction with the plane table, in addition to the spirit level used for levelling, includes a *sight rule* or *alidade*, and a *trough compass*, both of which are used for orienting the table when carrying out a survey. The great virtue of plane tabling is that all work is done in the field. Hence frequent checks are possible and the risk of blundering is slight. The disadvantages of plane tabling are: first, that dry and reasonably calm weather conditions are essential as all plotting and drawing are executed in the open; and secondly, the relative difficulty in setting up the instrument—a difficulty which is overcome by practice.

The preliminary work for plane tabling includes the measurement of a short base line on which the subsequent survey is virtually constructed by angle measurements. Any error in the measurement of the base line would not affect the relative positions of points which are plotted, but the scale of the map of course would be inaccurate. After the base line has been measured, the plane table, mounted with drawing paper, is set up at one end of the base line. The table is levelled and, with the use of a suitable scale, the base line is drawn on the plotting sheet. The table is then oriented by means of the trough compass.

A *trough compass* is simply a magnetic needle, pivoted so that when it lies in the magnetic meridian its axis will be parallel to the sides of the narrow trough in which the pivot is fixed centrally. A scale is provided, the line joining the zero point on the scale to the pivot being parallel to the sides of the trough. The long edge of the trough may be used as a ruler to draw in lines representing the magnetic meridian. It is essential, when using the trough compass, to ensure that magnetic fields other than the Earth's field do not affect the needle.

Having set up the table at one end of the base line, the table is slewed so that the line of sight of the base line coincides with its plotted position. The trough compass is then laid on the table and adjusted so that the end of the needle rests at the zero position of the scale. A line drawn along the edge of the trough compass then represents the magnetic north–south line; and, if sources of magnetism other than that of the Earth do not affect the compass, the table may be set up and oriented properly at any position in the area to be surveyed, provided that the Earth's magnetic field in the area is uniform at all places.

The principle of plane tabling is related to the correct orienta tion of the table whenever it is set up at an observation point. The table must never be set out of its original orientation, and it is essential to check the orientation frequently throughout the survey. Correct orientation of the table is facilitated by using the trough compass, and also by observing bearings and drawing *back rays* on the plotting sheet from points whose positions are known and which have been plotted on the sheet. If three back rays obtained from observations of three plotted marks do not meet at a point, the table is not correctly oriented, provided that the marks are plotted in their correct relative positions, and the back rays drawn in their correct directions. If three back rays do not meet at a common point, the table must be slewed in azimuth until they do. In plane tabling this process is normally done by intelligent guesswork; and, after a little practice, the process is found to be simple.

It has been said that if an embryo surveyor had to rely on learning how to use a plane table only from descriptions written in books, plane tabling would have died a natural death soon after it had been invented. The principles of the plane table are straightforward and simple, and the practice of plane tabling is not difficult to master.

At each new observation point, which has been fixed on the plotting sheet by previous observations, the table is oriented by slewing it until the trough compass, the edge of which has been set parallel to a magnetic north–south line on the plotting sheet, indicates the zero point on the scale. Then, to check the orientation, a mark whose position had been plotted is observed, to verify that the sight line is coincident with the bearing of the mark from the new observation point. Sighting of marks is facilitated by the sight rule or alidade.

There are four general methods of using a plane table, known respectively as the *radial, traverse, intersection* and *resection* methods.

The *radial method* involves setting up the table at a position which is centrally located in the area to be surveyed. The table is oriented properly using the trough compass, and it is then clamped. Rays are then drawn, using the sight rule, in the direction of objects which are to be mapped. Having fixed the directions of these objects, they may be plotted by measuring the distances to each of them from the observation point, and then marking off these distances to scale along the appropriate lines of sight.

The *traverse method* involves setting up the plane table at a suitable position in the area to be mapped, after which it is levelled and, using the trough compass, oriented properly. The sight rule is used to draw in the first leg of the traverse. The plane table is then set up at the second observation point, the distance between the first and second observation points being measured by a chain or tape. From this measurement the second observation point is marked on the plotting sheet. The table is levelled and oriented properly at the second observation point, and the sight rule used to mark in the second leg of the traverse. The length of the second leg is found by chaining or taping, and the third observation point is plotted. The survey continues in this way to the end of the traverse, which may be *closed* or *open*.

The *intersection method* of using a plane table involves the measuring of a suitably located base line, after which the table is set up and levelled at one end of it. The table is oriented by lining up the plotted base line with a mark which is set up at the other end of the base line. The sight rule is then used to draw in rays from the plotted position of the end of the base line at which the table is set up. The rays are drawn in the directions of marks which are to be mapped. Having drawn in the necessary rays, the table is moved to the other end of the base line and the same procedure is repeated. The points of intersection of corresponding rays from the ends of the base line are the plotted positions of the observed marks.

The method of intersection can apply only to marks that are visible from the observation points from which the rays are drawn. Marks such as points along stream beds or roads, which are not visible from plotted observation points, must be fixed if necessary by a process known as *resection*. Resection is analogous to the process of fixing a ship by a cross bearing of two or three charted marks visible from the offing.

When it is necessary to fix a mark by resection, the plane table is set up at or near the mark. After it is levelled and oriented, back rays from visible plotted marks are drawn. These rays should intersect at a common point provided that the plotted positions of the observed marks are correct, and the table is properly oriented. If the three back rays do not intersect at a common point, the three rays will form a *triangle of error*.

If, when employing the method of resection, a triangle of error appears, and if it is due to incorrect orientation of the table, the table must be slewed in azimuth to make the three rays meet at a common point. Two cases are possible: one in which the required position (at which the plane table is located) lies inside the triangle of error; and the other case when it lies outside the triangle.

The position is inside the triangle of error when, for any given azimuthal movement of the table, all three rays will move in the same direction, that is either clockwise or anticlockwise, around their pivotal points, so that the triangle increases or decreases in magnitude. The required position is distant from any ray by an amount which is proportional to the length of the ray. That is to say, the longer is the ray, the bigger is the displacement between the plotted ray and the true position of the observer.

If the position is outside the triangle of error—and this may readily be ascertained from the fact that one ray will have to swing in a direction different from that of the other two in order to decrease the size of the triangle of error—the sector in which the observer lies may easily be ascertained as the following illustration will show.

In Fig. 9, A, B and C represent the plotted positions of three conspicuous marks. Back rays AX, BY and CZ are drawn as shown and a triangle of error (shaded in the diagram) results through the table not being properly oriented.

It should be quite clear that the observer's position cannot be inside the triangle of error because as the arrows on the back rays suggest, this would require ray BY to swing in a direction opposite to that of the other two rays. The observer's position, therefore, lies outside the triangle. To ascertain in which of the six numbered sectors the observer lies, he would argue as follows.

To be in sector 1, requires rays AX and BY to swing in opposite directions. If the error is the same for both rays, this is not permissible, hence the observer cannot be in sector 1. By similar arguments he cannot be in sectors 2, 4 or 5. Remembering that the distance from the plotted ray to the observer's position is proportional to the length of the ray, it may readily be deduced that the observer's position is in sector 3 and not sector 6.

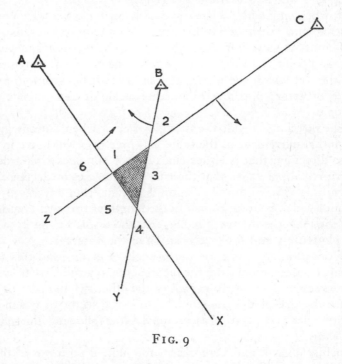

FIG. 9

The plane table provides for the field scientist the most suitable method of surveying. It demands the minimum of distance measuring if the methods of intersection and resection are used, and the time and energy so saved may be used for the study of the field interest. Plane tabling is most useful for surveying an area which has little or no relief, and one which is relatively clear of obstructions so that long rays may be employed. No assistance is necessary and, provided that the weather is clear, dry and calm, it is far superior as a survey method for the geographer, to chain-, traverse- or compass-surveying.

6. *The measurement of altitude*

Most maps, although they are drawn on a two-dimensional plane, portray the third dimension of altitude. Hence the relief of a mapped area may be visualized by studying the particular carto-graphic device used for representing relief.

When surveying an area, the heights of a number of points within an area are measured above some datum level, which is usually the level of the lowest point in the area. For coastal areas, and indeed for all areas portrayed on professionally-made maps, the sea level—usually the level of Mean High Water at Spring Tides (M.H.W.S.)—is used as a datum level. On Admiralty charts, the datum level below which charted depths are given— known as the level of *Chart Datum*—is, of necessity, a relatively low level—usually that of Mean Low Water at Spring Tides (M.L.W.S.).

One common form of altimeter works on the same principle as that of the aneroid barometer. Variations in air pressure which acts on a sealed metallic drum partially evacuated of air before being hermetically sealed, cause the volume of the drum to change. The resulting movement of one of the faces of the drum is transmitted to a pointer by means of a train of gears and chains. The pointer rides over a graduated scale of feet. Changes in level result in changes in air pressure, so that the altitudes of points within an area being surveyed may be ascertained by means of the variations of air pressure with altitude using an adaptation of an aneroid barometer.

The barometric method of ascertaining heights above or below some datum level suffers the disadvantage in that atmospheric pressure at any level changes with position and time. However if the necessary corrections are applied to altimeter readings, heights may be found to an accuracy of about 10 feet.

The commonly-used simple instrument for ascertaining heights of hill-tops and other landforms when surveying, is the *clinometer*, of which there are many varieties.

One form of clinometer is the *Indian clinometer*, the principal features of which are illustrated in Fig. 10.

After the instrument is levelled, the foresight is adjusted so that it lies on the same straight line as the line of sight to the feature

12

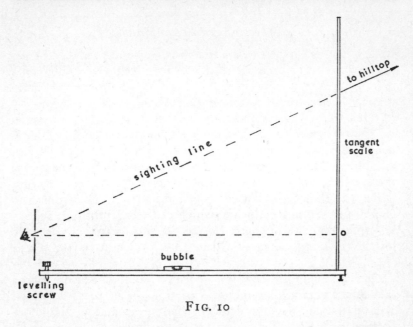

FIG. 10

whose height is required, the eye being placed at the back-sight as illustrated in Fig. 10.

The angle between the line of sight and the horizontal, together with the distance between the observer and the observed object, enables the observer to calculate the height of the object. Fig. 11 illustrates that the height of the object above the level of the observer is equal to the product of the distance between the observer and the object and the tangent of the angle of elevation.

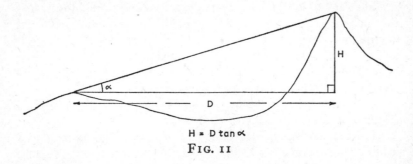

H = D tan α

FIG. 11

The Indian clinometer, as illustrated in Fig. 10, is provided with a tangent scale, so that trig tables are not required when using it.

The *Abney level*, which is illustrated in Fig. 12, consists of a sighting tube fitted with a horizontal cross wire as shown. Fitted within the tube is a half-silvered glass divided vertically and set at an angle of 45° to the axis of the sighting tube. Vertically above the half-silvered glass is a bubble, the image of which is reflected at the silvered part of the glass so that it is visible to an observer using the instrument. A scale of angles is fitted to the sighting tube. A pointer, which is engraved on an index arm to which the

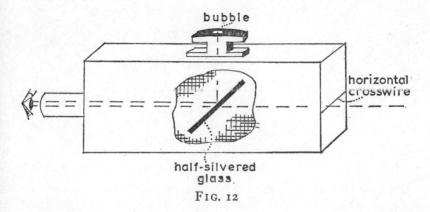

bubble

horizontal crosswire

half-silvered glass.

FIG. 12

bubble tube is attached, may be moved across the arc scale by means of a slow motion screw.

When using the Abney level, the instrument is directed to the object whose height is required, and the slow motion screw is turned until the direct image of the object, which is seen through the unsilvered part of the glass, is in horizontal alignment with the reflected image of the bubble. When this is so, as illustrated in Fig. 13, the angle which the axis of the sighting tube makes with the horizontal is read off the graduated scale. The height of the object above the level of the observer is then calculated from the formula:

$$H = D \tan \theta$$

where D is the distance off, θ the measured angle and H the required altitude.

The theodolite may be used to measure vertical angles of elevation or depression. This instrument, therefore, is often used for ascertaining altitudes.

The most accurate process of measuring the height of an eminence above a given datum level is known as *spirit levelling*, or more usually as simple '*levelling*'.

Levelling involves the use of a sensitive spirit level which is mounted on a telescope. The level is used in conjunction with two staves which are graduated very carefully in feet and inches.

When levelling by means of a spirit level, one staff is set up vertically at a point ahead of the level, and the other staff is set up

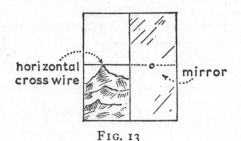

FIG. 13

likewise at about the same distance behind the level. The distance between the level and either staff is usually not more than about 50–100 yards. Observations on both staves are made, and the difference between the readings on the two staves is equivalent to the difference between the heights of the ground at the two points at which the staves are set. Fig. 14 illustrates the process of levelling by means of spirit level and staves.

Referring to Fig. 14, T_1 represents the first position of the level, and A and B the two staves. The difference in the readings on the two staves, which are 10′ and 4′ respectively, is a measure of the difference between the altitudes of the points where the staves are set up. This difference is six feet. After this set of observations has been made, staff A is moved to a position c ahead of the second position of the level T_2. The difference between the readings on the two staves will now give the difference between the altitudes at b and c. In our example this difference is 7 feet. In this way the relief of the area surveyed may easily be found.

If, when levelling in the way described above, a record of the successive differences between the readings on the two staves is

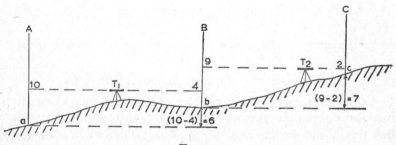

FIG. 14

kept, the algebraic sum of the differences should be equal to the difference between the altitudes of the starting and finishing points of the levelling traverse. In the event of a closed traverse having been made, the algebraic sum of the differences should be zero.

CHAPTER EIGHT

Map Projections

1. *The properties of map projections. Map scales*

For small areas, as we have noted in Chapter Seven, errors in mapping due to the curvature of the Earth's surface are negligible, but this is not so for large areas. The task of representing a spherical surface on a plane surface results in distortion. Distance, shape, direction and area cannot together be represented accurately, although it is possible to construct a map of a large area which suffers no distortion in shape OR distance OR direction.

Parallels of latitude and meridians (or parts of them), when represented on a plane surface, are said to be '*projected*'. The resultant network of lines which are the projected parallels of latitude and meridians is known as a *graticule*. There are many methods of projecting a spherical surface on to a plane surface, each being known as a *map projection*. But, as we have stated above, the graticule of every map projection is bound to be distorted in one way or another. The cartographer, therefore, in selecting a projection on which to construct a map, considers primarily the property which he desires most to preserve. If he wishes to produce a map on which geographical distributions are to be portrayed accurately, he would probably choose a projection in which there is uniform distortion of area throughout the map. Such a projection is described as an *equal-area projection*. If it is necessary to construct a map on which distances from a given point are to be represented truly, the map should be constructed on an *equi-distant projection*. If the cartographer desires several properties to be portrayed reasonably accurately, he must choose a projection which will be a compromise, so that the required properties are represented as faithfully as possible.

It is impossible to represent accurately shape and distance

together on any map, so that the property of *orthomorphism*—which means 'true shape'—has a special meaning when it is applied to a map projection. A map is orthomorphic when the exaggeration—which is expressed as a ratio between a short length on the globe and the corresponding length of its projection on the map—is the same at any point on the map in all directions. It follows, therefore, that shape on an orthomorphic map is truly represented only at a point on the map. In practice it is usually assumed that small areas on an orthomorphic map are portrayed without distortion.

The maps resulting from simple surveys, such as those described in Chapter Seven, are orthomorphic because the scale of distance at all parts of the map is constant, so that true shape is preserved. This follows from the fact that the area portrayed is such a small fraction of the Earth's total surface area that its curvature may justifiably be ignored. However a map of the whole of the Earth's surface, or at least a large part of it, may have the orthomorphic property, as we shall discover.

We shall be concerned in this chapter with map projections of the whole of the Earth's surface, or as much of it as the projections will allow. In this connection it must be remembered that a map is a representation of the Earth's surface on a reduced scale. We shall, therefore, consider some of the projections to be described as being full-scale projections of a model globe.

A model globe of the Earth's surface provides the only means of representing the Earth's surface without distortion of any form except, of course, area. For some purposes a model globe of the Earth is a splendid device but it suffers the serious disadvantages of being clumsy and expensive. Worse than these disadvantages is that, for most geographical purposes, its scale is too small. Maps, in contrast to model globes, are handy and inexpensive, and may be drawn to a sufficiently large scale for any practical purpose. The principal disadvantage of a map is that distortion in some way is bound to occur. When using a map, therefore, this ought always to be appreciated by the user.

The scale of a map is an expression of the ratio between a distance on the map and the distance on the Earth's surface which it represents. If, for example, a mile on the Earth's surface is represented by an inch on a certain part of a map, the scale of the map in this part could be expressed as being '*one inch to one mile*'. A *small-scale* map is one on which a relatively large distance on the Earth's surface is represented by a small length on the map. Thus a map whose scale is one inch to ten miles is a small-scale map compared with one on which the scale is one inch to one mile. But it is a *large-scale map* compared with one whose scale is one inch to a hundred miles.

The scale of a map, unless the map be of a very small area, usually varies with position on the map, so that when describing the scale, the position on the map to which the scale applies, should be stated. A conventional way of describing a map's scale is to state the ratio between a unit of distance on the map and the number of such units of distance along the Earth's surface it represents. This ratio is known as the *Representative Fraction* (R.F.) or *Natural Scale*. If a mile on the Earth is represented by an inch on the map, the R.F. is 1/63360. If the scale is one inch to ten miles, the R.F. is 1/633600. The smaller is the fraction, the smaller is the map scale. A map whose R.F. is 1/10000 has a linear scale of roughly 1 inch to 280 yards.

Map projections, for the purpose of orderly study, may be divided into two types, known respectively as *perspective* and *conventional*. All map projections are based on mathematical principles. The chief difference between projections of the two types, is that perspective projections are based on geometrical projection from a given point known as the *point of projection*: straight *lines of projection* extending from the point of projection, through the surface of a model globe, on to the surface of a cone which envelops, or is imagined to envelop, the model globe. It is useful to imagine the model globe, apart from the parallels of latitude and meridians which are engraved on it, as being transparent, and to imagine a point source of light to be located at the point of projection. The shadows of the parallels of latitude and meridians, which would be cast on to the enveloping cone, would form a geometrical or perspective projection.

The graticule of a perspective projection has a form which depends upon:

(1) the position of the point of projection

(2) the position of the enveloping cone

(3) the solid angle at the apex of the enveloping cone.

The limiting cases of a cone are, first, a plane surface, which is the case when the solid angle at the apex of the cone is maximum (2π); and secondly, a cylinder, which is the case when the solid angle at the apex of the cone is zero. For this reason perspective projections are divided into a three-fold classification as follows:

(1) Zenithal or Azimuthal

(2) Conical

(3) Cylindrical.

These are illustrated in Fig. 1, in which O is the centre of the model globe from which the projections are developed.

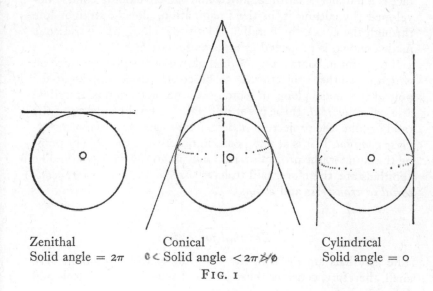

| Zenithal | Conical | Cylindrical |
| Solid angle $= 2\pi$ | $0 <$ Solid angle $< 2\pi \not> 0$ | Solid angle $= 0$ |

FIG. 1

In a perspective zenithal projection, the contact of the model globe and the plane of the projection is a point. In a perspective conical it is a small circle of the globe. In a perspective cylindrical it is usually (but not necessarily) a great circle of the globe.

Conventional projections are those which are constructed according to mathematical rules, and are not perspective. Most conventionals, although they are not perspective, are based on planes, cones, or cylinders, which are considered to envelop or intersect a model globe. The graticule of a conventional projection is produced, not from geometrical projection, but from mathematical devices employed to produce a certain property (such as equal-area, orthomorphism, or true representation of distance), in the projections of the parallels of latitude and meridians. For this reason some projections are called *conventional cylindricals*, or *conventional conicals*.

In most cylindrical projections the enveloping cylinder makes contact with the model globe along the equator, in which case parallels of latitude are projected from the globe's centre as parallel straight lines. In most conical projections, the line of contact is a parallel of latitude, and when the enveloping cone is developed (by cutting it, in the imagination, along a straight line through the apex), the parallel of latitude, along which the cone made contact, is projected as an arc of a circle.

The point of contact on a model globe, of the plane surface on which a zenithal projection is to be constructed, may be at the pole of the model globe, in which case the projection is described as a *polar zenithal*. If the point of contact is on the equator of the model globe, the projection is described as an *equatorial* or *transverse zenithal*. If it is at any position other than the pole or point on the equator, the projection is known as an *oblique zenithal*. The zenithals are, therefore, said to have three *cases*, viz., *polar*, *equatorial* or *transverse* and *oblique*.

2. Zenithal projections

The zenithals are perhaps the simplest of the projections. We shall, therefore, consider these before discussing the conicals and cylindricals (perspective and conventional).

Three of the five zenithals which we shall describe are perspective projections, the other two being conventionals.

a. GNOMONIC (PERSPECTIVE) POLAR CASE

Fig. 2 illustrates the construction of the polar case of the gnomonic projection.

Let the radius of the model globe which is illustrated in Fig. 2 be R. O is the centre of the globe, PP_1 lies in the plane of the zenithal projection, T, the point of contact, is located at the pole.

The point of projection in the case of the gnomonic lies at the centre of the globe at O. It should be clear that all meridians are projected as straight lines radiating from the point T. It should also be clear that all parallels of latitude in the hemisphere of which T is the pole, are projected as circles centred at T and radius r where

$$r = R \cot \phi$$

where ϕ is the latitude.

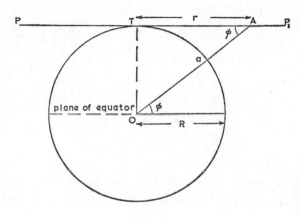

FIG. 2

The cotangent of an angle varies from infinity (∞) at $0°$ to unity at $90°$. It follows, therefore, that equidistant parallels on the globe are projected as circles whose distances apart increase as the latitude decreases. It should be clear that the equator cannot be projected on a polar gnomonic because $\cot 0° = \infty$.

The exaggeration along any projected parallel increases equatorwards at a rate different from that along any meridian in the vicinity of the parallel. On the globe the length of any parallel of latitude θ is $2\pi R \cos \theta$. On the map the length of the projection of the parallel of latitude θ is $2\pi r$ or $2\pi R \cot \theta$.

Therefore,

$$\text{Exaggeration of parallel} = \frac{2\pi R \cot \theta}{2\pi R \cos \theta}$$

$$= \operatorname{cosec} \theta$$

The exaggeration of any piece of the meridian, such as xy illustrated in Fig. 3, is different from this.

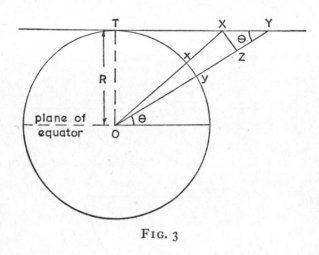

FIG. 3

In Fig. 3, the arc xy is projected as the line XY. The exaggeration of the piece of the meridian in the vicinity of the parallel of latitude θ:

$$= \frac{XY}{xy}$$

From Fig. 3:

$$OX = R \operatorname{cosec} \theta \quad \text{if xy is small}$$

Therefore,

$$\frac{XZ}{xy} = \frac{XO}{R}$$

and

$$XZ = \frac{xyR \operatorname{cosec} \theta}{R}$$

$$= xy \operatorname{cosec} \theta$$

In triangle XYZ:

$$\text{Angle } Y = \theta$$

$$XZ = xy \operatorname{cosec} \theta$$

$$XY = XZ \operatorname{cosec} \theta$$

Therefore, $XY = xy \operatorname{cosec}^2 \theta$

Therefore:

Exaggeration of a piece of a meridian in the vicinity of the parallel of latitude θ:

$$= \frac{XY}{xy} = \operatorname{cosec}^2 \theta$$

This is different from the exaggeration along the parallel. Therefore the gnomonic projection is not orthomorphic.

Because the point of projection lies in the plane of every great circle of the model globe, the projections of all great circles are straight lines. This feature of a gnomonic projection makes the projection valuable for great circle sailing in navigation.

Near the point of contact the representation of areas is satisfactory, for when θ is large the difference between $\operatorname{cosec} \theta$ and $\operatorname{cosec}^2 \theta$ is small, this difference decreasing as θ increases. For this reason Admiralty harbour plans having a natural scale greater than 1/25000, are often constructed on the gnomonic projection.

Fig. 4 illustrates the graticule of a polar gnomonic projection, developed from a model globe of radius one unit, for the area north of the parallel of latitude 30°N.

$R = 1$ unit	
Parallel θ	Radius $r = R \cot \theta$
30°	$1 \times \cot 30° = 1·73\ldots$
45°	$1 \times \cot 45° = 1·00$
60°	$1 \times \cot 60° = 0·58\ldots$
75°	$1 \times \cot 75° = 0·27\ldots$

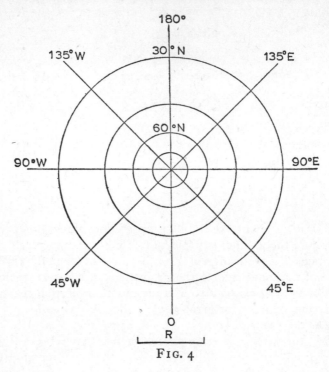

FIG. 4

b. STEREOGRAPHIC (PERSPECTIVE) POLAR CASE

Fig. 5 illustrates the construction of the polar case of the stereographic projection.

The point of projection, in the case of the stereographic projection, is the point on the model globe which is antipodal to the point of contact of the plane of the projection. In Fig. 5, O is the point of projection; PP_1 is in the plane of the projection; and T is the tangential point or point of contact.

Because O lies in the plane of all great circles which pass through T, therefore meridians are projected as straight lines radiating from T. Parallels of latitude are projected as circles centred at T. The radius r, of any parallel of latitude ϕ, as seen from Fig. 5, is:

$$r = 2R \tan (45° - \phi/2)$$

where R is the radius of the model globe.

The equator is projected as a circle of radius $2R$, and parallels of latitude on the side of the equator nearer the point of projection are projected as circles having radii greater than $2R$. More than a hemisphere may, therefore, be projected; but it is impossible to project a complete sphere.

Although the scale is increasingly exaggerated as the distance from the point of contact increases the map is orthomorphic. For this reason the projection is sometimes known as the *zenithal orthomorphic*.

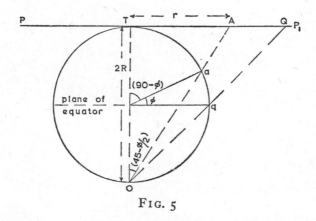

FIG. 5

A simple proof of orthomorphism in the stereographic projection is illustrated in Fig. 6.

In Fig. 6, X is the point of projection on a model globe centred at O; a and b are two points on the same meridian, and which are projected on to the plane of the projection at A and B respectively.

For orthomorphism, the exaggeration along any parallel of latitude must be equal to the exaggeration along any meridian in the vicinity of the parallel.

Exaggeration of projected parallel scale at A

$$= \frac{2\pi \text{TA}}{2\pi \text{ta}} = \frac{\text{TA}}{\text{ta}}$$

Exaggeration of meridian scale at A

$$= \frac{\text{AB}}{\text{ab}}$$

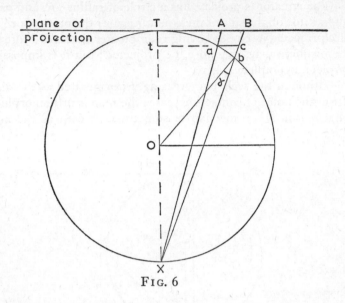

Fig. 6

Map is orthomorphic if

$$\frac{TA}{ta} = \frac{AB}{ab}$$

Consider the triangle abc:

as $ab \to O$

$ac \to ab$, because angle $abc \to (90 - \alpha)$

and angle $acb \to (90 - \alpha)$

Therefore, as $ab \to O$ $\quad \dfrac{AB}{ab} \to \dfrac{AB}{ac}$

Now, $\qquad \dfrac{AB}{ac} = \dfrac{AX}{aX}$ (similar triangles)

and, in the limit as $ac \to ab$,

$$\frac{AB}{ab} = \frac{AX}{aX}$$

Also, $\qquad \dfrac{TA}{ta} = \dfrac{AX}{aX}$ (similar triangles)

So, for an infinitely small piece of the meridian ab, we have:

$$\frac{AB}{ab} = \frac{TA}{ta}$$

Therefore the map is orthomorphic.

An alternative proof of orthomorphism in the stereographic is interesting because it illustrates a very important property of the projection, namely, all circles on the globe (*great* as well as *small*), are projected as straight lines or arcs of circles. The stereographic projection is, therefore, simple to construct geometrically— pencil, straight-edge and drawing compasses being the only instruments required.

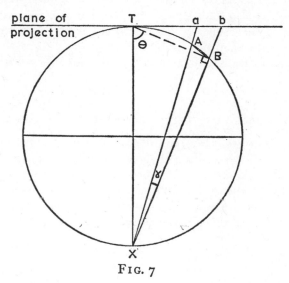

plane of projection

FIG. 7

Referring to Fig. 7 it may readily be proved that the triangles Xab and XAB are similar. Thus:

XBT is a semicircle, therefore: Angle XBT $= 90°$

Also,   angle TXB$+ \theta = 90°$

and,   angles BXT$+$XbT $= 90°$

Therefore,   angle XbT $= \theta$

Now angle XAB stands on chord XB.

Therefore,   angle XAB $= \theta$

13

Comparing triangles Xab and XAB:

α is common

$$XbT = XAB = \theta$$

therefore triangles are similar.

If triangles are similar, cones of rotation also are similar and the projection of a circle on the globe of diameter AB is a circle diameter ab. Therefore shape is accurately represented and the projection is, thus, orthomorphic.

The stereographic projection is often employed for world maps in two hemispheres (northern and southern, or eastern and western). It also finds great use in the hands of astronomers and navigators for solving astronomical- or celestial-navigational problems mechanically or geometrically.

Fig. 8 illustrates a polar stereographic for the area north of the equator.

c. ORTHOGRAPHIC (PERSPECTIVE) POLAR CASE

The point of projection, in the case of the zenithal orthographic, lies at an infinite distance along a line perpendicular to the plane of the projection at the point of contact, and which passes through the centre of the globe. All lines of projection are parallel to the diameter of the globe which terminates at the point of contact. The projection, therefore, appears as a photographic portrayal of the sphere's surface as seen from a great distance.

Fig. 9 illustrates the principle of the orthographic projection.

In Fig. 9, O is the centre of a model globe of radius R. PP_1 lies in the plane of the projection, and T is the point of contact. Lines of projection are parallel to OT.

The equator is represented by a circle of radius R; and all parallels of latitude are projected as circles centred at T. The radius of any projected parallel of latitude ϕ is $R \cos \phi$.

All meridians are projected as straight lines which radiate from the point of contact. A whole hemisphere may be projected using the orthographic projection; and the scale, in the case of the polar orthographic, is decreasingly exaggerated towards the projected equator. All parallels are projected true to scale, their lengths

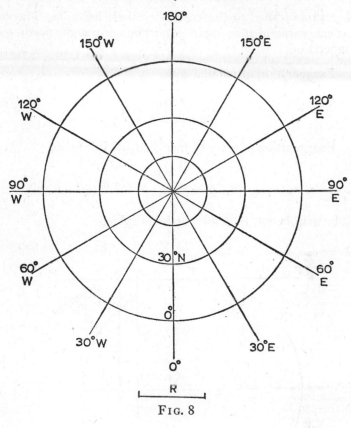

FIG. 8

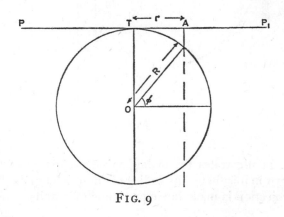

FIG. 9

being proportional to the cosines of their latitudes. The east–west exaggeration at any point is not the same as the north–south exaggeration.

Exaggeration of parallel scale

$$= \frac{2\pi R \cos \theta}{2\pi R \cos \theta} = 1$$

Exaggeration of piece of meridian BC in Fig. 10

$$= \frac{A_1 B_1}{BC} = \frac{AB}{BC} = \sin \theta$$

The map is not, therefore, orthomorphic.

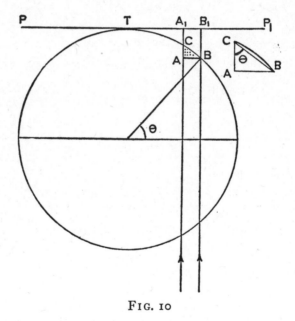

FIG. 10

Fig. 11 illustrates the orthographic projection of the Earth's northern hemisphere, the radius of the model globe from which the projection is made having a radius of 2 units.

$R = 2$ units

θ	$r = R \cos \theta$
$0°$	2·00
$15°$	1·93...
$30°$	1·73...
$45°$	1·41...
$60°$	1·00
$75°$	0·52...

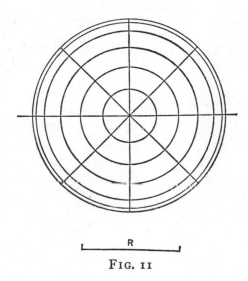

R

FIG. II

d. EQUIDISTANT (CONVENTIONAL) POLAR CASE

The zenithal equidistant (polar case), is a conventional projection in which meridians are projected as straight lines which radiate from a point which represents the Earth's pole. The parallels of latitude are projected as circles equidistantly spaced and centred at the projection of the pole. The radius of a projected parallel is proportional to the meridian distance of the projected parallel from the pole. If R is the radius of the model globe from which the projection is constructed, and $x°$ is the meridian distance of the parallel from the pole, that is the complement of the latitude of the parallel, the radius of the projected parallel is $x/180(\pi R)$.

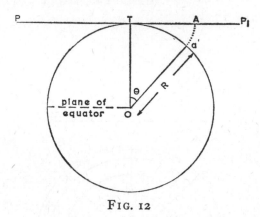

FIG. 12

Fig. 12 illustrates the principle of the polar equidistant projection. O is the centre of the model globe of radius R. PP_1 is in the plane of the projection. T, which lies at the pole of the globe, is the point of contact. The radius of the projected parallel of latitude through the point a, whose co-lat is θ, is TA where TA equals the arc length Ta.

Now $TA = \theta R$, where θ is expressed in radians

But $\theta° = \dfrac{\theta\pi}{180}$ radians

Therefore, radius of projected parallel whose co-lat is θ

$$= R\frac{\theta\pi}{180}$$

A whole sphere may be represented on the equidistant projection, the point on the globe which is antipodal to the point of contact being projected as a circle of radius πR. Fig. 13 illustrates a polar projection of the Earth developed from a model globe of radius 1 unit.

Co-lat θ	Radius of projected parallel
$R = 1$ unit	

Co-lat θ	Radius of projected parallel
0°	0
45°	0·78...
90°	1·57...
135°	2·35...
180°	3·14...

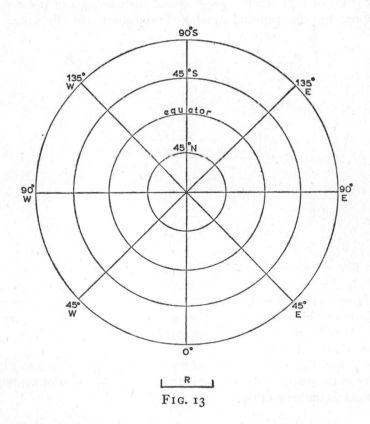

Fig. 13

The equidistant projection is useful because of correct scale of distance radially from the point of contact. On a polar equidistant, scale is correct along all projected meridians. It should be noted that distance along any line on the projection, other than those which radiate from the point of contact, is not correctly represented. The map is not orthomorphic: both shape and area being distorted. It finds its greatest use in the hands of polar explorers.

e. ZENITHAL EQUAL-AREA (CONVENTIONAL) POLAR CASE

A map on which areal distributions are to be portrayed should have the property of being *equal-area*. This means that areas on the map should be proportional to corresponding areas of the Earth. For representing geographical distributions of polar regions, the polar zenithal equal area projection is ideally suited.

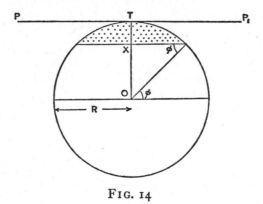

FIG. 14

The principle of projection is simply that the projected parallels of latitude, which are concentric circles centred at the point of contact (which is the pole of the model globe), enclose areas on the map which are equal to the areas of the polar spherical caps enclosed by the corresponding parallels on the globe. The principle is illustrated in Fig. 14.

In Fig. 14, O is the centre of the model globe of radius R. PP_1 lies in the plane of the projection; and T is the point of contact which is the pole of the globe.

Consider any parallel of latitude ϕ, polewards of which lies the spherical cap which is shaded in Fig. 14. The thickness of the cap is TX.

Now,
$$TX = TO - XO$$
$$= R - R \sin \phi$$
$$= R(1 - \sin \phi)$$

Now the area of a spherical cap is equal to the area of the circumscribing cylinder having the same thickness. Therefore, the area of the cap on the globe:

$$A = 2\pi R \times R(1 - \sin \phi)$$
$$= 2\pi R^2(1 - \sin \phi)$$

Let the circular area on the map which represents the polar cap north of the projected parallel of latitude be a, then:

$$a = \pi r^2$$

where r is the radius of the projected parallel.

The areas on the map and model globe are to be equal. Therefore:

$$a = A$$

and
$$\pi r^2 = 2\pi R^2(1 - \sin \phi)$$

from which:

$$r^2 = 2R^2(1 - \sin \phi)$$

and,
$$r = R\sqrt{2(1 - \sin \phi)}$$

The equal-area property is preserved by reducing the distance between projected parallels of latitude as the projected equator is reached.

Fig. 15 illustrates a polar zenithal equal-area projection developed from a model globe of radius 1 unit.

We shall now consider the transverse or equatorial cases of the gnomonic and stereographic projections.

The point of contact in the transverse case of a perspective zenithal is on the equator of a model globe.

$R = 1$ unit	
θ	$r = R \times 2(1 - \sin \theta)$
0	1·41...
15	1·22...
30	1·00
45	0·77...
60	0·52...
75	0·26...
90	0

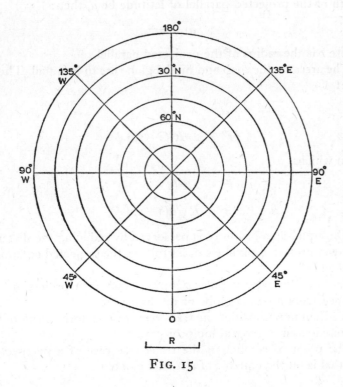

FIG. 15

f. GNOMONIC (PERSPECTIVE) EQUATORIAL CASE

The point of projection, in the case of the gnomonic projection, lies at the centre of the model globe. All great circles are projected as straight lines. The meridians are projected as parallel straight lines which cross the projected equator at right angles. The spacing of the projected meridians will increase away from the meridian which passes through the point of contact—a meridian known as the *central meridian of the projection.* The parallels of latitude will be projected as hyperbolae.

Fig. 16 illustrates the construction of the equatorial case of the gnomonic projection.

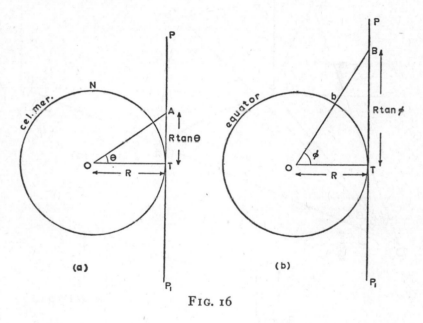

(a)   (b)

FIG. 16

In Fig. 16, in both diagrams PP_1 lies in the plane of the projection. In diagram (a), PP_1 represents the projected central meridian. In diagram (b) it represents the projected equator. T is the point of contact; and O is the point of projection at the globe's centre.

It will be evident from Fig. 16 that the projected distances between T and the point where any parallel of latitude θ crosses

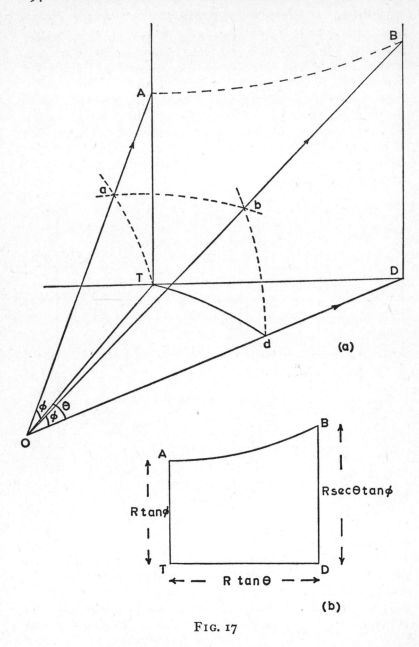

FIG. 17

the projected central meridian, is $R \tan \theta$. It should also be clear that the distance along the equator between the projected central meridian and any other projected meridian whose longitude differs from that of the central meridian by ϕ is $R \tan \phi$.

Fig. 17 is an attempt to show how a point in latitude ϕ whose longitude differs by $\theta°$ from that of the central meridian, is projected in the equatorial gnomonic.

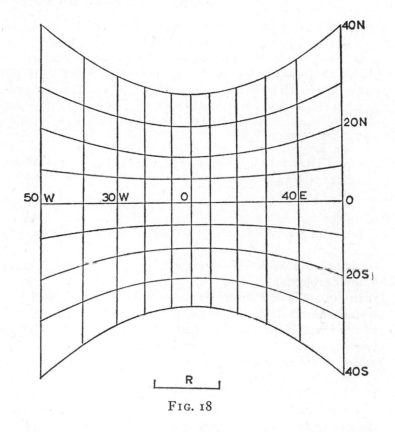

FIG. 18

In Fig. 17, O is the point of projection at the centre of a model globe of radius R. T is the point of contact. Td is an arc of the equator whose spherical length is $\theta°$. a and b are points on the parallel of $\phi°$N., a lying on the central meridian through T, and b lying on the meridian through d. The points a, b and d are projected on to the plane on which T stands, at A, B and D respectively. Referring to Fig. 17:

In the right-angled triangle OTD, $\quad$ OD $= R \sec \theta$

$\qquad\qquad$,, $\qquad\qquad$ OBD, $\qquad$ BD $= R \sec \theta \tan \phi$

$\qquad\qquad$,, $\qquad\qquad$ OTD, $\qquad$ TD $= R \tan \theta$

$\qquad\qquad$,, $\qquad\qquad$ OAT, $\qquad$ AT $= R \tan \phi$

Diagram (b) in Fig. 17 illustrates the projection of the spherical part of the globe Tabd. AB is the projection of the part of the parallel of latitude through a and b, and is an arc of a hyperbola.

Fig. 18 illustrates an equatorial gnomonic projection of that part of the Earth bounded by arcs of parallels 40°N., and 40°S., and arcs of meridians 50°E. and 50°W. The radius R of the model globe from which the projection is developed is 1 unit.

g. ZENITHAL STEREOGRAPHIC (PERSPECTIVE) EQUATORIAL CASE

The point of projection in a stereographic projection is at the end of a diameter the other end of which terminates at the point of contact. All great circles and small circles are projected as either arcs of circles or straight lines.

Fig. 19 illustrates the construction of an equatorial stereographic projection.

In Fig. 19, in both diagrams, C is the centre of the model globe whose radius is R. PP_1 lies in the plane of the projection. T is the point of contact lying on the equator. O is the point of projection. In diagram (a) in Fig. 19, PP_1 represents the projection of the central meridian; and in diagram (b) it represents the projection of the equator. The boundary of the hemisphere whose pole lies at T, is projected as a circle of radius $2R$.

The point a in diagram (a) in Fig. 19 lies on the central meridian in latitude $\phi°$N. Its projected position is at A, which is distant from T by an amount equal to $2R \tan \phi/2$, as illustrated.

The point b in diagram (b) is on the equator—its spherical distance from T being $\theta°$. It is projected at B, the distance of which from T along the projected equator is $2R \tan \theta/2$.

Fig. 20 illustrates how a point Y, in latitude $\phi°N$, and whose

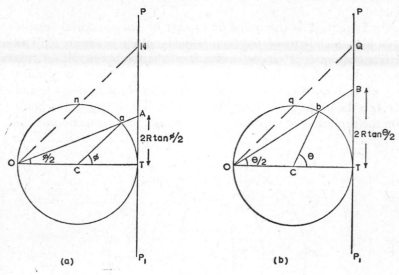

FIG. 19

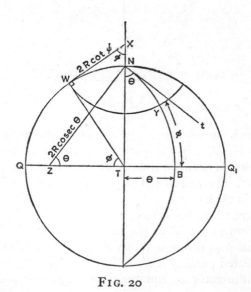

FIG. 20

longitude differs by $\theta°$ from that of the central meridian, is projected.

In Fig. 20 T is the point of contact on an equatorial stereographic which is projected from a model globe of radius R. The circle centred at T whose radius is $2R$, is the projection of two antipodal meridians which together form a great circle every point on which is 90° from T. N is the projection of the north pole and QQ_1 is the projection of half the equator. B is the projected point on the projected equator which is the point of intersection of Y's

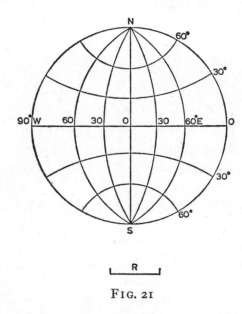

FIG. 21

meridian with the equator. The centre of the projection of Y's meridian is at Z. Nt is a tangent to the projected meridian at N. Clearly the angle between the projected central meridian and this tangent is $\theta°$. The radius of the projected meridian is, therefore, NZ which is 2R cosec θ.

The centre of the projected parallel through Y lies at X on the projected central meridian (or central meridian produced). Y's parallel must pass through W which is $\phi°$ north of Q. The radius of the projected parallel XW is clearly $2R$ cot $\phi°$.

Fig. 21 illustrates an equatorial stereographic projection of a hemisphere of the Earth, centred at latitude 0° longitude 0°, projected from a model globe of radius $R = 1$ unit.

We shall now discuss the oblique case of the stereographic projection. It will be remembered that in the oblique cases of a zenithal the point of contact of the plane of the projection with the model globe is not at the pole nor on the equator. We have chosen to illustrate the oblique case of the stereographic because all circles on the globe are projected as circles or straight lines on the map. It is, therefore, a relatively easy matter to construct an oblique stereographic geometrically using only protractor, drawing compass, straight edge and pencil.

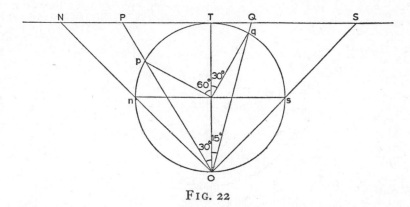

FIG. 22

To exemplify the method of construction, let us construct an oblique stereographic projection of a hemisphere of the Earth, the point of contact with the globe from which the projection is developed being at latitude 30°N., longitude 0°.

The boundary of the hemisphere to be projected is a circle of radius $2R$, where R is the radius of the model globe. The centre of this circle will represent lat. 30°N. long. 0°. The meridian of long. 0° will be represented by a diameter of the boundary circle.

Figs. 22 and 23 illustrate the principle of construction.

In Fig. 22, the circle represents the central meridian on the model globe of radius R. O is the point of projection and T is the point of contact in lat. 30°N. n and s are projected at N and S respectively. Points q and p are 30° and 60° respectively from T.

14

These points on the globe are projected at Q and P respectively. The line NS in Fig. 23 is the projection of the central meridian which appears as a diameter of the boundary circle of the projected hemisphere illustrated in Fig. 23.

The point P may be plotted geometrically, as illustrated in Fig. 23, from W (or E), by making arc Ea equal to 60°, and projecting the point a to W to cross the diameter NS at P. WT represents $2R$, therefore $PT = 2R \tan 60/2$. Point Q may be drawn geometrically in a similar way, arc Eb in this case being 30°, and b

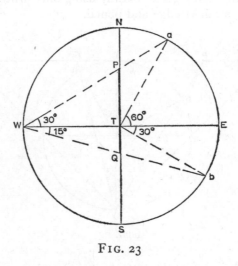

FIG. 23

is projected to W to cut the diameter NS at Q. Arc TQ is, therefore, $2R \tan 30/2$.

All parallels of latitude are projected as arcs of circles, so that if their centres of projection can be found, they can be constructed with ease.

The projected equator passes through Q, W and E in Fig. 24.

The centre of the projected equator lies on TN or TN produced. The projected equator crosses the central meridian produced at Q_1. Q_1 is at a position on the central meridian produced such that Q_1WP is equal to PWQ. If Q_1 is plotted, the centre of the projected equator may readily be found: lying as it does at c_Q which is the mid point of QQ_1.

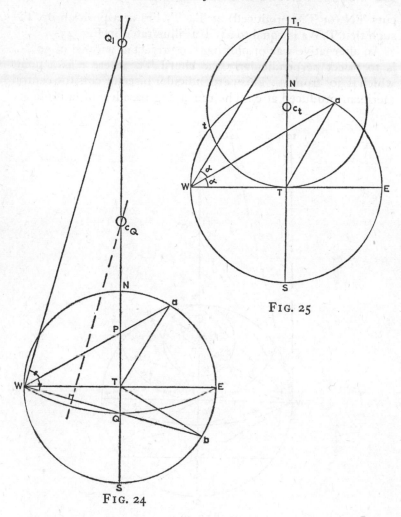

FIG. 25

FIG. 24

An alternative way of finding c_Q is to bisect perpendicularly the chord QW (or QE). This bisector crosses QQ_1 at the centre of the projected equator, as illustrated in Fig. 24.

Fig. 25 illustrates how the parallel of latitude of 30°N. is projected.

The projected parallel of 30°N. must pass through T. Its centre c_t lies on TN (or TN produced). The projected parallel cuts TN (or TN produced) at T_1. T_1 lies at a position on TN such that T_1Wa is equal to aWT as illustrated in Fig. 25.

An alternative way of plotting the projected parallel of 30°N., is to bisect perpendicularly the chord Tt, where t is a point which is 30° from W. This perpendicular bisector cuts the central meridian produced at c_t. The remaining parallels of latitude are

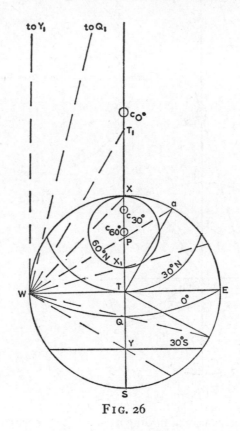

FIG. 26

projected in a similar manner to that described for the parallel of 30°N.

Referring to Fig. 26, the centre of the projected parallel of 60°N. is at c_{60} which is the mid point of XX_1 where X_1WP is equal to XWP. The centre of the projected parallel of 0° is at the mid point of QQ_1 where Q_1WP is equal to QWP. The centre of the projected parallel of 30°S. lies on WY_1. Y_1W is parallel to the central meridian because Y_1WP is equal to PWY. Therefore, the projected parallel of 30°S. is a straight line.

The projected meridians must pass through P and P_1: P_1 lying on TS produced. The arc PQ is equal to arc QP_1 each being 90°.

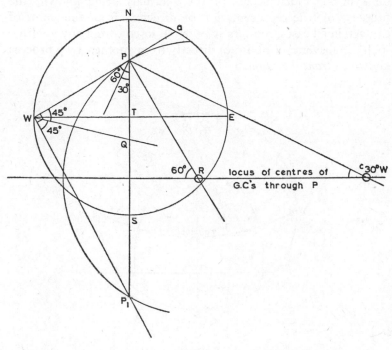

FIG. 27

The centres of all projected meridians, therefore, lie on the perpendicular bisector of PP_1. This line is usually called the locus of centres of great circles through P and P_1. The radius of the projected meridian 60°W. is PR, as illustrated in Fig. 27.

PR is at right angles to PW, the latter being the tangent to the projected meridian of 60°W. (Angles between two great circles are equivalent to the angles between the tangents to the great circles at the point of intersection.)

The remaining required meridians are projected, and the completed projection appears as illustrated in Fig. 28.

One important feature of all zenithal projections is that direction from the centre of the projection is true. Each zenithal differs from the others mainly in respect of the radial scale. The variations in the radial scales of the zenithals being known, the property of true representation of direction from the point of contact, in all cases, renders it possible to construct any zenithal (polar, transverse or oblique) directly from another, by a process known as *transformation*.

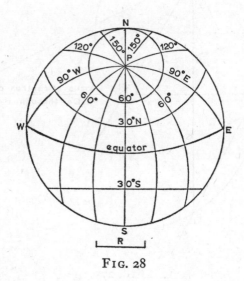

FIG. 28

Transformation provides a useful means of constructing a complex zenithal (which, in the normal way, would present difficulty in its construction), having first constructed another zenithal, of the same part of the same model globe, which has a less complex construction than that of the required projection.

The distance *r* from the centre of projection to any projected parallel of latitude θ in the polar cases of the zenithals—the model globe from which the projections are to be developed being *R*—are:

For the gnomonic $\quad r = R\cot\theta$
,, ,, stereographic $r = 2R\tan(45 - \theta/2)$
,, ,, orthographic $r = R\cos\theta$
,, ,, equal-area $\quad r = R\sqrt{2(1 - \sin\theta)}$
,, ,, equidistant $\quad r = \dfrac{R\pi}{180}(90 - \theta)$

The variations in radial scale away from the point of contact are best represented graphically as in Fig. 29.

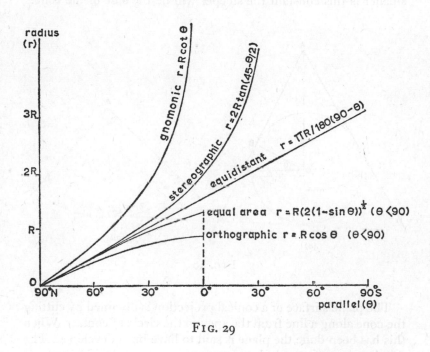

FIG. 29

The variations in the radial scales depicted in Fig. 29 apply to all cases of the zenithals. Thus, if it is required to construct an oblique equidistant projection of a hemisphere centred at lat. 30°N., long. 0°, the projection to be developed from a model globe of radius R, the task may be facilitated by transforming the oblique stereographic projection illustrated in Fig. 28, this having the same point of contact as that of the required projection.

3. Conical projections

The perspective conical projections are developed from a cone which envelops the model globe. In the simplest case, the cone makes contact with the globe along a small circle which is usually a parallel of latitude. In this case, the sine of the angle of latitude is an expression which describes the slope of the cone along a line extending from the apex of the cone perpendicular to the circle of contact. This expression is known as the *constant of the cone*. The smaller is this constant the steeper will be the side of the cone.

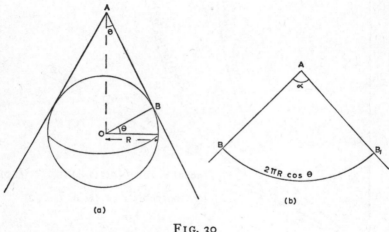

(a)

(b)

FIG. 30

The plane surface of a conical projection is obtained by cutting the cone along a line from the apex to the circle of contact. When this has been done the plane is said to have been developed. The development of a conical surface in this way results in a sector as illustrated in Fig. 30.

In Fig. 30(a), O is the centre of a model globe of radius R, which is enveloped by a cone whose apex is at A, and which makes contact with the globe along a parallel of latitude $\theta°$N.

The developed cone results in the sector illustrated in Fig. 30(b). The length of the circle of contact is $2\pi R \cos \theta$, where θ is the latitude and also the plane angle OAB. The radius of the

sector formed from the developed cone is $R \cot \theta$. Let the angle at the apex of the sector be α.
Then:

$$\frac{\alpha}{360} = \frac{2\pi R \cos \theta}{2\pi R \cot \theta}$$

$$= \sin \theta$$

$$= \text{constant of cone}$$

The angle at the apex of the sector is α and:

$$\alpha = 360 \times \sin \theta$$

The constant of the cone depends upon the latitude of the parallel of contact. This parallel of latitude is called the standard parallel.

a. SIMPLE (PERSPECTIVE) CONICAL

The simple perspective conical projection is developed from a cone which makes contact with a model globe along a chosen standard parallel. The point of projection is the centre of the globe. All meridians are projected as straight lines. The gnomonic projection may be regarded as being the limiting case of the simple perspective conical projection, the constant of the cone in the case of the polar gnomonic being unity, i.e. sine 90°.

The scale along the standard parallel is true; but the scale along the meridians is true only at the point where the meridian crosses the standard parallel.

To construct a simple perspective conical projection of the Earth for any given standard parallel the angle of the sector is first found, this being $360 \times \sin \theta$ where θ is the angle of the latitude of the standard parallel.

The radius of the projected standard parallel is $R \cot \theta$, as illustrated in Fig. 31.

The meridians are straight lines which radiate from the apex of the sector. The radius of the projected equator, as seen from Fig. 31, is $R \sec \theta \csc \theta$: and the radius of any other projected parallel of latitude ϕ is $R[(\cot \theta \pm \tan (\phi \pm \theta)]$. The projected parallels are concentric arcs centred at the apex of the sector.

The scale along parallels and meridians increases equator-wards of the standard parallel and decreases on the polewards side of it.

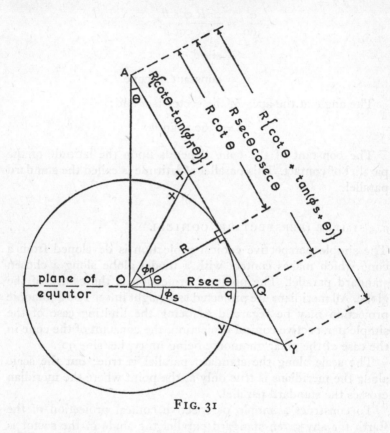

FIG. 31

Fig. 32 illustrates a simple perspective conical projection of the Earth's surface north of the parallel of 30°S., the standard parallel being 30°N., and the radius R of the globe from which the cone has been developed being one unit.

b. SIMPLE CONICAL (CONVENTIONAL)

The simple conical, as generally understood, is a non-perspective projection. It is similar to the perspective conical, but the spacing

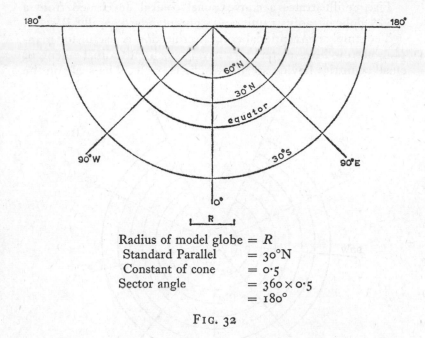

Radius of model globe = R
Standard Parallel = 30°N
Constant of cone = 0·5
Sector angle = 360 × 0·5
= 180°

FIG. 32

of the projected parallels of latitude is adjusted so that the scale along every meridian is correct. Equidistantly spaced parallels of latitude on the globe are, therefore, projected as equidistantly spaced concentric circles on the projection. As a consequence of this, the pole, which in the case of the perspective conical is a point at the apex of the sector, is an arc of a circle.

To construct a simple conventional conical projection for any given standard parallel of latitude θ, the sector angle α is first found thus: $\alpha = 360 \times \sin \theta$; and the sector is drawn. Centred at the apex of the sector, the arc representing the standard parallel is then drawn, the radius of this arc being $R \cot \theta$. The remaining parallels are then projected centred at the apex of the sector. The spacing of the projected parallels is marked off on the central meridian, this spacing being uniform for equidistantly spaced parallels on the globe. The spacing of projected parallels representing parallels on the globe which are $x°$ apart would be $x/360 \ 2\pi R$, where R is the radius of the model globe.

Fig. 33 illustrates a conventional conical developed from a model globe of radius 1 unit, and whose standard parallel is 45°N.

The simple conventional conical projection is useful for mapping narrow belts of territory having small latitudinal extent, or small countries having small latitudinal extent. The scale on the

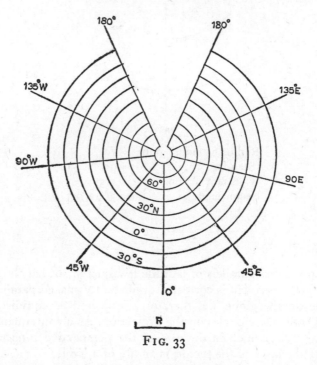

FIG. 33

projected standard parallel is correct, but away from this distortions of shape and scale increase. For mapping the Mediterranean Sea or the territory adjacent to the transcontinental railways of America or the U.S.S.R., the simple conventional conical is well-suited.

C. CONICAL WITH TWO STANDARD PARALLELS (CONVENTIONAL)

The conical with two standard parallels, as its name implies, is a conventional projection having true representation of distance along two projected parallels of latitude. It is suitable for mapping countries or seas of small latitudinal extent, and also belts of territory of large east–west extent. The general working rule for using the conical with two standard parallels is that about two-thirds of the area to be mapped should lie between the standard parallels.

To construct a conical with two standard parallels, the angle at the apex of the sector is first calculated as follows:

Refer to Fig. 34.

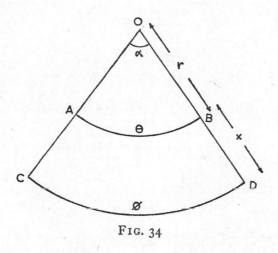

FIG. 34

Let AB and CD be the projections of arcs of the standard parallels θ and $\phi°$ north respectively. Given R, θ and ϕ:

$$x = \frac{\theta - \phi}{360} 2\pi R$$

$$\frac{r}{r+x} = \frac{\text{arc AB}}{\text{arc CD}} \quad \text{(similar sectors)}$$

that is,
$$\frac{r}{r+x} = \frac{2\pi R \cos \theta}{2\pi R \cos \phi}$$

that is,
$$r \cos \phi = r \cos \theta + x \cos \theta$$

and,
$$r = \frac{x \cos \theta}{\cos \phi - \cos \theta}$$

With these values of r and x, the standard parallels may be drawn.

The angle at the apex of the sector is found as follows:

$$\alpha^c = \frac{\text{arc AB}}{r}$$

i.e.

$$\alpha^c = \frac{2\pi R \cos \theta(\cos \phi - \cos \theta)}{x \cos \theta}$$

But,

$$x = \frac{(\theta - \phi)}{360} 2\pi R$$

Therefore,

$$\alpha^c = \frac{2\pi R \cos \theta (\cos \phi - \cos \theta)}{(\theta - \phi)/360 \; 2\pi R \cos \theta}$$

i.e.,

$$\alpha^c = \frac{(\cos \phi - \cos \theta) \; 360}{(\theta - \phi)}$$

and

$$\alpha^\circ = \frac{(\cos \phi - \cos \theta) \; 360 \; 180}{(\theta - \phi)\pi}$$

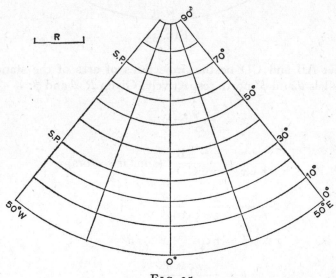

FIG. 35

The projected parallels, other than the standard parallels, are drawn correctly spaced on the central meridians; and the remaining meridians are projected after dividing the projected parallels of latitude.

Fig. 35 illustrates a Two-standard latitude conical projection of the part of the Earth's surface between the meridians of 50°E. and 50°W., and north of the parallel 0°. The standard parallels in this example are 30°N. and 70°N.

d. BONNE (CONVENTIONAL)

The Bonne is a conventional conical in which one selected parallel is drawn as if it were a standard of radius $R \cot \phi$, where R is the radius of the model globe, and ϕ is the selected parallel. All other projected parallels are drawn with the same curvature as that of the projected selected parallel. The projected parallels are drawn through points on the projected central meridian and are truly spaced. Parallels on the globe, which are $x°$ apart are represented by arcs of concentric circles spaced $x/360 \times 2\pi R$ apart on the projection of the central meridian.

Each parallel is divided correctly. If the spacing of the meridians on the globe is $y°$, the spacing of the projected meridians on any parallel is $y/360 \times 2\pi R \cos \theta$, where θ is the latitude of the parallel. After dividing the parallels, the meridians are drawn as smooth curves.

Fig. 36 illustrates a Bonne projection for the part of the Earth north of the equator and between the meridians of 50°E. and 50°W.

Because every parallel of latitude is projected true to scale, and since distance along the central meridian between selected parallels is true to scale, the area between selected parallels on the model globe is the same as that between projected parallels on the map. The equal-area property of the Bonne projection is its principal feature.

Provided that the central meridian and standard parallel are chosen carefully, the Bonne projection is suitable for mapping countries like France, Belgium or Holland. The chief function of the Bonne projection is for representing geographical distributions of middle latitudes.

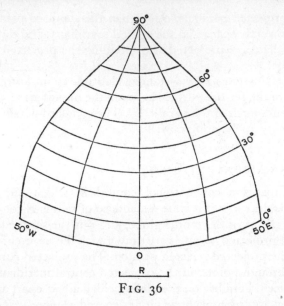

FIG. 36

If the equator is chosen as the standard parallel, the resulting projection is the *Sanson–Flamsteed sinusoidal projection* which is illustrated in Fig. 37.

The meridians on the Sanson–Flamsteed projection are projected as sine curves; and the parallels of latitude are projected as

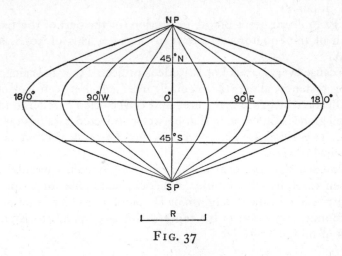

FIG. 37

straight lines equidistantly spaced on the central meridian and parallel to the projected equator.

e. POLYCONIC (CONVENTIONAL)

The optimum case of accuracy of scale along the projected parallels of a conical projection, occurs when every projected parallel is a standard parallel. This results in a polyconic projection on which every parallel is projected as an arc of a circle of radius $R \cot \theta$, where θ is the latitude of the parallel and R is the radius of the model globe. Each projected parallel has, therefore, a different point of projection.

On the polyconic projection the equator is projected as a straight line and the curvature of the projected parallels of latitude increases polewards.

The polyconic is widely used, often with modification, for topographical maps. A common modified polyconic projection is one in which the area to be mapped is divided into narrow east–west strips, each one being projected with its own central meridian.

Because every parallel of latitude is projected as a standard parallel, the curvature and scale of the projected parallels are quite independent of the position of the central meridian. Thus, when a large area is projected in the modified polyconic, adjacent north–south sheets of the mapped area will fit exactly. But if each strip has a different central meridian, the curvature of the boundary meridians of each sheet will be different from that of the neighbouring sheets. The east–west adjacent sheets are, therefore, said to have a 'rolling fit'.

The International 1/1,000,000 map is constructed on a modified polyconic. Each sheet of this map covers 4 degrees of latitude and 6 degrees of longitude. The meridian scale is true two degrees on each side of the central meridian, and the boundary meridians are drawn as straight lines to facilitate fitting adjacent east–west sheets.

Fig. 38 illustrates a polyconic projection of the part of the northern hemisphere between the meridians of 50°E. and 50°W.

15

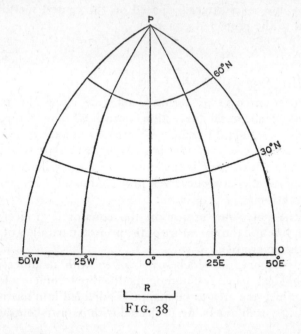

FIG. 38

f. LAMBERT'S CONICAL EQUAL-AREA (CONVENTIONAL)

The Lambert conical equal-area projection is a modified form of the conical projection with two standard parallels. The equal area property is gained at the expense of shape. The modification involves varying the distance between the projected parallels to achieve the equal-area property.

g. LAMBERT'S CONICAL ORTHOMORPHIC

The Lambert conical orthomorphic projection is an adaptation of the conventional conical projection with two standard parallels. In this case, the projected parallels at any part of the map, are spaced to the same extent as the spacing of the meridians in the same part of the map.

4. Cylindrical projections

We shall now discuss the more important of the cylindrical projections—both perspective and conventional.

a. SIMPLE CYLINDRICAL OR PLATE CARRÉE (CONVENTIONAL)

The simple conventional cylindrical projection has a rectangular graticule. The equator is projected as a straight line of length $2\pi R$, where R is the radius of the model globe; and all meridians are projected as straight lines which cut the projected equator at right angles. The meridians are projected true to length and are of length πR. All parallels of latitude are projected as straight lines parallel to the projected equator.

Scale along every meridian and along the equator is true, but the distortion of areas increases polewards.

Fig. 39 illustrates a Plate Carrée developed from a model globe of radius $R = 1$ unit.

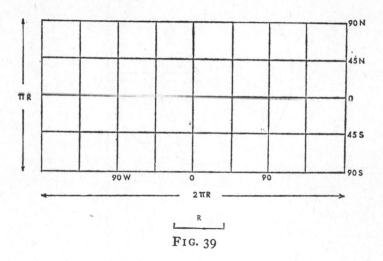

FIG. 39

b. SIMPLE CYLINDRICAL (PERSPECTIVE)

In the simple perspective cylindrical projection, the point of projection lies at the centre of the model globe, and lines of projection cut the globe's surface and meet the enveloping cylinder which makes contact with the globe along its equator.

The projected equator has a length of $2\pi R$, and all parallels of latitude have the same length as that of the equator. Meridians are projected as straight lines perpendicular to the projected equator. Scale along the projected equator is correct, but it increases polewards along the projected meridians. The distance along any projected meridian between the projected equator and any projected parallel of latitude is $R \tan \phi$ where ϕ is the latitude and R is the radius of the model globe.

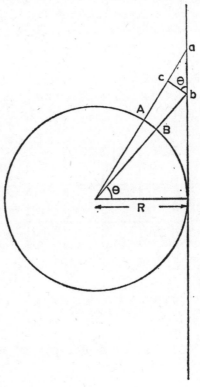

FIG. 40

Referring to Fig. 40:

$$\text{Exaggeration along meridian} = \frac{ab}{AB}$$

$$= \frac{bc \sec \theta}{AB}$$

But, $\dfrac{bc}{AB} = \dfrac{R \sec \theta}{R}$

Therefore, $\dfrac{ab}{AB} = \sec \theta \sec \theta$

                              $= \sec^2 \theta$

The exaggeration along any meridian is different from the exaggeration along any parallel, which latter is proportional to secant latitude. The map, therefore, is not orthomorphic.

Fig. 41 illustrates the method of constructing a simple cylindrical projection.

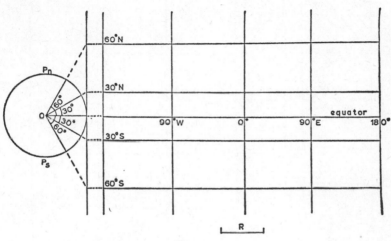

FIG. 41

c. MERCATOR (CONVENTIONAL)

The Mercator projection is a conventional cylindrical projection which is often mistaken for the perspective cylindrical.

The principal feature of the Mercator projection is that it is orthomorphic. Coupled with this is another important feature which is of great importance to seamen, viz., lines of constant course are projected as straight lines.

The graticule of the Mercator projection is rectangular. All parallels of latitude are projected as straight lines of length $2\pi R$.

The exaggeration along any parallel is proportional to the secant of the latitude of the parallel. Orthomorphism is achieved by exaggerating the meridian scale at any position to the same extent as the exaggeration of the latitude scale at that position. The exaggeration of the meridian scale at any parallel is also equal to the secant of the latitude of the parallel. Course angles, therefore, are

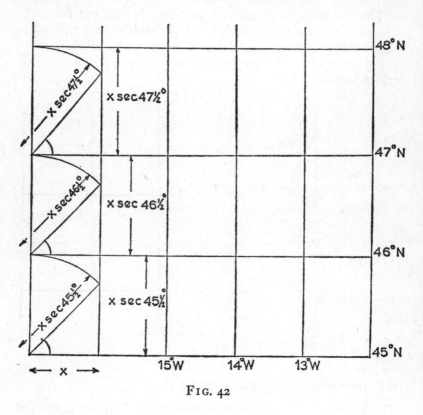

FIG. 42

truly represented, and course lines (rhumb lines) are projected as straight lines.

Mercator maps are constructed by using a table of meridional parts. These have been discussed in Chapter Four, in connection with problems related to sailing on the Earth's surface.

Fig. 42 illustrates a simple method of constructing a Mercator map of a small area, using the so-called Mercator principle, viz., *every line on a Mercator map is exaggerated proportional to the secant of the middle latitude of the line.*

Referring to Fig. 42, the spacing of parallels one degree apart is $x \cdot$ secant middle latitude, where x is the length representing $1°$ of longitude. By constructing angles equal to the middle latitude of any piece of the meridian, the parallels may be projected approximately correctly. The larger the scale of the map, the more accurately may the map be drawn using this method.

Polar regions cannot be represented on a Mercator map; and, although the map is orthomorphic, shape and area are distorted, the exaggeration increasing polewards. The projection finds its greatest use in the hands of navigators; but it is often used for mapping such geographical features as wind and current systems, and other flow patterns in which it is necessary for direction to be properly portrayed.

d. GALL'S STEREOGRAPHIC (PERSPECTIVE)

The Gall stereographic projection is a perspective projection, the point of projection lying at a point on the equator of the model globe, and the plane of the projection being developed from a cylinder which is imagined to cut the globe along the parallels of 45°N. and S. as illustrated in Fig. 43.

In Fig. 43, O is the point of projection. The point a in latitude $\theta°$N., is projected at Λ on the cylinder. The projection of the piece of any meridian between the projected equator and the projection of the parallel of latitude θ is d.

$$\begin{aligned}
\text{AD} &= \text{d} \\
&= \text{OD} \tan \theta/2 \\
&= (R + R \cos 45°) \tan \theta/2 \\
&= R(1 + \cos 45°) \tan \theta/2 \\
&= 1 \cdot 707 \ldots R \tan \theta/2
\end{aligned}$$

Gall's stereographic is neither orthomorphic nor equal-area. The scale along the parallels of latitude 45°N. and S. is correct; but polewards of these projected parallels the scale is too large, and between them it is too small.

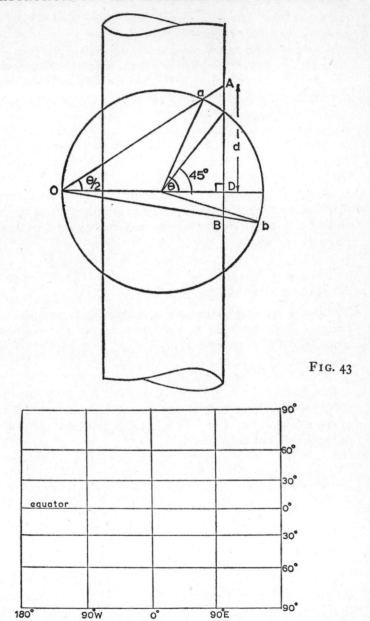

FIG. 43

FIG. 44

Although it is a good compromise projection on which geographical distributions are well displayed, the Gall stereographic projection is seldom used at the present time.

Fig. 44 illustrates a Gall's stereographic projection of the globe.

e. LAMBERT'S CYLINDRICAL EQUAL-AREA (CONVENTIONAL)

In the Lambert cylindrical equal-area projection, the property which gives its name to the projection is achieved by projecting the globe's surface on to a cylinder of east–west length $2\pi R$, and whose north–south breadth is $2R$.

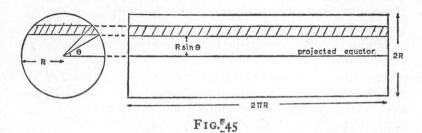

FIG. 45

The area of a zone of a sphere is equal to that of a circumscribing cylinder having the same depth (see Chapter Two). This is the principle on which the Lambert's cylindrical equal-area projection is based.

The diminishing spacing of the projected parallels, as the poles are reached, renders this projection unsuitable for portraying polar distributions.

Fig. 45 illustrates the principle of the construction of the Lambert's cylindrical equal-area projection. The shaded areas on both globe and map have the same 'width'. They are, therefore, equal in area.

f. TRANSVERSE MERCATOR (CONVENTIONAL)

In the case of the Mercator projection, the meridians are projected as parallel straight lines which intersect the projected equator at right angles. In the transverse Mercator (sometimes known as the *Gauss Conformal* or *Transverse Cylindrical Orthomorphic*), the cylinder which is imagined to envelop the model globe makes contact with the globe along a pair of antipodal meridians, both poles lying on the circle of contact. The poles, therefore, are projected as points which lie on the projection of the two meridians which make the great circle of contact. The two meridians are projected as a single straight line of length $2\pi R$, where R is the radius of the model globe.

The meridians, other than the two which make contact with the globe, are projected as curves which radiate from the projected poles. The parallels of latitude are projected as closed curves, which are almost circular near the projected poles, and which become increasingly elongated as the equator is reached, the equator itself being projected as a straight line which cuts the projected central meridian at right angles.

The mathematical principle of the transverse Mercator is the same as that of the Mercator projection. On the Mercator, the scale of distance at any point is proportional to the secant of the latitude of the point. On the transverse Mercator it is proportional to the secant of the spherical distance of an arc which joins the point to the equator and meets the equator at 90°.

The distortion of shape increases away from the central meridian, but along the central meridian it is correct. Any pair of antipodal meridians may be chosen in order to construct a transverse Mercator, the choice being related to the map required. The transverse Mercator is orthomorphic but rhumb lines are not projected as straight lines as they are on a Mercator projection.

g. CASSINI'S (CONVENTIONAL)

Cassini's projection is one in which the graticule is constructed in relation to a particular point on a particular central meridian and its antipodal meridian. The projection is often used for topographical maps: in particular those of the Ordnance Survey of Great Britain.

In contrast to the modified polyconic projection—which is also a favourite for topographical maps—the sheets of a map built on Cassini's projection fit perfectly.

The equator and a selected meridian are projected as perpendicular straight lines. These are divided true to scale. All other projected parallels and meridians are curves, every point on a particular curve being conditioned in that its perpendicular distance from the projected central meridian is true to scale.

Referring to Fig. 46, PP_1 is the central meridian and O is the fixed point on it, to which other projected points are related. Let the latitude of any point X, be $\lambda°$N., and let its longitude differ

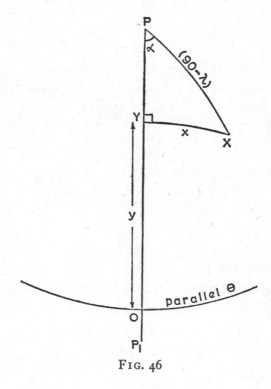

Fig. 46

from that of the central meridian by $\alpha°$. The arc XY is the great circle arc through X which crosses the central meridian at right angles.

Let the great circle distances XY and OY be denoted by $x°$ and $y°$. For the Cassini projection x and y corresponding to any point X, are calculated and used as rectangular coordinates related to the projected parallel and meridian through O which forms the point of origin of axes of reference formed by the projected selected parallel and central meridian as illustrated in Fig. 47.

For this reason Cassini's projection is sometimes referred to as *projection by rectangular coordinates*.

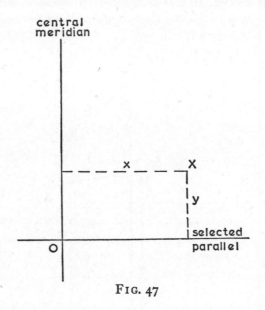

FIG. 47

Referring to Fig. 46.

In the spherical triangle YPX:

$$\text{angle YPX} = \alpha°$$
$$\text{arc PX} = (90 - \lambda)°$$
$$\text{angle PYX} = 90°$$

By Napier's Rules:

$$\sin x = \sin \alpha \cos \lambda \qquad (1)$$
$$\tan PY = \cos \alpha \cot \lambda \qquad (2)$$

From (2), $OY = y = (90 - \theta) - PY$

That is: $y = (90 - (\theta + PY))$

In the Cassini projection, meridians, other than the central meridian and its antipodal meridian, are projected as curves. As

the latitude increases, the outer meridians incline increasingly towards the projected central meridian. For small areas, the meridians are considered to be straight lines parallel to the projected
central meridian.

h. MOLLWEIDE (CONVENTIONAL)

The Mollweide projection is perhaps the most familiar of those
used for portraying geographical distributions on a world map. It
was invented in the early part of the 19th century and was pub-
licised in the mid 1900's when it was known as the *homolographic*.
Because meridians are projected as semi-ellipses, the Mollweide
is sometimes known as the *elliptical projection*.

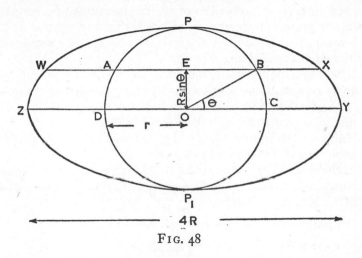

FIG. 48

The Mollweide projection is a conventional projection in which
parallels of latitude are projected as parallel straight lines, and
meridians are projected as semi-ellipses. Its principal property is
equal-area, which is achieved by adjustment of the spacing of the
projected parallels of latitude.

The area of an ellipse whose major and minor semi-axes are a
and b respectively is πab.

The boundary of a world map constructed on the Mollweide
projection is an ellipse whose semi-minor axis has a length r, and
whose semi-major axis has a length $4r$, as illustrated in Fig. 48.

Referring to Fig. 48:

If ZY = 2CD, then the ellipse has twice the area of the circle radius r, because:

$$\text{Area of circle} = \pi r^2$$

and $$\text{Area of the ellipse} = (\pi ab) = \pi r \times 2r$$

$$= 2\pi r^2$$

Let the circle represent half the area of a model globe of radius R, then:

$$\pi r^2 = 2\pi R^2 \quad \text{and} \quad r = R\sqrt{2}$$

To construct a Mollweide projection, the radius of the circle is first calculated; and, having drawn the circle, a diameter is extended equally on both sides of the circle to twice its length to form the projected equator. An ellipse is then constructed on this extended diameter as its major axis, the perpendicular diameter of the circle forming the minor axis.

The projected equator is then divided truly to scale; and semi-ellipses representing the meridians to be projected are drawn.

The parallels of latitude are projected as straight lines parallel to the projected equator in the following way.

Suppose we are to construct the parallel of $\phi°$N., the problem is to find the angle θ (refer to Fig. 48).

If the projection is to have the equal-area property, the area on the map represented by WXYZ in Fig. 48, is to be twice the area ABCD. If this be the case:

$$\text{Area ABCD} = \tfrac{1}{2} \times \text{area WXYZ}$$

Now $$\text{Area ABCD} = 2 \times \text{area sector BOC} + 2 \times \text{area EOB}$$

$$= 2(\tfrac{1}{2}r^2\theta°) + 2(\tfrac{1}{2}r^2 \sin \theta \cos \theta)$$

$$= r^2(\theta° + \sin \theta \cos \theta)$$

$$= \tfrac{1}{2}r^2(2\theta° + \sin 2\theta)$$

Therefore,

$$\text{Area WXYZ} = r^2(2\theta° + \sin 2\theta)$$

The area of a spherical zone between the equator and the parallel of latitude $\phi°$N.

$$= 2\pi R^2 \sin \phi$$

The area on the map between the projected equator and the projected parallel $\phi°$N., is equal to the area of the spherical zone on the model globe between the equator and the parallel of latitude $\phi°$N. Therefore:

$$r^2(2\theta^c + \sin 2\theta) = 2\pi R^2 \sin \phi$$

But, $$r = R\sqrt{2}$$

Therefore: $$2R^2(2\theta^c + \sin 2\theta) = 2\pi R^2 \sin \phi$$

from which: $$2\theta^c + \sin 2\theta = \pi \sin \phi$$

If ϕ is known then θ may be found.

By giving selected values between O and $\pi/2$ to θ, ϕ may be calculated for these selected values of θ, and the results graphed. From the graph the spacing of the projected parallels may be found with ease.

i. WHITTEMORE BOGG'S EUMORPHIC (CONVENTIONAL)

A conventional projection known as Whittemore Bogg's eumorphic, is derived from the sinusoidal and elliptical projection in a manner illustrated in Fig. 49, in which the pecked line, which lies between the sine curve of Sanson–Flamsteed's projection and the ellipse of Mollweide's, illustrates the outline of the eumorphic projection.

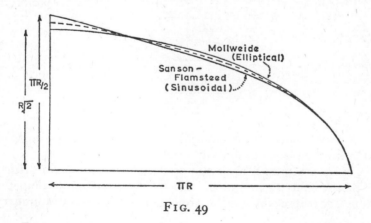

FIG. 49

j. COLONEL CRASTER'S PARABOLIC (CONVENTIONAL)

A projection similar to Mollweide's and which is useful for showing geographical distributions on a world map, is Colonel Craster's parabolic projection, in which meridians are projected as parabolas, and the spacing of the projected parallels of latitude (which are parallel straight lines) is adjusted to give the equal-area property.

k. GOODE'S HOMOLOSINE (CONVENTIONAL)

Another projection, similar to Whittemore Bogg's eumorphic, is Goode's homolosine, which is sinusoidal between 40°N. and 40°S., and Mollweideian polewards of these parallels.

l. AITOFF'S EQUAL-AREA (PERSPECTIVE)

The Aitoff projection is a projection of a projection. It is derived from the equatorial case of the zenithal equal-area, by projecting a hemisphere of the latter on to a plane which intersects the

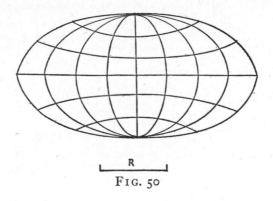

R

FIG. 50

central meridian of the equatorial equal-area, making an angle of 60° with the plane of the zenithal equal-area projection.

Circles are always projected on to a plane surface as either circles or ellipses; and, in the case of the Aitoff projection, the boundary ellipse which is the projection of the circular boundary

of the zenithal equal-area is an ellipse whose major axis is double
that of the minor axis.

The Aitoff projection is adapted as a world map by doubling
the longitudes of the meridians projected from those of the hemisphere of the equal-area projection on which it is based. The
projected parallels of latitude are curves which are convex to the
projected equator, so that near the boundary of the Aitoff world
map, the shape of the projected areas is better than that of a
Mollweide or sinusoidal having the same central meridian. The
Aitoff world map based on an equal-area projection constructed
from a model globe of radius R, is illustrated in Fig. 50.

5. *World maps*

World maps designed to portray geographical distributions are
usually based on an equal-area projection, such as Mollweide's
or Sanson–Flamsteed's. All of these projections suffer the disadvantage of considerable distortion of shapes near their boundaries. This disadvantage may be overcome by building up the

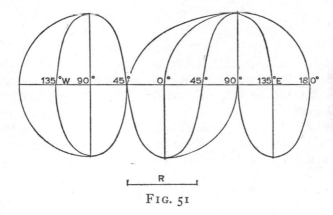

FIG. 51

projection on more than one central meridian (or half meridian),
in which case the projection is described as being *interrupted* or
recentred.

For representing continental distributions the projection would
normally be interrupted along meridians or semi-meridians

16

which pass through oceans. For representing oceanic distributions, the projection would normally be interrupted along meridians or semi-meridians which pass through continents.

The interrupted Mollweide, which is illustrated in Fig. 51, and whose central meridian is 0°, is recentred on the meridian of 90°W., the southern half of the meridian of 135°E., and the northern half of the meridian of 90°E.; the first of these passing

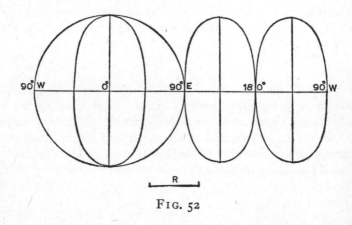

FIG. 52

through or close to the American continents, the second through mid-Asia, and the third through Australia. This recentred Mollweide is interrupted along the meridian of 45°W., which passes through the Atlantic, and along the southern half of the meridian of 90°E., through the central Indian Ocean.

The interrupted Mollweide illustrated in Fig. 52, is suitable for portraying oceanographical distributions. It is interrupted over continental masses, and recentred on ocean meridians.

6. Gridded maps

We have defined a graticule as a network of projected parallels of latitude and meridians. By means of the graticule, geographical positions of points on a map may be found or expressed.

On large-scale topographical maps, positions on the map are usually described, not by geographical coordinates of latitude and longitude, but by means of a *grid reference*. This is facilitated by superimposing on the map a system of *grid lines* which form a net-work of squares. The squares themselves may be lettered, so that a map position may be described as lying in square A or in square B, etc. In other cases, the grid pattern is lettered on one pair of opposite edges, and numbered on the other pair, so that a mapped position may be described as lying in square B6, or square D5, etc.

Topographical maps of the Ordnance Survey of Great Britain use a grid system based on Cartesian coordinates, the axes of reference passing respectively eastwards and northwards from a point of origin which lies well to the south-west of Britain. The location of the point of origin obviates the use of negative coordinates.

When making a grid reference, it is conventional to state the easterly coordinate first followed by the northerly coordinate. The coarse pattern of the grid is subdivided into less coarse patterns so that on large scale maps the grid reference facilitates describing positions very accurately.

A Selected List for
Further Reading

Barlow, C. W. C., and Bryan, G. H., *Mathematical Astronomy*, 5th edition revised by Sir H. Spencer-Jones, London, 1946.
Birch, T. W., *Maps, Topographical and Statistical*, 2nd edition, Oxford, 1964.
Bowditch, N., *The American Practical Navigator*, U.S.H.O.
Brown, Ll. A., *The Story of Maps*, Boston, 1949.
Bunbury, E. H., *History of Ancient Geography*, 1st edition, London, 1879.
Butterfield, A. D., *A History of the Determination of the Figure of the Earth from Arc Measurements*, Worcester, Mass., 1906.
Bygott, J., *Introduction to Map Work and Practical Geography*, 8th edition, London, 1964.
Clarke, A. R., *Geodesy*, Oxford, 1880.
Close, Sir C., *The Map of England*, London, 1932.
Clough-Smith, J. H., *Spherical Trigonometry*, Glasgow, 1966.
Cotter, C. H., *The Elements of Navigation*, London, 1953.
Crone, G. R., *Maps and their Makers*, London, 1953.
Debenham, F., *Map Making*, 2nd edition, London, 1940.
Dury, G. H., *Map Interpretation*, 2nd edition, London, 1960
Dutton, B., *Navigation and Nautical Astronomy*, U.S.H.O.
Hinkley, A., *Map Projections by Practical Construction*, London, 1942.
Hinks, A. R., *Map Projections*, 2nd edition, Cambridge, 1921.
——, *Maps and Survey*, London, 1947.
H.M.S.O., *Admiralty Manual of Navigation*, 3 vols.
——, *Admiralty Manual of Hydrographic Surveying*.
——, *Manual of Topographic Surveying*.
——, *Nautical Almanac*.
Jeans, Sir J., *The Growth of Physical Science*, London, 1950.
Jervis, W. W., *The World in Maps*, London, 1936.
Kellaway, G. P., *Map Projections*, London, 1946.
Mainwaring, J., *An Introduction to the Study of Map Projections*, London, 1942.

A SELECTED LIST FOR FURTHER READING   235

Melluish, R. K., *An Introduction to the Mathematics of Map Projections*, Cambridge, 1931.
Raisz, E., *Principles of Cartography*, New York, 1962.
Robinoon, A. H., *The Elements of Cartography*, 2nd edition, London, 1961.
Spencer-Jones, Sir H., *General Astronomy*, London, 1951.
Steers, J. A., *An Introduction to the Study of Map Projections*, 12th edition, London, 1960.
Taylor, E. G. R., *Ideas on the Shape, Size and Movements of the Earth*, Historical Association Pamphlet No. 126, London, 1943.
Todhunter, I., *A History of the Mathematical Theories of Attraction and the Figure of the Earth from the Time of Newton to that of Laplace*, 2 vols., London, 1873.
Tooley, R. V., *Maps and Mapmakers*, London, 1949.
Winterbottom, H. St. L., *A Key to Maps*, 2nd edition, London, 1945.
Wolf, A., *A History of Science, Technology and Philosophy in the Eighteenth Century*, 2nd edition prepared by Douglas MacKie, London, 1952.

Index

ACKNOWLEDGEMENTS

Many individuals and organizations assisted in making this book a reality. We would like to thank The Institute of Research for funding and providing the manpower to complete the project. Others include: our stars of tomorrow--Georgette, Paulette, George V and Marydna; Pluria Marshall, the National Black Media Coalition; the National Association of Black-Owned Broadcasters; Baha'i Spiritual Assembly of Carson, California; Television Academy of Arts & Science; Marion Quel for typing and editing parts of the manuscript.

Lastly, a big thanks to the students who attended Dr. Hill's first class on blacks and television. They will carry the message from their own experience.

I frankly believe that to a very great extent, white people in television have run out of ideas. They have expired their culture in terms of communicating it. Black culture has not even been scratched. I invite my colleagues cited in this book to come forth with material from our rich gold mine of black heritage; from our creative caverns of black contributions to this society and the world.

Neither is black America a monolith nor is ethnic or racial heritage a disadvantage. Conversely, racial heritage is an inclining factor in determining the life chances of a group in a culturally pluralistic society. It is this premise upon which we must base our new horizons in this medium of television.

Dr. George Hill and Sylvia Saverson Hill are to be commended for their research efforts in bringing together under one cover black involvement of every aspect of on-camera and behind-the-camera professions including producing, directing, soap operas, sports, religious broadcasting, child actors and much more.

Blacks have endured decades of negative images in this medium. I have chosen to use my exposure in this medium to combat the racist images. And I can tell you from firsthand experience that you need information and research to do it.

I challenge researchers, university professors, college students, and all others to take this abundance of data compiled by the authors and do the necessary research in this much overlooked area of broadcast communications.

Tony Brown
Executive Producer
Tony Brown's Journal

This bibliography, unlike most, has a plot. It offers the evidence for an indictment of the television and motion picture industries in America. It bears witness to the distorted image of blacks the world over, propagated by the industry's power structure. On these pages is the evidence provided by those of us that have been selected to portray and implement the images. We may not have been the most talented or gifted of artists, but we were, at that time, a combination of the proper temperament, talent, and image to satisfy television's top management.

In motion pictures and television you shall witness that we are but the pleasers who act out the carefully shaped and distorted images from Tarzan to Webster, and Birth of a Nation to Roots; the control of our images is not our own.

Dr. George Hill and Sylvia Saverson Hill are to be commended for taking the countless hours to bring black involvement in television to the forefront. After more than thirty-five years of network television, a book such as this is long overdue.

This bibliography will be quite useful to performers and entertainers who have not kept a scrapbook of their newspaper and magazine clippings. I recommend it to studio executives, network executives, cable outlets, stations, producers, directors, production companies, television historians, libraries, researchers and scholars.

Stu Gilliam
Actor/Comedian

This bibliography spans forty-five years of black involvement in television from Clarence Muse's appearance in 1939 on Los Angeles station W6XAO (California Eagle, 12/21/39), to the 1983-84 TV season of Mr. T. , The Jeffersons, The Jesse Owens Story, etc. This is the first book-length bibliography on the subject. We have included every possible area of interest from advertising to women's involvement and children's programs.

The authors and many other media professionals were quite surprised to learn of the vast amount of information that has been published on the subject. The bibliography contains more than 2800 entries. It is our sincere hope that this book will be the vehicle for the much-needed research on this subject by communications historians, researchers, scholars, and academicians. We have included hundreds of easy-to-locate articles from popular periodicals so that our book will be useful to the novice as well as the professional. These periodicals, primarily oriented toward the black consumer market, are the bedrock of exposure for the black artist and are the most lucrative places to find data on black involvement in television for the veteran or amateur researcher. Additionally, we have placed the books, dissertations, theses, and journal articles in separate sections for easier accessibility.

The bibliography is further divided into a number of useful sections. The first contains books that have some information on black involvement in television. It includes biographies and autobiographies of television personalities, and general TV books that have a satisfactory percentage of information on black programs. It also includes several books which are unique to the field. They are: McDonald's Blacks and White TV, the first full book on this subject; Ploski's series of books, with a variety of detailed information in each of the four volumes of The Afro American including the 1983 edition (which is not listed); the books by newsmen Gil Noble and Bob Teague; Dr. Hill's books Ebony Images: Black American & Television, the first anthology on this subject, and Airwaves to the Soul, which has a chapter discussing blacks on religious television and radio.

The chapter entitled Magazine and Newspaper Articles includes such sections as Awards, Soaps, Religious Broadcasting, and Cable Television. Due to their content, some articles could have been listed in more than one section, but they are not. One example of

this is entry 2273, "Cicely Tyson Views TV For Black People," is
in the Protest and Controversy section. It could have also been
listed in the Personalities-Actresses section. Entry 973, "Minority Broadcast Facilities Ownership Eyed by Government Agencies,"
is in the Organizations section. It could have also been listed in
the Government section.

Advertising, another section, focuses on agencies, black
talent in ads, racism in the advertising industry, commercials,
and advertising research. Awards and Honors contains entries on
national and local Emmy winners, NAACP Image Award winners,
honorary degrees, and so forth. In the section entitled Broadcasting, we discuss significant information on television and radio which
includes the FCC (Federal Communications Commission), former
FCC commissioners Ben Hooks and Tyrone Brown, and minorities
in broadcasting.

Children and Children's Programs contains entries about
successful programs such as Sesame Street, Electric Company,
and Bill Cosby's Fat Albert cartoon series. Another section is
devoted to black firsts from Adam Wade (game show host) to Max
Robinson (news anchor) to stations WGPR-TV (Detroit) and WHMM-
TV (Howard University). This section also includes programs such
as Roots, Today's Black Woman, and I Spy. General Television
has articles that would not normally be included in other sections,
such as overviews of TV seasons, comprehensive articles about
blacks and television, and so on. Government contains data on
government agencies such as the FCC, SBA (Small Business Ad-
ministration) and others. The Management section covers mostly
personalities who are in executive, middle, or lower management
positions. Music is one of the more succinct sections, because
only a few blacks have had the opportunity to become TV composers,
arrangers or music directors; many who have achieved are here.

The section News, covers broadcast journalists, their accomplishments, their perils and opinions, and their stations and
networks. A section entitled Organizations includes information
about media groups such as the National Association of Broadcasters, Atlanta Press Club, Media Forum; civil rights and civil liber-
ties groups such as NAACP, ACLU, PUSH, and Urban League; and
business organizations such as National Black Network, and Cox
Broadcasting Co. Ownership, the next section, has material on the
stations, production companies, and government regulations specifically related to minority ownership of stations. Personalities is
divided into five subsections. These are Actresses, Actors, Comedians, Singers, and Youth. The articles are about the lives, programs, careers, opinions, and comments of black performers on
television. Programs, another large section, has eleven subsections
which are Comedy, Detectives, Documentary, Drama, Game, Music, News, Talk, Roots, Specials, and Variety. These programs
are ones in which blacks have had starring or supporting roles, or
the program itself had a specific black orientation. Producers/
Directors/Writers is dedicated to these three off-camera fields.

Protest & Controversy is quite unique. It covers the people and programs about which there have been disagreement or conflict or where there have been protests by the NAACP, other civil rights groups, and/or individuals. Religious Broadcasting includes information on ministers and laypersons on TV since 1948 when Elder Lightfoot Solomon Michaux aired nationally on the DuMont network. Another section focuses on one of America's favorite daytime pastimes, The Soap Operas.

With the advent of all-sports channels and more professional teams, black sports figures have received much greater television exposure. The Sports section includes entries on athletes and sportscasters. These were taken primarily from TV Guide. Additional information can be obtained in Dr. Lenwood Davis' bibliography Black Athletes In the United States. The articles in the Women's section might have been lost in a work of this magnitude had they not been separated. Of course, there are many other articles about individual women as actresses, producers, news anchors, and so on. Cable Television, the last section, has five subsections. They are: Ownership, Programming, General, Personnel and Personalities, and Bidding and Government.

This book is a salute to those who have endured the stereotypical roles and those who sought to alter these characterizations that for too long have been the "order of the day" in white America.

Our Hats Are Off to:

Eddie Anderson, who portrayed Rochester on the Jack Benny Show which won several Emmy awards. Anderson, however, never received an Emmy nomination due to racism.

The NAACP, for always being in the forefront of eliminating discrimination in the television industry.

Harry Belafonte, for pioneering excellence by being the first black to receive an Emmy.

Stu Gilliam, who has been the voice of Curly Neal on the Harlem Globe Trotters cartoons series. He has never stopped loving humanity and helping people.

WGPR-TV, for pioneering black ownership in television.

Elder Lightfoot Michaux and Bob Howard, as the first blacks to have network programs.

Bill Cosby, the only black to win four Emmys. Cicely Tyson, Debra Allen, and Leontyne Price are not far behind with two each.

Sammy Davis, Jr. , Mr. Entertainment, for being one of the most visible black performers during television's first fifteen years. He has prime-time and daytime Emmy nominations to his credit.

Nat King Cole, who gave his all as host of the first black, half-hour network variety series.

The entire Amos 'n' Andy cast (Tim Moore, Spencer Williams, Alvin Childress, Ernestine Wade, Amanda Randolph, Johnny Lee, Nich Stewart), who made America laugh.

Tony Brown, for bringing information about black America into our homes each week for more than a decade.

Louis Gosset, Jr., for winning both Emmy and Oscar awards, and Howard Rollins, Jr., Quincy Jones, Ethel Waters, and Paul Winfield for being nominated for both.

Diahann Carroll and James Earl Jones, for each being nominated for Oscar, Emmy, Tony, and Grammy awards.

The entire The Jeffersons cast (Sherman Hemsley, Isabel Sanford, Marla Gibbs, Roxie Roker, Berlinda Tolbert), for having made America laugh for a decade.

Adam Wade, who was the first and only black game-show host.

Billy Daniels, whose quarter-hour show was the first to be broadcasted nationally by a single sponsor.

Gail Fisher, whose Emmy achievement was a first for a black woman.

Many articles in this bibliography are from Soul magazine (1966-1982). This publication covered black Hollywood and blacks in the recording industry better than any other magazine. If your local library does not have Soul, the microfilm can be obtained by contacting Microfilming Corp. of America, P. O. Box 10, 1620 Hawkins Ave., Sanford, N. C. 27330 or calling 800-334-7501.

Lastly, we are aware that we have not included every citation that might have been in this work; therefore, we welcome any additions or corrections, since we intend to update this book at a future time. Send information to: Dr. George Hill, P. O. Box 4721, Carson, CA 90749.

HISTORY OF BLACKS ON TELEVISION

by Cynthia E. Griffin and George H. Hill

Since network television began, it has projected an image of blacks that is as narrow and restricting as a single-lane highway in rush hour traffic. Even though the types of programs that blacks have appeared in range from musical varieties to Shakespearean productions, there is one fact that stubbornly sticks out. Historically, the black television shows or roles that were most popular and managed to last the longest were usually comedies or musical variety shows, not dramatic programs. Consequently, there has never been a balance for black performers or black America.

But this wasn't exactly what black America expected when the concept of network programming was first introduced. In July 1950, Ebony magazine went so far as to say that television offered better roles for blacks than any other media. At that point it was probably true. After all, the list of accomplishments was beginning to look quite significant. Bob Howard, pianist and singer, TV's jive bomber, had just finished a two-year run on his own show. He was the first black to have a network program. During that same time (1948-1949), Elder Lightfoot Solomon Michaux, a twenty-year broadcast veteran and top-notch businessman (he left an estate worth over $6 million) evangelized from his Washington D. C. church each week. CBS televised an all-black variety show, Uptown Jubilee, in 1949 (later called Sugar Hill Times), which was hosted by musician/ singer, Willie Bryant. Regulars included Timmie "Oh Yeah" Rogers, and Harry Belafonte. Unfortunately, it only aired for about a month. But this didn't matter because the promise was there. Hazel Scott, wife of Adam Clayton Powell, was the spirit of that promise when she became the first black woman to host a network series in July 1950.

Local television stations also got into the act providing shows like Harlem Detective. This 1953 WOR-TV (New York) program paired William Marshall with white actor William Harriston and featured the duo investigating crime in Harlem.

Ebony's high hopes and glowing words of praise were quickly tarnished. Television executives had begun to discover the lucrativeness of mass-audience programming, and one fact quickly became very clear: it would be bad business to change the skillfully crafted

1

and accepted black image film and radio had created. The Introduction of <u>Beulah</u> in October of 1950 began the short process of reestablishing the norm. This was the first comedy series to star a black performer and to offer a number of blacks television roles. <u>Amos 'n' Andy</u> followed in 1951, giving the race its first comedy series with an all-black cast. <u>Green Pastures</u> continued the tradition in 1951, when excerpts of the award-winning 1930 play were broadcast. These proved to be so popular that <u>The Hallmark Hall of Fame</u> assembled a cast of eighty black performers and produced a live ninety-minute version for TV in 1957. This was rebroadcast in 1959 with practically the same cast. In 1952, Billy Daniels marked another milestone: his fifteen-minute show was the first nationally broadcast program designed around a black entertainer to be sponsored by a single advertiser. Rybutol Vitamin Supplement set this precedent in the fall of 1952. The show ran for thirteen weeks.

Although all of these shows offered blacks more work, the victory was bittersweet. In <u>Beulah</u>, the first comedy series to have a black in the starring role, <u>Ethel</u> Waters (and later Louise Beavers) was an ever-faithful maid with a heart of gold, serving her white boss. <u>Amos 'n' Andy</u> featured blacks rolling their eyes and generally acting in a manner honed to a fine art during the movies of the 1920s and 1930s. <u>Green Pastures</u> was a biblical piece that seemed to feature blacks in a neverending fish fry, acting as happy as any mammy and her brood. Even "De Lawd" was portrayed as less than majestic.

There were other dramatic shows featuring blacks during the 1950s. On <u>Studio One</u>, talents like Juano Hernandez and Frank Silvera (1957) were showcased. <u>Kraft Theater</u> featured Ossie Davis in 1955, and on <u>The Hallmark Hall of Fame</u>, Staats Cosworth acted in <u>MacBeth</u> in 1954. But it was <u>Beulah, Amos 'n' Andy</u> and <u>Green Pastures</u> which were the most memorable because of their longevity and the number of blacks involved in the productions.

Blacks also appeared on a number of music and variety shows. <u>The Nat King Cole Show</u>, in 1956, was one of the most notable. Cole became the first major black performer to headline a network series. The program first aired on NBC in a fifteen-minute slot just before the network news. In the summer of 1957, the format was expanded to half an hour and aired at 10:00 p. m. Tuesdays. In September, Cole was shifted to 7:30 p. m. This was a tactical error, and, combined with other problems, led to the show's cancellation after about a year. <u>The Jack Benny Show</u> (1950-1965) offered Eddie "Rochester" Anderson the opportunity to have more exposure than any other black; while Steve Allen (1950-1952, 1956-1960 and 1961) and Ed Sullivan (1948-1971) provided a variety of black performers with instant exposure.

<u>The Ed Sullivan Show</u> proved to be an invaluable springboard for black talent, and the performers who worked on it were many. They include: The Jackson 5, Sammy Davis Jr. , Harry Belafonte,

Billy Eckstine, Ella Fitzgerald, The Four Step Brothers, The Nicholas Brothers, Leontyne Price, Fats Domino, Sam Cooke, The Coasters, and Pigmeat Markham. As the 1950s ended, it seemed to blacks like they were traveling through a twilight zone full of déjà vu. This new, oh-so-promising medium was shaping up to become no better than movies and certainly no better than radio.

In the first part of the 1960s, this trend continued. The roles blacks did get were generally characterized as "black parts" like the 1961 "Good Night Sweet Blues" episode of Route 66. Dying blues singer, Ethel Waters, wanted to see her old band together one last time. The main characters of the show fulfilled this request and in the process a long list of musicians and singers paraded across the television tube.

There was one genre of TV programs from which blacks were glaringly absent--Westerns. In the late 1950s and early 1960s, this was one of the most popular, but not one black had a main role in a Western. Several did, however, make an occasional appearance. Among these were Sammy Davis, Jr. in Zane Grey Theater in 1959, Lawman in 1961, and The Rifleman and Frontier Circus in 1962. Rex Ingram offered his bit to Black Saddle in 1959, while Frank Silvera worked on Johnny Ringo in 1960.

All this indicated that the 1960s would probably be business as usual when it came to what images of blacks were portrayed. But if there's one thing the 1960s could not be called, it would be "an era of business as usual. "

Television would definitely not be excluded from the changes that would roar through America during this time. When President John Kennedy came to office at the beginning of the decade, he made immediate changes. His appointees to the Federal Communications Commission began to demand that television stations consider affirmative action in their operations from top to the bottom. As a result, blacks began to see small changes. Civil rights organizations were demanding and protesting for equal access. Television became a potent ally in the fight. The Southern racists and Northern bigots could not hide their disdain for blacks, as they could be seen on the television news each night. TV became an ally of black Americans in their fight for freedom to ride in the front of the bus. Both Martin Luther King, Jr. and Malcolm X gained recognition as national leaders via television.

All these changes and more helped to make the 1960s a perfect environment to nurture these fledgling efforts. Blacks began finding themselves in more meaningful dramatic series and began proving that they could win awards for acting excellence. Two of the most significant series of the decade were I Spy (1965-68), and Eastside/Westside (1964).

I Spy starred Bill Cosby and Robert Culp as American agents, traveling all over the world on assignments. Cosby, who

won three Emmys for his role in the show, was the first black in
an adventure series, and the first black actor to have a starring
role in a noncomedic series. In Eastside/Westside, Cicely Tyson
was the only black with a continuing role. Although the series was
not primarily about blacks, it did feature several poignant portrayals of the black experience in the inner city. "No Hiding Place"
dealt with the real estate industry and white flight, while "Who Do
You Kill?" explored the attitudes that placed and maintained blacks
in poverty.

In addition to dramatic parts, blacks began to pick up roles
in daytime television. The first soap opera to offer blacks substan-
tially improved roles was One Life to Live, which premiered in
October 1968. This was producer Agnes Nixon's saga of the trials
and tribulations of a first-generation American family trying to
achieve social success. The show's orientation often focused on
relevant issues and this occasionally offered blacks more character
latitude. But as usual, there were limitations. Eleanor Holly's
case was a prime example. She played Carla Gray, a black secretary in love with her white boss. However, viewer anger caused
the show to be cancelled on one Texas station and Southern stations
threatened similar action. Nixon and the network realized a script
change was needed. Holly eventually married a black police lieutenant, Ed Hall, portrayed by Emmy winner Al Freeman, Jr.

The 1960s also found several blacks in short-lived but fairly
well-rounded roles. James Earl Jones and Cicely Tyson (later Ruby
Dee) portrayed Dr. Jim Frazier and his wife Martha on Guiding
Light. Jones was also Dr. Jerry Turner of As the World Turns.
Billy Dee Williams was an assistant district attorney on Another
World.

In addition to appearing in daytime roles, blacks began to
garner more industry recognition for their dramatic acting in prime
time. Harry Belafonte led off the awards for excellence in 1960
with an Emmy for Tonight With Belafonte, on the Revlon Revue.
He was the first black to earn this coveted accolade. Bill Cosby
followed six years later in 1966, winning for his role as Alexander
Scott on I Spy. But this talented entertainer didn't stop with a single
Emmy, he collected two additional consecutive awards for this same
role. Gail Fisher joined the Emmy winners in 1970, with an award
for best supporting actress in a dramatic series as Peggy on Mannix.

While winning an Emmy is the ultimate achievement, the
number of Emmy nomination blacks collected in the 1960s is definitely worth noting: Ethel Waters (Naked City, 1962); Ruby Dee (The
Nurses, 1964); James Earl Jones and Diana Sands (Eastside/West-
side, 1964); Eartha Kitt (I Spy, 1966); Diahann Carroll (Julia, 1969);
and Greg Morris (Mission Impossible, 1969). Morris went on to
pick up nominations in 1970 and 1971 as a part of the MI Force.

When put into perspective, these Emmy winners and nominees

fill a very important page in black entertainment history. Even
though blacks have been traditionally cast as comics in cinema, radio, and television, they have actually won more Emmys for dramatic acting than for comedy. Although all these awards and nominations didn't exactly translate into significantly more starring roles
for blacks in the 1960s, they did seem to be an indicator that maybe,
just maybe, things might be changing.

In many senses, the sheer numbers of blacks on television
in the 1970s appeared to be the big change. From 1970 to 1979
blacks had starring or strong supporting roles in at least fifteen
shows. Many of these had predominantly black casts. But looks
can often be deceiving, and in this case they were. Although blacks
had numerous roles on many shows, there was one glaring problem,
the majority of these shows were comedies. Detective shows ran
a distant second.

The comedy started with The Bill Cosby Show (1970) and Sanford and Son (1971) in the early years; peaked with Good Times
(1973), The Jeffersons (1974), and What's Happening (1976), and
ended up with Benson and Sanford in 1979. The detective series
included Shaft, Paris, Tenafly, Get Christy Love, Mannix, The
Rookies, Ironside and Mod Squad. But as with any tide, the surg-
ing surface froth hides the more deadly creep of erosion. While
outwardly, blacks got more and more starring and supporting roles
in the 1970s, the predominantly black comedies of the first part of
the decade slowly and inexorably gave way to a mix of black into
white during the twilight years.

In the early 1980s, one or two blacks integrated into the
casts of television shows was the order of the day. Nearly every
time blacks appeared they were part of the group. Obviously, this
caused white America, especially those living in urban settings, to
believe that blacks had it made, and were getting a piece of the
American pie. This was the feeling despite the fact that most whites
knew they didn't work with, live in the same neighborhood, or perhaps
even see anyone who was black except on television. This integrated
status made black performers quite visible. In the drama area,
Mr. T of NBC's The A Team seized the interest of many and the
hearts of millions of children. Madge Sinclair and Brian Mitchell
held down their hospital posts on M*A*S*H spin-off Trapper John,
M.D. Crime fighters on the top-rated Hill Street Blues were
Michael Warren and Taurean Blacque. Although many had high vis-
ibility in dramas, they still had roles as loyal followers and supporters of white heros. Roger Mosley was Tom Selleck's assistant
on Magnum P.I. Gregg Morris performed in a somewhat colorless
role in Vega$, as he had done a decade earlier in Mission Impos-
sible. Herb Jefferson, Jr. was a lackluster pilot in Battlestar Galactica.

Ted Lange continued as the comic bartender on Love Boat.
He also stepped from behind the bar to direct several episodes, as
did Debbie Allen on Fame. She also produced some of the Fame

shows in the 1904-05 season. Allen (the first black to win Emmys
for choreography), Gene Anthony Ray, and Janet Jackson excited
viewers so much that Fame did better in syndication than during its
first run on NBC.

Blacks were also still getting laughs on comedy programs.
Eddie Murphy of Saturday Night Live has made millions from his
mirth.   Robert Guillaume, Soap's butler, starred in his own series,
Benson, as a civil service executive.   He is the only black actor
to win an Emmy for a portrayal in a comedic series.   (Actress Isabel Sanford won an Emmy in 1981.)   Ron Glass of Barney Miller
and Demond Wilson of Sanford and Son teamed up as the New Odd
Couple, but the series was short-lived.   The producers seemed to
think that the old laugh-track responses and the outdated scripts of
the 1970s Odd Couple with Tony Randall and Jack Klugman would
suffice.   They didn't!   The Diff'rent Strokes scene changed a little
when Todd Bridges (Willis) grew a mustache and acquired a girl-
friend--youthful singing sensation Janet Jackson, of the famed Jackson family.   Gary Coleman (Arnold) moved on to junior high school
and had a few romances himself.   ABC aired Diff'rent Strokes look-
alike, Webster, with Emmanuel Lewis in the starring role.   The
charisma, warmth, and chuckle of Lewis seemed to carry the show
even though it did not do well in the ratings.

The 1980s was the era when blacks also became hosts and
cohosts of several programs.   Former Los Angeles sportscaster
Bryant Gumbel moved to the Today show.   Byron Allen was seen
weekly on Real People.   Songstress Marilyn McCoo became the host
of Solid Gold.   People Are Funny viewers enjoyed Flip Wilson for
the first time in nearly a decade since his Flip Wilson Show had
aired.

Two now-famous Jacksons, Jesse and Michael, received not
only national, but worldwide popularity via the tube in 1983 and 1984.
Michael Jackson's music changed the look of television with record
videos.   Cable station MTV (Music Television) had initially refused
to air black singers.   Michael's "Beat It" and "Billy Jean" videos
brought an abrupt halt to MTV's racist practice.   Shortly thereafter,
primarily due to the success of Michael's music, most network and
independent stations began broadcasting music video programs.
Jesse Jackson moved into America's livingrooms via television as
a presidential candidate.   Most had watched him crisscross America as they became familiar with his rhyming, rhythmic orations.
His charismatic mannerism, progressive ideas and diplomatic insight captured the hearts and hopes of millions.   Many newscasters,
skeptics, and other Americans gained a new respect for Jesse and
his Rainbow Coalition, after hearing his speech on the second night
of the National Democratic Convention.

In retrospect, 1960-1970 was probably the most significant
decade for blacks on television.   It offered a depth of roles which
had never been available before.   Blacks were seen as doctors,
nurses, secretaries, law enforcement officials, entertainers, social

workers, and more.   They were beginning to be seen as multidimensional people with troubles and joys.   The decade from 1970-1980, for the most part, stunted this growth.   These years represented the two-steps-forward, one-step-backward syndrome that has been an integral part of black progress in America.   The early 1980s brought a mixed blessing.   Blacks were integrated into white television, but in much smaller numbers.   The roles they portrayed, in general, lacked true depth and offered a sterile picture of black people.

Behind the scenes in television's upper management and production, the number of blacks in such positions would probably fit comfortably on one city bus.   The first five years of the 1980s found blacks wrestling with a demon that had plagued them throughout their television history: lack of balance in the images of blacks presented to America.

No one knows what the last five years of the decade will bring to this most persuasive, yet evasive medium.   Hopefully, there will be a move toward balance; with more blacks in every phase of the medium, including executive producers and other top positions.   America's conservative mode will change.   It always has and always will.

1 Archer, Leonard C. Black Images in the American Theater:
   NAACP Protest Campaigns--Stage, Screen, Radio and Television. Brooklyn, NY: Pageant-Poseidon, Ltd. , 1973, 351 p.
   Archer traces the black image in television and recounts
the struggle through the concerted efforts of W. E. B. Du Bois, James
Weldon Johnson, Roy Wilkins, and Herbert Hill to deinstitutionalize
the black stereotypes in the media. In Chapter 11, "Blacks in Radio
and Television," Archer describes the NAACP's fight to end discrimination in television and obtain employment for blacks. He cites the
results achieved by the NAACP through the television protest campaigns. These were: (1) public attention was focused on issues of
radical discriminatory stereotypes, and racial segregation; (2) winning support of other organizations for these protest campaigns; (3)
successfully securing a statement of policies favorable to black performers from broadcasters; (4) directing the attention of protest
groups which posed a threat of mass boycott to television advertisers and their products. Archer discusses the NAACP's successfully
passed resolutions to condemn The Amos 'n' Andy Show and the dis-
agreements of organized black performers with the NAACP tactics
and changing views. He cites several TV programs where black
actors appeared in roles that were not stereotypical, such as Ed
Sullivan's Toast of the Town, Arthur Godfrey's Talent Scouts, Sid
Caesar's Your Show of Shows, Steve Allen's The Tonight Show, and
The Milton Berle Show. There were also shows with predominantly
black casts or with black stars/hosts, such as Harlem Detective,
Winner by Decision with Harry Belafonte and Ethel Waters, A Man
Is Ten Feet Tall with Sidney Poitier, and The Nat King Cole Show.
Archer includes information on the first successful two-hour televi-
sion blackout launched by the Coordinating Council of Negro Perform-
ers and the NAACP in 1955. Supporters of the blackout did not
watch television for the two hours.

2 Cole, Barry G. Television: A Selection of Readings from TV
   Guide Magazine. New York: Free Press, 1970, 605 p.
   This book contains a variety of articles which appeared in
TV Guide. There were two articles about blacks in 1968. In Martin Maloney's "Black Is the Color of Our New TV" (November 16,
1968, p. 255-258), the author discusses the new and old shows with
blacks, such as Julia, I Spy and Mission Impossible. Art Peters'
"What the Negro Wants from TV," (January 20, 1968, p. 259-264),
discusses the need for more positive images for blacks on TV. It
quotes Bill Cosby, George Norford of Westinghouse Broadcasting,
actor P. Say Sidney, and Walter Carroll.

3 Hill, George H. Airwaves to the Soul: The Influence and Growth
   of Religious Broadcasting in America. Palo Alto, CA: R &
   E Associates, 1983, 156 p.
      This book examines the history, demographics, and expan-
   sion of religious radio and TV. Chapter 6, on blacks, is the first
   research on black involvement in the field. The author discusses
   the backgrounds of the major black telecasters Cleophus Robinson,
   Fred Price, Clay Evans, Rev. Ike, and Ben Kinchlow. He includes
   biographical sketches on the first blacks to have programs on TV
   and/or radio in New York, Atlanta, St. Louis, Los Angeles, Washington, D.C. , Chicago, and Dallas/Fort Worth. This book has
   chapters on the Christian networks--PTL, CBN, TBN--and covers
   the early pioneers, broadcasters in Souther California, and the pros
   and cons of religious broadcasting.

4 _____. Black Media, USA. Chicago: Path Press, 1985,
      163 p.
      This is a compilation of articles on black involvement in
   media, which includes historical data on books, newspapers, magazines, radio, television, public relations, and advertising. The book
   contains many biographical sketches of outstanding communicators
   such as John H. Johnson, Earl Graves, Ed Lewis, Jack L. Cooper,
   Al Benson, Max Robinson, Moss H. Kendrix, LeRoy Jefferies, and
   Barbara Proctor. It also has articles about Howard University's
   WHUR Radio, black book publishers, The National Association of
   Television and Radio Artists (NATRA), and the first black-owned
   radio station, Atlanta's WERD. The book also lists blacks accred-
   ited by the Public Relations Society of America.

5 _____. Ebony Images: Black Americans and Television.
      Carson, CA: Daystar Publishing Company, 1985, 110 p.
      This is the first anthology on black involvement in TV. It
   lists Emmy award winners, black-owned stations and cable facilities,
   and programs that starred blacks. There are articles examining the
   years of negative imagery of blacks on TV, which includes thirty
   years of NAACP protests. The book covers black involvement in
   the soap operas, sportscasting, news, cartoons, religious broadcasting, game shows, cable television, the roles black child stars have
   played on programs such as Our Gang, Diff'rent Strokes, and Julia.
   There are biographical sketches on the following artists: Don Cornelius, Tony Brown, Adam Wade, Eddie "Rochester" Anderson,
   Bryant Gumbel, Charlene Hunter-Gault, Ed Bradley, Max Robinson,
   and religious broadcasters Fred Price, Rev. Ike, and Ben Kinchlow.
   Articles on several historical programs such as "Roots" and "Harris
   and Company" are included.

6 _____. Black Media of America: A Resource Guide. Boston:
      G.K. Hall, 1984, 333p.
      This is the first bibliography covering the broad scope of
   black involvement in media, including public relations, advertising,
   magazines, newspapers, books, television, radio, marketing, con-
   sumerism, and cable television. This work has more than 3800 entries from books as well as sections on journal, newspaper, and

magazine articles.   There is also a biographical section of outstanding communicators.

7 _____ . Religious Broadcasting, 1920-1983: A Selected Annotated Bibliography of Books, Dissertations, Theses, and Articles.   New York: Garland Publishing Company, 1984, 243 p.
     This is the first bibliographical text on religious broadcasting.   It covers religious television networks CBN, TBN, and PTL, National Association of Religious Broadcasters, the FCC, and every aspect of religious radio and TV.   It includes citations on blacks such as Elder Lightfoot Solomon Michaux, the most popular religious broadcaster from 1920 to 1955.   He was among the first blacks to have a nationally telecasted program (it began on October 31, 1948).   The book has citations on contemporary, nationally syndicated telecasters Fred Price, Cleophus Robinson, Ben Smith, Clay Evans, and Reverend Ike.   It also cites CBN cohost Ben Kinchlow, international broadcasters Howard Jones and Ernie Wilson, Wallace D. Muhammed's Islamic program, black all-gospel stations WYCB, KMAX, KTYM and WUST, B. Sam Hart's WYIS, and the first black-owned television station, WGPR-TV in Detroit.

8 Hunter, Julius K. and Gross, Lynn S.   Broadcast News, The Inside Out.   St. Louis: The C.V. Mosby Company, 1980, 267 p.
     This is one of the first college textbooks on broadcast journalism to be authored by a black television newsman.   Hunter is anchorman for KMOX-TV in St. Louis.   He and Gross cover a broad range of topics including the background of broadcast news, needs of news, basics of news, and controversies of news.   The text has much useful and current information such as recent journalistic trends. Glossary.   Appendix of universities with accredited journalism and mass-communications departments.   Index.

9 Kirk, Onnie and others.   Contemporary Black America.   Nashville, TN: The Southwestern Company, 1980, 531 p.
     This book has a brief history of blacks in television in the subsection "Television and Radio: Projecting Diverse Images."   The book cites many shows in which blacks have had starring and major supporting roles such as I Spy and Roots.

10 Low, W. Augustus and Clift, Virgil.   Encyclopedia of Black America.   New York: McGraw-Hill Book Company, 1971, 985 p.
     The authors give a brief summary of the history of black involvement in television on pp. 723-726.   The book cites early 1950s programs such as Beulah and Amos 'n' Andy, Emmy award winner Bill Cosby, and Nipsy Russell as cohost on the Les Crane Show for a season, marking the first time that a regularly employed black master of ceremonies appeared on a nationally televised program.

11 MacDonald, J. Fred.   Blacks in White TV.   Chicago: Nelson-Hall, 1983, 288 p.

12   Blacks On Television

The author divides this study into three parts. The first
covers the formative period, from 1948-1957, when blacks believed
that TV would not adopt the racist stereotyping that had flourished
in radio and film. Ebony magazine epitomized this sentiment, when
it reported in 1950 that TV offered better roles for blacks than any
other medium. As television became nationally distributed and enor-
mously profitable, the hopes of blacks were shattered. The second
part of the book covers the "Age of Civil Rights" (1957-1970), the
most lucrative era for blacks. They received exposure on the news
and in prime-time programs, but had no real voice.

The third part covers a period called the "Age of the New
Minstrelsy," from 1970 to the present, during which the medium has
reverted to stereotypical images of blacks as clowns, mammies, and
buffoons. Blacks have been depicted as people not to be taken seriously. However, blacks held on to a few gains of the 1960s, and
now participate in most aspects of programming from newscasts and
situation comedies, to various dramatic formats, commercials, and
TV movies. MacDonald concludes by saying that even with the gains,
one cannot feel satisfied with the manner in which the medium has
received blacks. Television has been less than honorable in its
treatment of blacks. Bibliography. Index.

12 Noble, Gil. Black Is the Color of My TV Tube. Secaucus, NJ:
      Lyle Stuart, 1981, 190 p.
        Noble, a four-time local Emmy award winner and host of
Like It Is, shares a look at his world as a telecaster. The book is
the first autobiography of a black network anchorman. Noble offers
a warm and sincere insight into himself, his ancestry, and his people. He shares his perspective on his interviews with such notables
as Martin Luther King, Jr. , Malcolm X, Eubie Blake, and Dizzy
Gillespie.

13 Ploski, Harry and Marr, Warren. The Afro American. New
      York: The Bellwether Company, 1976, 1,206 p.
        In Section 25, "The Black Press and Broadcast Media," the
authors provide brief profiles of thirteen television news people. Included are local Emmy award winner Gil Noble and Lem Tucker.
TV station acquisitions by blacks up to 1974 are listed. The book
cites Black Journal and Black Perspectives on the News as the only
black-oriented Public Broadcasting programs. Section 21, "The
Black Entertainer in the Performing Arts," offers profiles of many
performers who have had starring or major supporting roles in
prime-time series, specials or made-for-TV movies, including Bill
Cosby, Adam Wade, Ethel Waters, Diana Ross, Redd Foxx, J. J.
Walker, and dozens more. In Polski's similar 1967 volume entitled
The Negro Almanac, the television data are on pages 710-711. The
TV material in the 1971 volume is on pages 761-765.

14 Schechter, William. The History of Negro Humor in America.
      New York: Fleet Press Corp. , 1970, 214 p.
        Schechter looks at black humor in Africa prior to slavery
and he discusses present-day situation comedies on television. The
derivation of "dozens contests" is highlighted in the first chapter.

In Chapter 5, "Enter Radio, Movies, and a New Uncle Tomism,"
and Chapter 8, "The Age of Soul--Its Humor," he discusses black
humor on radio and television.

15 Sharp, Saundra. 1980 Directory of Black Film/TV: Technicians,
    West Coast. Los Angeles: Togetherness Productions, 1980,
    310 p.
        This directory lists almost 500 black professional craftsper-
sons working in the film and TV industry on the West Coast (Los
Angeles, San Francisco, San Diego and Seattle). It is the first directory about blacks who work behind the cameras. It lists companies and individuals. Company listings include the company's spe-
cialty, principal owners, credits, and awards. Individual listings
include agents, union membership, two industry references, training,
credits, and awards. Where a listing has credits, training, or union
membership in another skill, his/her name is cross-referenced to
that category.

16 Spradling, Mary Mace. In Black and White. Detroit: Gale Re-
    search Company, 1980, 2 vols., 1,263 p.
        This is a listing and guide to magazine and newspaper arti-
cles and books about more than 15,000 black individuals and groups
in a broad variety of careers and occupations. In the index, the author cites 325 people as television personalities and telecasters.

17 Teague, Bob. Line and Off-Color: News Biz. New York: A
    & W Publishers, 1982, 239 p.
        Teague, a black reporter and anchorman for New York's
WNBC-TV, shares the inside story, the human side of television
news. The book relates the behind-the-scenes reality and the amusing anecdotes of television. The author analyzes how and why local
TV reporting has become more like entertainment than news. Teague
provides a frank look at what electronic journalism is all about--the
triumphs and problems. He offers a provocative, iconoclastic, but
eminently practical scenario for revamping the "news biz" to achieve
its awesome potential. Teague shares an uncompromising and hu-
morous look at the inner workings of local news.

18 Tinney, James S. and Rector, Justine J., eds. Issues and
    Trends in Afro-American Journalism. Lanham, MD: Univer-
    sity Press of America, Inc., 1980, 362 p.
        The authors, professors at Howard University, have compiled
a wide variety of information about blacks in media. Rector's section, Part 2, discusses blacks in broadcasting. There are several
chapters on television in this section. Chapter 22, "Blacks in News
Jobs," by Mary Ellen Perry, cites Washington, D.C. as the city
having the highest representation of black newspeople, including Jim
Vance, Delores Handy, Max Robinson and others. Chapter 18, by
Richard Pride and Daniel Clarke, "Race, In the Television News,"
evaluates the networks' (ABC, NBC, CBS) coverage of race relations,
examining coverage of black militants, white racists, blacks in general, and the police. They conclude that the militants and racists
were portrayed negatively and blacks and police were not. "Television

Use and Self-Esteem of Blacks," Chapter 25, by Alexis and Gerdean
Tan, examines high TV entertainment viewing and low self-esteem
among black audiences. "Women and Minorities in Network News,"
Chapter 24, is by the U.S. Commission on Civil Rights.

19 Westbrooks, Logan H. and Williams, Lance A. The Anatomy
      of a Record Company: How to Survive in the Record Business.
    Los Angeles: Logan Westbrooks, 1981, 180 p.
      The authors cover the importance of a record's exposure on
television, citing Don Cornelius' Soul Train as a case in point on
pages 73-75. The book cites Soul Train as the most successful
black-oriented television program in history. It has been on the
air for more than thirteen years. Westbrooks and Williams provide
an insight into why the show has been so successful and they explain
its value in giving artists exposure.

20 Withey, Stephen B. and Abeles, Ronald P. Television and So-
      cial Behavior: Beyond Violence and Children. Hillsdale, NJ:
    Lawrence Erlbaum Associates, 1980, 258 p.
      This is a study of the long- and short-term effects of tele-
vision on children, the language of TV violence and children's ag-
gression, and other related items. There are three chapters on
blacks and television, they are: "Television and Afro-Americans--
Past Legacy and Present Portrayals"; "Social Trace Contaminants:
Subtle Indicators of Racism on TV"; and "Psychological Effects of
Black Portrayals on Television. "

21 Wolper, David L. The Inside Story of "Roots." New York:
      Warner Books Company, 1978, 303 p.
      Wolper explains the worldwide success of the eight-night
TV series, how the script was derived from the book, and discusses
reviews of the series from black and white newspapers.

Selected Individual Biographies

          Armstrong, Louis
22 Satchmo: My Life in New Orleans (A). New York: Prentice-
      Hall, 1954.

23 and Richard Meryman. Louis Armstrong--A Self-Portrait (A).
      New York: Eakins Press, 1971.

          Bailey, Pearl
24 The Raw Pearl (A). New York: Harcourt, Brace and World,
      1968.

25 Talking to Myself (A). New York: Harcourt, Brace and World,
      1971.

(A) = Autobiography

Belafonte, Harry
26 Shaw, Arnold. Harry Belafonte: An Unauthorized Biography.
New York: Chilton, 1960.

27 Wright, Charles. Songs Belafonte Sings. New York: Duell,
1962.

Blake, Eubie
28 Carter, Lawrence. Eubie Blake: Keys to Memory. Detroit:
Bealamp, 1979.

29 Rose, Al. Eubie Blake. New York: Schirmer Books, 1979.

Calloway, Cab
30 Of Minnie the Moocher and Me (A). New York: Crowell, 1976.

Charles, Ray
31 and David Ritz. Brother Charles: Ray Charles' Own Story (A).
New York: Dial, 1978.

Cole, Nat King
32 Cole, Maria Ellington. Nat King Cole: An Intimate Biography.
New York: William Morrow, 1971.

Cosby, Bill
33 Olsen, James. Bill Cosby: Look Back in Laughter. Creative
Education, 1970.

Dandridge, Dorothy
34 and Earl Conrad. Everything and Nothing: The Dorothy Dandridge Tragedy (A). New York: Abelard-Schuman Ltd. , 1970.

Davis, Sammy Jr.
35 Yes I Can (A). New York: Farrar Straus & Giroux, 1965.

36 Hollywood In a Suitcase. New York: Berkley Publishing, 1980.

Dunham, Katherine
37 A Touch of Innocence (A). New York: Harcourt, Brace and
Company, 1959.

38 Biemiller, Ruth. Dance: The Story of Katherine Dunham. New
York: Doubleday, 1969.

Foxx, Redd
39 The Redd Foxx Encyclopedia of Black Humor. Los Angeles:
Ward Ritchie Press, 1977.

40 Price, Joe X. Redd Foxx, B.S. Chicago: Contemporary
Books, 1979.

Gregory, Dick
41 Nigger: An Autobiography (A). New York: Dutton, 1964.

42 The Shadow That Scares Me (A). Garden City, NY: Doubleday,
    1968.

        Holiday, Billie
43 Lady Sings the Blues (A). New York: Doubleday, 1956.

44 Chillon, John. Billie's Blues: The Billie Holiday Story. New
    York: Stein & Day, 1975.

        Horne, Lena
45 and Carlton Moss. In Person, Lena Horne (A). New York:
    Greenberg, 1950.

46 and Richard Schickel. Lena (A). New York: Doubleday, 1965.

        Kitt, Eartha
47 Alone with Me (A). Chicago: Henry Regnery, 1976.

48 Thursday's Child (A). New York: Duell, Sloan and Pearce,
    1956.

        Michaux, Lightfoot
49 Webb, Vivian Ashcraft. About My Father's Business. West-
    port, CT: Greenwood Press, 1983.

        Parks, Gordon
50 A Choice of Weapons (A). New York: Harper & Row, 1966.

        Poitier, Sidney
51 This Life (A). New York: Doubleday, 1980.

52 Keyser, Lester. The Cinema of Sidney Poitier. San Diego:
    A. S. Barnes, 1980.

53 Marell, Alvin. The Films of Sidney Poitier. New York: Cit-
    adel Press, 1978.

        Pryor, Richard
54 Nazel, Joe. Richard Pryor. Hollywood: Holloway House,
    1980.

55 Robbins, Fred and David Ragan. Richard Pryor: This Cat's
    Got 9 Lives. New York: Delilah Books, 1981.

        Robeson, Paul
56 Here I Stand (A). New York: Othello Associates, 1958.

57 Davis, Lenwood. A Paul Robeson Research Guide: A Selected
    Annotated Bibliography. Westport, CT: Greenwood Press,
    1982.

        Ross, Diana
58 Berman, Connie. Diana Ross Supreme. New York: Popular
    Library, 1978.

59 Haskins, James. I'm Going to Make You Love Me: The Story of Diana Ross. New York: Dial, 1980.

60 Pitts, Leonard. Diana Ross. Cresskill, NJ: Star Books, 1983.

Simpson, O. J.
61 A Bear for the FBI (A). New York: Trident Press, 1968.

62 The Education of a Rich Rookie (A). New York: Macmillian, 1970.

Waters, Ethel
63 with Charles Samuels. His Eye Is on the Sparrow (A). Garden City, NY: Doubleday, 1951.

64 To Me It's Wonderful (A). New York: Harper & Row, 1972.

Wonder, Stevie
65 Haskins, James. Stevie Wonder. New York: Lothrop, Lee and Shepard, 1976.

66 Marianne, Ruth. Stevie Wonder. Hollywood: Holloway House, 1980.

67 Wilson, Beth. Stevie Wonder. New York: Putnam, 1972.

Collective Biography

68 Abdul, Raoul. Famous Black Entertainers of Today. New York: Dodd, Mead and Company, 1974, 159 p.
The author has included biographies of eighteen blacks whose popularity and/or accomplishments were especially noteworthy in the early 1970s. The Introduction gives a brief overview as to why he chose these individuals. The book is for young readers, but can be beneficial to anyone wanting information about the following persons: Alvin Ailey, dancer; Martina Arroyo, opera singer; Alex Bradford, gospel singer; James DePriest, symphonic conductor; Gloria Foster, actress; Aretha Franklin, pop singer; Micki Grant, composer/performer; Ellis Haizlip, television producer; James Earl Jones, actor; Arthur Mitchell, ballet dancer; Carmen Moore, music critic/composer; Ron O'Neal, actor; Diana Ross, singer/actress; and Cicely Tyson, actress.

69 Rollins, Charlemae. Famous Negro Entertainers of Stage, Screen, and TV. New York: Dodd, Mead and Company, 1967, 159 p.
After a short introduction about the origin of Negro entertainment on the Southern plantations and the careers of The Black Swan, Black Patti and Blind Tom, the author of this book for young

readers presents sixteen outstanding black entertainers in various
fields. Each chapter begins with an account of the entertainer's
life and, in turn, leads to an appraisal of the subject's professional
career. Those who have appeared regularly on television are:
Harry Belafonte, Nat "King" Cole, and Sammy Davis, Jr. Others
include Ida Aldridge, Marian Anderson, Louis Armstrong, Josephine
Baker, Duke Ellington, Lena Horne, Eartha Kitt, Sidney Poitier,
Leontyne Price, and Paul Robeson.

General Television Books

70 Brooks, Tim and Marsh, Earle. The Complete Directory to
    Prime Network TV Shows, 1946-Present. New York: Ballan-
    tine Books, 1979, 1,001 p.
        This is an encyclopedia listing: (1) every regular series
ever carried on the four commercial networks during "prime time"
--roughly 7:30-11:00 p.m., E.S.T.; (2) all network series carried
in the early evening, 6:00-7:30 p.m., and late night after 11:00 p.m.;
(3) the top syndicated programs of all time that were aired primarily
in the evening hours. The book covers the entire history of television networking from 1946 to 1979. The appendices list Emmy
award winners, top-rated programs by season, longest-running series, prime-time spin-offs, prime-time shows that also aired on radio, song hits from television, and series airing on more than one
network.

71 Brown, Les. Encyclopedia of Television. New York: New York
    Zoetrope, 1982, 496 p.
        This covers an A-to-Z listing of television programs, net-
work executives, behind-the-camera personnel and television jargon.
The book cites very few blacks or black-oriented programs as compared to other TV encyclopedias. Some of them are: Bill Cosby,
Roots, Black Entertainment Network, Black Journal, Black Perspectives on the News, Ed Bradley, former FCC commissioners Ben
Hooks and Tyrone Brown, Good Times, The Jeffersons, Leslie Uggams, Max Robinson, WLBT, and several others. The book's best
use is for quick reference to historical data.

72 Grossman, Gary H. Saturday Morning TV. New York: Dell
    Publishing Company, 1981, 398 p.
        Grossman cites scores of Saturday morning TV programs
over the past thirty years that touched the kid in all Americans.
Beginning in the infancy of TV itself with movie matinee perennials
like Laurel and Hardy, the Little Rascals, and Flash Gordon, the
book cites many classic fun-and-adventure programs such as Smilin'
Ed's Gang, Captain Midnight, Sky King, Beany and Cecil, and dozens
of others. The author includes data on the stars, the stories, the
theme songs and slogans, the memorable commercials and premiums
(Secret Squadron Decoder Ring). The book has information on black
cartoon shows such as Fat Albert, The Jackson 5, Muhammad Ali,
and The Harlem Globetrotters.

73 McNeil, Alex. Total Television: A Comprehensive Guide to
    Programming from 1948 to 1980. New York: Penguin Books,
    1980, 1,088 p.
        This is an encyclopedia listing more than 3,400 series, net-
work and syndicated, prime-time and daytime programs. It also
lists 570 noteworthy specials, prime-time fall schedules from 1948
to 1979, Emmy and Peabody award winners, and top-rated series
from 1949 to 1979. It includes many black shows not in other historical television books such as Adam Wade's Musical Chairs, PBS'
Black Journal, Black Omnibus, Tony Brown's Journal, and Sammy
Davis' Sammy and Company.

74 Maltin, Leonard, ed. TV Movies, 1983-1984. New York:
    Signet Books, 1982, 884 p.
        This book lists nearly every movie that has appeared on
television (including cable TV). It has more than 1,000 entries with
a description of each movie, the editor's rating of the film, the
year aired, main characters, length in minutes, and a brief plot
summary.

75 Mapp, Edward. Directory of Blacks in the Performing Arts.
    Metuchen, NJ: The Scarecrow Press, Inc., 1978, 429 p.
        This is a reference source to black performing artists in
film, television, nightclubs, theater, opera, ballet, jazz, and classical concerts. Each entry lists the performer's name, nickname,
date and city of birth, special interests, address, honors, and career
data. Other facts on each performer might include films, musical
compositions, television, radio, theater, publications, and education.
The book has a directory of organizations, bibliography, and index.
It is an excellent work.

76 Marill, Alvin. Movies Made for Television. New York: Da
    Capo Press, 1981, 399 p.
        The author lists by season the made-for-TV movies from
1964 to 1979, giving the principal actors and directors. The book
covers 1,000 miniseries and films. It also has an index of actors
and directors. Some of the black movies include: Roots, Back-
stairs at the White House, Get Christie Love, and King.

77 Mitz, Rick. The Great TV Sitcom Book. New York: Richard
    Marek Publishers, 1980, 440p.
        This is a historical listing of top-rated situation comedies
on television from 1949 to 1980. Even though blacks appeared in
many comedies, they did not have starring roles (excluding Amos
'n' Andy). They weren't important or popular enough to be mentioned in this book until the 1968-1969 season with Diahann Carroll's
Julia show. Other programs with blacks listed in starring roles
are: The Bill Cosby Show, Sanford and Son, Temperatures Rising,
Good Times, Roll Out, The Jeffersons, What's Happening, Baby I'm
Back, The Sanford Arms, Diff'rent Strokes, and Soap. The book
also has Emmy winners, top-rated shows, and longest-airing programs.

78 Terrace, Vincent. Television 1970-1980. San Diego: A.S.

Barnes and Company, 1981, 322 p.
This is an encyclopedic listing of more than 1,900 entertainment programs. The book covers network and syndicated telecasts between January 1, 1970 and October 26, 1980 (a program addendum covers October 27, 1980 to March 1, 1981); network and syndicated pilot films for the same period; and the British series on which American programs are based. This book includes much information not found elsewhere, and has more than 140 photographs.

79 Armstrong, George. "Interpersonal and Mass Media Impacts on Beliefs About Race and Race Relations." Master's thesis, Michigan State University, 1981.

This study assessed mass-media and interpersonal influences on four sorts of beliefs about racial and social inequality, using freshmen at Michigan State University. The results showed television entertainment exposure predicted greater favorability of stereotypes of blacks. TV sports exposure was associated with more negative black stereotypes. Exposure to TV news was related to more negative judgements of both black character traits and economic input. The greater the newspaper exposure, the less the degree to which individual differences were seen as the cause of social inequality, and the less racial inequality was perceived.

80 Bowmani, Kwame N. "Black Television and Domestic Colonialism." Doctoral dissertation, Stanford University, 1977.

Bowmani explores whether television tends to foster, maintain, or close the socio-economic-political gaps between blacks and whites in America. The main conclusions were: TV maintains and probably fosters existing gaps between blacks and whites; TV tends to provide homogenized, imitative programming that reinforces the domestic colonialism mentality and status of blacks; and the outlook for TV as a tool for black decolonization is not promising.

81 Brenner, William M. "Comparative Analysis of Black and White Student Attitudes toward Television." Master's thesis, Ohio State University, 1971.

82 Clift, Charles E. "The WLBT-TV Case, 1964-1969: An historical Analysis." Doctoral dissertation, Indiana University, 1976.

In 1964, during the height of the civil rights movement, a group of cornered individuals petitioned the FCC to deny the license of WLBT-TV in Jackson, Mississippi. The petition alleged that during the 1961-1964 renewal period, the station had failed to serve blacks who comprised nearly half of the service area. This dissertation sequences the chronology of the events during the five years between the initial petition and the U.S. Court of Appeals' second decision. The roles of the petitioners, the station, the FCC and the Court during this period are analyzed. The WLBT-TV case produced a landmark decision guaranteeing the public legal standing before the FCC. The history of the case illustrates the FCC's

concern with maintaining the status quo and the extraordinary effort
necessary to change the system.

83 Colle, Royal D. "The Negro Image and the Mass Media."
    Doctoral dissertation, Cornell University, 1967.
        This work examines the depiction of blacks in mass media
    (i. e., newspapers, magazines, film, radio and television) and the
    efforts made by each medium to effect changes in the portrayed im-
    ages of blacks. The author traces the record of the media's treat-
    ment of the Negro from the turn of the century to the mid-1960s,
    using published materials, news releases, policy statements, codes
    of performance, personal interviews, letters, and other documents
    as sources.

84 Cosby, William H. Jr. "An Integration of the Visual Media Via
    'Fat Albert and the Cosby Kids' into the Elementary School
    Curriculum as a Teaching Aid and Vehicle to Achieve Increased
    Learning." Doctoral dissertation, University of Massachusetts,
    1976.
        The purpose of the study was to develop an alternative
    source of instructional materials to aid elementary classroom teach-
    ers in creating a more positive learning environment as well as an
    environment that is free from racial bias and prejudice. An eval-
    uation of Fat Albert and the Cosby Kids indicates that the film ser-
    ies can serve as a useful addition to existing curriculum materials.
        The study examines failure of urban schools to meet the
    educational needs of minority children as it analyzes three program
    series--Sesame Street, The Electric Co. and Fat Albert and the
    Cosby Kids. The creative aspects involved in the production of the
    Fat Albert show are presented. Attention is given to the medium
    of television as a purveyor of intellectual development and thought
    in children. Lastly, Cosby establishes the effectiveness of Fat Al-
    bert and the Cosby Kids as a vehicle to aid elementary teachers in
    the classroom.

85 Czech, Elizabeth S. "Interaction Between Black and Corporate
    Culture in Broadcast Management." Doctoral dissertation,
    Ohio State University, 1972.
        Czech identifies what special problems may be anticipated
    and overcome when radio and television broadcasters seek to pre-
    pare young blacks for managerial positions in broadcasting. Major
    findings reveal that anticipatable problems are a matter of socioeco-
    nomic background more than that of race. Many behaviors stereo-
    typed as black were found to be common to people of many ethnic
    origins who live in a state of poverty. Included were some ex-
    cellent suggestions for future study.

86 Dates, Jannette Lake. "The Relationship of Demographic Var-
    iables and Racial Attitudes to Adolescent Perceptions of Black
    Television Characters." Doctoral dissertation, University of
    Maryland, 1979.
        An examination of differences that exist in adolescent per-
    ceptions of black television characters related to differences in race,

sex, socioeconomic status, academic achievement, amount of time
spent viewing black television characters, and general racial attitude.
Two of the seven findings were that there were significant differences
between low and high socioeconomic status youngsters in their perceptions of black television characters, and that high academic
achievers had positive racial attitudes and low academic achievers
had negative racial attitudes.

87 Esch, Pamela S. "Blacks in Broadcasting: Minority Access to
    Programming and Employment." Master's thesis, Michigan
    State University, 1971.

88 Ferguson, Gloria Haithman. "From 'Amos 'n' Andy' to 'San-
    ford and Son': An Historical Survey and Critical Analysis of
    the Characteristics and Images of Blacks on American Network
    Television and Drama." Master's thesis, University of South-
    ern California, 1975.
        Ferguson describes the changes in the characterizations and
images of blacks in American television network comedy and drama
series over three decades (1944-1974). The author concludes that
there was no significant change in the kinds of images. Blacks have
been portrayed as either extraordinarily "white" (programs like Julia,
I Spy, etc.), or extraordinarily bad (drug pushers, hustlers, or
hookers). However, the author does point out that blacks have gone
from being only servants in episodes to playing starring roles.

89 Ferguson, Richard. "The Role of Blacks in Magazine and Tele-
    vision Advertising." Master's thesis, University of South Caro-
    lina, 1970.

90 Fricke, Charles H. "Study to Determine How the Advertiser
    Can Reach Negroes with Radio, Television, Magazines and
    Newspaper." Master's thesis, University of North Carolina,
    1967.

91 Gallatin, Martin V. "Reverend Ike's Ministry: A Sociological
    Investigation of Religious Information." Doctoral dissertation,
    New York University, 1979.
        The author examines how Reverend Ike, the leader of a
large, mostly black, fundamentalist church in New York City, was
able to institute important ideological changes in his ministry that
brought his philosophy more in line with the ideals of the New Thought
movement. Study traces the development and evolution of Reverend
Ike's presentation of the gospel. His ministry is divided into three
time frames: Conversationist (1958-1968); Transitional (1969-1972);
and Gnostic (1973-1976). Gallatin determined that Reverend Ike was
able to change the orientation of his church from Fundamentalist
Christian to New Thought for five reasons. They are: 1) the evan-
gelist's charismatic qualities and cult of personality; 2) his well-
established following; 3) the manner in which important ideological
innovations were introduced; 4) the characteristics of the new belief
system; and 5) the payoff for his adherents.

92 Haley, Mary P. "'SIX30'--Some of the News, Some of the
    Time: A Case Study of Minority Access to Television. " Doc-
    toral dissertation, Northwestern University, 1973.
        SIX30, a five-night-a-week, half-hour, live news program
on WHA-TV (a public television station at the University of Wisconsin), was an experiment in giving minorities access to television.

93 Hill, George H. "The Development and Expansion of Religious
    Radio and Television in America." Doctoral dissertation,
    City University, Los Angeles, 1980.
        A study of the history and demographics of religious broad-
casting in the continental United States. Compares the views of
people in Los Angeles and Long Beach, California. Includes information on the first black broadcasters to produce or host programs
in New York, Los Angeles, Chicago, St. Louis, Atlanta, and Dallas/
Fort Worth. Includes data on six major black television broadcasters: Reverend Ike, Fred Price, Cleophus Robinson, Clay Evans,
Ben Smith, and CBN's Ben Kinchlow on the 700 Club. All of these
telecasters' programs air in more than five states.
        This study discusses the only five published surveys on re-
ligious broadcasting from 1010 to 1982, and contains information on
the electric church in Hollywood and on the Christian networks, CBN,
TBN, and PTL.

94 _____. "Women's World: A Television Special on the Baha'i
    Faith." Master's project, California State University at Do-
    minguez Hills, 1978.
        A project in an interdisciplinary major of communications
and religion known as Religious Information. The television special
was a half-hour program sharing women's perspectives of the Baha'i
Faith. Sylvia Saverson Hill and Muhtadi Saallam coordinated the
telecast.

95 Jackson, Harold. "From 'Amos 'n' Andy' To 'I Spy': A Chron-
    ology of Blacks in Prime Time Network Television Program-
    ming, 1950-1964. " Doctoral dissertation, University of Mich-
    igan, 1982.
        The author identifies and discusses the roles played by black
actors and performers who appeared on weekly prime-time network
series that premiered in the fall of each year between the hours
7:00 p.m. to 11:00 p.m. from 1950 to 1964. It follows a chronological pattern of the development of characters and personalities on
programs that featured black actors on a continuing basis.
        The research materials include black publications, personal
papers on television performers, producers and directors, information on programs provided by NBC, CBS, ABC and the Alan DuMont
television network. The study examines a number of programs which
were not aired during prime time which featured black performers,
in order to illustrate the performers' television exposure.
        Jackson has divided the study into six chapters. Three
chapters deal with the chronological development of characters, personalities and programs. Chapter 3 covers the period 1950 to 1956,
and Chapter 4, the period from 1956 to 1964. Chapter 5 is an

interview with Ossie Davis, a black actor who appeared on many programs during this time peri od.

The study reveals that black actors appeared on 8, 500 hours of prime-time television out of 62, 000 hours of prime-time and that there were 310 black actors who appeared regularly on television. The author concludes with a discussion of data and a complete alphabetical listing of all black performers and lists their TV credits by program, date, and time.

96   Jewell, Karen Sue Warren. "An Analysis of the Visual Development of a Stereotype: The Media's Portrayal of Mammy and Aunt Jemima As Symbols of Black Womanhood. " Doctoral dissertation, Ohio State University, 1976.

The statement best characterizing this study is essentially the premise upon which this research is based. The mass media historically has developed and portrayed an image of black womanhood based on the images of mammy and Aunt Jemima; and that inherent in these images are myths and stereotypes which are generalized to all black women in America irrespective of social class or age. Further, these images are the antithesis of American society's conception of womanhood, beauty, and femininity.

97   Maddox, Gilbert A. "A Study of CPT: Public Television Programming for Detroit's Black Community. " Doctoral dissertation, Wayne State University, 1970.

CPT was a case study of a fourteen-week television series that was produced by and for the black television viewer, utilizing a magazine format.

98   Merritt, Bishetta D. "A Historical-Critical Study of a Pressure Group in Broadcasting--Black Efforts for Soul in Television. " Doctoral dissertation, Ohio State University, 1974.

Merritt examines three ideas about BEST, a pressure group in broadcasting founded in 1969 and designed to stimulate "Black Efforts for Soul in Television. " This study relates the effect of the BEST campaign on the FCC; the Senate, and the broadcast industry. It examines the effects of the BEST campaign as a catalytic agent in relation to securing participation of more consumers, especially blacks, in the broadcasting process. Finally, the dissertation seeks to deal with implications of BEST activities for rhetoric in the mass media. The author concludes: 1) BEST created an awareness in black communities through its programs which educated and sensitized blacks to the process of broadcasting. This was accomplished by such activities as lobbying for a black FCC commissioner, working for black employment, and stimulating an interest among blacks to become involved in cable television; 2) BEST had a significant impact on the FCC, the Senate and the broadcast industry; and 3) the study revealed several implications for rhetoric in the mass media and limitations to BEST.

99   Miller, Oliver R. "An Investigation of the Cognitive Effectiveness of Color and Monochrome Presentations with Black Elementary School Children in Relation to the Predominant Home

Television Viewing Mode." Doctoral dissertation, University
of Southern California, 1972.

100   Poe, Lillian A. "Elder Lightfoot Solomon Michaux: His Social
      and Political Interests and Influence." Doctoral dissertation.
      The College of William and Mary in Virginia, 1975.
      Elder Michaux was one of the first blacks to have a nation-
wide television program. It was telecast on the DuMont network
from 1947 to 1949. He was also regularly featured on local Washington, D.C. television on DuMont's WTTC. Michaux lived from
1884 to 1969, and was the most well-known black religious broadcaster of the 1930-1950 period.
      The study was designed to probe the nature of the religious
movement which he founded in 1919, and to determine the extent of
his social and political interests and influences in the nation and
within the black community. A number of questions are answered
concerning Michaux's background, his self-image, his motives, his
psychological and material needs, the nature of his appeal as a minister, the dynamics of his leadership, the nature of his membership
and followers, and the benefits accrued to him, and his movement.
These issues are addressed in such a way as to provide a capsuled
view of a very complex and multitalented black minister and his
church as he steered through society, especially as he operated in
the nation's capital. Conclusions are that Michaux, a man with a
sense of mission, was sensitive to the vicissitudes of black people
in the United States. In his preachments, he espoused a desire to
help eradicate social-economic deprivations of blacks and other disinherited people. He used the Church as an instrument toward acquiring economic and political power, but failed to make it a liberat-
ing force.

101   Solomon, Paul J. "A Laboratory Experiment to Assess the
      Aspect of Black Models in Television Advertising." Doctoral
      dissertation, Arizona State University, 1974.
      This study tested whether black or white models had a
different effect in eliciting product-choice behavior on college
students (both black and white). The products used were Zest soap
and Annie Green Springs wine. Major findings were: (1) that there
were no differences in the behavioral responses of blacks or whites
to soap television ads that contain either a black or a white model;
and (2) black subjects responded behaviorally in more favorable
manner to black models in wine ads than to white models in
wine ads.

102   Stephens, Lenora C. "Telecommunications and the Urban
      Black Community: An Interdisciplinary Study of Public Tele-
      vision, 1952-1975." Doctoral dissertation, Emory University,
      1976.
      The study traces the relationship, from 1952 to 1975, of
materials disseminated by the media, the FCC, black media groups,
and individuals. It includes interviews of public TV activists. New
York, Washington, D.C., and Atlanta are used to meter the develop-

ment of public TV. The relationship of blacks and public television are examined for the periods 1952-66, 1967-73, and 1974-75.

103 Thornton, Lee. "Is Denver Television Programming Meeting the Needs of the Black Community?" Master's thesis, University of Colorado, 1970.

104 Vannoni, John R. "Television Viewing Behavior of Black and White Senior High School Students in Grades 10-12 of the Public School System of Philadelphia, Pennsylvania." Doctoral dissertation, Pennsylvania State University, 1974.

This study determined that there were significant differences in the viewing preferences of specific programs of black and white senior high school students, but also that there were some marked similarities in preferences of program categories.

105   Alexander, H. B.   "Negro Opinion Regarding 'Amos 'N' Andy.'"
      Sociological and Social Research, March 1932, p. 345-354.

106   Allen, R. L. and Chaffee, S. H.   "Mass Communication and the
      Political Participation of Black Americans."   Nimmo, D.,
      ed. Communication Yearbook 3, New Brunswick, N. J.: Trans-
      action Books, 1979, p. 407-522.

107   _____ and Clarke, D. E.   "Ethnicity and Mass Media Behav-
      ior: A Study of Blacks and Latinos."   Journal of Broadcast-
      ing, Winter 1980, p. 23-24.

108   Allen, T. H.   "Mass Media Use Patterns in a Negro Ghetto."
      Journalism Quarterly, Autumn 1968, p. 525-527.

109   Balan, R. E.   "Impact of Roots On A Racially Heterogeneous
      Southern Community: An Exploratory Study."   Journal of
      Broadcasting, Summer 1978, p. 299-307.

110   Balan, Robert; Philport, Joseph; and Beadle, Charles.   "How
      Sex and Race Affect Perceptions of Newscasters."   Journal-
      ism Quarterly, Spring 1978, p. 160-164.

111   Barnett, C. A.   "Role of the Press, Radio and Picture and
      Negro Morale."   Journal of Negro Education, July 1943, p.
      474-489.

112   Barry, T. E. and Hansen, R. W.   "How Race Affects Children's
      TV Commercials."   Journal of Advertising Research, Octo-
      ber 1973, p. 63-68.

113   Barry, T. and Sherkh, A. A.   "Race As A Dimension In Chil-
      dren's TV Advertising: The Need for More Research."   (Bib-
      liography).   Journal of Advertising, No. 3, Fall 1977, p. 5-
      10.

114   Bush, R. F. and others.   "There Are More Blacks in TV Com-
      mercials."   (Bibliography).   Journal of Advertising Research,
      February 1977, p. 21-25.

115   Clark, Cedric.   "Television and Social Controls: Some Obser-
      vations on the Portrayals of Ethnic Minorities."   Television
      Quarterly, Spring 1969, p. 18-22.

116 Colle, Royal D. "Negro Image in the Mass Media Market:
     A Case Study in Social Change." Journalism Quarterly,
     Spring 1968, p. 55-60.

117 Cripps, T. "Noble Black Savage: A Problem in the Politics
     of Television Art." Journal of Popular Culture, Spring 1975,
     p. 687-695.

118 Darden, Betty and Bayton, James. "Self-Concept and Blacks'
     Assessment of Black Leading Roles in Motion Pictures and
     Television." Journal of Applied Psychology, 1977, p. 62.

119 Dominic, J. R. and Greenberg, B. S. "Three Seasons of Blacks
     On Television." Journal of Advertising Research, April 1970,
     p. 21-27.

120 Donohue, T. R. "Black and White Children: Perceptions of TV
     Commercials." (Tables). Journal of Marketing, October
     1978, p. 38-40.

121 _____. "Effect of Commercials on Black Children." Jour-
     nal of Advertising Research, December 1975, p. 41-47.

122 Drabman, Ronald S. and Thomas, Margaret Hanratty. "Chil-
     dren's Imitation of Aggressive and Prosocial Behavior When
     Viewing Alone and in Pairs." Journal of Communication,
     1977, p. 199-205.

123 Fedler, Fred. "The Media and Minority Groups: A Study of
     Adequacy of Access." Journalism Quarterly, Spring 1973,
     p. 109-117.

124 Fine, Marilyn G.; Anderson, Carolyn; and Eckles, Gary.
     "Black English on Black Situation Comedies." Journal of
     Communications, Summer 1979, p. 21-29.

125 Goldberg, M. E. and Gorn, G. J. "Television's Impact on Pref-
     erences for Non-White Playmates: Canadian Sesame Street
     Inserts." Journal of Broadcasting, Winter 1979, p. 27-32.

126 Greenberg, B. and Dervin, B. "Mass Communication Among
     the Urban Poor." Public Opinion Quarterly, Summer 1970,
     p. 224-235.

127 Greenberg, Bradley. "Children's Reactions to TV Blacks."
     (Based On Interviews with Fourth- and Fifth-Grade Children
     from Several Michigan Public Schools Fall 1970) Journalism
     Quarterly, Spring 1972, p. 5-14.

128 Haefner, James. "Can TV Advertising Influence Employers to
     Hire or Train Disadvantaged Persons." Journalism Quarterly,
     Summer 1976, p. 211-215.

129 Hinton, J. L. "Tokenism and Improving Imagery of Blacks in TV Drama and Comedy, 1973." Journal of Broadcasting, Fall 1974, p. 423-432.

130 Howard, J. "Response to 'Roots': A National Survey." Journal of Broadcasting, Summer 1978, p. 279-287.

131 Hur, K. K. "Impact of 'Roots' on Black and White Teenagers." Journal of Broadcasting, p. 289-298.

132 _____ and Robinson, J. P. "Social Impact of 'Roots.'" Journalism Quarterly, Spring 1978, p. 19-24.

133 Kassarjian, Waltraud. "Blacks As Communicators and Interpreters of Mass Communications: Data on Black Media Use Patterns are Mixed; Content Studies Document Increased Presence of Blacks in Ads and All Media." Journalism Quarterly, Summer 1973, p. 285-291.

134 Lemon, Judith. "Women and Blacks On Prime-Time Television." Journal of Communications, Vol. 4, 1977, p. 70-79.

135 Lindley, William R. "Communications Theories and Racial Tensions." Journalism Quarterly, Spring 1969, p. 147-148.

136 McCombs, Maxwell. "Negro Use of Television and Newspapers for Political Information, 1952-1964." Journal of Broadcasting, Summer 1968, p. 216-266.

137 MacDonald, J. F. "Black Perimeters--Paul Robeson, Nat King Cole and the Role of Blacks in American TV." Journal of Popular Film and Television, Vol. 3, 1979, p. 246-264.

138 "Mass Media and Intergroups Relations: Suggested Guidelines." Journal of Intergroup Relations, Summer 1961, p. 205-212.

139 Mendelsohn, Harold. "Socio-psychological Perspectives on the Mass Media and Public Anxiety." Journalism Quarterly, Autumn 1969, p. 499-504.

140 Meyer, Timothy; Donohue, Thomas; and Heneke, Lucy. "How Black Children See TV Commercials." Journal of Advertising Research, October 1978, p. 51-58.

141 Reid, P. T. "Racial Stereotyping On Television: A Comparison of the Behavior of Both Black and White Television Characters." Journal of Applied Psychology, October 1979, p. 465-471.

142 Riddick, Lawrence. "Educational Programs for the Improvement of Race Relations: Motion Pictures, Radio, The Press and Libraries." Journal of Negro Education, Summer 1944, p. 1.

143 Roberts, C. "The Presentations of Blacks in Television Network Newscasts." Journalism Quarterly, Spring 1975, p. 50-55.

144 Roberts, Churchill. "The Portrayal of Blacks on Network Television (on programs and in commercial advertisements over American television)." Journal of Broadcasting, Winter 1970-71, p. 45-53.

145 Sargent, L. W. and Stempel, G. H. "Poverty, Alienation and Mass Media Use." Journalism Quarterly, Summer 1968, p. 9.

146 Scherer, Klaus. "Stereotype Change Following Exposure to Counter-Stereotypical Media Heroes." Journal of Broadcasting, Winter 1970-1971, p. 91.

147 Seggar, J. F. "Television's Portrayal of Minorities and Women, 1971-1975." Journal of Broadcasting, Fall 1977, p. 435-446.

148 Shankman, A. "Black Pride and Protest: The 'Amos 'N' Andy' Crusade." Journal of Popular Culture, Fall 1978, p. 236-252.

149 Spaulding, Norman. "Bridging the Color Gap: Effective Communication with the Black Community Calls for an Understanding of Its Media and Leading Organizations." Public Relations Journal, April 1969, p. 8-11.

150 Stevenson, Robert. "Use of Public Television by Blacks." Journalism Quarterly, Spring 1979, p. 141-147.

151 Suber, Howard. "Television's Interchangeable Ethics: Funny They Don't Look Jewish." Television Quarterly, Winter 1975, p. 49-56.

152 Tan, A. S. "Evaluation of Newspapers and Television By Blacks and Mexican Americans." Journalism Quarterly, Winter 1978, p. 673-681.

153 _____ and Tan, G. "Television Use and Self-Esteem of Blacks: Ethnic Studies in Black and White." Journal of Communication, Winter 1979, p. 129-135.

154 Tickton, Stanley and Jones, Patricia. "Racial Minorities in Broadcast Education." Journal of Broadcasting, Vol. 1, 1978, p. 87-93.

155 Vandor, Phillip. "On the Meaning of 'Roots.'" Journal of Communications, Vol. 4, 1977, p. 64-69.

156 Young, Witney M. "The Social Responsibility of Broadcasters." Television Quarterly, Spring 1969, p. 6-17.

Advertising

157 "ABA Approves Lawyer Ads on TV." Baltimore Afro American, August 19, 1978, p. I-7.

158 "ABA Okays Lawyer Advertising on TV." Bilalian News, September 1, 1978, p. I-18.

159 "Ad Council to aid Negro; Planned Campaigners Deal with His Economic Status and How to Improve It." Broadcasting, September 13, 1965, p. 42.

159a "Ad Men Agree on Roles of Minorities." Broadcasting, August 19, 1968, p. 39-40.

160 "Advertisements Show Most Negroes OK Blatz Xmas Show." Advertising Age, August 13, 1951, p. 9.

161 "Admen Rapped for Keeping Negro 'The Invisible Man.'" Editors & Publishers, November 18, 1967, p. 16+.

162 "Agencies Blamed for Race Bias in TV." Advertising Age, April 22, 1963, p. 96.

162a "All-Negro Cast to Tout Supreme Beauty Items in TV Spots." Advertising Age, September 30, 1968, p. 4.

163 Allen, Bonnie. "In Focus: Blacks in Ads." Essence, February 1980, p. 19.

164 "America's Black Forum Show Praises Advertisers." Norfolk Journal & Guide, August 4, 1978, p. B-15.

165 "Ana-Four A's Clinic Screens Integrated TV." Advertising Age, August 19, 1968, p. 1.

166 "An All-Star Commercial." TV Guide, March 7, 1970, p. 12-15.

166a "Black Parents' Effort to Get Their Children in TV Ads Viewed." Chicago Daily Defender, April 5, 1979, p. 12.

167   "Blacks & TV Views Advertising." Washington Post, September 2, 1974, p. D-1.

167a "Blacks in TV Commercials." (Editorial). Michigan Chronicle, January 7, 1979, p. A-6.

167b "Breakthrough in TV Alerts Advertisers (to Negro Market)." Sponsors, Part 2, October 22, 1962, p. 10-12+.

168   "Children and Television Advertising." (Editorial). Chicago Daily Defender, April 1, 1981, p. 11.

169   Christopher, M. "Desegregate Ads TV Lever Tells Agencies; Advertiser Urges More Use of Minorities in Print, TV, Ads, Shows." Advertising Age, August 12, 1963, p. 1+.

169a "Chicago's Drill Team Makes Coca-Cola Commercial." Atlanta Daily World, August 15, 1978, p. I-5.

170   "Commercial TV's Influence on Americans." (Editorial). Atlanta Daily World, May 16, 1980, p. I-6.

170a "Curbing TV Ads Aimed at Children." Bilalian News, December 2, 1977, p. I-13.

170b "Filming of Miller Airline TV Commercial." Atlanta Daily World, February 22, 1979, p. 3.

171   "FTC Hearings on Proposed Kids' TV Ad Rules." Bilalian News, June 1, 1979, p. 23.

172   "Getting into TV Commercials." New York Amsterdam News, November 26, 1977, p. D-12.

172a "Group Questions Whether TV Shows Enough Negroes; Sees Improvement In Commercials (New York Society for Ethical Culture)." Advertising Age, December 14, 1964, p. 62.

173   Harris, L. "TV Ads Intensify Negro's Drive for Rights." Advertising Age, October 21, 1963, p. 3.

173a Hayakawa, S.I. "Yesterday's TV Ad-viewing Tots Are Now Integration Activists." Advertising Age, August 19, 1963, p. 1+; Discussion, C.H. Turner, September 2, 1963, p. 1+.

173b 'Illinois Bar Association Prohibits Lawyers' TV and Radio Ads." Chicago Daily Defender, June 23, 1979, p. I-7.

174   "Impact of TV Commercials on Children." (Editorial). Atlanta Daily World, June 11, 1978, p. I-4.

174a "Junk Food Ads on Children's Programs Protested." Bilalian News, May 20, 1977, p. I-11.

175 "Legal fund of organization asked TV ad inquiry told FCC surveys show possibility of racial bias in TV commercials, stars, extras." Wall Street Journal, August 24, 1967, p. 10.

176 "Marla Gibbs Films TV Commercials." World Muslim News, February 5, 1982, p. 16.

177 "Martine Rita Dalton Sings TV Commercials in N.Y.C. with Roy Eaton, Negro Arranger with Benton and Bowles Advertising Agency." Jet, November 24, 1960, p. 60.

178 "Moral Majority and Commercial TV." (Robertson column). Los Angeles Sentinel, July 9, 1981, p. A-6.

179 "Negroes Don't Like the Same T.V. Shows as Whites, SRDS Data Study Finds." Advertising Age, April 6, 1974, p. 3.

180 "Negroes Sought for TV Commercials Program." Sponsor, September 5, 1966, p. 54-57.

181 "No Sears Ads Run on Violent TV Programs." Pittsburgh Courier, February 19, 1977, p. 2-12.

182 "Pearl Bailey Advertises for Greyhound." Pittsburgh Courier, February 26, 1977, p. 3-17.

183 "Pharmaco Uses Negro Talent In TV Commercials." Broadcasting, October 1, 1962, p. 30.

184 "Procter and Gamble's Stand on TV Advertising." (Editorial). Atlanta Daily World, July 9, 1981, p. 4; September 24, 1981, p. 4.

185 "R. Ferguson to Raise Money for NAB Minority Fund." Atlanta Daily World, December 16, 1979, p. 3.

186 "Research Underlines Large Negro Consumption of TV." Sponsor, August 17, 1964, p. 48-49.

187 Revett, J. "Minority Folk Learn TV Ads in GAP Workshop." Advertising Age, February 24, 1969, p. 166.

188 Ribowsky, M. "Ralph MacDonald Does TV Commercials and Records." Sepia, June 1977, p. 72-78.

189 "Roper Organization Survey on Children & TV Advertising." Pittsburgh Courier, March 17, 1979, p. 2-13.

190 "Roy Eatons Writes 'Hit' TV Commercial." Ebony, September 1958, p. 59-63.

191 Shayon, Robert Lewis. "Commercials in Black and White." Saturday Review, October 5, 1968, p. 48.

192   "Singing Saleswomen; Television Advertising." Ebony, April
      1964, p. 143-144.

193   "Three Largest Soap Makers to Include Negroes in Television
      Commercials." Wall Street Journal, August 21, 1963, p. 3.

194   Tripp, G. "Ways To Use Minority Groups in Commercials."
      Television, August 1968, p. 105-106+.

195   "TV Ads." (Ingram column). Michigan Chronicle, December
      31, 1977, p. B-10.

196   "TV Ads, Shows Still Lag Use of Negro and Other Races Says
      American Civil Liberties Union." Advertising Age, April 11,
      1966, p. 128.

197   "TV Commercial Attempts to Sell to Blacks." New York Ams-
      terdam News, May 20, 1978, p. D-5.

198   "TV Commercials." New York Amsterdam News, July 1,
      1970, p. D-11.

199   "Washington Post Article on TV Ads and Blacks." New York
      Amsterdam News, June 10, 1978, p. D-11.

200   Webber, H. H. and Taylor, N. "Two Views of Negroes In TV:
      The Adman, The Activist." Sponsor, August 17, 1964, p.
      50-52.

                          Awards and Honors

201   "ABC Receives SCLC Award for 'Roots.'" Michigan Chronicle,
      August 27, 1977, p. B-4.

202   "ABC-TV Wins Peabody Award for 'Roots.'" New York Ams-
      terdam News, May 6, 1978, p. D-16.

203   "Al Freeman Jr., Award as Best Soap Opera Actor." Jet,
      June 14, 1979, p. 56.

204   "The American Black Achievement Awards; Ebony Pays Tribute
      to 55 Honorees on Nationwide TV Show." Ebony, 1979, p.
      130-132.

205   "Arleigh Prelow Wins Atlanta Emmy for 'Sweet Auburn Show.'"
      Los Angeles Sentinel, August 9, 1979, p. B-4A.

206   "Atlanta's WAGA-TV Wins Mental Health Award." Atlanta
      Daily World, March 29, 1977, p. I-5.

207 "Big Story; Philadelphia Reporter Wins TV Award for Daring Probe." Ebony, June 1957, p. 131-134.

208 Bingham, Joe. "Beat the Deficit Dragon." (NAACP Image Awards). Sepia, August 1974, p. 68-73.

209 "Black Broadcasters' Hall of Fame." Black Radio Exclusive, March 27, 1981, p. 7.

210 "Black Filmmaker Hall of Fame Awards 'Black Oscars' in Oakland." Soul, March 29, 1976, p. 1.

211 "'Black Filmmakers Hall of Fame' Slated." Michigan Chronicle, May 7, 1977, p. B-4.

212 "Black Filmmakers' Hall of Fame Special Slated." Norfolk Journal & Guide, March 26, 1977, p. B-15.

213 Bradley, B. "Were Negro TV Winners Coached?" Sepia, February 1960, p. 15-17.

214 Bright, Daniel. "Emmy Award for Cicely." Sepia, April 1974, p. 16-20.

215 Caulfield, Deborah. "NAACP's Image Awards Salute Black Artists." Los Angeles Times, December 7, 1982, p. 4-10.

216 "Chicago Emmy Awards Presented." Chicago Daily Defender, June 14, 1979, p. 27.

217 "Cicely Tyson's Emmy for 'Jane Pittman.'" Sepia, April 1974, p. 16-20.

218 "Clarence Muse Honored by Law School." Bilalian News, June 23, 1978, p. I-31.

219 "Convention on Household Employment to Honor Marla Gibbs." Los Angeles Sentinel, October 5, 1978, p. A-12.

220 Dee, Ruby. "At the Emmy Time!" Freedomways, 1980, p. 38-40.

221 "'Denise L.' Dennis Wins Academy of TV Arts Scholarship." Atlanta Daily World, July 8, 1979, p. 3.

222 "Diahann Carroll, Greg Morris and Ossie Davis Nominated for Emmy Awards." Jet, May 29, 1969, p. 58.

223 "'Down at the Dunbar,' TV Special Wins Peabody Award." Los Angeles Sentinel, April 24, 1980, p. A-5.

224 "Endowment Awards Made for Black Programs." New York Amsterdam News, August 27, 1977, p. D-3.

225 "Enola Aird Gets Broadcasting Association Fellowship." Cleveland Call & Post, February 3, 1979, p. B-9.

226 "Flip Wilson Wins Two Emmy's, Mark Warren Gets One." Jet, May 27, 1971, p. 56.

227 "Fred Silverman Gets Award for Putting 'Roots' on Air." Michigan Chronicle, July 23, 1977, p. B-4.

228 "Gentlemen's Quartet in L.A. Honors Roger Mosley and K. Patterson." Los Angeles Sentinel, August 16, 1979, p. A-13.

229 "Good Image Brings Early Christmas to NAACP Honorees." Jet, December 27, 1982, p. 58-62.

230 "'Good Times' Amos, Stands To Receive Image Awards." Jet, June 5, 1975, p. 58.

231 "'Good Times' Episode Wins Award." New York Amsterdam News, December 10, 1977, p. D-5.

232 "Isabel Sanford Wins Genii Award from California Radio and TV Association." Los Angeles Sentinel, March 19, 1981, p. B-7.

233 "L. A. Academy of TV Arts and Sciences Cites W. Wilson." Los Angeles Sentinel, June 19, 1980, p. A-10.

234 "Lloyd Wilkins Gets Acting Award from American College Theater Association." Los Angeles Sentinel, March 16, 1978, p. A-10.

235 "'Mama' Wins Performing Arts Award for KNBC-TV." Los Angeles Sentinel, March 3, 1977, p. B-4A.

236 Mink, Eric. "Hunter Named Recipient of Medal of Honor." St. Louis Post Dispatch, March 23, 1981, p. 6D.

237 "NAACP Image Awards." Soul, July 31, 1978, p. 16.

238 "NAACP Image Awards Nominees Announced." Los Angeles Sentinel, December 27, 1979, p. 1.

239 No entry.

240 "The NAACP Image Awards: Image Builders or Imageless?" Right On, March 1983, p. 44-45.

241 "NAACP Image Glows Star-Bright." Sepia, February 1971, p. 25-29.

242 "Nelson Grace, WTOL-TV Named Toludos Man of the Year." Jet, April 22, 1971, p. 12.

243   "Ninth Annual Image Awards." Soul, March 29, 1976, p. 6-7.

244   "Only 3 Blacks Win Emmys Despite Record Nominations." Jet,
      October 11, 1982, p. 59.

245   Rachal, Thomas. "Oscar Micheaux Awards: The Black Os-
      cars." Soul, May 8, 1978, p. 13.

246   "Redd Foxx, Lawanda Page Inducted into Stars Hall of Fame
      in Florida." Jet, June 30, 1977, p. 58-60+.

247   "Redd Foxx Wins Two Clio Awards." Jet, July 17, 1978, p.
      18.

248   "Regina O'Neal Gets Detroit Emmy." Michigan Chronicle, July
      7, 1979, p. B-7.

249   "Renee Ferguson Wins Emmy for TV Report on Marva Collins."
      Chicago Daily Defender, June 10, 1982, p. 25.

250   Robinson, Leroy.   "Together They Did It!--The 12th Annual
      NAACP Image Awards." The Crisis, May 1980, p. 162-174.

251   "'Roots' & Green Eyes Win Humanities Prizes." New York
      Amsterdam News, July 19, 1977, p. 3.

252   "'Roots' Receives Sidney Hillman Award." Atlanta Daily World,
      May 14, 1978, p. I-10.

253   "'Roots' Sweep Emmy Awards." Pittsburgh Courier, Septem-
      ber 24, 1977, p. 3-19.

254   "'Roots' Wins Clarion Award." Los Angeles Sentinel, July 20,
      1978, p. B-4A.

255   "'Roots' Wins Peabody Award." Los Angeles Sentinel, May 18,
      1978, p. B-1A.

256   "Scatman Crothers Honored." Los Angeles Sentinel, October
      13, 1977, p. a-1.

257   "6 Media Forum Members Win 10 Emmys." Los Angeles Sen-
      tinel, June 10, 1982, p. A-2.

258   "35th Annual Golden Globe Award Winners Announced." Los
      Angeles Sentinel, February 9, 1979, p. B-3A.

259   "Timmie 'Oh Yeah!' Rogers Nominated for Emmy." Jet, May
      14, 1970, p. 54.

260   "Top Actor of the Year." Ebony, March 1964, p. 123-126+.

261   "Tyson Captures Actress Of Year Emmy." Jet, June 13, 1974, p.
      62.

262   "Tyson and Cole Selected 'Ladies' Home Journal' Women of the
       Year." New York Amsterdam News, July 1, 1978, p. D-10.

263   "[Ben] Vereen Receives Israel's Cultural Award." Los Angeles
       Sentinel, July 6, 1978, p. B-2A.

264   "Vernee Watson Wins LA Area Emmy Award for Angel Dust:
       The Wack Attack." Grapevine, October 1980, p. 15.

265   "WETV-TV Bronze Jubilee Awards." Atlanta Daily World,
       February 8, 1979, p. 1.

266   "What Happens To TV Winners." Ebony, October 1958, p. 138.

267   "WVIT-TV Wins Black Communications Institute National Award."
       Atlanta Daily World, November 23, 1979, p. 6.

                              Broadcasting

268   "Art Gilliam to Fill Slot on Broadcasting Rating Council."
       Cleveland Call & Post, January 26, 1980, p. B-5.

269   "Black Broadcasters." (Moore column). Chicago Daily De-
       fender, February 26, 1977, p. I-18.

270   "Black Broadcasters Association Elects Officers." Atlanta
       Daily World, July 3, 1977, p. I-10.

271   "Black Broadcasters Association Eyes Media Content." Bilalian
       News, February 18, 1977, p. I-11.

272   "Black Caucus and the Broadcasting Industry." (Robertson
       column). Los Angeles Sentinel, April 12, 1979, p. A-6.

273   "Black Media Group Criticizes National Association of Broad-
       casters. Atlanta Daily World, March 9, 1978, p. I-8.

274   "Black Owners Eye Racial Policy on National Association of
       Broadcasters." Baltimore Afro American, March 18, 1978,
       p. I-15.

275   "Black Ownership in Broadcasting." (Hooks column). Atlanta
       Daily World, August 11, 1977, p. I-4.

276   "Black Radio-TV Owners Face Uphill Battle." Bilalian News,
       August 12, 1977, p. I-24.

277   "Blacks Bridging Gap in Broadcasting Field." Michigan Chron-
       icle, July 15, 1978, p. A-2.

278 "Broadcasters." (Hooks column). Chicago Daily Defender, April 16, 1977, p. I-6.

279 "Broadcasters Favor SBA Proposal." Norfolk Journal & Guide, December 17, 1977, p. B-21.

280 "Broadcasters Form New Organization." Norfolk Journal & Guide, July 2, 1977, p. B-16.

281 "Changes in Broadcast Planning Urged." Michigan Chronicle, June 4, 1977, p. B-4.

282 Douglas, Carlyle. "Ben Hooks: Watchdog of the Airwaves." Ebony, June 1975, p. 56-59.

283 "Minorities and Broadcasting." (Hooks column). Baltimore Afro American, May 20, 1977, p. I-4.

284 "Minorities in Broadcasting." (Martin column). Chicago Daily Defender, February 25, 1978, p. I-8.

285 No entry.

286 "Minority Broadcasting." (Hooks column). Baltimore Afro American, June 18, 1977, p. I-5.

287 "Minority Broadcasting." (Hooks column). Chicago Daily Defender, April 16, 1977, p. I-6.

287a "Minorities in TV and Radio Broadcasting." (Payne column). Baltimore Afro American, June 20, 1981, p. 5.

288 "National Association of Broadcasters Backs SBA Plan to Aid Blacks." Atlanta Daily World, December 22, 1977, p. I-6.

289 "Plight of Blacks in Broadcasting." (Hooks column). Atlanta Daily World, June 9, 1977, p. I-4.

290 "Public Broadcasting Challenged by Black Radio-TV Group." Michigan Chronicle, May 28, 1977, p. D-5.

291 "Rep. Clay Speaks on Minorities in the Media Before House." Norfolk Journal & Guide, November 12, 1977, p. B-11.

292 "Television Broadcasting." (Hooks column). Atlanta Daily World, June 17, 1977, p. I-4.

293 "2 Black Women Who Hold Production Jobs in TV Broadcasting." New York Amsterdam News, April 4, 1981, p. 27.

294 "United Church of Christ Battles Job Bias in Broadcasting." Norfolk Journal & Guide, August 19, 1981, p. 10.

294a "U.S. Civil Rights Commission Releases Report on TV

Broadcasting." Pittsburgh Courier, April 7, 1979, p. 3-
19.

Children and Children's Programs

295 "The ABC's of Children's TV." Essence, September 1972, p.
      58-59.

296 "ABC's Reduction In Ads Aimed at Children." Atlanta Daily
      World, February 11, 1979, p. 4.

297 "Action for Children's TV Releases Film on TV Advertising."
      Atlanta Daily World, March 1, 1979, p. 6.

298 "Annenberg School Report on Violence and Kids' TV." Bilalian
      News, May 18, 1979, p. 23.

299 "Bill Cosby to Host Fat Albert Cartoons." Jet, May 18, 1972,
      p. 58.

300 "Bill Cosby Translates Boyhood Memories into Pictures."
      Michigan Chronicle, October 28, 1978, p. B-5.

301 "Children & TV Advertising in LA." Los Angeles Sentinel,
      February 8, 1979, p. C-1.

302 "Clarice Taylor Joins 'Sesame Street.'" Pittsburgh Courier,
      February 15, 1977, p. 3-19.

303 "Debbie Allen, Performer on 'Vegetable Soup II.'" Michigan
      Chronicle, September 16, 1978, p. B-4.

304 "Educator Views Effects of TV on Children." Bilalian News,
      February 11, 1977, p. I-18.

305 "Effects of TV Violence on Black Children." Pittsburgh Cour-
      ier, June 18, 1977, p. I-3; June 25, 1977, p. 3-23.

306 "'Electric Company' Sparks Reading." New York Amsterdam
      News, October 1, 1977, p. D-2.

307 "Fat Albert Goes to School in September." Jet, June 17, 1976,
      p. 60.

308 "Fat Albert and Friends." TV Guide, August 2, 1969, p. 12-
      13.

309 "FTC to Control Ads Aimed at Children." Bilalian News, No-
      vember 11, 1977, p. 1-23.

310 "Group Complains About Children's Programming." Bilalian News, December 23, 1977, p. I-29.

311 "Haywood Nelson, 'What's Happening' Star Branching Into Cartoons." Jet, June 16, 1977, p. 53.

312 "Kids In TV Commercials." Ebony, June 1978, pp. 102-105+.

313 Kisner, Ronald. "Cosby Makes Millions Teaching Manners and Moral Lessons on TV." Jet, May 11, 1978, p. 58-61.

314 "LeVar Burton Goes to 'Rebop' TV Youth Program." Cleveland Call & Post, October 14, 1978, p. A-18.

315 "LeVar Burton to Host PBS' 'Reading Rainbow.'" Jet, January 17, 1982, p. 60.

316 Levin, E. "Infinity Factory." TV Guide, July 17, 1976, p. 44.

317 _____. "PBS's New Series 'Interface' Will Explore Ethnic America." TV Guide, January 19, 1974, p. 34.

318 _____. "'Rebop.'" PBS Series for 9 to 13 Year Olds." TV Guide, September 11, 1976, p. 35.

319 "'Popeye's Playhouse': Negro and White Children Romp Together on TV Program in South." Ebony, 1960, p. 50+.

320 "'Rebop' Children's Program." Bilalian News, February 18, 1977, p. I-8.

321 "Relation Between Child Behavior and TV Violence." Michigan Chronicle, March 19, 1977, p. D-1.

322 "Roscoe Orman's Role as Gordon in 'Sesame Street.'" Chicago Daily Defender, July 29, 1978, p. I-9.

323 "'Sesame Street' Top Rated PBS Show." Norfolk Journal & Guide, October 29, 1977, p. B-18.

324 "'Sesame Street' Top Show on Public TV." Pittsburgh Courier, November 5, 1977, p. 3-23.

325 "Sing Out With Charity (Children's TV)." Our World, February 1955, p. 12-15.

326 Singer, Dorothy. "Fat Albert." TV Guide, December 12, 1981, p. 44-45.

327 "Small Boy's Big Moment." Ebony, March 1957, p. 9.

328 No entry.

329   "Study of Women, Children and Minorities on TV Programs
        Viewed." Christian Science Monitor, November 6, 1979,
        p. 9; November 20, 1979, p. 10.

330   "A Toddle Down 'Sesame Street.'" Ebony, January 1970, p.
        36.

331   "The TV Kids." Ebony, March 1982, p. 82-86.

332   "TV Schoolmarm To 24,000 Children." Ebony, April 1960,
        p. 60-62+.

333   "TV Spelling Champ." Ebony, November 1955, p. 111-112+.

334   "TV Sunday School." Ebony, April 1956, p. 81-84.

335   "TV Teacher To Philly Tots." Ebony, October 1964, p. 147-
        150.

336   "TV's Effects On Children." (Editorial). Michigan Chronicle,
        February 24, 1979, p. A6.

                                    First

337   "ABC-TV Tabs Max Robinson 1st Black for Co-Anchor News
        Spot." Jet, May 11, 1978, p. 23-24.

338   "Adam Wade to Debut as First Black TV Game Show Host."
        Jet, May 29, 1975, p. 58.

339   "Alabama A & M Gets First Black Educational Station." Jet,
        May 3, 1973, p. 30.

340   "Alex Haley's 'Roots' Had Biggest TV Audience Say Neilsen
        Ratings." San Francisco Chronicle, February 2, 1977, p. 1.

341   "Blacks Acquire Television Station in DC, A First." Jet, Feb-
        ruary 15, 1973, p. 28.

342   "Blacks Operating First TV Station in Virgin Isles." Jet, De-
        cember 27, 1973, p. 18.

343   "First Black-Owned TV Network Planned." Jet, October 2,
        1980, p. 16.

344   "First Black TV Station to Broadcast in Full Color." Jet,
        June 28, 1973, p. 29.

345   "First Black TV Station, WGPR, in Detroit." Chicago Tribune,
        March 18, 1976, p. 1.

346 "First Black TV Station WGPR-TV in Detroit, to Broadcast in Full Color." Jet, June 28, 1973, p. 26.

347 "First Black Woman Nominated By ABC." Los Angeles Times, April 24, 1973, p. CAL-1.

348 "First Negro to Break Directorial Barriers in TV." Sepia, April 1960, p. 59.

349 "First TV Commercials for Products Used Exclusively by Negroes to be Shown in Prime Time in Five Major Cities Starting Oct. 1." Wall Street Journal, September 30, 1968, p. 15.

350 "First TV Series Aimed At Black Women to Debut." Jet, June 23, 1977, p. 59.

351 "First Woman Chosen for Director's Program." Jet, August 9, 1973, p. 54.

352 "'I Spy': Comedian Bill Cosby Is First Negro Co-Star In TV Network Series." Ebony, September 1965, p. 65-66+.

353 "John Amos Will He Be First Producer of Movie Glorifying Black Heroes?" Sepia, March 1976, p. 34-36.

354 "John Small Pioneers; Joins WNBC-TV As First Negro Salesman." Advertising Age, February 15, 1965, p. 12.

355 Karrim, Talib. "WGPR, Taking A Corner of the Media." Bilalian News, February 18, 1977, p. 6.

356 Matthews, C.L. "Detroit's WGPR-TV; Struggling Strat for Black TV." Black Enterprise, November 1976, p. 63+.

357 "Nation's First Black-Owned TV Station To Open In Detroit." Los Angeles Times, June 20, 1975, p. 20.

358 "New Detroit University To Mark Blacks' Entry Into Ranks of TV Ownership." Broadcasting, June 18, 1973, p. 38.

359 "New TV Show Record, Bill Cosby." Jet, May 6, 1978, p. 61.

360 "Nielsen Rating Report 'Roots' Had TV's Biggest Audience." San Francisco Chronicle, February 2, 1977, p. 1.

361 "Prosper: Washington's WOOK-TV." Sponsors, August 17, 1964, p. 53.

362 Poole, Isaiah J. "TV First At Howard." Black Enterprise, December 1980, p. 22-23.

363 "Radio and TV Women Name 1st Black President." Cleveland Call & Post, January 7, 1979, p. A-9.

364 Randall, Rick. "Howard University To Begin TV Broadcast." The Capitol Spotlight, November 13, 1980, p. 7.

365 "'Roots' Biggest Event in TV Entertainment History." Broadcasting, January 31, 1977, p. 19.

366 "Site Chosen For Macon's First Black TV Station." Jet, December 11, 1980, p. 8.

367 Stevens, William K. "Black TV Station, WGPR-TV, Opens In Detroit." New York Times, September 30, 1975, p. 1.

368 "Struggle For WLBT, NBC Affiliate, Jackson, Mississippi." New York Times, February 24, 1977, p. 70.

369 "Three-Way Fight for WOOK-TV: Negro Formated Station Attracts Interest of Two Washington Groups." Broadcasting, September 5, 1966, p. 104.

370 Trescott, Jacqueline. "Prime Time for Howard; The University's New Television Station, WHMM, Signs On." Washington Post, November 18, 1980, p. B1, B3.

371 "Tuning In By Satellite." Black Enterprise, July 1979, p. 12.

372 "WGPR-TV, 1st Black TV Station In U.S., Opened In Detroit." Bilalian News, February 18, 1977, p. 6.

373 "WGPR-TV In Detroit, Nation's 1st Black TV Station." Chicago Tribune, March 18, 1976, p. 1.

374 "WHMM-TV Goes On Air." The Capitol Press Club News," November 1980, p. 1.

375 "Why CBS Fired Kennedy From NFL Today." (Young column). Los Angeles Sentinel, August 7, 1980, p. A1.

376 "Why I Quit My TV Show, by Nat King Cole." Ebony, February 1958, p. 29-34.

377 "WNTV In Nigeria Is Africa's 1st TV Network." Jet, March 3, 1960, p. 14.

General

378 "Actors' New Boss." Ebony, June 1964, p. 58-60+.

379 "Added Attractions." TV Guide, November 14, 1970, p. 40-
     41.

380 "Aftermath: Here is Marva." Our World, July 1953, p. 12-
     13.

381 Alexander, D. R. "Common Ground." Essence, September
     1980, p. 69.

382 Alexander, Daryl Royster. "Leap into the Twilight Zone."
     Essence, September 1980, p. 69.

383 Ali-Beyah, Zakia. "Television Programming." The Black Col-
     legian, October/November 1980, p. 27.

384 Allen, B. "TV." Essence, February 1980, p. 19.

385 Allen, Bonnie. "Piece of the Pie." Essence, November 1980,
     p. 22.

386 Allen, S. "Talent Is Color-Blind." Ebony, September 1955,
     p. 41-42+.

387 "Alpha Epsilon Rho, Norfolk University Produces Television
     Announcements." Norfolk Journal & Guide, April 9, 1980,
     p. 1-12.

388 "Amsterdam News Looks at 1980's Film & TV." New York
     Amsterdam News, January 1980, p. 21.

389 "And So They Laughed." TV Guide, March 11, 1967, p. 12-
     13.

390 Anderson, Janelle. "Television 5 Years Ago: No Color, Just
     Gray and White." Soul, May 10, 1976, p. 10-12.

391 _____. "What Do TV's Blacks Think of Blacks on TV?"
     Soul, May 10, 1971, p. 14-16.

392 Antoine, Roane. "Blacks in TV Programs." Sepia, November
     1980, p. 35-41.

393 "Apollo Story." Sepia, January 1966, p. 14-20.

394 Ariade, Folami. "Freedom and the Independents." Essence,
     July 1980, p. 10.

395 Barrow, W. "Gallery of Leading Men." Negro Digest, Octo-
     ber 1963, p. 45-48.

396 Beale, Lewis. "TV's Black Perspective Is the Only One."
     Essence, May 1978, p. 12+.

397   _____ . "Would You Buy Jell-o from Bill Cosby?"
       National Leader, November 25, 1982, p. 21.

398   "Belafonte Sours On Films, Disco Music, TV Racism, Back-
       sliding Blacks." Jet, April 6, 1979, p. 30-33+.

399   Belman, D. "Success Story." Newsweek, November 10, 1975,
       p. 54.

400   "Bern'Nadette Stanis And Her Own Fashion." Black Stars, p.
       58-60.

401   "Beverly Payne Urges Career In TV." Michigan Chronicle,
       February 26, 1977, p. B2.

402   "Bilalian (Black) Relationship to Public TV." Bilalian News,
       May 19, 1978, p. I-21.

403   "Bilalians on TV." (Earle Chisolm column). Bilalian News,
       June 15, 1979, p. 26.

404   "Billye Aaron Glad to Be Back On TV For NBC's WTMJ in
       Milwaukee." Jet, May 8, 1975, p. 6.

405   "Billye Williams Resigns TV Post In Atlanta For Spouse."
       Jet, August 1, 1974, p. 18.

406   "Black Actors Finding Few TV Jobs." Baltimore Afro Amer-
       ican, March 29, 1980, p. 4.

407   "Black Actors 'Hustling' for Jobs: Calvin Lockart." Jet, No-
       vember 23, 1978, p. 50.

408   "Black Artist for Action Organization Eyes Black Image on TV."
       Los Angeles Sentinel, December 6, 1979, p. A-3.

409   "Black Excellence in the Wasteland." Ebony, March 1972, p.
       44-51.

410   "Black Experience in Film & TV." (Series). Los Angeles
       Times, February 11, 1979, p. CAL-3; February 18, 1979,
       p. CAL-7; May 6, 1979, p. CAL-32.

411   "Black Images on Radio and TV." (Tony Brown column).
       Norfolk Journal & Guide, May 14, 1980, p. 6.

412   "Black On The Channels." Time, May 24, 1968, p. 74.

413   "Black-Operated TV Training Program in NYC Seeks Funding."
       New York Amsterdam News, April 24, 1982, p. 3.

414   "Black-owned TV A Possibility in Washington." Broadcasting,
       October 2, 1972, p. 34-35.

415   "Black Press' View of TV and Films." (Robertson column).
      Los Angeles Sentinel, August 5, 1982, p. A-6.

416   "Black Psyc Looks At Blacks On Television." Jet, March 30,
      1978, p. 30.

417   "Black Stars." New York Amsterdam News, March 10, 1979,
      p. 30.

418   "Black Stereotype Characters Appear in Programs." Pitts-
      burgh Courier, December 24, 1977, p. 3-17.

419   "Black TV." Newsweek, September 29, 1975, p. 18.

420   "Black TV Image Month." (Editorial). St. Louis Argus, No-
      vember 4, 1982, p. 2-4.

421   "Black TV; its problems and promises." Ebony, September
      1969, p. 88-90+.

422   "Blacks And Public TV. As Squeeze Play Misfires Blacks
      Challenge White Control of Tax-Supported Medium." Black
      Enterprise, January 1974, p. 31-33.

423   "Blacks and Television in DC." (Payne column). Baltimore
      Afro American, June 13, 1981, p. 5.

424   "Blacks & The Boob Tube." Michigan Chronicle, November
      17, 1979, p. A-6.

425   "Blacks and TV Programs." (Roger Mosley column). Los
      Angeles Sentinel, July 26, 1979, p. B-3A.

426   "Blacks Call for Boycott of Black TV Shows & Sponsors."
      Pittsburgh Courier, July 23, 1977, p. 1.

427   "Blacks in Film and TV Industries." (Robertson column).
      Los Angeles Sentinel, February 28, 1980, p. A-6; March 6,
      1980, p. A-6; March 13, 1980, p. A-6; March 20, 1980,
      p. A-6.

428   "Blacks Must Work To Change Bad TV Images." Jet, July 10,
      1980, p. 38.

429   "Blacks On TV." (1980-81 Season). Jet, November 27, 1980,
      p. 54-59.

430   "Blacks on TV: A Dark Picture." (Editorial). Soul, August
      2, 1976, p. 1.

431   "Blacks on TV: A Disturbing Image." Time, March 27, 1978,
      p. 101-102.

432 "Blacks on TV and in Motion Picture Industry." Michigan
     Chronicle, May 27, 1978, p. C-10.

433 "Blacks on TV in 1978." Black Panther, March 18, 1978, p.
     21.

434 "Blacks on TV '71." Soul, November 8, 1971, p. 1.

435 "Blacks on TV: They Laugh at Us But They Won't Cry with
     Us." Soul, November 7, 1977, p. 2.

436 "Blacks Rejected By Three Networks." Washington Post, Feb-
     ruary 3, 1971, p. A-3.

437 Bond, J. C. "Flip Wilson, the 'Mod Squad,' 'Mission Impos-
     sible': Is This what it's really like to be Black?" Redbook,
     February 1972, p. 82-83+.

438 Bond, Jean Carey. "The Media Image of Black Women."
     Freedomway, Winter 1975, p. 34-37.

439 Breitenfeld, F. Jr. "A Look at Minority Programming." TV
     Guide, January 25, 1975, p. 22-23.

440 Bright, Hazel V. "TV Versus Black Survival." Black World,
     December 1973, p. 30-42.

441 Brown, G. F. "Decline of Negro Show Business." Sepia,
     January 1959, p. 36-39.

442 Brown, L. "Integration on Network TV Shows: Fall 1966."
     Integrated Education, 1966, p. 47-48.

443 Brown, W. "Gallery of Leading Men." Negro Digest, October
     1963, p. 45-48.

444 Buck, Jerry. "Something Different for TV." Oakland Tribune,
     May 11, 1980, p. 3, 11.

445 Buck, Maril. "It's Hard for Black History on the TV." San
     Fernando Valley News, September 27, 1978, p. 8.

446 Cambridge, Godfrey. "Use More Negroes in Significant TV
     Roles." Advertising Age, August 9, 1965, p. 19.

447 Campanella, Roy Jr. "Television Programming." Black Col-
     legian, November 1980, p. 193-197.

448 "Can Sammy Davis Jr., Crash Network TV?" Ebony, October
     1954, p. 33-40.

449 "Can TV Crack America's Colorline?" Ebony, May 1951, p.
     33-40.

450 "Candance Carruthers & Bonnie Boswell, Overseas Editors,"
     New York Amsterdam News, August 6, 1977, p. D-2.

451 "Carlie Neal Joins TV in Detroit." Michigan Chronicle, May
     7, 1977, p. B-1.

452 "Carolyn Comes Home; On TV Program." Our World, Decem-
     ber 1953, p. 27-31.

453 "Carson Gulley, TV Chef Cook on WATV in Madison, Wis."
     Ebony, September 1955, p. 5.

454 Carter, Bill. "Racial Humor--Some Good, Some Bad--Current
     Fad of the Networks." Baltimore Sun, September 15, 1977,
     p. 9.

455 Casey, C. "Cops, Corn, and Commercials." New American
     Movements, November 1975, p. 14.

456 "The Cast Is Dyed." TV Guide, March 28, 1970, p. 32-33.

457 "Celebrities Flock to Eckstine Party." Ebony, March 1952,
     p. 27-28+.

458 "C'est la Vie." TV Guide, February 18, 1967, p. 10-11.

459 "Chris Moore Resigns From KETC-TV Staff and Goes to WQED-
     TV." St. Louis Argus, June 1980, p. 1-1. (Editorial). June
     19, 1980, p. 1-10.

460 Christopher, M. "Integration Drive Momentum in TV Indus-
     try." Advertising Age, September 20, 1963, p. 105.

461 _____. "Television: F.C.C. WLBT and Negroes." Nation,
     August 5, 1968, p. 93-94.

462 Coats, Carl. "TV Needs Blacks," Los Angeles Sentinel, June
     17, 1976, p. B-4.

463 Colle, R. D. "Color on TV." Reporter, November 30, 1967,
     p. 23-25.

464 Collier, Eugenia. "Black Shows for White Viewers." Free-
     domway, 1974, p. 209-217.

465 _____. "New Black TV Shows Still Evade the Truth." TV
     Guide, January 12, 1974, p. 6-10.

466 Collins, Lisa. "Dawn's Case Against Tony Orlando." Sepia,
     January 1980, p. 35-38.

467 "Coloring TV in Mississippi." Ebony, March 1973, p. 108-
     110+.

468 "Community Television Network ask FCC to Approve Low
     Power Network in 14 Cities." Washington Post, April 10,
     1980, p. B-5.

469 Compton, N. "Television and Reality." Commentary, Septem-
     ber 1968, p. 84-86.

470 Crosby, John. "Ain't Dat Sumpin." Collier's, October 16,
     1948, p. 30.

471 Cummings, Mark. "National Pay TV Network Narrow-Casting,
     A Model and Simutation of A System Serving Blacks," (Notes).
     Black Political Economics, Fall 1974, p. 69-93.

472 "Dancing Brothers: Powells Make Early Bid for Fame on
     Television." Ebony, May 1956, p. 50-52.

473 "Data Black Poll on Entertainment Preferences." New York
     Amsterdam News, March 1, 1980, p. 5.

474 Dawling, E. "Color Us Black; Failure of Commercial TV to
     Report Adequately on Race Relations and Ghetto Problems."
     New Republic, June 8, 1968, p. 41-43.

475 Deeb, Gary. "TV Ending Its Racist Ways." San Fernando
     Valley News, July 12, 1979, p. 18.

476 "Diahann Carroll Wins Fame, Fortune and a Celebrity's Head-
     aches On TV Talent Show." Our World, May 1954, p. 12-
     17.

477 Doan, R. K. "Public-TV Officials Looking for More Black
     Programming." TV Guide, January 11, 1975, p. A-3.

478 _____. "Shows with Negroes Are Status Symbol in TV."
     TV Guide, May 18, 1968, p. A-3.

479 _____. "TV'S Campaign for Racial Understanding." TV
     Guide, August 17, 1968, p. 9-11.

480 "Does TV Have A Secret Formula For Blacks?" Ebony, Jan-
     uary, 1980, p. 104+.

481 Dominick, J.R. and Greenberg, B.S. "Three Seasons of Blacks
     on Television." Journal of Advertising-Research, April 1970,
     p. 21-7.

482 Douglas, Pamela. "Television Authorship in Hollywood." Es-
     sence, December 1973, p. 64-65+.

483 "Dramatic TV Shows with Black Actors." (Robertson column).
     Los Angeles Sentinel, October 11, 1979, p. A-6.

484 Dunbar, E. "Look Black-On-White TV." Look, September 7, 1971, p. 31.

485 No entry.

486 Dunjee, Roscoe. "Tis the Set of the Sail." The Crisis, January, 1956, p. 23.

487 Edwards, J. "Hollywood ... So What!" Our World, December 1953, p. 56-59.

488 "Effects of 'Roots' Will Be With TV For a Long Time." Broadcasting, February 7, 1977, p. 52-56.

489 Elshof, Phyllis Ten. "How we kicked the TV Habit." Christian Life, February 1979, p. 28-29+.

490 Fairfax, Jean. "Contributing to Black Rage." Educational Broadcasting Review, October 1970, p. 8-10.

491 Feather, Leonard. "Hollywood in Glorious Black and White." Entertainment World, December 12, 1969, p. 27.

492 Ferdinand, Val. "Making the Image Real: Black Producers of theater, film and television." Black Collegian, March/April 1977, p. 54-58.

493 Fife, Marilyn Diane. "Black Image in American TV: The First Two Decades." Black Scholar, November 1974, p. 7-15.

494 Fine, Marilyn G. "Dialectual Features of Black Characters in Situation Comedies on Television." Phylon, December 1980, p. 396-409.

495 "First Negro Crowned Miss Teen L.A. on KTLA's 'Shebang.'" Soul, November 24, 1966, p. 1.

496 Forkan, J.P. "Arbitron Study Charts Ethnic TV Viewing Habits." Advertising Age, October 22, 1979, p. 20.

497 "Foundation Gets $121 Gs to Examine TV & Blacks." Jet, April 10, 1975, p. 46.

498 Fourzon, Pamela and Johnson, Connie. "From an Emmy to Tacos and Back on Top Again." Soul, September 13, 1976, p. 6.

499 "From Heartbreak Hill to Peyton Place." Sepia, February 1967, p. 48-53.

500 "A Gallery of Black Stars." Negro Digest, April 1967, p. 45-48.

501   Gehman, R. "The Negro in Television." TV Guide, June 20,
      1964, p. 15-23; June 27, 1964, p. 15-22.

502   Gent, George. "Exit Darkies, Enter Blacks." The New York
      Times, July 3, 1968, p. 71.

503   Greeley, Andrew M. "Black and White Minstrels." The Re-
      porter, March 21, 1968, p. 40.

504   "Gregory Takes To Task On Civil Rights; CBS TV's Dann Notes
      Revolution in Industry." Broadcasting, November 18, 1963,
      p. 82.

505   Gipson, Gertrude. "ABC's of Movieland. So You Want to
      Crash the Movies and Be a Star?" Our World, September
      1952, p. 60-64.

506   "Girl with TV Dream." Ebony, December 1962, p. 37-40.

507   Gite, Lloyd. "Blacks at a Standstill in Television." Black
      Collegian, November 1980, p. 84.

508   Goodlett, Carlton B. "Mass Communications, U.S.A.: Its
      Feet of Clay." Black Scholar, November 1974, p. 7-15.

509   Haddad, M. George. "Altovise Davis, Joi Foxx and Johanna
      Poitier: Tricks They Use To Keep Their Husbands Happy."
      Black Stars, September 1978, p. 32-35.

510   Haggerty, Sandra. "TV and Black Womanhood." Los Angeles
      Times, November 6, 1974, p. 4-1.

511   "Hal Jackson and Operation Santa Claus." (Gipson column).
      Los Angeles Sentinel, December 9, 1982, p. B-7.

512   "Hal Williams Discusses TV Programming and Blacks." Los
      Angeles Sentinel, July 1, 1982, p. C-10.

513   No entry.

514   Harding, H. "Actor P. Jay Sidney Testifies That Negroes Are
      Not Employed for Radio and TV Roles." TV Guide, Novem-
      ber 10, 1962, p. A-1.

515   _____. "Two Blacks Sign Contracts." TV Guide, Septem-
      ber 8, 1962, p. A-1.

516   Harmon, Sidney. "How Hollywood Is Smashing the Color Bar."
      Films and Filming, March 1959, p. 7+.

517   Harrison, Bernie. "From Chas On The Tube Comes...."
      Washington Star, March 9, 1979, p. 36.

518 Hartman, Hermene. "TV In American Culture." Crisis, January 1978, p. 15-18.

519 "Heap O'Rhymin." Time, March 19, 1951, p. 85.

520 "Her Image Is the Same On and Off the TV Screen." St. Petersburg (Fla.) Times, February 27, 1978, p. 9.

521 Hickey, N. "Detroit: Television on Trial." TV Guide, June 1, 1968, p. 6-10; June 8, 1968, p. 16-20.

522 "Highlights of 'Black Families and the Medium of Television.'" Atlanta Daily World, July 22, 1982, p. 5.

523 "Highlights of Michigan University Conference on Black Families and TV Medium." Michigan Chronicle, June 14, 1980, p. B-1.

524 "Highlights of NYC Seminar on Minorities in Film and TV." New York Amsterdam News, July 3, 1982, p. 34.

525 Hinton, James and others. "Tokenism and Improving Imagery of Blacks in TV Drama and Comedy." Journal of Broadcasting, Fall 1974, p. 423-432.

526 "Hiring of Minorities For TV." Baltimore Afro American, January 15, 1977, p. 8.

527 "History of Blacks On TV Recounted." Bilalian News, September 16, 1977, p. 4.

528 Hobson, D. "The Latest in Hollywood Fashions--for the Male." TV Guide, August 16, 1969, p. 4-7.

529 Hobson, Sheila Smith. "The Rise and Fall of Blacks in Serious Television." Freedomway, 1974, p. 185-199.

530 Holly, Ellen. "Where Are the Films About Real Black Men and Women?" Freedomway, 1974, p. 270-273.

531 "Hollywood's New Breed." Sepia, June 1963, p. 20-25.

531a Holsendolph, E. "Coloring the Image On Public Television." Black Enterprise, March 1979, p. 13.

532 "Host With The Most." Time, September 23, 1957, p. 56+.

533 "How Liberal Is Show Business?" Sepia, March 1963, p. 40-43.

534 "Image of Blacks On TV." Baltimore Afro American, (Yette column), August 27, 1977, p. 1-5.

535 "Image of Blacks On TV Programs." Los Angeles Times, September 18, 1974, p. 1.

536   "Image Makers." Ebony, April 1961, p. 88-89.

537   "The Image Makers." Negro History Bulletin, December 1962, p. 127-128.

538   "In-Depth Look At History and Future of Blacks In Entertainment." St. Louis Argus, April 24, 1980, p. 3-1.

539   "Insider Discusses Plight of Black Script Writers." Jet, March 2, 1978, p. 34.

540   "Is Your TV Set Killing You." Sepia, January 1969, p. 48.

540a "It Happened in Our World." Our World, December 1952, p. 14-15.

541   Ivie, Ardie. "The New Blacks for Color TV." Soul Illustrated, Fall 1968, p. 17-20, 61.

542   Jacob, John. "TV Accused of Perpetuating Stereotypes." Washington Post, August 16, 1977, p. 27.

543   "Jesse Jackson Speaks to Academy of TV Arts and Sciences." Los Angeles Sentinel, July 5, 1979, p. A-10.

544   "Jobs Hard To Find For Black Actors, Says 'Room 222" Star, Denise Nicolas." Jet, June 3, 1971, p. 59.

545   "John Murphy's Views on Blacks and the Media." (Chisolm column). Bilalian News, May 25, 1979, p. 28.

546   Johnson, Albert. "Beige, Brown or Black." Film Quarterly, Fall 1959, p. 39-42.

547   "Joseph Jackson Invents Device to Pre-Program TV Set." Los Angeles Sentinel, May 17, 1979, p. A-5.

548   "Julian Bond Deplores Multiple Media Ownership." Jet, December 11, 1975, p. 33.

549   "Julian Dixon Column on TV Programming & Blacks," Los Angeles Sentinel, November 8, 1979, p. A8.

550   Kael, Pauline. "Notes on Black Movies." New Yorker, December 2, 1972, p. 9.

551   Kelly, Marlene. "Television Being Used for Learning, Teaching." California State University Dominguez Hills Panorama, Spring 1979, p. 2.

552   King, Pamela. "Taking a Few Shots at Uncle Walter and Company." Los Angeles Herald Examiner, October 14, 1978, p. 18.

553   Kirk, Cynthia.   "Black TV Shows Are Still Programmed for
      Whites."   Soul, May 26, 1975, p. 6-10.

554   _____.   "The Screen Goes to Black as TV Opens Its Eyes."
      Soul, April 29, 1974, p. 22-24.

555   Kisner, Ronald.   "Blacks Get Bigger Roles This TV Season."
      Jet, September 22, 1977, p. 58-61.

556   Lemon, R.   "Black Is the Color of TV's Newest Stars."   Sat-
      urday Evening Post, November 30, 1968, p. 42+.

557   Levin, E.   "Television Takes to the Streets."   TV Guide, De-
      cember 28, 1974, p. 12-13.

558   Levine, Richard M.   "Why Unconscious Racism Persists."
      TV Guide, July 18, 1981, p. 2-6; July 25, 1981, p. 26-32.

559   "Linda Avery Discusses Blacks and Minorities in TV Industry."
      Michigan Chronicle, July 11, 1981, p. A-3.

560   "Living Color on Television; Negroes On the Screen."   Satur-
      day Review, November 24, 1962, p. 25; February 9, 1963,
      p. 57.

561   Lucas, Bob.   "Blacks on TV."   Jet, March 1980, p. 54-56.

562   _____.   "New Faces, New Shows and Old Racism Mark New
      Television Season."   Jet, October 23, 1975, p. 55-57.

563   McGhee-Jordan, Kathleen,   "View from Within: Television As
      A Profession."   Encore, May 17, 1976, p. 48.

564   McQueen, Michel.   "High-Powered TV Opportunities at How-
      ard."   Washington Post (The District Weekly), p. 1-2.

565   McPherson, Andrew.   "Negroes and Television."   Essence,
      November 1975, p. 13.

566   Maloney, Martin.   "Black Is the Color of Our New TV."   TV
      Guide, November 16, 1968, p. 7-10.

567   "Mariners; Democracy In TV."   Our World, December 1951,
      p. 36-39.

568   "Martha Davis & Spouse; Marriage and TV Break Up Put Com-
      edy Team On Top."   Ebony, June 1958, p. 33+.

569   "Mass TV's Face Renewal Roadblock."   Broadcasting, March
      27, 1972, p. 39.

570   "Memory Lingers On."   Our World, September 1954, p. 46-
      49.

571 "Minorities and TV Viewers' Surveys." (Earle Chisolm column).
     Bilalian News, July 6, 1979, p. 24.

572 "Minorities In Public Broadcasting Report Scores Public TV."
     Los Angeles Times, November 17, 1978, p. 4-37.

573 "Minority Employment In TV Field Survey." New York Ams-
     terdam News, February 12, 1977, p. D-5.

574 "Minority Training Grants Available." Norfolk Journal & Guide,
     June 4, 1977, p. B-16.

575 Moore, Jere. "Television 68." Soul, December 2, 1968, p.
     2.

576 "More Negroes on TV." Jet, October 1953, p. 60.

577 Morris, Allen. "One Hundred Years of Negro Entertainment."
     Ebony, September 1963, p. 122-124.

578 Morton, C. A. "Public Service for Black Viewers, Some Other
     Choices Besides Off/On." Black Enterprise, August 1979,
     p. 49.

579 Moses, K. "Black Image on Television: Who Controls It?"
     Black Enterprise, September 1979, p. 33-6+

580 "Most Black Journalism Students Want TV Jobs." Jet, Decem-
     ber 24, 1981, p. 24.

581 "Motown Sets Expansion into TV, Movies, Broadway." Soul,
     June 23, 1966, p. 5.

582 "Move for Integration of Negroes into AM-TV Shows Gains Mo-
     mentum." Variety, July 18, 1951, p. 1, 18.

583 "Mrs. Mastermind of TV Black Technical School." Ebony,
     May 1972, pp. 12-17+; pp. 102-104.

584 "NAACP Freedom TV Spectacular." Crisis, April 1964. p.
     249-256.

585 "Name's the Same." Our World, February 1954, p. 57.

586 "National TV and the Black Interest." Michigan Chronicle,
     November 3, 1979, p. A8.

587 "NBC Show Ask Sammy, Wife To Help Ratings." Jet, Novem-
     ber 23, 1978, p. 61.

588 "Negro Actors in Dramatic Roles." America, September 17,
     1966, p. 298-300.

589 "Negroes and Television." Sepia, April 1976, p. 5.

590   "The Negro and TV." Our World, February 1954, p. 17.

591   "Negro and White Love Scenes That Shock-it-to-you." Coronet, April 1969, p. 10-17.

592   "The Negro in Cinema." Films and Filming, May 1957, p. 9-11.

593   "Negro Performers Win Better Roles on TV Than in Any Other Entertainment Medium." Ebony, June 1950, p. 22-25.

594   "New Study of TV Violence Shows Number of Weapons Displayed." Michigan Chronicle, December 31, 1977, p. B-7.

595   "New TV Bosses K.O. 'd Sammy Davis." Sepia, May 1966, p. 8-10.

596   "New TV UHFs Aim for Negro Audience." Broadcasting, February 4, 1963, p. 56.

597   "Nielsen Poll Indicates That 47% More Black Viewers Watch Public TV in October 1976 Than in 1975." New York Times, June 13, 1977, p. 57.

598   "Nita Bason, WKTU Talk Show Host." New York Amsterdam News, January 5, 1980, 6.

599   "$1.5 Million UNCF Fund Begun by TV Guide Creator, Walter Annenberg." Jet, January 14, 1982, p. 37.

600   Ortez, Maria. "Television Survey." Soul, June 5, 1978, p. 22.

601   "PBS Media Short Changes Blacks; Task Force Reports." Jet, December 21, 1978, p. 46.

602   "Personnel Changes at Cleveland TV Station." Cleveland Call & Post, March 19, 1977, p. 1.

603   "Personnel Changes at WEWS-TV in Cleveland." Cleveland Call & Post, December 11, 1982, p. A-14.

604   Peters, A. "What the Negro Wants from TV." TV Guide, January 20, 1968, p. 6-10.

605   "Photographers Pick Most Beautiful Face in TV." Jet, March 4, 1971, p. 56-57.

606   Pitts, Leonard. "Black Hollywood: A Requiem." Right On-Focus, Spring 1983, p. 67-68.

607   _____. "Norman Lear and the Black TV Image." Soul, June 5, 1978, p. 20-22.

608 _____. "Stalking the Elusive Perfect Black Image." Soul,
     July 3, 1978, p. 19.

609 _____. "What Is Soul? Is It Only Black?" Soul, June 20,
     1977, p. 2-3.

610 "Playboy Penthouse Show Losing Money; Some Southern Stations
     Refuse to Run It, Negro Entertainers and Mixed Groups Often
     Appear on Show." Jet, March 3, 1960, p. 60.

611 "Poitier Credits Robeson With Much of His Success." Jet,
     September 14, 1978, p. 58.

612 "The portrayal of minorities and women on television hasn't
     improved in recent years and neither has their employment
     in the industry the U.S. Civil Rights Commission reported."
     Wall Street Journal, January 16, 1979, p. 34.

613 Poussaint, Alvin F. "Education and Black Self-Image." Free-
     domway, Fall 1968, p. 334-339.

614 Rahn, Pete, "Julius Hunter Praises Radio, Puts Down Rumor."
     St. Louis Post Dispatch, October 17, 1980, p. 10F.

615 "Redd Foxx TV Roasting to Raise College Funds." Jet, Novem-
     ber 8, 1973, p. 86.

616 Reed, Claude. "Film and TV: Blacks Still in the Background."
     National Scene Supplement, January 1983, p. 14-17.

617 "Researcher Says TV Teaches Stereotypes About Race Rela-
     tions." Norfolk Journal & Guide, November 10, 1978, p.
     B-11.

618 "Richard Pryor Gets Sued for $1 Million by NBC Page." Jet,
     April 3, 1975, p. 57.

619 No entry.

620 "Robin Smith, KMOX-TV, To Emcee Sickle Cell Relief Fund
     Benefit." St. Louis Argus, March 13, 1980, p. 4.

621 Robinson, Eugene. "Happy Negroes Make A Comeback: A
     Critique of the Treatment of Blacks in TV Programs." New
     West, July 16, 1979, p. 72.

622 Robinson, Lawrence." Effects of Television Violence." Es-
     sence, November 1976, p. 26.

623 Robinson, Louie. "TV Discovers the Blackman." Ebony, Feb-
     ruary 1969, p. 27-30.

624 " 'Roots' Reunion." Jet, February 15, 1982, p. 64.

625 Rose, Arnold. "TV Bumps into the Negro Problem." Printer's Ink, July 20, 1951, p. 36.

626 Sampson, C. A. "Black Image; The More It Changes, The More It Remains The Same." Encore, May 1980, p. 40-42.

627 Sanders, Charles L. "Is Archie Bunker the Real White America? Interview with Carroll O'Connor." Ebony, June 1972, p. 186-188.

628 "Sara Jay Smith, Public Service Director, WBMG-TV in Birmingham." Ebony, June 1972, p. 7.

629 "Satellite Communication." Bilalian News, September 28, 1979, p. 22.

630 "Satellite TV Teaching By North Carolina A & T State University." Norfolk Journal & Guide, February 25, 1978, p. 6.

631 Scarupa, Harriet Jackson. "Is There Life Without Television." Essence, November 1977, p. 123+.

632 Scotch, Norman A. "The Vanishing Villains of TV." Phylon, Spring 1960, p. 58-62.

633 Shayon, Robert Lewis. "Living Color on Television." Saturday Review, November 24, 1962, p. 25; February 9, 1963, p. 57.

634 Slater, Jack. "Does TV Have a Secret Formula for Blacks?" Ebony, January 1980, p. 104.

635 _____. "Satellite TV and Minorities." Los Angeles Times, May 23, 1980, p. 4-2.

636 Spiegelman, Judy. "More Black Shows, More Blacks Working." Soul, October 5, 1970, p. 4-6.

637 _____. "TV in the 70s." Soul Illustrated, February 1970, p. 22, 63.

638 "Star Studded: 'Soul Train' Feast and Party." Soul, March 1, 1976, p. 9.

639 "Station Rankings To Shift In Ethnic-Rating Storm?" Television/ Radio Age, February 19, 1973, p. 23-25.

640 "Stereotyped Black TV Roles Discussed." Chicago Defender, December 17, 1977, p. A-10.

641 Stewart, Gail. "Black Comedy TV Shows Replacing Shoe Shine Boy." Soul. February 16, 1976, p. 6-7.

642   Stewart, Ted. "Blacks & Television." Sepia, February 1979,
      p. 82.

643   _____. "Negroes and Television." Sepia, November 1975,
      p. 82.

644   _____. "What's Happening To Black TV Stars." Sepia,
      October 1974, p. 36+.

644a Stoehr, Chris. "Where Have All the Black Series Gone." De-
      troit Free Press, August 20, 1978, p. 1.

645   "Stokes Strikes Blow For TV, Radio Freedom." Jet, Decem-
      ber 4, 1975, p. 47.

646   "Stokes Wants to Use TV Post to Aid Blacks." Jet, May 4,
      1974, p. 24.

647   "Storer Broadcasting Forms Minority Broadcasting Investment
      Fund." Atlanta World, October 26, 1979, p. 5.

648   "The Story Behind Haley & Lear Television Team." Jet, April
      3, 1980, p. 48-49.

649   "Study Shows Black Viewing Trends." New York Amsterdam
      News, May 7, 1977, p. B-5.

650   "Study Shows Portrayal of Women on TV." Bilalian News,
      September 23, 1977, p. 31.

651   Sullivan, E. "Can TV Crack America's Color Line?" Ebony,
      May 1951, p. 58-62+.

652   "Summary of Major Provisions of Proposed Communications
      Act." New York Amsterdam News, July 1, 1978, p. D-5.

653   "Television." Ebony, June 1950, p. 22-23.

654   "Television; Black Man's Saga." Economist, February 5, 1977.

655   "Television 5 Years Ago." Soul, May 10, 1971, p. 12.

656   "Television Industry Hiring of Women, Minorities Comes Under
      Fire From Communications Industry Critics at the United
      Church of Christ." Wall Street Journal, January 13, 1976,
      p. 1.

657   "Television Interviews About Departure of Andrew Young."
      Los Angeles Times, August 27, 1979, p. 1-1.

658   "Television '78 Close Up." Soul, October 2, 1978, p. 13.

659   "Television's Educational Effects in the Drive for Equality."
      TV Guide, July 6, 1968, p. 4.

660 Terry, Mike. "TV Roundup: Movies, Minis and Miscellaneous."
     Soul, October 2, 1978, p. 16, 20.

661 "This Is Show Business." Our World, September 1953, p. 32-
     36+.

662 "3 Challenges to Blacks." (Editorial). Cleveland Call &
     Post, October 14, 1978, p. A-14.

663 "TV & Learning." (Editorial). Baltimore Afro American,
     September 3, 1977, p. 4.

664 "TV and Publishing Industries and Blacks." (Bill Lane column).
     Baltimore Afro American, May 10, 1980, p. 11.

665 "TV Bias Against Blacks." (Billy Rowe commentary). New
     York Amsterdam News, March 29, 1980, p. 20.

666 "TV Careers and Computers." (Buzz Lutrell column). Michi-
     gan Chronicle, May 22, 1982, p. CRS-6.

667 "TV Images of Black People." (Julian Dixon column). Cleve-
     land Call & Post, January 19, 1980, p. A-9.

668 "TV Industry Careers." (Diana Lewis column). Michigan
     Chronicle, May 19, 1979, p. CRS-47.

669 "TV Industry's Biased Treatment of Blacks." (Robertson col-
     umn). Los Angeles Sentinel, October 7, 1982, p. A-6.

670 "TV Is Rated First in Care About Blacks; The Harris Survey."
     Washington Post, August 30, 1971, p. A3.

671 "TV: It's Not A Negro Medium." Sponsor, July 5, 1967, p.
     52-55.

672 "TV Jobs Open Up, But Not For Minorities, Study Says," Ad-
     vertising Age, January 12, 1976, p. 10.

673 "TV Medium & Black Family Conference." Michigan Chronicle,
     June 14, 1980, p. B-4.

674 "TV Movie Industry Sign Equal Opportunity Pact." Jet, April
     16, 1970, p. 55.

675 "TV; New Force In Selling To US Negroes." Sponsor, August
     17, 1964, p. 44-48.

676 "TV Portrayals of Blacks." (Editorial). New York Amsterdam
     News, April 21, 1979, p. 37.

677 "TV Programs Panned." Bilalian News, October 21, 1977, p.
     I-28.

64   Blacks On Television

678   "TV Programs Viewed." Bilalian News, October 28, 1977,
      p. I-16.

679   "TV Show and Careers." Soul, January 8, 1979, p. 12-13.

680   "TV Showcase; Baritone Zooms To National Prominence On
      Fred Waring Show." Our World, October 1952, p. 10.

681   "TV Technicians." Ebony, August 1954, p. 25-28+.

682   "TV 'Turnabout' Host." Baltimore Afro American, January
      14, 1978, p. 1.

683   "TV Viewing Makes For Lonely Children." Jet, April 15,
      1976, p. 24.

684   "TV Viewing Patterns." Bilalian News, January 27, 1978,
      p. 4.

685   "TV Watching." (Silvia Hill column). Chicago Daily Defender,
      May 16, 1979, p. WA-2.

686   "TV'S White Male Enclaves: Jenning's Findings." Christian
      Century, December 27, 1972, p. 13.

687   "25 Leading TV Markets With the Largest Number of Black
      Prospects." (Table). Sales & Marketing Management, Octo-
      ber 29, 1979, p. 9+.

688   "Two TV Stations Promise To Hire and Recruit Blacks." Jet,
      March 11, 1978, p. 7.

689   "UCC Find TV Slightly Improved As EEO Employer, But Sus-
      pects Input For Study Is Off." Broadcasting, January 24,
      1977, p. 30+.

690   "University of Michigan Doctoral Fellow Eyes Black Images on
      TV." Atlanta Daily World, August 24, 1980, p. 2.

691   "Variety Calls Chicago a Lily White TV Town; No Negro on the
      4 TV Commercial Outlets There Above Janitor." Jet, Feb-
      ruary 25, 1960, p. 57.

692   "Violence and TV." (Editorial). Atlanta Daily World, July 5,
      1977, p. I-6.

693   "Wanted: Black Talent; Apply Hollywood." Sepia, October
      1968, p. 16-18.

694   Ward, Renee. "Lights! Camera! Action! Black Movies Make
      It Big." Soul, May 26, 1975, p. 12-14.

695   "WCIU-TV Sponsors Inner City Forum In Chicago." Baltimore
      Afro American, January 26, 1979, p. 22.

696 "Watch Your Mouth. " Atlanta Daily World, February 27, 1977,
     p. I-8.

697 Webster, Ivan. "Three Black TV Pilots Stay A Ground. "
     Encore, July 16, 1979, p. 40-41.

698 Weisman, A. "He Passed As a Negro. " Negro Digest, Oc-
     tober 1951, p. 16-20.

699 West, Hollie I. "The Uncertain Legacy Of 'Amos 'N' Andy. ' "
     Washington Post, December 10, 1977.

700 "What Do Negroes Want from TV?" (Contest for Chicago's
     UHF Channel 38 at issue). Broadcasting, April 19, 1965,
     p. 71.

701 "What Happens to TV Winners?" Ebony, October 1958, p. 65-
     66+.

702 White, A. "From Tom-Toms to Television. " Our World,
     February 1951, p. 30-38.

703 "Will New TV Series About A Negro Open Eyes of Some Whites?"
     Wall Street Journal, April 18, 1968, p. 1.

704 "WKYC In Cleveland Hires Al Roker As Weatherman. " Cleve-
     land Call & Post, February 3, 1979, p. A1.

705 "Woman With A Dream (On TV). " Services, April 1950, p. 9.

706 Young, A. S. "New Look in Hollywood. " Sepia, March 1959,
     p. 30-34.

                             Government

707 "Federal Communications Commission Orders More Blacks. "
     Soul, May 10, 1971, p. 14.

708 "Federally Funded Radio and Television Editorials. " (Editorial).
     Atlanta Daily World, April 7, 1978, p. I-6.

709 "Government Regulation of TV. " (Christensen commentary).
     Atlanta Daily World, May 6, 1979, p. 10.

710 "Government Support for Minorities in Media. " Atlanta Daily
     World, October 6, 1977, p. I-4.

711 "House Committee to Probe TV Broadcast Ratings. " Atlanta
     Daily World, December 15, 1977, p. I-3.

712   Jordon, Milton.   "Tuning in Mississippi."   Black Enterprise,
      June 1980, p. 61-62.

713   "Minority Broadcast Facilities Ownership Eyed by Government
      Agencies."   Cleveland Call & Post, March 18, 1978, p. A-
      14.

714   "NAB Raps SBA for Not Helping Blacks Buy Radio-TV Stations."
      Pittsburgh Courier, June 3, 1978, p. 3-22.

715   "Report on Minorities in Radio and TV."   Chicago Daily De-
      fender, November 18, 1978, p. I-1.

                              Management

716   "Agnes W. Snowden, Operations Manger for CBS In Hollywood."
      Ebony, May 1970, p. 7.

717   Anderson, Janelle.   "Blacks Finally Behind Scenes in TV."
      Soul, May 10, 1971, p. 18.

718   _____.   "Joe Dyer and Chuck Jackson in TV Community Re-
      lations."   Soul, May 10, 1971, p. 20.

719   "Arnold Wallace Named Manager of Howard University's WHMM-
      TV."   Michigan Chronicle, September 27, 1980, p. B-7.

720   "Black TV Executive Gets Top Post At California Station."
      Jet, April 10, 1980, p. 22.

721   "Blacks Seek Management Level in TV Industry."   Bilalian
      News, February 18, 1977, p. 10.

722   "Broadcasting Executive Bernadine Washington."   Chicago Daily
      Defender, January 12, 1980, p. AN-1.

723   "Cliff Lane Named Editorial Director of WABC-TV."   New
      York Amsterdam News, November 25, 1979, p. 8.

724   "Communications Expert; T. V. Executive Lionel J. Monagas."
      Sepia, March 1962, p. 58.

725   "David Crippens, Station Manager of KCET-TV."   Los Angeles
      Sentinel, September 18, 1980, p. B-5.

726   "Don Marbury, TV Producer and Program Director."   Pitts-
      burgh Courier, July 15, 1978, p. 2-13.

727   "Don Mitchell Named To Do TV Movie Post."   Jet, December
      11, 1975, p. 63.

728 "Evan Fannell, KMOX-TV Accounting Manager." St. Louis Argus, April 24, 1980, p. 2-8.

729 "Full-Time Negro TV Outlet Continues to Prosper: Washington's WOOK-TV." Sponsor, August 17, 1964, p. 53.

730 "G. Gordon Cooper Named Showtime Program Executive." New York Amsterdam News, April 4, 1981, p. 8.

731 "Herbert Davis, Program Director WTOP-TV, a CBS affiliate in Washington, D.C." Ebony, November 1957, p. 5.

732 Hobson, D. " 'I Spy''s Photographer vs. The Establishment." TV Guide, March 23, 1968, p. 22-27.

733 "J. Taber Bolden, Jr., Vice President, Station Affairs, NBC-TV in Washington." Ebony, March 1977, p. 6.

734 "Jessie Maple, Camerawoman, Writes Book on Subject." New York Amsterdam News, December 17, 1977, p. B-5.

735 "Jewell McCabe Named Channel 13 Manager." New York Amsterdam News, December 17, 1977, p. B-6.

736 "Johnathan Rogers Named News Director, KNXT Los Angeles." Jet, April 10, 1980, p. 22; Los Angeles Times, April 10, 1980, p. 22; Los Angeles Sentinel, March 20, 1980, p. A-1.

737 "Joseph Dyer Named Dir., Community Affairs, KNXT-TV, LA." Los Angeles Wave, January 29, 1981, p. 8.

738 "Katherine Johnson Named KTVI's Director of Minority Affairs." St. Louis Argus, July 31, 1980, p. 2-1.

739 "Lack of Trained Blacks in TV Viewed by TV Station Manager." Atlanta Daily World, May 4, 1978, p. I-6.

740 "Le Vern Brown Is Named Night Manager at WGN-TV, Chicago." Chicago Daily Defender, February 26, 1977, p. ENT-9.

741 Lowe, Buddy. "Connie King, Director of Community Relations at KTLA in Los Angeles." Soul, December 14, 1970, p. 6.

742 "Manager of WLBT-TV Testifies in U.S. House on FCC Regulations." Chicago Daily Defender, May 26, 1979, p. I-5.

743 "Meeting Held to Discuss New Manager for Channel 56 in Detroit." Michigan Chronicle, March 31, 1979, p. 1.

744 "Negro-Orientated Programming to be Beamed by WOOK-TV, Washington Starting." Wall Street Journal, October 25, 1962, p. 1.

745   "On Stage with Mr. Lights." Our World, October 1955, p. 24-
       27.

746   "Orlando White Named Urban Affairs Manager at Chicago's
       WGN-TV." Chicago Daily Defender, March 12, 1977, p. I-
       9.

747   "Paul Gardner Named Chief KNBC-TV's South Los Angeles
       News Bureau." Jet, March 5, 1970, p. 31.

748   "Public TV Stations To Buy 3 New Series On Minority Groups."
       Los Angeles Times, April 3, 1980, p. 4-8.

749   Reid, Craig W.   "Chuck Smiley: Television's Little-Known
       Super-Achiever." Sepia, August 1980, p. 46-50.

750   "Robert Guillaume Secures 'Soap' Theatrical Rights." Jet,
       April 19, 1982, p. 60.

751   "Robert Jackson Named Sales Director for National Black Net-
       work." Bilalian News, January 5, 1979, p. 20.

752   "Saundra Willis Promoted to Manager at KNBC-TV." Cleve-
       land Call & Post, February 9, 1980, p. B-3; Los Angeles
       Sentinel, February 20, 1980, p. B-5A.

753   "Stan Myles Named NBC Variety Programs Manager." (Bur-
       rell column). Soul, December 8, 1975, p. 4.

754   "Stanley Robertson Appointed West Coast Director of Motion
       Pictures for NBC-TV." Jet, April 30, 1970, p. 59.

755   "Stanley Robertson Named West Coast VP of Motion Pictures
       for Television, NBC." Soul, June 7, 1971, p. 5.

756   "Thaddeus Garrett Named VP of Public Broadcasting." Cleve-
       land Call & Post, September 24, 1977, p. A-1.

757   "W. Clinton Powell Gets Public Broadcasting Post." Jet, May
       3, 1973, p. 30.

758   "William Whittaker Becomes KNBC's Press & Publicity Man-
       ager." Los Angeles Sentinel, April 10, 1980, p. A-10.

759   "WLBT's Dilday: Competition Is His Motivation." Broadcast-
       ing, April 21, 1980, p. 105.

                                   Music

760   "The Asphalt Jungle," an Hour-Long Dramatic Series on ABC-

TV; Music Score by Duke Ellington." Jet, January 12, 1961, p. 19.

761 "Benny Carter, Negro Jazz Musician Writes Music for 'The M-Squad' TV Series." Jet, February 11, 1960, p. 29.

762 No entry.

763 "Billy Taylor Named Musical Director of 'The David Frost Show' Starting July 7, 1969." Jet, July 3, 1969, p. 56.

764 "Documentary Features 2 Detroit Musicians." Michigan Chronicle, October 1, 1977, p. B-4.

765 "Duke Ellington Composed Music for ABC-TV Show 'Asphalt Jungle, ' Show's Theme Song Issued as a Single Record by Columbia Records." Jet, September 7, 1961, p. 61.

766 "Duke Ellington Writes Musical Score for ABC-TV's New 'Asphalt Jungle' Series Titled 'The Lady and Lawyer.'" Jet, April 27, 1961, p. 60.

767 "'Ed Sullivan Show'; Count Basie and Band, with Joe Williams, CBS-TV, May 29, 1960." Jet, June 2, 1960, p. 66.

768 "Harry Belafonte: One Hour CBS-TV Spectacular Coming up Has Music Written by John Lewis of the Modern Jazz Quartet." Jet, November 10, 1960, p. 63.

769 "'High Society'; New Movie with Jazz Angle Has Role Made for Satchmo." Ebony, July 1956, p. 103-105.

770 Lucas, Bob. "Merv Griffin TV Show to Spotlight 'Ebony' Music Poll." Jet, August 14, 1975, p. 53-60.

771 "Luther Henderson, Network Music Director." Ebony, January 1958, p. 5.

772 "Master Musician Scores and Success." Ebony, September 1958, p. 59-62.

773 "Oliver Nelson, TV Series Musical Scorer, Dies at 42." Jet, November 13, 1975, p. 55.

774 Salvo, Patrick. "'Soul Train': Television's Most Successful Show." Sepia, August 1976, p. 33-38.

Networks

775 "ABC Files $5 Million Suit Against Redd Foxx." Jet, September 14, 1974, p. 56.

776 "ABC News--'Washington Post' Poll on Racial Progress Re-
     leased." Atlanta Daily World, April 9, 1981, p. 1; Balti-
     more Afro American, April 18, 1981, p. 3.

777 "ABC Releases Research Study on Impact of 'Roots.'" Los
     Angeles Sentinel, June 28, 1979, p. B-2A.

778 "ABC-TV Files Million Suit Against Redd Foxx." Jet, Septem-
     ber 14, 1978, p. 56.

779 "ABC's 12-hour Adaptation of 'Roots.'" Los Angeles Times,
     July 6, 1976, pp. 4-14.

780 "B. Hooks to be Interviewed by ABC on Eve of NAACP Conven-
     tion." Atlanta Daily World, June 22, 1979, p. 3.

781 "CBS Criticized on Minority Hiring." Broadcasting, November
     29, 1971, p. 67-68.

782 "CBS Girl on the Go." Sepia, February 1966, p. 28-33.

783 "CBS News Calls for Inquiry Into Martin Luther King Murder."
     Los Angeles Times, January 2, 1976, p. 1-21.

784 "CBS Sued By Motown Records." New York Amsterdam News,
     February 19, 1977, p. 2.

785 "CBS Supports Black Caucus Internship Program." Atlanta
     Daily World, September 30, 1977, p. I-5.

786 "CBS-TV Cancels New TV Show in Wake of Black Caucus Pro-
     test." Chicago Tribune, March 9, 1979, p. 2-3.

786a "CBS-TV Fires Jayne Kennedy For Taking Job With NBC."
     Los Angeles Sentinel, July 10, 1980, p. A-1.

786b "Corporation for Public Broadcasting Announces Training
     Grants." Atlanta Daily World, January 9, 1977, p. I-7.

787 "CPB to Study Status of Minorities in Broadcasting." Atlanta
     Daily World, February 11, 1977, p. I-2.

788 "Data On Black Panthers Sought From CBS." New York Times,
     February 22, 1970, p. 74.

789 "Donna Summers Signs Contract With NBC-TV." Atlanta
     World, August 21, 1981, p. 6.

790 "E. Holsendolph Speaks in Cleveland About Black TV Network."
     Cleveland Call & Post, May 31, 1980, p. 1.

791 "50 Picket at Cleveland CBS Affiliate over Decoders for the
     Deaf." Cleveland Call & Post, May 29, 1982, p. A-1.

792   Finnigan, J. "ABC Introduces New Summer Series Called
      'Love Thy Neighbor.'" TV Guide, May 19, 1973, p. 1.

793   "Foxx Explains Stories About Dispute With NBC." Jet, March
      28, 1974, p. 54.

794   "Jayne Kennedy In Fight to Switch TV Networks." Jet, July
      10, 1980, p. 65.

795   "Kennedy Fired By CBS for Taping NBC Show." Jet, July 24,
      1980, p. 62.

796   "Motown Sues CBS over the Jackson Group." Michigan Chron-
      icle, February 26, 1977, p. A-1.

797   "NBC Affiliate WCR-TV Charged With Race Bias." Jet, May
      4, 1972, p. 21.

798   "NBC, CBS Join Columbia University's Minority Journalism
      Program." Jet, April 22, 1971, p. 12.

799   "NBC, Citing Fear that Radio-TV Stability is Threatened by
      License Challenges by Minority Groups, Reluctantly Asks
      FCC to Set Quantitative Standards." New York Times, No-
      vember 16, 1971, p. 3.

800   "NBC Gives Bryant Gumbel A Long-Term Contract." Los An-
      geles Sentinel, July 24, 1980, p. B-3.

801   "NBC's 'Talent Has No Color' Projects Negro Contributes to
      New High in '52." Variety, March 18, 1952, p. 1, 34.

802   "PBS to Present 'After Bakke Who Gets Ahead?'" Atlanta
      Daily World, May 28, 1978, p. I-10.

803   "Pryor Blasts NBC." Soul, October 24, 1977, p. 2.

803a "Scottsboro Victim: Sues NBC." Atlanta World, July 12,
      1977, p. 3.

804   "Sonny Hill, Petition Drive to Save His Job With CBS." Pitts-
      burgh Courier, September 17, 1977, p. 3-22; Michigan Chron-
      icle, September 24, 1977, p. B-2.

805   "Southern California Psychologists Association Tells ABC It
      Supports Max Robinson." Los Angeles Sentinel, April 9,
      1981, p. A-2.

806   "Suits Against ABC-NCAA Pact by Warner Cable and Ohio At-
      torney General." Atlanta Daily World, August 4, 1978, p.
      I-4.

807   "Three Networks Deny Blacks Equal Times." Black Times,
      February 15, 1971, p. 20.

808   "TV Networks Deny Negro Bias: Rep. Powell Hears Pro and
      Con Testimony." Broadcasting, November 5, 1962, p. 68.

809   "TV Networks React to TV Violence Issue." Bilalian News,
      March 25, 1977, p. I-19.

                                News

810   "ABC News Anchorman, Max Robinson, Speaks at Nevada Uni-
      versity." World Muslim News, May 7, 1982, p. WNE-5.

811   "ABC News Anchorman Max Robinson's Speech at Smith Col-
      lege." Chicago Daily Defender, February 14, 1981, p. 3.

812   "ABC News Anchorman Robinson Interviewed While in Cleve-
      land." Cleveland Call & Post, June 6, 1981, p. B-4.

813   "ABC Newsman Max Robinson." (Al Sweeney column).   Balti-
      more Afro American, March 7, 1981, p. 13.

814   "ABC Newsman Max Robinson's Smith College Speech." Los
      Angeles Sentinel, February 12, 1981, p. A-1.

815   "ABC-TV and News Anchorman Max Robinson." (Editorial).
      Baltimore Afro American, February 21, 1981, p. 4.

816   "ABC TV Newsman, Max Robinson, Explains His Speech at
      Smith." Bilalian News, February 27, 1981, p. 5.

817   "ABC-TV Station Files Suit to Keep NYC Newsman from Quit-
      ting." Baltimore Afro American, April 12, 1980, p. 1.

818   "Allan Davis, Cleveland TV News and Sports Reporter." Cleve-
      land Call & Post, April 12, 1980, p. A-2.

819   "Amyre Makupson, Anchor of WKBO-TV News." Michigan
      Chronicle, April 1, 1978, p. B-4.

820   "Amyre Porter Makupson Named WKBD-TV's News & Public
      Affairs Manager." Michigan Chronicle, September 10, 1977,
      p. B-5.

820a "Anchorman Ben Frazier's Status at WDIV-TV." Michigan
      Chronicle, November 21, 1981, p. A-1.

821   "Angela Black Touted for Hostess of 'A.M. Los Angeles.'"
      Los Angeles Sentinel, November 26, 1981, p. A-1.

822   "Anna Bond: Correspondent/Eyewitness News." Blacktress,
      January 1981, p. 42.

823   "Art Edgarton, Reporter & Musical Director, WTOL-TV in
      Toledo, Ohio." Ebony, April 1967, p. 101-106.

824   "B. Draper Leaves Job at WJBK-TV." (Charles Adams col-
      umn). Michigan Chronicle, September 11, 1982, p. A-6.

825   "Ben Frazier and WDIV-TV in Detroit." (Adams column).
      Michigan Chronicle, November 28, 1981, p. A-6.

826   "Ben Perry Leaves Atlanta's Channel 11 Team." Atlanta Daily
      World, January 11, 1980, p. 1.

827   "Beverly Draper Leaves Her Job at WJBK-TV." (E. Hood
      column). Michigan Chronicle, September 11, 1982, p. A-6.

828   "Bias Faced by Black TV Newspeople." (Cleaver column).
      Los Angeles Sentinel, February 19, 1981, p. A-7.

829   "Bias in TV News Reporting in Detroit." (A. Watkins column).
      Michigan Chronicle, September 11, 1982, p. A-9.

830   "Bill Greene, Macon Newsroom on WMAZ-TV Banned From
      Covering Speech." Jet, February 19, 1976, p. 8.

831   Binns, M. L. "TV Newswoman Gail Christian." TV Guide,
      June 12, 1976, p. 18-20.

832   "Black Broadcast Journalists on TV." New York Amsterdam
      News, September 6, 1980, p. 63.

833   "Black Journalists in White Newsrooms." (D. Wilson column).
      Michigan Chronicle, September 11, 1982, p. A-3.

834   "'Black Perspective on the News' Returns." Bilalian News,
      October 7, 1977, p. I-3.

835   "Black Television Newsmen." Race Relations Reporter, March
      1, 1970, p. 9.

836   "Blacks and Electronic News Media." (A. Watkins column).
      Michigan Chronicle, December 5, 1981, p. D-8.

837   "Blacks and TV News Programs." (Charles Adams column).
      Michigan Chronicle, November 21, 1981, p. A-6.

838   "Blacks Make TV History--Roz Adams & Joe Washington,
      WXIA in Atlanta; Darcel Grimes, WTWV, Tupelo, Miss."
      Jet, July 27, 1978, p. 19.

839   "Blacks on the Other Side of the News--TV Broadcasting."
      (Jake Jacobs, Steve Roland and Bill Woods). Soul, May 10,
      1971, p. 24.

840 "Bob Reid." Bilalian News, January 1, 1977, p. 7.

841 "Bob Teague Celebrates His 20th Year as NYC TV Journalist."
     Norfolk Journal & Guide, April 7, 1982, p. NSC-4.

842 "Bob Teague's Book About TV News Business." Baltimore
     Afro American, August 28, 1982, p. 6.

843 "Bradley Named CBS Anchorman." Cleveland Call & Post,
     January 1, 1977, p. B-14.

844 Brandt, Pat. "Edith Huggins: WCAU-TV's First Lady of the
     News ... This is Her Inside Story." New Lady, September
     1969, p. 12-18, 42-45.

845 Brown, Roxanne. "Max Robinson: Anchor Man for ABC-TV."
     Sepia, November 1979, pp. 39-43.

846 "Bryant Gumbel and 'Today Show.'" Baltimore Afro American,
     December 19, 1981, p. 9.

847 "Careers of Three Black People Working in TV News in NYC."
     New York Amsterdam News, April 5, 1980, p. 2.

848 "Carol Richardson Named Staff Director at ABC." New York
     Amsterdam News, March 19, 1977, p. D-8.

849 "Carole Simpson, NBC News, Assigned to U.S. House." Mi-
     chigan Chronicle, June 16, 1979, p. B-4; Norfolk Journal
     Guide, June 22, 1979, p. B-18.

850 "CBS Medical Reporter Glenda Wina." Los Angeles Sentinel,
     June 21, 1979, p. A-3.

851 "Charlene Mitchell Gets Week-end Anchor Post on WNAC-TV,
     Boston." Jet, July 27, 1978, p. 18.

852 "Christopher Cartwright WAVY-TV News Artist." Baltimore
     Afro American, December 29, 1979, p. 2-12.

853 "Chuck Stone to Host PBS Series 'Black Perspective on the
     News.'" Michigan Chronicle, September 30, 1978, p. B-4.

854 "Coalition Formed to Investigate Detroit TV Stations' Bias."
     Michigan Chronicle, September 4, 1982, p. A-1.

855 Collins, Lisa. "Gail Christian: News Director, KCET in Los
     Angeles." Sepia, October 1977, p. 28-30.

856 Condon, M. "Mayor Carl Stokes Is on the Air." TV Guide,
     January 4, 1969, p. 24-26.

857 "Corrice Collins, Newscaster on WLBT-TV." Ebony, August
     1971, p. 6.

858 "D. McMillan Joins Broadcast Team of WABC-TV 'Eyewitness News.'" New York Amsterdam News, October 25, 1980, p. 31.

859 "Dana Waddell Named Assignment Editor for WAND-TV News." St. Louis Argus, April 22, 1982, p. I-19.

860 "David A. Hepburn Employed in CBS-TV News Department." Jet, May 5, 1960, p. 18.

861 "Deborah Horne Named Reporter for WPRI-TV." Norfolk Journal & Guide, November 25, 1981, p. 4.

862 "Detroit News Media and Blacks." (Charles Adams column). Michigan Chronicle, September 25, 1982, p. A-6.

863 "Detroit TV Newsman Ben Frazier." (Charles Adams column). Michigan Chronicle, October 31, 1981, p. A-8.

864 "Detroit Voter Apathy and News Media Bias." (A. Watkins column). Michigan Chronicle, October 17, 1981, p. A-9.

865 "Dorothy Reed Named WCBS-TV News Correspondent." New York Amsterdam News, July 15, 1978, p. A-2.

866 Dowling, E. "Color Us Black; Failure of Commercial TV to Report Adequately on Race Relations and Ghetto Problems." New Republic, June 8, 1968, p. 41-43.

867 "Ed Bradley, Black Journalist on TV," (Harris column). New York Amsterdam News, September 6, 1980, p. 63.

868 "Ed Bradley Named Anchorman." Cleveland Call & Post, January 1, 1977, p. 1.

869 "Ed Bradley Named Co-Editor of '60 Minutes.'" Michigan Chronicle, September 20, 1980, p. B-6.

870 Efron, E. "Why Has TV News Forgotten Black Civil-Rights Cause." TV Guide, November 30, 1974, p. A-3, A-4.

871 "Emery King Named NBC-TV White House Correspondent." Norfolk Journal & Guide, October 13, 1982, p. 15.

872 "Ethel Payne Discusses Flap over Max Robinson's Smith Speech." Michigan Chronicle, February 28, 1981, p. A-1.

873 "Felicia Jeter Leaves KHJ-TV." Los Angeles Sentinel, June 25, 1981, p. A-15.

874 "Felicia Jeter to Anchor CBS News Overnight." Jet, September 27, 1982, p. 60.

875 "Felicia Jeter to Anchor CBS-TV Show Called 'Nightwatch.'" Atlanta Daily World, October 3, 1982, p. 3.

875a Ferdinand, Val. "Taking the Weight: TV Broadcasting of News." (Max Robinson). Black Collegian, November-December 1978, p. 56-57+.

875b "4 Black NBC News Correspondents." New York Amsterdam News, February 21, 1981, p. 46.

875c "Gail Christian, News Director at KCET in L.A., Resigns." Los Angeles Sentinel, February 23, 1979, p. A-1.

876 "Glenda Wina, KNXT-TV Reporter." Los Angeles Sentinel, March 8, 1980, p. TV-14.

877 "Gloria Rojas: Correspondent 'Eyewitness News.'" Blacktress, January 1981, p. 50.

878 Good, Paul. "Is Network News Slighting the Minorities?" TV Guide, March 5, 1977, p. 4+.

879 Harding, H. "ABC Is Selecting First Negro Network News Reporter." TV Guide, August 18, 1962, p. A-1.

880 "How Fair Are TV Networks To Black Newsmen?" Sepia, November 1971, pp. 14-16.

881 "Hunter-Gault Named Public TV Correspondent." Norfolk Journal & Guide, October 22, 1977, p. 6; Baltimore Afro American, October 28, 1977, p. 9.

882 "Inside the Television Newsroom." New York Amsterdam News, April 29, 1978, p. D-7.

883 "Jim Scott Named NBC News Correspondent in Pittsburgh." Norfolk Journal & Guide, September 15, 1978, p. B-15.

884 "Jo Ann Williams To Host WFLD-TV's 'P.M. Evening Magazine.'" Baltimore Afro American, August 14, 1980, p. 2-1.

885 "John Baker Named Vice President of Cable News Network." Atlanta Daily World, September 16, 1980, p. 3.

886 "John Johnson: Correspondent 'Eyewitness News.'" Blacktress, January 1981, p. 45.

887 "Johnny Davis, Reporter KMJ-TV, Fresno." Grapevine, September 1970, p. 34.

888 "Johnathan Rogers Named Executive Producer of KNXT-TV '5 O'Clock News.'" Los Angeles Sentinel, February 23, 1979, p. A-1.

888a "Lee Thornton CBS News Correspondent." (Garland column). Pittsburgh Courier, p. ENT. 6.

889 "Lee Thornton, CBS News Correspondent, Speaks In Norfolk." Norfolk Journal & Guide, March 28, 1980, p. 1.

890 Leslie, Connie. "TV News: Power Is Behind the Camera." Black Enterprise, June 1981, p. 107-114.

891 Levin, E. "Reginald Bryant of 'Black Perspectives on the News.'" TV Guide, February 8, 1975, p. 36.

892 Levine, Richard. "The Plight of Black Reporters: Why Unconscious Racism Persists." TV Guide. July 18, 1981, p. 2-6; July 25, 1981, p. 26-32.

893 "Lloyd Gite Joins Staff of WTVS-TV 'Evening Edition News.'" Michigan Chronicle, January 2, 1982, p. B-5.

894 McFadden, M. "He'd Rather Do It Himself." TV Guide, July 29, 1972, p. 4-5.

895 Maloney, M. "'Six30' Something Different in News Programs." TV Guide, August 29, 1970, p. 24-26.

896 "Margo Williams Named Reporter for WKBD-TV." St. Louis Argus, November 25, 1982, p. I-7.

897 "Margo Williams, Radio and TV Broadcaster." St. Louis Argus, April 22, 1982, p. 2-6.

898 Marshall, Marilyn. "Black Anchorwomen: Making It in the Tough World of TV News." Ebony, November 1981, p. 52-56.

899 "Max Robinson." (Payne column). Baltimore Afro American, February 21, 1981, p. 5.

900 "Max Robinson, ABC News Anchorman." Baltimore Afro American, October 13, 1979, p. DWN 20.

901 "Max Robinson, ABC-TV Black Newscaster." (Jarrett column). Chicago Tribune, May 19, 1978, p. 3-4.

902 "Max Robinson and L.A. Times Critic D. Hunt." (Lane column). Baltimore Afro American, March 7, 1981, p. 11.

903 "Max Robinson, Black News Anchorman." Chicago Defender, February 10, 1979, p. 7.

904 "Max Robinson Honored at Golden State Minority Foundation Banquet." Los Angeles Herald Dispatch, May 5, 1983, p. 1.

905 "Max Robinson, New Co-Anchor For Revised ABC News."
     Los Angeles Times, July 10, 1978, p. 4-1.

906 "Max Robinson Speaks at Atlanta University Commencement."
     Atlanta Daily World, May 22, 1980, p. I-1.

907 "Max Robinson Speaks in Detroit about Black Viewer's Attitudes."
     Michigan Chronicle, October 4, 1980, p. A-1.

908 "'NBC News' Carole Simpson Assigned to U.S. House." Mi-
     chigan Chronicle, June 16, 1979, p. B-4.

909 "Nerissa Williams, WSOC-TV Newscaster." Norfolk Journal
     & Guide, July 15, 1981, p. 12.

910 "News Anchorman Max Robinson." Pittsburgh Courier, July
     21, 1979, p. ENT-6.

911 "Norma Quarles Named NBC News Correspondent in Chicago."
     Michigan Chronicle, November 11, 1978, p. B-6.

912 Perry, Mary Ellen. "Blacks in Television News Jobs." Wash-
     ington Star, January 23, 1977, p. 18.

913 Peterson, F. "How Fair Are TV Networks To Black Newsmen."
     Sepia, November 1971, pp. 14-23.

914 "President Reagan's Criticism of TV News Reporting." Chi-
     cago Daily Defender, June 28, 1982, p. 13.

915 "Randall Pinkston Joins New York City Channel 2 News Team."
     New York Amsterdam News, March 1, 1980, p. 39.

916 "Rene Ford Becomes News Director of WANX-TV." Atlanta
     Daily World, March 30, 1980, p. 10.

917 "Reporter Russ Ewing." Chicago Daily Defender, December 27,
     1982, p. 5; December 28, 1982, p. 6; December 29, 1982,
     p. 6; December 30, 1982, p. 6.

918 "Responsibilities of TV News Commentators." (Editorial).
     Atlanta Daily World, July 17, 1981, p. 6.

919 "Richard Gibson, Newswriter for CBS." Ebony, August 1959,
     p. 7.

920 "Robert Warfield, Assistant WDIV-TV News Director." Michi-
     gan Chronicle, June 7, 1980, p. B-6.

921 "Russ Ewing Becomes Reporter for WLS-TV (Chicago)." Chi-
     cago Daily Defender, August 12, 1981, p. 2.

922 "Shauna Singletary Joins 'NBC News' as Correspondent." At-
     lanta Daily World, March 14, 1982, p. 6.

923 Simon, Roger. "Max Robinson: No Longer Invisible." TV
     Guide, December 2, 1978, p. 18-21.

924 "St. Louis TV News Anchorperson." St. Louis Argus, Novem-
     ber 20, 1980, p. 2-9.

925 Stump, A. "Danny Villanueva--Making Points as a Broadcas-
     ter." TV Guide, June 23, 1973, p. 4-7.

926 "Sue Simmons to Co-Anchor WNBC-TV 11 O'Clock News."
     Baltimore Afro American, December 15, 1979, p. 27.

927 "Susan Kidd, WTVI-TV Anchorperson." St. Louis Argus,
     April 22, 1982, p. 2-5.

928 Tait, E. V. "Ed Bradley--Life in the Fast Lane." Encore,
     August 1, 1977, p. 26-31.

929 "Ted Turner Launches 'Cable News Network.'" Atlanta Daily
     World, June 3, 1980, p. I-2.

930 "Television News." (Editorial). Atlanta Daily World, Novem-
     ber 13, 1981, p. 4.

931 "Television's Personality Girl; Mary Holt on WJMO and KYM-
     TV in Cleveland." Ebony, December 1957, p. 102-105.

932 "Three Blacks on TV News." New York Amsterdam News,
     April 5, 1980, p. 2.

933 Townley, Rod. "Slow Down, Ed Bradley, Slow Down!" TV
     Guide, February 20, 1982, p. 28-32.

934 "Trudy Gallant Joins WTVS-TV Staff as News Reporter." Mi-
     chigan Chronicle, October 16, 1982, p. B-4.

935 "TV News." New York Amsterdam News, April 8, 1978, p.
     D-15.

936 "TV News and Politicians." (Column). Atlanta Daily World,
     August 3, 1982, p. 6.

937 "TV News 'Blacks and Women Cyclops.'" Life, June 30, 1972,
     p. 20.

938 "TV News 'Events.'" (F. Williams column). Baltimore Afro
     American, January 17, 1981, p. 4.

939 "TV News Hens," Ebony, September 1966, p. 34-36+.

940 "TV News: Power Is Behind the Camera." Black Enterprise,
     June 1981, p. 107-110.

941   "TV Newscast On Gang Members In Schools." Los Angeles
      Sentinel, November 22, 1979, p. A6.

942   "TV Newsman Ben Frazier." Michigan Chronicle, December
      26, 1981, p. A-1.

943   "TV Personalities Bob Teague and Gil Noble." New York Ams-
      terdam News, December 11, 1981, p. 29.

944   "TV's S. Walter Jacobson." (Verner Reid column). Chicago
      Daily Defender, July 22, 1982, p. 12.

945   "The Typical TV Viewer." Pittsburgh Courier, June 10, 1978,
      p. I-1.

946   "Upsurge In TV News Girls." Ebony, June 1971, pp. 168-176.

947   "U.S. Rep. Fauntroy Calls for Boycott of Detroit Free Press
      and TV2." Michigan Chronicle, September 18, 1982, p. A-1.

948. "Walter Jacobson, WBBM-TV News Anchorman." Chicago Daily
      Defender, August 10, 1982, p. 14.

949   Warga, Wayne. "Focus On TV Anchor Women." Cosmopolitan,
      June 1981, p. 262-267.

950   Weisman, John. "For Ed Bradley the White House Is Not a
      Home." TV Guide, August 20, 1977, p. 10-13.

951   "WJBK-TV News Anchor, B. Draper." (Charles Adams column).
      Michigan Chronicle, August 28, 1982, p. A-6.

952   "Wiley Daniels, TV Newsman Dies." Baltimore Afro American,
      December 17, 1977, p. 7.

953   Wolcott, James. "Black Perspectives on the News." Village
      Voice, October 24, 1977, p. 51.

954   Wood, B. "Black Woman In Television News." Essence, July
      1972, p. 3, 31.

                              Organizations

955   "Atlanta Press Club Bid to Televise Williams Trial Denied."
      Atlanta Daily World, August 27, 1981, p. 1; Baltimore Afro
      American, September 5, 1981, p. 6.

956   "Atlanta Press Club to Seek New Georgia Rule on TV in Court."
      Atlanta Daily World, August 28, 1981, p. 1.

957 "Atlanta Press Club Wants Wayne Williams Trial Televised."
     Atlanta Daily World, August 23, 1981, p. 1.

958 "B. A. D. C. Organization Combats Negative Images of Blacks
     in TV and Movies." Los Angeles Sentinel, December 16,
     1982, p. A-1.

959 "Black Actresses Form Charity Group Called 'Kwanza.'" Nor-
     folk Journal & Guide, December 28, 1979, p. NSC-4.

960 "Black Broadcasters." Michigan Chronicle, January 1, 1977,
     p. A-13.

961 "Black Citizens for Fair Media Organization Fights Bias in TV
     Industry." New York Amsterdam News, November 22, 1980,
     p. 36.

962 "Blacks in Media Broadcasting Club Promote Jogging as Pro-
     test." Los Angeles Sentinel, January 4, 1979, p. A-3.

963 "Broadcasters Form Organization for Blacks." Cleveland Call
     & Post, August 27, 1977, p. A-9.

964 Burrell, Walter. "Black Stuntmen's Association, Hollywood's
     Militant Stepchild." Soul, November 30, 1970, p. 12.

965 "Church of Christ Studies EEO in Radio and TV Industries."
     Baltimore Afro American, December 11, 1982, p. 8.

966 "Dwight Ellis Appointed VP of National Association of Broad-
     casters." Atlanta Daily World, March 27, 1980, p. 6.

967 "Georgia Supreme Court Gets Petition on Televising Williams
     Trial." Atlanta Daily World, September 18, 1981, p. 1.

968 "Highlights of Minorities and Telecommunications Conference
     in California." Los Angeles Sentinel, May 20, 1982, p. A-3.

969 "Impact of GE-Cox Merger on Minority Business." Atlanta
     Daily World, October 12, 1979, p. 3.

970 "Impact of GE-Cox Merger on Minority Groups." Norfolk
     Journal & Guide, October 5, 1979, p. A-3.

971 "Media Forum Panel on Minorities and the FCC." (Ivory col-
     umn). Los Angeles Sentinel, February 7, 1980, p. A-1.

972 "Media Workers Forming National Black Media Group." (Mar-
     tin column). Michigan Chronicle, March 4, 1979, p. A-6.

973 "Minority Broadcast Facilities Ownership Eyed by Government
     Agencies." Cleveland Call &Post, March 18, 1979, p. A-14.

974   "Minority Groups Battle Proposed Deregulation of Broadcast-
      ing." New York Amsterdam News, June 23, 1979, p. 37.

975   "Minority Video Company Opened." Pittsburgh Courier, June
      3, 1978, p. 2-16.

976   "NAACP and ACLU Sign Agreement with Cox Broadcasting."
      Atlanta Daily World, January 11, 1981, p. 1.

977   "NAB Minority Investment Fund to be Operational in 1980."
      Atlanta Daily World, December 25, 1979, p. 3.

978   "National Association of Broadcasters Completes Study of TV
      Programming." Cleveland Call & Post, April 29, 1978, p.
      B-8.

979   "National Association of Broadcasters Criticizes SBA Aid to
      Minorities." Atlanta Daily World, June 11, 1978, p. I-2.

980   "National Black Network Ends Strike in New York." Baltimore
      Afro American, June 3, 1978, p. I-3.

981   "National Broadcasters' Association Forms Minority Executive
      Council. Michigan Chronicle, October 27, 1979, p. A-7.

982   "Negroes Step Up Drives on Radio-TV; CORE Bids for Jobs in
      Commercials." Broadcasting, August 12, 1963, p. 62-64.

983   "Now a Negro Push on Radio-TV; NAACP Opens Campaign for
      Jobs Throughout Broadcast System." Broadcasting, July 1,
      1963, p. 27-29.

984   "P.U.S.H. Works for Black Employees of ON-TV." Chicago
      Daily Defender, December 12, 1981, p. 3.

985   Shayon, Robert Lewis. "FCC on the Carpet." Saturday Re-
      view, August 24, 1968, p. 54.

986   "Storer Broadcasting Forms Minority Broadcast Investment
      Fund." Atlanta Daily World, October 26, 1979, p. 5.

987   "3 Added to Task Force of National Association of Broadcast-
      ers." Baltimore Afro American, December 24, 1977, p.
      I-7.

988   "Urban League Focuses on Image of Blacks in Films and TV."
      Atlanta Daily World, August 3, 1978, p. I-7.

Ownership

989   "Alex Haley Starts TV Company." Soul, September 27, 1976,
      p. 9.

990   Bernstein, Margaret. "Group Launches Plans for Black Sta-
       tion." Los Angeles Wave, March 23, 1983, p. 1.

991   "Bertram Lee Among Owners of WNAC-TV." Norfolk Journal
       & Guide, May 12, 1978, p. A-1.

992   "Black Chicago Group Will Buy Wisconsin TV Station." Jet,
       October 12, 1978, p. 25.

993   "Black Group Seeking License to Operate Detroit TV Station;
       if Agency Grants Applications it Would Be Nation's First
       TV Outlet Controlled By Blacks." Wall Street Journal,
       November 14, 1972, p. 17.

994   "Black-Owned TV/Radio Stations and Cable Companies."
       Black Enterprise, June 1981, p. 103-105.

995   "Black-Owned TV Station in Detroit." (Hooks column). Nor-
       folk Journal & Guide, June 18, 1977, p. A-9.

996   "Black Ownership of TV Facilities." Michigan Chronicle,
       March 17, 1979, p. A-8; Pittsburgh Courier, March 17,
       1979, p. 1-6.

997   "Black Purchases WHEC-TV in Rochester." Soul, October 2,
       1978, p. 2.

998   "Black Station, WGPR-TV, Starts Dance Show." Soul, Jan-
       uary 17, 1977, p. 11.

999   "Black TV Station." Chicago Defender, July 9, 1977,
       p. 16.

1000   "Black TV Station Struggles For Survival." Michigan Chron-
       icle, July 9, 1977, p. 1.

1001   "Black TV Station's Survival Assured." Michigan Chronicle,
       July 16, 1977, p. A-4.

1002   "Blacks Get TV Station License in New Jersey." Jet, March
       1, 1979, p. 15.

1003   "Blacks May Direct Largest TV Station in Mississippi!" Jet,
       December 21, 1978, p. 46.

1004   "Bob Johnson's Black Entertainment Network Debuts." Wash-
       ington Post, January 25, 1980, p. D-1.

1005   "Cosby Forms TV Company, Opens with 14-City Market."
       Jet, March 12, 1981, p. 16.

1006   "Dennis Brownlee Launches Satellite Television Company."
       Jet, December 13, 1982, p. 46.

1007　"Dennis Brownlee Plans Satellite Broadcasting Company."
　　　　Jet, March 15, 1982, p. 40.

1008　"Detroit Black Media Brings U.S. 1st Black TV and Radio
　　　　Stations." Michigan Chronicle, July 22, 1978, p. A-1.

1009　"Detroit's Black TV Station." (Hooks column). Norfolk Jour-
　　　　nal & Guide, June 25, 1977, p. A-8.

1010　"Esther Rolle Opens Her Own Production Firm, Rollaway Pro-
　　　　ductions." Soul, September 4, 1978, p. 2.

1011　"FCC Approved Change in Owner of Station Accused of Negro
　　　　Bias Would Permit Lamar Life Insurance Co. to Buy Back
　　　　80% of WLBT-TV in Mississippi." Wall Street Journal,
　　　　December 6, 1965, p. 9.

1012　"FCC Gives Herman Russell, Atlanta Contractor, O.K. to
　　　　Build TV Station in Macon, Georgia." Jet, February 2,
　　　　1980, p. 24.

1013　"FCC Judge O.K.'s TV License for Black Group in Mississippi."
　　　　Jet, May 10, 1973, p. 58.

1014　"FCC Policy on Black Broadcast Ownership." Atlanta Daily
　　　　World, March 17, 1977, p. I-5.

1015　"Financiers of the Airwaves: New FCC Rules Open Owner-
　　　　ship." Black Enterprise, January 1981, p. 93-99.

1016　"Fund Set up to Help Minorities Buy Broadcast Facilities."
　　　　Norfolk Journal & Guide, January 5, 1979, p. B-15.

1017　Gupta, Udayan. "Black Television Station Owners; How They
　　　　Did It." Black Enterprise, February 1980, p. 106-111.

1018　"Herman Russell, Atlanta Contractor Receives FCC Contract
　　　　to Build TV Station in Macon, Ga." Jet, February 7,
　　　　1980, p. 27.

1019　"Howard University Television Station Opening Set for Novem-
　　　　ber 17." Washington Afro American, November 15, 1980,
　　　　p. 18.

1020　"Inner City Broadcasting: Countdown to Takeoff." Black En-
　　　　terprise, June 1982, p. 128-135.

1021　"Integrating the Airwaves: Black Ownership in Broadcasting."
　　　　Black Enterprise, January 1982, p. 125-127.

1022　Levin, Eric. "Under New Management (TV Station WLBT in
　　　　Mississippi Emphasizes Black Programs, Management)."
　　　　TV Guide, April 5, 1975, p. 3+.

1023 "Listing of Black-Owned Commercial Stations." Black Enter-
      prise, July 1, 1978, p. 48-49.

1024 Little, Harlee. "WHMM-TV Goes On the Air Today." The
      Capstone, November 17, 1980, p. 1, 3.

1025 Livingston, G. "WNAC-TV Black Investor Holds Only Minor-
      ity Stake." Variety, May 10, 1978, p. 176, 188.

1026 "Minority Broadcast Ownership." (Hooks column). Atlanta
      Daily World, October 13, 1977, p. I-4.

1027 "Minority Media Ownership." Norfolk Journal & Guide, No-
      vember 12, 1977, p. A-8.

1028 "Minority-Owned Television Stations." Chicago Tribune, Jan-
      uary 7, 1980, pp. 5-11.

1029 "Minority Ownership of Broadcast Stations Backed by NAB."
      Norfolk Journal & Guide, April 28, 1978, p. B-18.

1030 "Minority Ownership of Radio and TV Stations Backed by FCC."
      Norfolk Journal & Guide, June 16, 1978, p. B-15.

1031 "Mississippi Group Seeks Black Control of TV Station." At-
      lanta World, June 12, 1977, p. 1.

1032 "Mississippi TV Station WLBT." New York Times, June 17,
      1979, p. 22.

1033 "Morgan State Gets TV Network." Jet, September 2, 1971,
      p. 28.

1034 "NAB Backs Minority Ownership of Media." New York Ams-
      terdam News, April 29, 1978, p. A-7.

1035 "NAB Helps Minorities to Secure Own TV and Radio Stations."
      Norfolk Journal and Guide, June 9, 1978, p. B-15.

1036 "National Broadcasters' Minority Ownership Foundation Seeks
      Funds for Goal." Los Angeles Sentinel, February 22,
      1979, p. B-1A.

1037 "National Broadcasting Task Force on Minority Ownership
      Names Board." Atlanta Daily World, February 27, 1979,
      p. 3.

1038 "New Black TV Station, WTSG-TV, Albany, GA." Jet, March
      22, 1982, p. 15.

1039 "Pastore Bill Restricts Black TV Ownership." Soul, Novem-
      ber 17, 1979, p. 18.

1040   "Plight of Black TV Licensee." (Hooks column). Norfolk
       Journal & Guide, June 18, 1977, p. A-9.

1041   "Poitier Heads Production Company." Chicago Daily Defender,
       December 16, 1978, p. I-13.

1042   Poole, Isaiah J. "TV First at Howard." Black Enterprise,
       December 1980, p. 22.

1043   "Proposed Overhaul of Nation's Communication Law." Bila-
       lian News, August 18, 1978, p. I-21.

1044   "A Push For Black-Owned TV." Newsweek, July 2, 1979,
       p. 57.

1045   Robertson, E.   "New Image In Newark (Connections Commu-
       nications)." Black Enterprise, June 1980, p. 55.

1046   "Seaway Communications Buys Wis. Network Station." Jet,
       May 5, 1979, p. 14.

1047   Tempest, R.   "Detroit's Black TV Station." TV Guide, March
       13, 1976, p. 28-29.

1048   "TV Station Sale To North Carolina Mutual Life Insurance
       Company Canceled." Jet, May 22, 1980, p. 40.

1049   "Tyrone Brown Named to Broadcast Capital Fund Board."
       Baltimore Afro American, October 3, 1981, p. 2.

1050   "Washington, D.C. Gets Black-Owned STV." NABOB News,
       July/August 1980, p. 1.

                        Personalities--Actresses

1051   "Actress in the Making." Our World, August 1950, p. 24-26.

1052   "Alice Demery Travis Hosts "For You ... Black Woman."
       Michigan Chronicle, September 3, 1977, p. B-4.

1053   "Amy Irving." Chicago Daily Defender, May 20, 1978, p.
       ENT-11.

1054   "At Home with Ethel Waters." Time, October 5, 1953, p.
       78.

1055   "Barbara Lewis, NYC Actress and Critic." New York Ams-
       terdam News, July 28, 1979, p. 30.

1056   "Barbara McNair: The Activity Debut of a Singer." Sepia,
       July 1960, p. 58-60.

1057 "Barbara-O." (Lee Ivory column). Los Angeles Sentinel,
       November 15, 1979, p. B-4A.

1058 Barber, R. "'The Jeffersons' Isabel Sanford." TV Guide,
       October 30, 1976, p. 20-23.

1059 "Beah Richards." Pittsburgh Courier, January 21, 1978,
       p. 3-20; Chicago Daily Defender, January 21, 1978, p.
       ENT-3.

1060 _____. Pittsburgh Courier, March 4, 1978, p. 3-18.

1061 Beals, Melba. "Essence Woman: Carol Munday Lawrence."
       Essence, March 1980, p. 38.

1062 "Beauty That Is Barbara McNair." Sepia, November 1970,
       p. 72-73.

1063 "BernNadette Stanis: Another Side of 'Good Times' TV
       Daughter." Jet, August 28, 1975, p. 35-39.

1064 "BernNadette Stanis of 'Good Times.'" TV Guide, July 31,
       1976, p. 12-13.

1065 Berry, Bill. "Growing Up With The Real Mrs. Jefferson--
       Isabel Sanford." Jet, October 18, 1979, p. 57-61.

1066 "Beverly Ann." Baltimore Afro American, December 23, 1978,
       p. I-11.

1067 Burke, T. "All's Fair: Bernadette Peters." TV Guide, Oc-
       tober 9, 1976, p. 26-31.

1068 "Butterfly McQueen." New York Amsterdam News, March 31,
       1979, p. 39.

1069 "Career of Caledonia." Chicago Daily Defender, June 4, 1977,
       p. I-4.

1070 "Chance of a Lifetime: Diahann Carroll Wins Fame, Fortune
       and a Celebrity's Headaches on TV Talent Show." Our
       World, May 1954, p. 12-17.

1071 "Charges Against Gail Fisher Dropped." Pittsburgh Courier,
       July 8, 1978, p. 3-18.

1072 "Chelsea Brown." Sepia, June 1867, p. 80+.

1073 "Chelsea Brown: New Star of 'Laugh-In.'" Sepia, February
       1969, p. 34-37.

1074 Chenault, Julie. "Many Faces of Leslie Uggams." Jet, Jan-
       uary 28, 1982, p. 58-62.

1075   Cllp and Kim Fields." Baltimore Afro American, August
       26, 1978, p. I-11.

1076   "Cicely Tyson." Baltimore Afro American, August 18, 1979,
       p. 2-11.

1077   "Cicely Tyson." Bilalian News, February 16, 1979, p. 14.

1078   "Cicely Tyson." Chicago Daily Defender, January 23, 1979,
       p. 17.

1079   "Cicely Tyson." Michigan Chronicle, December 23, 1978, p.
       A-1.

1080   "Cicely Tyson." Pittsburgh Courier, December 30, 1978, p.
       2-10.

1081   "Cicely Tyson's Performance in Atlanta." Atlanta Daily World,
       April 29, 1979, p. 5.

1082   "Cicely Tyson Speaks in Indianapolis on Roles for Blacks."
       Bilalian News, August 17, 1979, p. 12.

1083   "Cicely Tyson Speaks to Black Women's Forum in L.A." Los
       Angeles Sentinel, July 26, 1979, p. A-1.

1084   Collins, Lisa. "Irene Cara." Right On, February 1976, p.
       28-29.

1085   _____. "Sydney Goldsmith: Hollywood's Brightest, Funni-
       est Comedienne." Sepia, June 1980, p. 48-54.

1086   "Damita Jo Freeman of 'Soul Train' Fame, on 'Private Benja-
       min.'" Jet, August 16, 1982, p. 59.

1087   "Dandridge Gets Red Carpet Treatment." Ebony, August 1956,
       p. 24+.

1087a Davidson, B. "Introducing Melba Moore." TV Guide, June
       17, 1972, p. 30-32.

1088   "Debbi Morgan's Role in 'Roots 2.'" Michigan Chronicle,
       February 24, 1979, p. D-8.

1089   "Debbie Allen." Chicago Daily Defender, May 20, 1978, p.
       ENT-2.

1090   "Debbie Allen: A Real Down-to-Earth Lady." Right On, June
       1979, p. 52.

1091   "Debbie Allen: Torrid on TV." Jet, May 17, 1982, p. 58-
       60.

1092 "Deborah Allen: On Acting." Right On, August 1979, p. 43.

1093 DeBose, Troy. "The Maid Wore Costly Wigs and Dressed
      Like No Maid We'll Ever See." New York Times, Sep-
      tember 1, 1968, p. D9.

1094 "Dee Dee Bridgewater." Chicago Daily Defender, June 2,
      1979, p. AW-1.

1095 "Della Reese to be TV Hostess." Soul, March 3, 1969, p. 1.

1096 "Denise Nichols." Michigan Chronicle, January 27, 1979, p.
      B-4.

1097 "Denise Nichols; A Star in 'Room 222.'" Sepia, June 1974,
      p. 48-52.

1098 "Diahann Carroll." People, August 23, 1976, p. 54-59.

1099 "Diahann Carroll Models Donald Brooks Fashions." TV Guide,
      July 8, 1967, p. 26-29.

1100 "Diahann Carroll Stars in Sisters." Los Angeles Sentinel,
      February 1, 1979, p. B-1A.

1101 "Do Negroes Have a Future in Hollywood?" Ebony, Decem-
      ber 1955, p. 24+.

1102 "Do You Remember ... Our Gang?" Negro Digest, Decem-
      ber 1950, p. 69-70.

1103 "Dorothy Dandridge." Baltimore Afro American, December
      2, 1978, p. I-5.

1104 Durslag, M. "Triple Threat Lola Falana." TV Guide, June
      23, 1973, p. 18-20.

1105 "Eartha Kitt." Baltimore Afro American, July 14, 1979, p.
      2-11.

1106 "Eartha Kitt." Chicago Daily Defender, February 11, 1978,
      p. ENT-3.

1107 "Eartha Kitt." Norfolk Journal & Guide, June 2, 1978, p. B-
      12.

1108 "Eartha Kitt." Pittsburgh Courier, February 18, 1978, p.
      4-25.

1109 "Eartha Kitt." TV Guide, December 17, 1955, p. 10-11.

1110 "Eartha Kitt Invited Back to White House after 10 Years."
      Baltimore Afro American, February 4, 1978, p. I-1.

1111 "Eartha Takes Off." Ebony, March 1956, p. 24.

1112 Efron, E. "Diahann Carroll's Struggle Between Two Worlds."
      TV Guide, May 27, 1967, p. 12-15.

1113 "Erica Gimbel, Playing the 'Fame' Game." Right On, July
      1982, p. 40.

1114 "Esther Lets 'God Times' Rolle Without Her." Soul, Novem-
      ber 7, 1977, p. 5-6.

1115 "Esther Rolle Discusses 'Good Times' Role." Baltimore Afro
      American, May 27, 1978, p. I-8.

1116 "Esther Rolle Returns to 'Good Times.'" New York Amster-
      dam News, September 23, 1978, p. D-8.

1117 "Ethel Waters Dies at 76." Soul, October 24, 1977, p. 2.

1118 "Faye Fielder Girl Friday to TV Commentator at CBS."
      Ebony, Oct. 1960, p. 6.

1119 "Fearless Ed Sullivan." (Ethel Waters). TV Guide, June 19,
      1953, p. 5-7.

1120 Fee, Debi. "Damita Co-Star, 'Private Benjamin.'" Right
      On, May 1983, p. 68-69.

1121 _____. "Irene Cara: Out Here on My Own!" Right On,
      July 1982, p. 18, 64.

1122 _____. "Nell Carter: She Deserves a Break Today."
      Right On, October 1982, p. 24-25.

1123 Fisher, Gail. "I'm a Very Private Person." Black Stars,
      p. 50-55.

1124 Fuller, Marilyn. "Versatile Deborah Allen." Soul, May 9,
      1977, p. 8.

1125 "Gail Fisher Cleared of All Charges by L.A. Municipal Court."
      Los Angeles Sentinel, June 22, 1978, p. A-1.

1126 "Gail Fisher of 'Mannix.'" Sepia, March 1969, p. 34-38.

1127 "Gloria Calomee." Michigan Chronicle, May 20, 1978, p.
      B-7.

1128 "Going Places and Doing Things with Mittie Lawrence."
      Sepia, November 1970, p. 16-19.

1129 "Hallelujah, It's Leslie Uggams." TV Guide, April 27, 1968,
      p. 24-27.

1130   "Hattie McDaniel."   New York Amsterdam News, April 28,
       1979, p. 37.

1131   "Hattie McDaniel."   Newsweek, November 3, 1952, p. 71.

1132   Hepburn, D.   "How Evil Is Eartha?"   Our World, September
       1954, p. 9-15.

1133   "Hollywood's New Glamour Queen; With Two New Film Roles,
       Dorothy Dandridge Is Groomed as No. 1 Glamour Girl."
       Ebony, April 1951, p. 48-50+.

1134   Horne, Lena.   "I'm Proud To Be a Mother."   Ebony, April
       1959, p. 56-58+.

1135   Horner, Cynthia.   "Sydney Goldsmith: The Girl with Some-
       thing."   Right On, July 1980, p. 28-29.

1136   _____.   "'Up and Coming's' Cindy Herron."   Right On,
       June 1982, p. 32.

1137   "Irene Cara."   Right On, October 1980, p. 27.

1138   "Irene Cara: A Show Biz Veteran at Age 22."   Ebony, July
       1982, p. 88-92.

1139   "Irene Cara: Anyone Can See She's Found 'Fame!'"   Right
       On, June 1982, p. 16-17.

1140   "Isabel Sanford's California Hideaway."   Ebony, April 1982,
       p. 31-35.

1141   "Isabelle Cooley; Brown Bombshell of Paris Bistros."   Our
       World, February 1953, p. 7-8+.

1142   "Jackie Gleason's 'Billboard' Girl, Lulu Guerrero."   Ebony,
       December 1958, p. 32-36.

1143   "Jane-Ellen Dawkins Promoted by KTLA-TV."   Los Angeles
       Sentinel, November 11, 1982, p. A-10.

1144   "Janet Langhart, Co-Host of 'A.M. New York.'"   Bilalian
       News, April 27, 1979, p. 12; New York Amsterdam News,
       May 12, 1979, p. 29.

1145   "Janet Lanhart Host New York Talk Show."   Jet, March 15,
       1979, p. 58.

1146   "Janet Maclachlan Grabs Filmland's Brass Ring."   Sepia,
       March 1970, p. 54-58.

1147   "Jayne Kennedy."   Atlanta Daily World, June 17, 1979, p. 6.

1148   "Jayne Kennedy." Los Angeles Sentinel, February 2, 1978,
       p. ENT-1.

1149   "Jayne Kennedy: How She Became A Ding-A-Ling." Sepia,
       June 1973, p. 36-38.

1150   "Jayne Kennedy Survives Media Brickbats." Sepia, April
       1980, p. 39-45.

1151   "Jayne Kennedy Tells: Why A Girl Needs a Husband In Holly-
       wood." Sepia, April 1975, p. 36-42.

1152   "Jean Renee Foster." New York Amsterdam News, November
       3, 1979, p. 31.

1153   "Jeanette Dubois: Actress of Many Faces." Sepia, May 1964,
       p. 68-71.

1154   "Jedda; Colored Australian's Star." Ebony, March 1957, p.
       108+.

1155   Jenkins, Flo. "Roxie Roker, Co-Star of TV's 'The Jeffer-
       sons' Advises." Grapevine, September/October 1979,
       p. 40-42.

1156   Jenkins, W. "Portrait of Gail Fisher." Sepia, March 1969,
       p. 34-37.

1157   "Jo Baker Takes New York." Our World, August 1951, p.
       40-44.

1158   Johnson, Boni. "Berlinda Tolbert: Television's First Prime
       Time Mulatto." Soul, March 19, 1979, p. 10.

1159   Johnson, Robert. "Della Reese." Jet, March 29, 1982, p.
       54-58.

1160   _____. "Lola Falana." Jet, April 26, 1982, p. 58-60.

1161   "Josephine Baker Suggests Debbie Allen to Star in 'Josephine.'"
       Chicago Daily Defender, May 15, 1979, p. 22.

1162   "Judy Pace on 'The Young Lawyers.'" TV Guide, September
       19, 1970, p. 18-19.

1163   "Kim Bass: Top TV Actor in Japan." Ebony, September
       1982, p. 48-50.

1164   Kitt, Eartha. "Fame Can Be Lonely." Ebony, December
       1957, p. 83-86+.

1165   LaFontaine, Beverly. "Esther Rolle: Star and Lady." Soul,
       June 20, 1977, p. 20.

1166 _____ . "Saundra Sharp: What Will She Yet Become?" Soul, July 4, 1977, p. 14, 17.

1167 Lane, Bill. "Lena Horne Changes Course." Sepia, June 1980, p. 34-38.

1168 "Lena Horne." Ebony, May 1980, p. 39-45.

1169 "Lena Horne Enjoys Her Longest Vacation." Ebony, December 1954, p. 64-68+.

1170 "Lena Horne: 'Our World's' First Cover Girl." Our World, April 1950, p. 11-13.

1171 "Lena's Daughter Makes Stage Debut." Ebony, November 1960, p. 129-13.

1172 "Leslie Uggams." Chicago Daily Defender, January 13, 1979, p. 11.

1173 Lewis, R. W. "The Importance of Being Julia." TV Guide, December 14, 1968, p. 24-28.

1174 Lewis, R. "Teresa Graves of 'Get Christie Love!'" TV Guide, November 30, 1974, p. 20-23.

1175 "Linda Clifford." Cleveland Call & Post, May 6, 1978, p. A-16.

1176 "Living, Breathing Picture Gallery; Chelsa Brown On 'Laugh-In.'" Ebony, April, 1969, p. 54-56+.

1177 "Lonette McKee, Actress-Singer-Writer." Michigan Chronicle, September 2, 1978, p. B-7.

1178 "Naomi Sims." Washington Post, October 17, 1976, p. B-3.

1179 "Nell Carter Marries." Jet, March 31, 1982, p. 59.

1180 "Nichelle Nichols Discusses Her Role in 'Star Trek.'" Baltimore Afro American, December 8, 1979, p. 2-11.

1181 "Nichelle Nichols Joins Black Pilots." Los Angeles Sentinel, June 1, 1978, p. B-3A.

1182 "Nichelle Nichols, New Star in the TV Heavens." Ebony, January 1967, p. 71-80.

1183 Nolan, Tom. "Says Nell Carter ... 'There Was a Time I Didn't Like Nell.'" TV Guide, August 21, 1982, p. 17-20.

1184 Norman, Shirley. "The Real Ja'Net DuBois." Sepia, March 1978, p. 19-23+.

1185 _____. "Lena Horne At 60." Sepia, June 1977, p. 26-33.

1186 "Madame Sul-Te-Wan; At 80 She's the Oldest Negro Actress in Hollywood." Our World, February 1954, p. 80-82.

1187 "Madge Sinclair." Chicago Daily Defender, January 20, 1979, p. AW-12.

1188 "Madge Sinclair's Role in 'Uncle Joe Shannon.'" Baltimore Afro American, January 20, 1979, p. 2-11.

1189 "Marian Anderson." TV Guide, December 28, 1957, p. 14.

1190 "Marla Gibbs." Cleveland Call & Post, February 4, 1978, p. B-8.

1191 "Marpessa Dawn; American Actress Makes a Big Splash in Europe." Ebony, November 1959, p. 85-88+.

1192 Marsh, Antoinette. "Jonelle Allen: Broadway Actress Tackles Tinseltown." Black Stars, September 1978, p. 20-25.

1193 "Meet Mitch Miller's Leslie Uggams." TV Guide, January 20, 1962, p. 26-28.

1194 "Melba Moore." New York Amsterdam News, March 4, 1978, p. D-8.

1195 "Melba Moore." New York Amsterdam News, September 15, 1979, p. 31.

1196 "Million Dollar Beauty, Lena Horne." Sepia, January 1958, p. 7-13.

1197 Mills, Jon. "Esther Rolle: A Television Mother Speaks Out!" Right On, December 1979, p. 44-45.

1198 "Miss Waters Regrets." Ebony, February 1957, p. 56-60.

1199 Morrison, A. "Ethel Waters Comes Back." Negro Digest, April 1950, p. 6-10.

1200 _____. "Mother Role Brings Broadway Fame." Ebony, May 1960, p. 97-100+.

1201 Murphy, Frederick. "Debbie Allen: A View From Within The Heart of An Actress." Black Stars, April, 1979, p. 7-10.

1202 "My Biggest Break." (Louise Beavers). Negro Digest, December 1949, p. 21-22.

1203 "Mystery of Dorothy Dandridge." Color, March 1956, p. 7-9.

1204   "Off Stage with Eartha Kitt." Our World, January 1953, p.
       44-45.

1205   "On the Hotline with Irene Cara." Right On, August 1979,
       p. 12-13.

1206   Ostroff, R. "Ja'net DuBois of 'Good Times.'" TV Guide,
       July 19, 1975, p. 10-12.

1207   "Passing of 'Beulah.'" Our World, February 1953, p. 12-15.

1208   "A Pooped Pearlie Mae." Ebony, April 1958, p. 55-56+.

1209   Powell, Pauline. "Marla Gibbs: A True Humanitarian."
       Grapevine, February 1981, p. 36-38.

1210   "Private World of Dorothy Dandridge." Ebony, June 1962,
       p. 116-121.

1211   Raddatz, L. "'Mannix's' Girl Friday--Gail Fisher." TV
       Guide, October 19, 1968, p. 23-24.

1212   _____. "Theresa Merritt of 'That's My Mama.'" TV
       Guide, January 18, 1975, p. 20-22.

1213   "Rediscovering Chelsea Brown." TV Guide, November 21,
       1970, p. 21-24.

1214   Reed, Claude. "Marla Gibbs." National Scene Supplement,
       January 1983, p. 11.

1215   "Ren Woods Plays Sybil in 'Youngblood.'" Baltimore Afro
       American, May 6, 1978, p. I-11.

1216   Riley, J. "Esther Rolle of 'Good Times.'" TV Guide, June
       29, 1974, p. 16-18.

1217   Robinson, Louie. "Jayne Kennedy." Ebony, April 1981, p.
       33-36.

1218   "Ruby Dee." Chicago Daily Defender, May 26, 1979, p. 2-9.

1219   Salvo, Patrick and Salvo, Barbara. "Denise Nicholas: It
       Take A Hell of A Man To Put Up With Me." Sepia, Feb-
       ruary 1975, p. 36-42.

1220   Sanders, Charles. "Debbie Allen." Ebony, March 1983, p.
       74-80.

1221   _____. "Diahann Carroll Talks About Marriage." Ebony,
       September 1976, p. 152+.

1222   No entry.

1223 _____. "Jayne & Leon Kennedy." Ebony, January 1982,
     p. 116-125.

1224 "Sandra Brown Bender, Co-Host of 'Omelet' on WHAS-TV in
     Louisville," Ebony, March 1972, p. 7.

1225 "Secretary by Day, Actress by Night." Sepia, August 1964,
     p. 46-50.

1226 See, C. "Diahann Carroll's Image." TV Guide, March 14,
     1970, p. 26-30.

1227 "Shari Belafonte." Jet, May 24, 1982, p. 58-60.

1228 "Sharon Brown." Michigan Chronicle, February 25, 1979,
     p. B-9.

1229 "Shaw, Ellen. "Roxie Roker." TV Guide, April 4, 1981,
     p. 12-14.

1230 Sissle, Noble. "How Jo Baker Got Started." Negro Digest,
     August 1951, p. 15-19.

1231 Slaton, Shell. "Berlinda Tolbert of 'The Jefferson.'" Right
     On, December 1979, p. 26-27.

1232 St. John, Michael. "Debbie Allen Swings on a Star." En-
     core, October 2, 1978, p. 26-29.

1233 "Thelma Hopkins." Jet, July 26, 1982, p. 55.

1234 Torgerson, E. "Della Reese of 'Chico and the Man.'" TV
     Guide, December 4, 1976, p. 39-40.

1235 "TV's Personality Girl: Ohio Housewife Has Two Shows on
     TV, Three on Radio." Ebony, December 1957, p. 102-
     106.

1236 Ward, Renee. "Rosalind Cash: Prayer Has Kept Me Going."
     Soul, September 1, 1975, p. 8.

1237 Waters, Ethel. "Men in My Life; Famous Actress Looks Back
     to Recall Intimate Off-Stage Story of Tumultuous Loves in
     Her Stormy Life on Stage." Ebony, January 1952, p. 24-
     32+.

1238 Webster, Ivan. "A Woman Called Tyson." Encore, Novem-
     ber 6, 1978, p. 24-28.

1239 "Whatever Happened to Charlayne Hunter?" Ebony, June
     1972, p. 138.

1240 "Whatever Lola Wants ... Lola Falana Gets." Sepia, April
     1967, p. 32-36.

1241 Winter, Jason. "LaWanda Page: A Cinderella Story." Black
      Stars, December 1977, p. 28-30+.

1242 Young, A. S. "Dorothy Dandridge Marries." Sepia, Septem-
      ber 1959, p. 38-43.

1243 _____. "Life and Death of Dorothy Dandridge." Sepia,
      December 1965, p. 8-12+.

1244 "Young Actress Kimberly Webb." Chicago Daily Defender,
      November 25, 1978, p. ENT-15.

1245 "Zara Cully Brown Dies." New York Amsterdam News, March
      4, 1978, p. D-4; Baltimore Afro American, March 11,
      1978, p. I-11.

                    Personalities--Actors

1246 "Actor Ray Vitte's Death." Los Angeles Wave, April 20,
      1983, p. 1, 3.

1247 "Actor/Singer Clarence Muse on Thomas Lee New Television
      Station, W6XAO in Los Angeles." California Eagle, De-
      cember 21, 1939, p. 6-B.

1248 "Adam Wade." Chicago Daily Defender, June 30, 1979, p.
      AW-5.

1249 "Adam Wade." Sepia, August 1962, p. 68.

1250 "Adam Wade Collects Bet." Jet, September 14, 1961, p. 27.

1251 Alder, D. "Richard Roundtree of 'Shaft.'" TV Guide, April
      20, 1974, p. 26-28.

1252 "Alex Haley." (Hooks column). Baltimore Afro American,
      March 12, 1977, p. I-5.

1253 "Antoine, Roane. "When Will Richard Pryor's Ordeal End?"
      Sepia, August 1980, p. 16-22.

1254 "Antonio Fargas." Baltimore Afro American, January 13,
      1979, p. 2-11.

1255 "Antonio Fargas." Los Angeles Sentinel, May 18, 1978, p.
      B-2A.

1256 Barber, R. "'Good Times' with Jimmie Walker." TV Guide,
      December 14, 1974, p. 28-32.

1257 _____. "James Earl Jones Comes to TV." TV Guide,
     October 12, 1974, p. 12-17.

1258 "Belafonte Power." Newsweek, February 19, 1968, p. 101.

1259 Bennett, L., Jr. "Hollywood's First Negro Star; Sidney Poi-
     tier Breaks Film Barrier." Ebony, May 1959, p. 100-
     103+.

1260 "Ben Vereen." Chicago Daily Defender, November 11, 1978,
     p. ENT-2.

1261 "Ben Vereen." Pittsburgh Courier, February 18, 1978, p. 4-
     27. "Breaks Film Barrier." Ebony, May 1959,

1262 Benny, Jack. "My 24 Years with Rochester." Sepia, March
     1962, p. 34-37.

1263 "Benny and Rochester; TV's Hottest Team." Our World,
     August 1955, p. 51-55.

1264 Berkow, I. "John Amos of 'Good Times.'" TV Guide, Au-
     gust 17, 1974, p. 15-18.

1265 "Bernie Casey and Minority Actors." Bilalian News, August
     24, 1979, p. 24.

1266 "Bill Cosby Comes Home." TV Guide, August 19, 1967, p.
     4-6.

1267 "Bill Cosby; Cool Hip Spy." Sepia, July 1966, p. 22-27.

1268 "Billy Daniels Hits the Top." Ebony, September 1950, p. 40-
     44.

1269 "Billy Dee Williams." Chicago Daily Defender, March 6,
     1979, p. 11.

1270 "Billy Dee Williams--A Man for all Seasons." Right On,
     March 1982, p. 22-25.

1271 "Billy Dee Williams Has Two Television Projects." Soul,
     August 30, 1976, p. 1.

1272 "Big Payoff; St. Louis Newlyweds Enjoy a Week in Paris after
     Copping $8,000 'Big Payoff' Jackpot." Our World, Feb-
     ruary 1953, p. 30-33.

1273 Black, Doris. "Clarence Muse." Sepia, October 1976, p.
     80.

1274 _____. "What's Next for Bill Cosby?" Sepia, June 1971,
     p. 44-48.

1275 "Black 'Roots 2' Actors Who Had Their Roots in Ohio. " (Editorial). Cleveland Call & Post, February 24, 1979, p. A-8.

1276 "Boy Wonder: Bill Cosby. " TV Guide, March 16, 1968, p. 28-29.

1277 Brack, Fred. "Yaphet Kotto. " Dial, February 1982, p. 44+.

1278 "Brock Peters. " Ebony, June 1962, p. 186-188.

1279 "Brock Peters. " Ebony, June 1963, p. 106-108+.

1280 Burrell, Walter. "Robert Hooks: Black Where It Counts. " Soul, November 16, 1970, p. 16-17.

1281 _____. "Whatever Happened to Woody Strode? " Ebony, June 1982, p. 140-141.

1282 "Butterbeans and Susie; Oldest Negro Song and Dance Act Celebrates Its 35th Anniversary in Show Business. " Ebony, April 1952, p. 59-63.

1283 "Carl Weathers. " Baltimore Afro American, June 30, 1979, p. 2-11.

1284 "Carl Weathers. " Chicago Daily Defender, July 7, 1979, p. AW-12.

1285 "Carl Weathers. " Chicago Daily Defender, August 8, 1979, p. WER-1.

1286 "Carl Weathers. " Michigan Chronicle, December 23, 1978, p. B-6.

1287 Cash, Rita. "Michael Roberts Is 'Rooster' on 'Baretta. '" Soul, May 8, 1978, p. 8.

1288 "The Charisma of Billy Dee Williams. " Right On, November 1981, p. 20-22.

1289 "Chronology of Paul Robeson's Life. " Michigan Chronicle, April 29, 1978, p. A-3.

1290 "Clarence Muse Dies at Age 90. " Los Angeles Sentinel, October 18, 1979, p. A-1; New York Amsterdam News, October 27, 1979, p. 28.

1291 "Clarence Muse's Acting Career Recalled. " Baltimore Afro American, October 27, 1979, p. 2-11.

1292 "Clarence (Pops) Foster Dies. " New York Amsterdam News, September 10, 1977, p. D-6.

1293   "Cleavon Little." Chicago Daily Defender, May 6, 1978, p.
        ENT-3.

1294   "Cleavon Little." Pittsburgh Courier, June 3, 1978, p. 3-19.

1295   "Clifton Davis." Baltimore Afro American, August 4, 1979,
        p. 2-11.

1296   Cole, Deborah. "Hal Williams." Black Stars, p. 10-15.

1297   Collier, Aldore. "Roger Mosley: An Actor with a Conscience."
        Ebony, November 1982, p. 79-85.

1298   _____. "Ron Glass and Demond Wilson Bounce Back as
        TV's New Odd Couple." Jet, November 22, 1982, p. 62-
        65.

1299   _____. "Whatever Happened to the Nicholas Brothers?"
        Ebony, May 1983, p. 103-106.

1300   Collins, Lisa. "Lawrence Hilton-Jacobs: 'Cool 'n' Struttin.'"
        Black Stars, April 1976, p. 14-18.

1301   _____. "Ray Vitte: Stardom is Rewarded." Black Stars,
        September 1978, p. 6-11.

1302   Cooper, K. "Les Edwards: A 60 Minutes Man." Essence,
        September 1980, p. 13-14.

1303   "Craziest Act in Show Business; Red Caps Seem to Have a
        Right Formula." Our World, March 1953, p. 42-45.

1304   "Curtis Wilson Hosts Cleveland Television Series." Cleveland
        Call & Post, March 26, 1977, p. A-5.

1305   "Dancing Brothers: Young Powells Make Early Bid for Fame
        on Television." Ebony, May 1956, p. 50-52.

1306   Daniel, B. "Bernie Hamilton: A Great Star in the Making."
        Sepia, August 1961, p. 59-63.

1307   Davidson, B. "Redd Foxx--the World's Funniest Ex-Dishwasher."
        TV Guide, March 17, 1973, p. 26-30.

1308   Davis, Curt. "Tony Martinez--A Man of La World." Encore,
        November 7, 1977, p. 27-28.

1309   "Davis Roberts: The Man Everybody Has Seen but Nobody
        Knows." Ebony, September 1981, p. 48-51.

1310   "Demond Wilson Misses Two Weeks' Work; No Reason." Jet,
        April 24, 1975, p. 56.

1311 de Roos, R. "Bill Cosby: the Spy Who Came in for the
      Gold. " TV Guide, October 23, 1965, p. 14-17.

1312 "Detroit Relives Life and Times of Paul Robeson. " Michigan
      Chronicle, April 15, 1978, p. A-1.

1313 "Detroit's Celebration of Robeson's Life. " (Adams column).
      Michigan Chronicle, April 29, 1978, p. A-8.

1314 "Do Black Actors Make Good Fathers?" Sepia, December
      1969, p. 32-34.

1315 "Do You Remember ... Stepin Fetchit?" Negro Digest, No-
      vember 1950, p. 42-43.

1316 "Don Cornelius Recovering from Surgery in LA. " Jet, De-
      cember 20, 1982, p. 55.

1317 Dongee, Ron. "Ray Vitte: Pyramid Power. " Soul, August
      29, 1977, p. 13.

1318 Dreyfuss, Joel. "Bryant Gumbel: A Man for Today. " Black
      Enterprise, April 1982, p. 32.

1319 Durslag, M. "Fred Williamson of 'Julia. '" TV Guide, De-
      cember 26, 1970, p. 15-18.

1320 Ebert, A. "How Sammy Davis Jr. Met Disaster. " TV Guide,
      July 9, 1966, p. 4-9; July 16, 1966, p. 22-26.

1321 "Eddie Murphy Does Dangerous Comedy Called 'Playing Doz-
      ens. '" Jet, August 23, 1982, p. 58.

1322 "Edric Connor: Theatrical Genius. " Sepia, December 1963,
      p. 52-55.

1323 Efron, E. "Robert Hooks of 'N. Y. P. D. '" TV Guide, Feb-
      ruary 10, 1968, p. 22-24.

1324 English, Lori and Rush, Jeffrey. "Lawrence Hilton-Jacobs. "
      Black Stars, p. 32-39.

1325 Ernest, E. "Gil Noble: Media's Warrior. " Encore, October
      1981, p. 21-23.

1326 "Fabulous Gales. " Our World, August 1951, p. 32-35.

1327 Fee, Debi. "Brian Mitchell of 'Trapper John. '" Right On,
      May 1982, p. 52; January 1983, p. 24-25.

1328 _____. "Leon Kennedy: The Truth Behind the Breakup. "
      Right On, March 1982, p. 16-17.

1329 _____. "Mr. T.: The Gentle Giant." Right On, August
     1982, p. 58-59.

1330 "Frank Silvera; Famous Negro Character Actor Portrays
     Many Nationalities and Races But Seldom His Own."
     Ebony, March 1952, p. 51-55.

1331 "From Actor to College Prof.; Star Juano Hernandez Returns
     to Native Puerto Rico for Teaching Job." Ebony, Novem-
     ber 1952, p. 122-126+.

1332 Fuller, Marilyn. "Eddie 'Rochester' Anderson Dies." Soul,
     April 11, 1977, p. 4.

1333 Gantt, H. "Why I Turned Down Stardom in Paris." Negro
     Digest, December 1961, p. 45-48.

1334 "Gary Coleman." Pittsburgh Courier, June 10, 1978, p. 3-
     17.

1335 "Gary Coleman Voted Top Performer at Peoples' Choice
     Awards." Jet, April 4, 1982, p. 56.

1336 Gelman, Steve. "Robert Guillaume." TV Guide, September
     15, 1979, p. 26.

1337 "Gene Anthony Ray." Right On, July 1982, p. 48.

1338 "Gene Anthony Ray: Will 'Fame' Make Him Famous?" Right
     On, September 1980, p. 26-27.

1339 "Gene Williams, Child Actor." New York Amsterdam News,
     January 21, 1978, p. D-4.

1340 "George Kirby; Mimic with A Thousand Faces and Voice Range
     That Matches Is New Nightclub Sensation." Ebony, Jan-
     uary 1952, p. 61-62+.

1341 "Glynn Turman." New York Amsterdam News, January 27,
     1979, p. 58.

1342 "'Good Times' J. J. Character Eyed." Baltimore Afro Amer-
     ican, November 5, 1977, p. I-1.

1343 "Greater Philadelphia's Newest TV Star." Color, January
     1956, p. 5.

1344 "Greenberg, P. "Georg Stanford Brown of 'The Rookies.'"
     TV Guide, May 4, 1974, p. 21-26.

1345 "Greg Morris Family Beats Show Business Jinx." Ebony,
     May 1981, p. 33-36.

1346 "Greg Morris Speaks Out On Blackness and Black Movies."
Sepia, December 1973, p. 46-50.

1347 Haley, Alex. "My Search for 'Roots.'" TV Guide, January
22, 1977, p. 6-9.

1348 "Haley Named Reader's Digest Roving Editor." Los Angeles
Wave, April 20, 1983, p. 3.

1349 Hampton, Lee Curtis. "D'Urville Martin: Gave up Sugar
Mama for Showbiz." Soul, March 1, 1976, p. 13.

1350 "Harry Belafonte." TV Guide, January 10, 1959, p. 13-15;
December 5, 1959, p. 12-13.

1351 "Heshimu Cunbuk: Jason of 'Room 222.'" Soul, August 28,
1978, p. 15.

1352 Hicks, Jack. "Ted Lange." TV Guide, July 19, 1980, p.
22+.

1353 Higgins, R. "Flip Wilson, the Gentle Spoofer." TV Guide,
January 17, 1970, p. 35-40.

1354 Hobson, D. "Lloyd Haynes Calls His Class to Order." TV
Guide, November 1, 1969, p. 31-34.

1355 _____. "The Odyssey of Otis Young." TV Guide, March
1, 1969, p. 18-22.

1356 _____. "On Maneuvers with Hari Rhodes." TV Guide,
April 20, 1968, p. 18-19.

1357 _____. "Sherman Hemsley of 'The Jeffersons.'" TV
Guide, June 21, 1975, p. 20-22.

1358 "Hollywood's Handsome Henry." Ebony, February 1959,
p. 45+.

1359 "Hollywood's Hottest Negro Actor; Dynamic Juano Hernandez
Gets His Fourth Important Role in Single Year in 'The
Breaking Point.'" Ebony, August 1950, p. 22-26.

1360 Horner, Cynthia. "Michael Warren of 'Hill Street Blues.'"
Right On, May 1982, p. 30-31.

1361 "How Sidney Poitier Won an Oscar." Sepia, June 1964, p.
14-17.

1362 Hyman, E. "Black Actor in Norway." Negro Digest, February 1964, p. 32-36.

1363 Ingram, R. "I Came Back From the Dead." Ebony, March
1955, p. 48-51+.

1364 "Ivan Dixon at Home." Sepia, February 1967, p. 38-41.

1365 "Ivan Dixon's Hard Climb from the Ranks." TV Guide, September 16, 1967, p. 35-36.

1366 Ivory, Steve. "Mr. T.: My Bodyguard." Right On, December 1982, p. 50-51, 64-65.

1367 _____. "Sherman Hemsley: I Never Look at 'The Jeffersons.'" Soul, June 20, 1977, p. 14.

1368 "Jack Benny's Man 'Rochester.'" TV Guide, August 27, 1955, p. 20-21.

1369 "James Earl Jones." Negro Digest, October 1962, p. 43-44.

1370 "James Earl Jones, Actor Still Climbing." Ebony, April 1965, p. 98-100+.

1371 "James Earl Jones' Goal Is to Become Great Actor." Sepia, February 1964, p. 72-76.

1372 "James Earl Jones: Race Is Still the Important Thing." Sepia, January 1971, p. 16-20.

1373 "James Earl Jones Signs to Play Haley in 'Roots.'" Los Angeles Sentinel, August 17, 1978, p. B-2A.

1374 Jenkins, W. "Allison Mills; Image of Hollywood's New Breed." Sepia, July 1970, p. 14-17.

1375 "Jim Tilmon, TV Weatherman In The Skies." Sepia, December 1975, p. 56-5.

1376 "John Moultrie." Chicago Daily Defender, November 3, 1979, p. AW-15.

1377 Johnson, Boni. "Terry Carter of 'Battlestar Galactica.'" Soul, December 11, 1978, p. 16.

1378 Johnson, Robert. "Al Freeman Talks About TV Career and His Designing Wife." Jet, August 13, 1981, p. 60-63.

1379 _____. "Sidney Poitier's Book Talks About His Marriage, Black Films and Tensions in Life." Jet, May 22, 1980, p. 56-62.

1380 "Johnny Brown Laughs Way To TV Stardom." Jet, June 17, 1971, p. 56-57+.

1381 Jones, Hughes. "Sid McCoy: The Freedom of Self-Expression." Black Collegian, November 1980, p. 205-207.

1382   Jordon, Milton. "Bill Dilday: Sitting in the Eye of a TV
       Storm. " Sepia, November 1979, p. 31-35.

1383   Kaiser, R. "Cleavon Little of 'Temperature's Rising. ' " TV
       Guide, April 28, 1973, p. 11-16.

1384   "King of the Con Men; Single-Handed on a New York TV Show,
       Edward Lee Woods Duped 15 Million People to Win this
       Title. " Our World, September 1953, p. 61-65.

1385   Klemesrud, Judy. "Fred--Don't Compare Me with Sidney. "
       New York Times, March 18, 1973, p. 27.

1386   Lane, Bill. "Ted Lange: 'Love Boat's' Dream Boat. " Sepia,
       February 1979, p. 65-70.

1387   "Larry McCormick, Anchorman, KTLA, Los Angeles. "
       (Young column). Los Angeles Sentinel, January 22, 1981,
       p. A-7.

1388   "LaVar Burton. " Atlanta Daily World, July 9, 1978, p. I-10.

1389   "LaVar Burton Interviewed about His Sudden Fame. " Michigan
       Chronicle, September 2, 1978, p. A-1.

1390   "Lawrence Hilton-Jacobs. " Chicago Daily Defender, March
       10, 1979, p. 9.

1391   "Lawrence Hilton-Jacobs. " Chicago Daily Defender, August
       25, 1979, p. AW-10.

1392   "Lawrence Hilton-Jacobs. " Michigan Chronicle, April 29,
       1978, p. B-6; Atlanta Daily World, May 4, 1978, p. I-6.

1393   "Lawrence Hilton-Jacobs. " Michigan Chronicle, October 7,
       1978, p. A-1; New York Amsterdam News, February 25,
       1978, p. D-7; New York Amsterdam News, May 5, 1979,
       p. 39.

1394   "Lawrence Hilton-Jacobs. " Pittsburgh Courier, October 21,
       1978, p. 3-17.

1395   "Leon Isaac Kennedy. " Cleveland Call & Post, December 8,
       1979, p. B-2.

1396   "LeVar Burton Wins Ron Leflore TV Role. " Los Angeles
       Sentinel, April 13, 1978, p. B-2A.

1397   Levin, E. "Black Star of 'Tenafly' Talks About Growing up
       Near Tenafly, N. J. " TV Guide, December 29, 1973, p. 2.

1398   Levin, E. "Robert Hooks Talks About Black Theater. " TV
       Guide, April 6, 1974, p. 2.

1399   "'Like It Is' and Gil Noble." New York Amsterdam News, October 8, 1977, p. D-8.

1400   "Lion Man; Woody Strode Plays Comic Beast in 'Androcles and the Lion.'" Ebony, August 1952, p. 39-42+.

1401   "Lloyd Richards Talks About Robeson." New York Amsterdam News, March 4, 1978, p. D-6.

1402   "Lou Gossett Playing Satchel Paige on TV." (A.S. Young column). Los Angeles Sentinel, December 20, 1979, p. A-7.

1403   "Lou Gossett to Star in 'The Lazarus Syndrome.'" Bilalian News, August 3, 1979, p. 30.

1404   Lucas, Bob. "Grady Bids For TV Stardom on His Show." Jet, December 18, 1975, p. 58-60.

1405   _____. "Mr. and Mrs. Broadway: Ruby Dee and Ossie Davis Have Built Outstanding Careers." Sepia, April 1960, p. 51-53.

1406   _____. "Redd Foxx Marries Again." Jet, March 1980, p. 60-62.

1407   _____. "Redd Foxx Sheds His TV Image." Jet, December 4, 1975, p. 52-55.

1408   _____. "Scatman Crothers' 56 Years of Show Biz, 44 Years of Marriage." Jet, June 11, 1981, p. 28-31.

1409   _____. "Switch to ABC-TV Changes Lifestyle of Redd Foxx." Jet, May 6, 1976, p. 58-60.

1410   McHarry, Charles. "Adam Wade." New York Daily News, September 16, 1961, p. 1.

1411   "'Magnum PI's' Roger Mosley Says Jet Story Added Blacks to Show's Staff." Jet, December 27, 1982, p. 62.

1412   "Man Who Created Emperor Jones." Sepia, May 1958, p. 41.

1413   "The Man Who Does 'Good Times' Dyn-o-mite Paintings." TV Guide, July 10, 1976, p. 10-11.

1414   "Mantan Moreland's Acting Career." Bilalian News, July 6, 1979, p. 24.

1415   "Many Faces of Ivan Dixon." Sepia, July 1965, p. 32-36.

1416   "Many Faces of Oscar Brown, Jr." Sepia, September 1962, p. 72-74.

1417 "Mark Warren, TV's Black Skyrocket." Ebony, April 1979, p. 113-118.

1418 Marshall, Marilyn. "Prime Time for Michael Warren." Ebony, April 1982, p. 48-52.

1419 "Max Robinson." Us, July 25, 1978, p. 56-57.

1420 "Max Robinson." Washingtonian, September 1978, p. 8.

1421 "Michael Moriarty." Chicago Daily Defender, September 9, 1978, p. ENT-13.

1422 "Mike Evans Plays Lionel in 'All in the Family.'" Soul, March 8, 1971, p. 4.

1423 "Mike Evans Quits 'The Jeffersons.'" Soul, August 4, 1975, p. 1.

1424 Mortimer, O. "Ira Aldridge, Shakespearean Actor." Crisis, April 1955, p. 202-214.

1425 "Most Unusual Stand-In." Sepia, December 1959, p. 18-19.

1426 No entry.

1427 "Mr. and Mrs. Broadway; Ruby Dee, Ossie Davis Blend Stage, Marriage." Ebony, February 1961, p. 110-114.

1428 "Mr. Black Magic: Billy Daniels, Florida's Gift to Cafe Society." Our World, April 1951, p. 45-48.

1429 Murphy, Frederick and Davis, Curt. "Can Percy Sutton Go the Distance?" Encore, April 4, 1977, p. 8-15.

1430 "NAACP Executive Director Hoods Speaks in Los Angeles." Los Angeles Sentinel, June 19, 1980, p. A-4.

1431 Nadel, G. "Scatman Crothers of 'Chico and the Man.'" TV Guide, March 13, 1976, p. 21-26.

1432 "New Faces on 'The White Shadow': Art Holliday, Wolfe Perry, Larry Flash Jenkins." Right On, October 1980, p. 22-24.

1433 "The New Odd Couple: Ron Glass and Demond Wilson." Right On, December 1982, p. 5.

1434 Nipson, H. "Job for Officer Barnes." Negro Digest, December 1950, p. 95.

1435 Norman, Shirley. "Clifton Davis." Sepia, May 1976, p. 68-78.

1436 _____. "Ron Glass: TV's Top Black Detective." Sepia,
        May 1977, p. 54-60.

1437 _____. "Television's Top Black Detective." Sepia, May
        1977, p. 54-56+.

1438 Norment, Lynn. "Howard Rollins." Ebony, February 1982,
        p. 115-120.

1439 _____. "Lou Gossett: The Agony and Ecstasy of Success."
        Ebony, December 1982, p. 142-146.

1440 Norton, F. "Audacity of Sidney Poitier." Holiday, June 1962,
        p. 103.

1441 O'Conner, John J. "Topper Carew Has A New Angle of Vi-
        son." New York Times, May 18, 1980, p. 36.

1442 "Oscar Brown, Jr.:   The Flop That Flipped." Sepia, May
        1963, p. 18-22.

1443 "Oscar Brown to Host 'From Jumpstreet.'" Chicago Daily
        Defender, July 14, 1979, p. 2-9.

1444 "Ossie Davis." Pittsburgh Courier, September 1, 1979, p.
        ENT-4.

1445 "Ossie Davis and Ruby Dee." Chicago Daily Defender, Sep-
        tember 8, 1979, p. 2-7.

1446 "Ossie Davis Lauds Strict School Rules in Richmond." Balti-
        more Afro American, September 9, 1978, p. I-8.

1447 "Otto Sterman, the Man of a Hundred Faces." Our World,
        February 1955, p. 17-23.

1448 "Paul Robeson." (George Crockett commentary). Michigan
        Chronicle, February 24, 1979, p. B-4.

1449 "Paul Robeson." New York Amsterdam News, February 17,
        1979, p. 43.

1450 "Paul Robeson Celebration." Michigan Chronicle, April 8,
        1978, p. A-8.

1451 "Paul Robeson Honored at United Nations." New York Ams-
        terdam News, October 21, 1978, p. A-3.

1452 "Paul Robeson Week Activities Planned in Detroit." Michigan
        Chronicle, April 8, 1978, p. A-1.

1453 "Paul Winfield to Portray MLK in TV Movie." Michigan
        Chronicle, April 23, 1977, p. B-4.

1454   Peck, J. L. H.   "Hollywood's Bronze Valentino."   Our World,
       February 1950, p. 26-29+.

1455   "Peter Wise."   Right On, October 1978, p. 40.

1456   Peterson, F.   "I Spy on Bill Cosby."   Sepia, August 1969,
       p. 8-11.

1457   Peterson, Franklynn.   "Mr. Black Journal: Tony Brown."
       Sepia, March 1972, p. 51-58.

1457a Pitts, Leonard.   "Adam Wade's Success Game Plan."   Soul,
       July 4, 1977, p. 13.

1457b _____.   "Bryant Gumbel: Behind the Scenes with Amer-
       ica's Mr. Perfect."   Right On--Class, Spring 1983, p.
       21-23.

1458   _____.   "Louis Gossett Jr. Won an Emmy for 'Roots.'"
       Soul, April 24, 1978, p. 6.

1459   _____.   "Ron Glass."   Soul, July 3, 1978, p. 6.

1460   Poitier, Sidney.   "Why I Became an Actor."   Negro Digest,
       December 1961, p. 80-97.

1461   Pyatt, Richard I.   "Will Moses Gunn Shoot Down Father Time?"
       Encore, January 3, 1977, p. 29-30.

1462   Raddatz, L.   "'Ironsides' Don Mitchell."   TV Guide, Novem-
       ber 30, 1968, p. 21-25.

1463   _____.   "Lloyd Haynes of 'Room 222.'"   TV Guide, Sep-
       tember 15, 1973, p. 20-22.

1464   "Ragan Henry Entrepreneur."   Norfolk Journal & Guide, May
       21, 1977, p. A-3.

1465   "Raymond St. Jacques."   Baltimore Afro American, September
       30, 1978, p. I-11.

1466   "Redd Foxx: How He Went From Blue Jokes to Black."
       Sepia, June 1972, p. 38-41.

1467   "Redd Foxx May Be Relieved of His Taft Police Duties."   Jet,
       April 17, 1975, p. 55.

1468   "Redd Foxx Presents Redd Foxx."   Sepia, June 1967, p. 42-
       46.

1469   "Redd Foxx: Television's Unhappy Millionaire."   Sepia, Jan-
       uary 1976, p. 34-40.

1470   "Requiem for the Kingfish." Ebony, July 1959, p. 57-58+.

1471   "Robert Earl Jones Eyes James Earl Jones' Career." Bila-
       lian News, April 13, 1979, p. 24.

1472   "Robert Guillaume." Oui, March 1979, p. 112.

1473   Robinson, Louie. "Belafonte: Portrait of an 'Angry' Legend."
       Ebony, November 1981, p. 79-84.

1474   _____. "J.J. In Search of Jimmie Walker." Ebony, April
       1975, p. 136-141.

1475   _____. "Sammy Davis, Jr.: The Kid Turns 50." Ebony,
       July 1972, p. 52-59.

1476   _____. "Sidney Poitier Tells How To Stay On Top in Holly-
       wood." Ebony, November 1977, p. 53-64.

1477   "Rochester in London." Our World, November 1950, p. 20-
       24.

1478   "Roger Mosley and Tom Selleck: Black TV Star Rose from
       Ghetto to Fame." Jet, October 4, 1982, p. 62-65.

1479   "Ron Glass: Living in the Glass House." Right On, March
       1983, p. 31-32.

1480   "Ron O'Neal." Los Angeles Sentinel, December 21, 1978, p.
       A-12.

1481   "Ron O'Neal Speaks at Clark College." Atlanta Daily World,
       April 26, 1979, p. 7.

1482   Rubine, Naomi. "Obnoxious Egomaniac Fred Williamson
       Blows His Cool." Soul, August 4, 1975, p. 2-3.

1483   Russell, Dick. "Lou Gossett, Jr." TV Guide, April 8, 1978,
       p. 39+.

1484   Salvo, Pat. "John Amos." Sepia, March 1976, p. 24-33.

1485   _____. "Robert Guillaume." Sepia, June 1979, p. 39+.

1486   "Sammy Davis." Sepia, February 1966, p. 8-13.

1487   "Sammy Davis, Jr. at 25." Ebony, December 1950, p. 45-
       49.

1488   "Sammy Davis, Jr. Proves a Point." Sepia, November 1962,
       p. 55-58.

1489   "Sammy Davis's World of Children." TV Guide, November
       20, 1965, p. 28-29.

1490 Sanders, C. L. "Raymond the Magnificent." Ebony, November 1969, p. 175-178+.

1491 _____. "Sidney Poitier: The Man Behind the Star." Ebony, April 1968, p. 172-174+.

1492 "Sandy Lewis Fights for Stardom." Sepia, June 1965, p. 68-73.

1493 "Scat-Man Crothers." Our World, June 1953, p. 21.

1494 "Scatman Crothers; After 50 Years in Show Biz, An 'Overnight' Success." Ebony, July 1978, p. 62-67.

1495 "Sid McCoy." Sepia, March 1963, p. 70-74.

1496 "Sidney Poitier--Diahann Carroll: What Will It Be?" Sepia, June 1965, p. 8-12+.

1497 Sildn, Isobel. "Clifton Davis." Pageant, November 1976, p. 118-123.

1498 Shelton, Eugene. "Kene Holliday and Vernee Watson of Carter Country." Soul, June 19, 1978, p. 2-3.

1499 _____. "Rodney Allen Rippy: He Just Keeps on Stepping." Soul, December 25, 1978, p. 30.

1500 _____. "Terry Carter of 'Battlestar Galactica.'" Soul, December 11, 1978, p. 17.

1501 Slater, Jack. "Robert Guillaume, Television's Prime Time Black Man." Ebony, December 1979, p. 124+.

1502 Slaton, Shell. "Byron Allen: The 'Real People' Person." Right On, April 1980, p. 12-13.

1503 _____. "The Fred Williams Experience." Right On, December 1979, p. 52-53.

1504 _____. "'Trapper John M. D.' Presents--Brian Mitchell." Right On, September 1980, p. 64-65.

1505 "Stan Shaw." New York Amsterdam News, February 11, 1978, p. B-4.

1507 "Stevie Wonder Interviewed on TV." Michigan Chronicle, February 19, 1977, p. B-4.

1508 "Sudden Stardom for James Earl Jones." Sepia, June 1969, p. 52-55.

1509 Sye, Robert. "David Franklin: Maker of Star." Sepia, January 1978, p. 32-35.

1510 "Ted Lange." Baltimore Afro American, September 9, 1978,
      p. I-11.

1511 "Ted Ross in 'The Wiz.'" Baltimore Afro American, Decem-
      ber 30, 1978, p. I-11.

1512 "Ted Ross Plays the Lion in 'The Wiz.'" Chicago Daily De-
      fender, November 25, 1978, p. ENT-11.

1513 "Terry Carter." Los Angeles Sentinel, July 5, 1979, p. B-
      1A.

1514 Terry, Mike. "Robert Guillaume: No Man's Servant." Soul,
      August 28, 1978, p. 3.

1515 "Theodore (Teddy) Wilson Stars in 'Sanford Arms.'" New
      York Amsterdam News, October 15, 1977, p. D-8.

1516 "Tim Moore: Case of the Missing Roast Beef." Ebony, April
      1958, p. 143-146.

1517 "Tim Reed of 'WKRP.'" Jet, March 15, 1982, p. 58-60.

1518 "Tony Brown." Cleveland Call & Post, April 29, 1978, p.
      B-4.

1519 "Tony Brown: A Man for the People." Essence, October
      1980, p. 22+.

1520 "Topper Carew: A Bit of A Success Story; Producer of Pub-
      lic TV's 'Righteous Apples.'" Black Enterprise, April
      1980, p. 50.

1521 Torgerson, Ellen. "Ernest Thomas." TV Guide, March 18,
      1978, p. 29-32.

1522 _____. "Lawrence Hilton-Jacobs." TV Guide, August 19,
      1978, p. 25+.

1523 _____. "Ron Glass." TV Guide, September 23, 1978, p.
      36-38.

1524 Tucker, M. "Mister Johnson vs. Mr. Hyman." Crisis, Jan-
      uary 1958, p. 13-16+.

1525 "TV Host Adam Wade." Los Angeles Sentinel, January 12,
      1978, p. ENT-1.

1526 "Two KMOX-TV Employees Profiled." St. Louis Argus,
      April 24, 1980, p. 2-10.

1527 "Ulysses Newkirk Joins Channel 56 As Announcer." Michigan
      Chronicle, October 29, 1977, p. D-16.

1528   Unger, Norman. "Demond Wilson: Black & Proud of His
       Image." Black Stars, November 1979, p. 28-31.

1529   "Wallace D. Muhammad Appears on Public TV Special." Nor-
       folk Journal & Guide, June 18, 1977, p. B-15.

1530   Watson, Vernee. "Fame Has Its Problems." Black Stars,
       April 1979, p. 20-23.

1531   Weisman, John. "Ed Bradley." TV Guide, August 20, 1977,
       p. 10-12.

1532   "What Happened to the TV Stars of 'Amos 'n' Andy?'" Jet,
       December 10, 1981, p. 55-57.

1533   Whitney, D. "Mike Evans of 'All in the Family.'" TV
       Guide, June 2, 1973, p. 28-32.

1534   _____. "Sammy Davis Jr." TV Guide, November 10,
       1973, p. 22-30.

1535   Whitney, Dwight. "Sherman Hemsley: Don't Ask How He
       Lives or What He Believes In." TV Guide, February 6,
       1982, p. 30-32.

1536   "William Dilday, Jr., General Manager, WLBT-TV in Jack-
       son, Miss." NABOB News, September, Conference Edi-
       tion 1980, p. 7.

1537   William Marshall." Chicago Daily Defender, November 17,
       1979, p. AW-1.

1538   "William Melvin Kelley." Negro Digest, October 1962, p.
       44-46.

1539   Williams, Ron and Don. "Truman Jacques." Soul, January
       4, 1972, p. 6A.

1540   "Willie Tyler and Lester: An Odd Couple." Ebony, October
       1981, p. 77-82.

1541   Wickham, Phyllis. "Ted Lange Becomes ... Isaac Washing-
       ton." Soul, May 15, 1978, p. 15.

1542   "Winfield Discusses 'King' Role." Chicago Daily Defender,
       February 11, 1978, p. I-5.

1543   Winters, Jason. "Sammy Davis, Jr.: The World's Greatest
       Entertainer." Black Stars, July 1978, p. 20-24.

1544   _____. "Scatman Crothers: A Star at Last." Jet, De-
       cember 1977, p. 56-60.

1545   "Yaphet Kotto." Chicago Daily Defender, May 19, 1979, p.
       AW-12.

1546   Young, A. S. "Fastest Gun in the West." Sepia, February
       1962, p. 51-54.

1547   _____. "Hollywood's Busiest Starlet." Sepia, May 1959,
       p. 40-45.

1548   Young, D. "Hollywood's Most Versatile Starlet." Sepia,
       December 1958, p. 42-46.

1549   Young, J. R. "Demond Wilson of 'Sanford and Son.'" TV
       Guide, October 5, 1974, p. 21-26.

                        Personalities--Comedians

1550   "Aaron and Freddie Named Sheriff's Field Deputy of Safety
       Education." Los Angeles Sentinel, April 21, 1983, p. B-9.

1551   Bennett, Lerone. "Why Richard Pryor Stopped Saying 'Nig-
       ger.'" Ebony, July 1982, p. 118-126.

1552   Bersamin, Rose. "Stu Gilliam." Soul Illustrated, December
       1969, p. 22, 52.

1553   "Bert Williams." Cleveland Call & Post, June 24, 1978, p.
       B-9.

1554   "Bill Cosby." Baltimore Afro American, October 15, 1977,
       p. I-11.

1555   "Bill Cosby Comments on 'California Suite.'" Chicago Daily
       Defender, December 9, 1978, p. ENT-11.

1556   "Bill Cosby Earns Doctoral Degree." Michigan Chronicle,
       April 23, 1977, p. A-1.

1557   "Bill Cosby to Appear at Mill Run Theater in Chicago." Chi-
       cago Daily Defender, June 30, 1979, p. AW-15.

1558   "Bill Trotman, 'Trinidad Bill.'" New York Amsterdam News.
       May 26, 1979, p. 45.

1559   "Black Comedians on TV." (Editorial). Baltimore Afro
       American, October 8, 1977, p. I-4.

1560   "Black Humor." New York Amsterdam News, August 19,
       1978, p. D-4.

1561 Brown, G. F. "Rapid Rise of Dick Gregory." Sepia, February 1962, p. 42-45.

1562 _____. "Timmie Rogers on the Art of Comedy." Sepia, September 1961, p. 48-51.

1563 Bunn, Howard. "Dewey Pigmeat Markham." Soul Illustrated, December 1969, p. 50-51.

1564 "Close-up of Bill Cosby." Michigan Chronicle, December 3, 1977, p. B-4.

1565 "Comedy Row's Top Ten." Ebony, April 1966, p. 105-108+.

1566 "Complaint Filed Against Richard Pryor in L.A." Cleveland Call & Post, January 7, 1978, p. A-1.

1567 "Cosby Does His Own Growling While Camille Tends the Cubs." Soul, January 5, 1976, p. 2-4.

1568 Davidson, M. "Bill Cosby--Ph. D." TV Guide, August 18, 1973, p. 28-30.

1569 "December Is Bill Cosby's Month." Soul, December 8, 1966, p. 18.

1570 "Dick Gregory." Ebony, May 1961, p. 67-70+.

1571 Doan, R. K. "Foxx's Demands Scare Network, May Kill Show." TV Guide, March 23, 1974, p. A-1.

1572 "Eddie Murphy OKs 4th Season on 'Saturday Night Live.'" Jet, May 9, 1983, p. 56.

1573 Finnigan, J. "Redd Foxx Moves to ABC in 1977." TV Guide, April 24, 1976, p. A-3, A-4.

1574 "Flip Wilson Returns to Vegas." Los Angeles Sentinel, April 6, 1978, p. B-2A.

1575 "Franklyn Ajaye." Baltimore Afro American, July 14, 1979, p. DWN-16; Chicago Daily Defender, July 21, 1979, p. DWN-16.

1576 "Franklyn Ajaye." Right On, October 1978, p. 26-27.

1577 "Funny World of Stu Gilliam." Sepia, August 1969, p. 35-38.

1578 "George Kirby." Chicago Daily Defender, November 26, 1977, p. ENT-3.

1579 "George Kirby." (Cleaver column). Los Angeles Sentinel, May 19, 1977, p. A-1.

1580   "Gilliam Opens Another Shoe Store in L. A." Soul, July 13,
       1970, p. 7.

1581   "Happy Face of Chelsea Brown." Sepia, February 1969, p.
       34-36.

1582   "J. J. Walker Responds to Criticism of TV Role." New York
       Amsterdam News, November 5, 1977, p. B-1.

1583   "Jimmy Walker." Pittsburgh Courier, October 29, 1977, p.
       3-21.

1584   "Johnny Brown Jogging Along with 'Laugh-In.'" TV Guide,
       November 21, 1970, p. 12-13.

1585   Johnson, B. "In the Wake of Gregory, Cosby Becomes a
       Star." Negro Digest, October 1966, p. 39-42.

1586   "Kirby Bail Reduced by U. S. District Judge." Baltimore Afro
       American, April 22, 1978, p. I-3.

1587   Kisner, Ronald E. "Pryor Adds Fireworks to Star-Spangled
       Gay Night." Jet, October 6, 1977, p. 54-56.

1588   _____. "Pryor Stuns Friends with Wedding: Off to Oz in
       'Wiz.'" Jet, October 13, 1977, p. 56-57.

1589   _____. "Richard Pryor's Richest Xmas." Jet, December
       29, 1977, p. 56-58.

1590   Lane, Bill. "Richard Pryor: He's Moving on up--Fast."
       Sepia, August 1977, p. 34-35.

1591   "LaWanda Paige." New York Amsterdam News, December
       30, 1978, p. B-5.

1592   Leavy, Walter. "Eddie Murphy Scores Hit." Ebony, April
       1983, p. 88-91.

1593   Lewis, Bobbi Jean. "Richard Pryor." Soul Illustrated, Sum-
       mer 1968, p. 14-18.

1594   Lewis, R. W. "Cosby Takes Over." TV Guide, October 4,
       1969, p. 12-15.

1595   Lucas, Bob. "New Redd Foxx Finds Success with New Show."
       Jet, November 3, 1977, p. 58-61.

1596   _____. "Pam and Richard: Movie Love Turns into Real
       Thing." Jet, June 2, 1977, p. 58-61.

1597   _____. "Redd Foxx at Home with His New Bride." Jet,
       February 3, 1977, p. 46-49.

1598   "Luke Walker." Los Angeles Sentinel, January 25, 1979, p.
       B-3A; Los Angeles Sentinel, April 26, 1979, p. B-3A.

1599   Marsh, Antoinette.   "Stu Gilliam: The Ambassador of Mirth
       Gets Serious." Black Stars, April 1979, p. 66-69.

1600   Marshall, Marilyn.   "The New Comedians." Ebony, June
       1982, p. 38-42.

1601   "Moms Mabley--Anybody That Comes to Me, I'll Help 'Em."
       Soul, June 30, 1966, p. 2.

1602   Morehead, H.   "Redd Foxx Spoofs the World." Sepia, Jan-
       uary 1963, p. 27-31.

1603   Mungen, Donna.   "Richard Pryor: Not Many Women Can
       Stand My Act for Long." Soul, December 8, 1975, p.
       2-3, 18.

1604   "NBC Censorship of Pryor's Show." Los Angeles Sentinel,
       September 15, 1977, p. A-1.

1605   "Out of the Mouths of Pros: A Look at the First Black Laugh-
       makers." Soul Illustrated, December 1969, p. 16-18.

1606   Pierce, P.   "All Flip over Flip." Ebony, April 1968, p.
       64-66+.

1607   "Pigmeat Markham: De Judge Has Arrived." Soul Illustrated,
       Fall 1968, p. 28-31.

1608   Pitts, Leonard.   "Franklyn Ajaye." Soul, July 17, 1978, p.
       10.

1609   _____.   "The Many Faces of Richard Pryor." Right On,
       October 1982, p. 44-45, 67.

1610   _____.   "Richard Pryor: Putting the Pieces Together."
       Soul, June 5, 1978, p. 10-16.

1611   "Problems of Richard Pryor." Pittsburgh Courier, October
       7, 1978, p. 3-18.

1612   "Pryor Proves You Can Always Go Home Again." Jet, June
       2, 1977, p. 22-24.

1613   "Pryor Returns to Concert Stage and PUSH Benefits." Jet,
       January 7, 1982, p. 60-62.

1614   "Pryor Signs with Warner Bros. Studios for Millions." Soul,
       September 12, 1977, p. 2.

1615   "Pryor Takes Bride, Debbie McGuire." Soul, October 24,
       1977, p. 2.

1616 "'Raceless' Bill Cosby." Ebony, May 1964, p. 131-132+.

1617 "Redd Foxx." Chicago Daily Defender, July 18, 1978, p. I-11.

1618 "Redd Foxx." Michigan Chronicle, January 14, 1978, p. A-1.

1619 "Redd Foxx." Michigan Chronicle, June 17, 1978, p. A-1.

1620 "Redd Foxx Angry over Cancellation of TV Show." Michigan Chronicle, August 19, 1978, p. A-1.

1621 "Redd Foxx Contractual Relations with ABC-TV." Baltimore Afro American, November 18, 1978, p. I-11.

1622 "Redd Foxx Inks $10 Million Contract." Pittsburgh Courier, January 28, 1978, p. 3-19.

1623 "Redd Foxx Presents Redd Foxx." Sepia, June 1967, p. 42-47.

1624 "Redd Foxx Recounts Experiences of Early Days in New Book." Pittsburgh Courier, July 1, 1978, p. 2-13.

1625 "Redd Foxx Says Comedy Hardest Form of Entertainment." Michigan Chronicle, July 8, 1978, p. B-6.

1626 "Renaldo Rey's Show in Los Angeles." Los Angeles Sentinel, September 20, 1979, p. B-4A.

1627 "Richard Pryor." Chicago Daily Defender, November 5, 1977, p. ENT-13; Michigan Chronicle, November 19, 1977, p. B-4.

1628 "Richard Pryor." (Cleaver column). Los Angeles Sentinel, May 31, 1979, p. A-7.

1629 "Richard Pryor." Los Angeles Sentinel, January 4, 1979, p. B-4A.

1630 "Richard Pryor." Michigan Chronicle, October 28, 1978, p. B-6.

1631 "Richard Pryor." New York Amsterdam News, June 25, 1977, p. D-14.

1632 "Richard Pryor." Pittsburgh Courier, June 24, 1978, p. 3-17.

1633 "Richard Pryor Alleged to be 'Black Magic' Victim." Michigan Chronicle, June 10, 1978, p. A-1.

1634 "Richard Pryor and Pam Grier: Is It Love?" Soul, January 31, 1977, p. 1.

1635 "Richard Pryor and Word 'Nigger.'" (Ida Peters commentary).
     Baltimore Afro American, July 28, 1979, p. I-1.

1636 "Richard Pryor Explains the Making of an Oscar." Chicago
     Tribune, March 25, 1973, p. 9-18.

1637 "Richard Pryor Featured in NBC Special." Michigan Chron-
     icle, May 7, 1977, p. B-4.

1638 "Richard Pryor, Jackie Gleason Team Up for Laughs in 'The
     Toy.'" Jet, January 10, 1983, p. 60-62.

1639 "Richard Pryor--Live in Concert." New York Amsterdam
     News, March 3, 1979, p. 48.

1640 "Richard Pryor Signs Contract with NBC-TV." Michigan
     Chronicle, May 21, 1977, p. B-8.

1641 "Richard Pryor Speaks Out." Right On, December 1981, p.
     24-25.

1642 "Richard Pryor Sued for $2.8 Million by Ala Enterprises."
     Soul, September 29, 1975, p. 14.

1643 "Richard Pryor Telethon Raises $140,000." Los Angeles
     Sentinel, July 24, 1980, p. A-5.

1644 "Richard Pryor Vows Never to Use Word 'Nigger' Again."
     Los Angeles Sentinel, July 12, 1979, p. A-1.

1645 "Richard Pryor Wants to Ban Word 'Nigger.'" Bilalian News,
     August 3, 1979, p. 30.

1646 "Richard Pryor's Appearance at Brotherhood Crusade Concert."
     Los Angeles Sentinel, February 16, 1978, p. A-6.

1647 "Richard Pryor's Case." Los Angeles Sentinel, January 5,
     1978, p. A-1.

1648 Robinson, L. "Why Negro Comics Don't Make It Big." Ebony,
     October 1960, p. 108-110+.

1649 Robinson, Leroy. "Bill Cosby: A Funny Success." Soul
     Illustrated, December 1969, p. 42-45.

1650 Robinson, Louie. "Dr. Bill Cosby." Ebony, June 1977, p.
     130-132+.

1651 Ryan, C. "Bill Cosby: The Man in Studio 41." TV Guide,
     February 3, 1973, p. 28-31.

1652 Sanders, Charles. "Richard Pryor: Is He the Biggest, Rich-
     est Black Movie Star?" Ebony, December 1981, p. 141-
     146.

1653   "76 Big Year for Pryor." Soul, August 30, 1976, p. 1.

1654   "Shirley Hemphill Tells of Her Hard Times in Hollywood."
        Jet, April 3, 1980, p. 44.

1655   "Slappy White Stars at the Cotton Club." New York Amster-
        dam News, April 1, 1978, p. D-10.

1656   "Stu Gulliam." Sepia, August 1969, p. 35-38.

1657   "Stu Gilliam on 'Playboy After Dark.'" (Burrell column).
        Soul, June 29, 1970, p. 6.

1658   "Stu Gilliam Signed for Cartoon Show." (Burrell column).
        Soul, June 29, 1970, p. 6.

1659   "Stu Gilliam Talks About Redd Foxx." Soul Illustrated, De-
        cember 1969, p. 28-29.

1660   Terkel, Pauline. "Richard Pryor Uncensored." Sepia, Au-
        gust 1977, p. 284.

1661   "$3.1 Million Ruling in Favor of Richard Pryor Challenged
        by Lawyer." Jet, August 30, 1982, p. 61.

1662   "Timmy Rogers; Comic Moves Towards Stardom after 23
        Years As Entertainer." Ebony, January 1951, p. 39-40+.

1663   "Trenier Twins; Madcap Comic Team Dazzles Spectators with
        Hilarious Act." Ebony, July 1954, p. 31-34.

1664   "Two Time Winner Richard Pryor in 5 Films." Soul, April
        26, 1976, p. 5.

1665   Whitney, D. "Flip Wilson--He's on the Case." TV Guide,
        January 8, 1972, p. 20-25.

1666   _____. "Jimmie Walker: Coping with Overnight Success."
        TV Guide, June 25, 1977, p. 6-11.

1667   "Will the Real Richard Pryor Please Stand?" Soul, Septem-
        ber 15, 1966, p. 10.

1668   Wilson, Reggie. "Pryor ... To What?" (Richard Pryor).
        Right On-Focus, Spring 1983, p. 41-47.

1669   Wood, Collette. "Richard Pryor." Soul Illustrated, Decem-
        ber 1969, p. 22, 25.

1670   "Woody Henderson." (Calloway column). Chicago Daily De-
        fender, September 26, 1979, p. I-19.

1671   "Yari Lawrence." New York Amsterdam News, September 8,
        1979, p. 26.

1672 Young, A. S. "Funniest Man in the World." Sepia, March
      1961, p. 50-53.

Personalities--Singers

1673 "Aretha Franklin and Glynn Thurman." Pittsburgh Courier,
      May 6, 1978, p. 3-18.

1674 "Aretha Franklin Makes Plans for Wedding." Michigan Chron-
      icle, April 15, 1978, p. A-1.

1675 "Barbara McNair: The Acting Debut of a Singer." Sepia,
      April 1964, p. 74-78.

1676 "Billy and Marilyn: Out There on Their Own." Soul, April
      26, 1976, p. 7.

1677 "Chubby Checker, Dick Clark and the Twist." TV Guide,
      January 6, 1962, p. 22-25.

1678 Cole, N. and Bennett, L., Jr. "Why I Quit My TV Show."
      Ebony, February 1958, p. 29-34.

1679 "Crooner Nat King Cole Turns Actor." Ebony, June 1957,
      p. 74+.

1680 "Diana Ross Defends Role in 'The Wiz.'" Chicago Daily De-
      fender, September 23, 1978, p. I-13; Pittsburgh Courier,
      September 30, 1978, p. 3-20.

1681 "Diana Ross Defends 'Wiz.'" Michigan Chronicle, October 7,
      1978, p. A-4; Los Angeles Sentinel, October 12, 1978, p.
      B-3A.

1682 "Eubie Blake Returns to Broadway." Chicago Daily Defender,
      September 16, 1978, p. I-9.

1683 "Fifth Dimension Filming TV." Soul, June 22, 1967, p. 9.

1684 Hobson, D. "The Fifth Dimension on How Sinatra Did His
      Thing." TV Guide, November 23, 1968, p. 28-35.

1685 Johnson, Connie. "Marilyn McCoo & Billy Davis, Jr.: Don't
      Call Us the Black Sonny and Cher." Soul, August 1, 1977,
      p. 8-9.

1686 Johnson, Robert. "Jennifer Holliday." Jet, July 19, 1982,
      p. 54-57.

1687 "King Cole Turns Actor." Our World, April 1953, p. 45-47.

1688   Lucas, Bob. "Gladys Knight and the Pips Get Own TV Show."
       Jet, July 31, 1975, p. 58-61.

1689   "Marilyn and Billy Get Own TV Show." Soul, December 20,
       1976, p. 5.

1690   "Marilyn and Billy Go Solo, 5th Breakup after 10 Years."
       Soul, December 8, 1975, p. 1.

1691   "Marilyn McCoo and Andy Gibb: Hot Duo Sizzle on 'Solid
       Gold.'" Jet, February 11, 1982, p. 60-62.

1692   "Marilyn McCoo's Acting Debut on 'It Takes a Thief' Series."
       (Burrell column). Soul, July 19, 1971, p. 4.

1693   Massaquoi, Hans. "Diana Ross." Ebony, November 1981,
       p. 38-50.

1694   "Nancy Wilson's Singing Fashion." TV Guide, August 13,
       1966, p. 20-23.

1695   "Nat King Cole Has an Important Role on Television." TV
       Guide, September 7, 1957, p. 14-15.

1696   O'Hallaren, Bill. "Marilyn McCoo of 'Solid Gold': I'm the
       Biggest Square You're Likely to Meet." TV Guide, Jan-
       uary 8, 1983, p. 10-12.

1697   "Sing Out with Charity." Our World, February 1955, p. 12-
       15.

1698   "A Step in the Right Direction: Nat King Cole Discusses His
       Role in Television." Jet, September 7, 1955, p. 15.

1699   Terry, Mike. "Billy Davis & Marilyn McCoo: Did They Lose
       Their Credibility On TV?" Soul, January 8, 1979, p. 12-
       13.

1700   "This Is Nancy Wilson." TV Guide, July 17, 1965, p. 26-27.

1701   "This Is Your Life." (Nat King Cole). Jet, January 21,
       1960, p. 30, 58.

                          Personalities--Youth

1702   "At Home with Fred Berry." Right On, June 1979, p. 2.

1703   "At Home with Gary Coleman." Jet, June 28, 1982, p. 10-11.

1704   Austin, Chaz. "Todd Bridges: Fish's Kid Is Just the Bridges'
       Kid." Soul, May 8, 1978, p. 1-3.

1705 Burrell, Walter. "'Our Gang's' Farina." Soul, July 3, 1978,
      p. 14.

1706 Carter, Ralph. "Ralph Carter: I Have Two Different Person-
      alities." Black Stars, p. 60-63.

1707 Collier, Aldore. "Kim Fields." Jet, July 5, 1982, p. 22-25.

1708 _____. "Todd Bridges and Janet Jackson: The Problems
      of Teen Age Stars." Ebony, February 1983, p. 58-62.

1709 "Dancing Brothers; Young Powells Make Early Bid for Fame
      on Television." Ebony, May 1956, p. 50-52.

1710 "David Hubbard, NBC's 'James at 16.'" Right On, October
      1979, p. 12.

1711 "David Hubbard: TV Star At 18." Sepia, July 1978, p. 41-
      45.

1712 Davidson, Bill. "Gary Coleman." Family Circle, October
      9, 1979, p. 48+.

1713 "The Double Life of Marc Copage." Ebony, December 1969,
      p. 174.

1714 "Erik Kilpatrick: 'White Shadow' Co-Star." Right On, June
      1979, p. 54-55.

1715 "Fat Freddie." New York Amsterdam News, May 27, 1978,
      p. D-24.

1716 Fee, Debi. "Kim Fields: Growing Up Too Fast?" Right On,
      January 1982, p. 28-29.

1717 _____. "Todd Bridges: His Life, Loves and Ladies."
      Right On, May 1982, p. 41, 62.

1718 "59 Inches of Dynamite." Our World, October 1951, p. 53-
      55.

1719 "Gary Coleman." Chicago Daily Defender, June 30, 1979,
      p. 2-9.

1720 "Gary Coleman." Ebony, June 1980, p. 33-38.

1720a "Gary Coleman and 'Diff'rent Strokes.'" New York Amster-
      dam News, December 9, 1978, p. D-16.

1721 "Gary Coleman: Just a Little Boy." Panorama, August 1980,
      p. 80-83.

1722 "Gary Coleman, New Video Rich Kid." Jet, September 6,
      1979, p. 61.

1723 "Gene Williams, Television's Tiny Salesman." Ebony, November 1976, p. 181+.

1724 "'Good Times' Ralph Carter Has Disco Album." (Dorothy Brunson column). Soul, January 19, 1976, p. 11.

1725 "Has Kim Fields Hooked Todd Bridges?" Right On, July 1982, p. 41.

1726 "Hollywood's Eligible Bachelors: Ernest Harden, Michael Dorn, James Bridges, Jr. and Erik Washington." Right On, November 1981, p. 44-48.

1727 Horner, Cynthia. "Wolfe Perry on 'White Shadow.'" Right On, January 1982, p. 24.

1728 "James Bond, 12, Acts in 'The Fish That Saved Pittsburgh.'" Pittsburgh Courier, August 12, 1978, p. 3-17.

1729 "Janet Jackson: Singing Is a Diff'rent Stroke." Right On, December 1982, p. 16-17.

1730 "Janet Jackson: Through the Years." Right On, November 1982, p. 32.

1731 Jenkins, Walter. "A Friendly Visit With Marc Copage." Black Stars, June 1976, p. 28-31.

1732 Johnson, Hershel. "Rae Dawn Chong." Ebony, June 1982, p. 126-132.

1733 "Kevin Hooks: Father of the Year." Right On, October 1979, p. 46.

1734 Kiester, Edwin. "Todd Bridges." TV Guide, December 6, 1980, p. 35.

1735 "Lawrence Hilton-Jacobs Stars in 'Youngblood.'" Baltimore Afro American, April 8, 1978, p. I-11.

1736 "Leslie Crayne, MGM's Pint-Sized Vocal Discovery, Is Veteran Performer at Age of Ten." Our World, August 1953, p. 42-45.

1737 "The Little Angels; Los Angeles Family Makes National TV Hit." Ebony, February 1961, p. 35-37.

1738 Marsh, Antoinette. "Gary Coleman and Todd Bridges: Little Kids With Big Minds." Black Stars, March 1979, p. 40-45.

1739 _____. "Todd Bridges: Older Is Better." Black Stars, June 1979, p. 6-10.

1740 "Philadelphia's Newest TV Star." Color, January 1956, p. 5.

1741 Pitts, Leonard. "Danielle Spencer: Little Pitcher with Big
      Career." Soul, October 24, 1977, p. 14-15.

1742 Plato, Dana. "I'm Going to Spill the Beans on Todd Bridges
      and Gary Coleman." Right On, November 1981, p. 28-29.

1743 Robinson, Louie. "Rodney Allen Rippy." Ebony, February
      1974, p. 100-105.

1744 "Rodney Allen Rippy: Hottest Property in Show Business."
      Sepia, November 1973, p. 72-75.

1745 "Rodney Allen Rippy Sues TV Producer." Soul, January 6,
      1975, p. 12.

1746 "Rodney Allen Rippy Wins Contract Tiff." Jet, July 24, 1975,
      p. 61.

1747 "Rodney Allen Rippy Wins Dispute." Soul, August 18, 1975,
      p. 13.

1747a Seligson, Marcia. "Gary Coleman." TV Guide, March 3,
      1979, p. 26+.

1748 Shaw, Ellen. "Kim Fields." TV Guide, June 6, 1981, p.
      18-20.

1749 Shelton, Eugene. "Gary Coleman and Todd Bridges: Mighty
      Mouth & Friend." Soul, December 25, 1978, p. 24-25.

1750 _____. "Marc Copage, Julia's Son, Grows Up." Soul, De-
      cember 25, 1978, p. 28.

1751 _____. "Rodney Allen Rippy." Soul, December 25, 1978,
      p. 30.

1752 "Small Boy's Big Moment." Ebony, March 1957, p. 64-67.

1753 "Small Wonder; Leslie Crayne, MGM's Pint-Sized Vocal Dis-
      covery, Is Veteran Performer at Age of Ten." Our World,
      August 1953, p. 42-45.

1754 "'Soul Train' Dance Contest Winner Anthony Jo Wright."
      Soul, October 13, 1975, p. 4.

1755 "Stoney Jackson." Right On, March 1980, p. 7.

1756 "Talented High School Senior Is a Shining Star at 17." Sepia,
      October 1966, p. 55.

1757 "Teen-Age TV Star; Joan Proctor Gets Big Break on 'Horace
      Heidt Show.'" Ebony, October 1955, p. 26-30+.

1758   "Todd Bridges: Is He Lost on 'Diff'rent Strokes'?"   Right
       On, June 1979, p. 26.

1759   "Todd Bridges of 'Diff'rent Strokes.'"   Grapevine, July/August
       1979, p. 31.

1760   "TV's Fresh New Faces: LeVar Burton, Janet Jackson, Kirk
       Calloway, Fred Berry and Danielle Spencer."   Right On,
       August 1977, p. 7-9.

1761   "TV's Miniature Millionaires: Rodney Allen Rippy, Lea Jack-
       son, Alene Wilson, Damon Woodruff, Bunky Butler."
       Right On, February 1979, p. 66.

1762   "The Untold Story of Julia's TV Son 'Corey.'"   Jet, May 22,
       1969, p. 54-59.

1763   Washington, Erik. "Mark James."   Right On, December 1981,
       p. 29.

1764   Whitney, D. "Marc Copage Meets His Public."   TV Guide,
       June 28, 1969, p. 10-13.

1765   "Why Millionaire Gary Coleman Needs Bodyguard."   Jet, Jan-
       uary 17, 1980, p. 44-45.

1766   Young, A. S. Doc. "Gary Coleman: Little Boy Star of
       'Diff'rent Strokes.'"   Sepia, April 1979, p. 39-46.

1767   "Young Actor Deno Brown."   Chicago Daily Defender, October
       28, 1978, p. ENT-15.

                    Producers, Directors and Writers

1767a "Actor/Director Tom Moses."   Los Angeles Sentinel, Novem-
       ber 15, 1979, p. A-9.

1768   "Alpha Epsilon Rho's Norfolk State Unit Produces TV Announce-
       ments."   Norfolk Journal & Guide, April 9, 1980, p. I-12.

1769   "Angie Gordon Promoted to New Job at WJKW-TV."   Cleve-
       land Call & Post, March 1, 1980, p. B-10.

1770   "Arden Hill, TV Editor at NBC-TV in New York."   Ebony,
       October 1954, p. 5.

1771   "Batman's Backstage Helper."   Ebony, April 1966, p. 40-42+.

1772   "'Bill Cosby Show' Has Eight Black Writers."   Jet, June 22,
       1972, p. 52.

1773 "Bill Duke Debut as TV Director." Jet, May 17, 1982, p. 56.

1774 "Billy Wilson, Production Coordinator, KFSN TV in Fresno." Grapevine, March 1972, p. 27.

1775 "Black Directors are Getting a Chance." Washington Post, April 12, 1970, p. F-4.

1776 "Black Playwrights Get A Break." Sepia, November 1968, p. 21-22.

1777 "Black TV Directors." Sepia, May 1971, p. 28-32.

1778 "Black TV Writers Threaten to Picket Cosby Show." Soul, September 27, 1976, p. 1.

1779 "Black Woman Named Casting Director For National TV Program." Los Angeles Sentinel, August 4, 1977, p. 1.

1780 "Blacks Get TV Station." Jet, February 15, 1973, p. 28.

1781 "Bonita Cornute Named Public Affairs Reporter for KETC-TV." St. Louis Argus, September 11, 1980, p. 1-3.

1782 Bryan, Bob. "Gil Moses Director in 'Roots' Series." Soul, March 14, 1977, p. 13.

1783 "Candance Carruthers-Morrow, Editorial Director, WABC-TV in New York." Ebony, July 1977, p. 6.

1784 "Candance Carruthers Named Producer 'AM New York.'" Norfolk Journal & Guide, July 30, 1980, p. 9.

1785 "Candance Carruthers, WABC-TV, Editorial Director." New York Amsterdam News, March 31, 1979, p. 19.

1786 Chapman, Debriah. "Felicidad: The Lady Behind 'For You Black Woman.'" Blacktress, September 1980, p. 20.

1787 "Charles Haines, TV Art Director, TV Pioneer in Indiana." Ebony, April 1957, p. 55-56+.

1788 "Christine Houston, Chicago Student Wins Chance to Write TV Show." Jet, May 11, 1978, p. 25.

1789 Coller, Aldore. "Ted Lange Is Also a Writer and a Director on 'Love Boat.'" Jet, October 11, 1982, p. 60-62.

1790 "Darlene Hayes, Associate Producer on 'Phil Donahue.'" Ebony, January, 1975, p. 6.

1791 "Darlene Hayes, Producer of 'Donahue Show.'" Ebony, December 1981, p. 98-102.

1792   "Darlene Hayes Produces 'Donahue Show.'"   Pittsburgh Cour-
       ier, November 5, 1977, p. 3-22.

1793   "D.C. Businessman Wins 8-year Battle For Pay TV." Jet,
       July 24, 1980, p. 55.

1794   "David Crippens, Producer/Director, KCET-TV, Los Angeles."
       Ebony, September 1975, p. 6.

1794a "Denise Nichols Tries a New Life Behind the Cameras."
       Sepia, January 1981, p. 27-31.

1795   "Earl Bradley, KMJ-TV Cameraman." Grapevine, November
       1970, p. 23.

1796   "Eddie Madison, Community Service Director, WMAL-TV, and
       WMAL Radio." Jet, January 29, 1970, p. 51.

1797   "First Negro to Break Directorial Barrier in TV." Sepia,
       April 1960, p. 59.

1798   "Fred Norfleet, Public Affairs Director, NBC's KGTV in San
       Diego." Grapevine, December 1980, p. 27.

1799   "Georg Stanford Brown to Direct New TV Episodes." Jet,
       January 7, 1982, p. 58.

1800   "Gerren Keith Director of 'Diff'rent Strokes.'" Ebony, De-
       cember 1982, p. 42-44.

1801   "Hatti Jackson Named Community Affairs Director for WXIA-
       TV." Atlanta Daily World, January 20, 1980, p. 6.

1802   "Hollywood's Most Sought After Man, Black Casting Director,
       R. Cannon." Ebony, July 1980, p. 62+.

1803   "Jeffrey Hollis Seeks Funds to Produce Screenplay." Pitts-
       burgh Courier, February 3, 1979, p. 3-21.

1804   "John Tweedle, Producer/Director of 'Our People' on WTTW-
       TV in Chicago." Ebony, April 1972, p. 7.

1805   "Johnathan Rogers Named Executive Producer of KNXT-TV
       5 O'Clock News." Los Angeles Sentinel, February 23,
       1978, p. A-1.

1806   Jones, Michael.   "Lonnie Elder." Soul, February 22, 1979,
       p. 8-9.

1807   "Joseph Wilcot, 'Roots II' Cameraman." Jet, March 15, 1979,
       p. 58.

1808   "Juan Thorton, TV Producer at CBS' WTOP-TV, Washington."
       Ebony, September 1971, p. 6.

1809 "Kathryn Goree Joins Staff WKYC-TV." Cleveland Call & Post, June 14, 1979, p. B5.

1810 Killens, J. O. "A Black Writer Views TV." TV Guide, July 25, 1970, p. 6-9.

1811 Kirk, Cynthia. "So You Wanna Be a ... Television Program Director." Soul, July 17, 1978, p. 21.

1812 "Lemuel Johnson, TV Cameraman, WEMS-TV, Cleveland." Ebony, 1955, p. 4.

1813 "Liz Gant, Producer NBC Affiliate, WBZ-TV, Boston." Ebony, May 1980, p. 5.

1814 McClarn, Agnes S. "Essence Woman: Sue Booker (Founds New Bureau For Black Community)." Essence, November 1973, p. 9.

1815 "Mark Warren To Produce Ebony's Premiere 'Black Achievers Awards' for TV." Jet, December 14, 1978, p. 18.

1816 "Melody Jackson Promoted to Staff Producer at KTTV in Los Angeles." Jet, March 22, 1979, p. 19.

1817 "Minority Television Company Produces Series for PBS." Jet, May 22, 1980, p. 40.

1818 "On Stage With Mr. Lights." Our World, October 1955, p. 25-27.

1819 "Orville Hurt Television Illustrator at Kline Studios." Ebony, January 1955, p. 5.

1820 "Quincy Jones Producing Special for Pay TV." Jet, May 10, 1982, p. 64.

1821 "Richard Durham, Editor of Newspaper Muhammad Speaks Is Chief Writer for 'Bird of the Iron Feather' a Daily Soul Drama on WTTW Chicago's Channel 11, About Life in the Chicago Ghetto." Jet, October 30, 1969, p. 72.

1822 Riley, Lew. "Writing For Television: All White Or All American?" Emmy, Spring 1980, p. 32-39+.

1823 "Robert L. Goodwin Writes Scripts for 'Big Valley' Lou Rawls in Cast." Jet, January 30, 1969, p. 58.

1824 "Robert Pettus, TV Transmitter Engineer at WEWS-TV in Cleveland." Ebony, July 1955, p. 5.

1825 "Roy Campanella: Hollywood Film and TV Director." Ebony, September 1982, p. 69-73.

1826 Shapiro, Marc. "Lonnie Elder III: The Screenwriter As Black
      Media Gadfly. " Soul, February 22, 1979, p. 8-9.

1827 "Stan Myles Produces Movie-for-TV About Louis Armstrong
      Starring Ben Vereen. " Soul, January 5, 1975, p. 16.

1828 "Sylvia Smith, News Film Editor at Chicago's NBC-TV Affil-
      iate. " Ebony, January 1972, p. 7.

1829 "Television Art Director; Charles Haines Is TV Pioneer at
      ABC's WTTV in Bloomington, Ind. " Ebony, April 1957,
      p. 55-58.

1830 "Tiffini Hall, Engineer With KPLR-TV in St. Louis. " Ebony,
      January 1977, p. 6.

1831 "Tony Brown Named Executive Producer of NET's Emmy Award
      Winning 'Black Journal' Series. " Jet, June 18, 1970, p.
      60.

1832 "TV Floor Manager. " Ebony, April 1954, p. 105-106.

1833 "Walter Brooks, Education TV Producer Maryland Center for
      Public Broadcasting. " Ebony, February 1970, p. 3.

1834 "Xerona Clayton, Producer/Host of 'Open Up' Appointed Mi-
      nority Affairs for TBS. " National Leader, January 13,
      1983, p. 24.

Programs--Comedy

1835 Adler, D.   "Sanford and Son. " TV Guide, May 13, 1972, p.
      28-32.

1836 Amory, C.   "Grady. " TV Guide, February 14, 1976, p. 1.

1837 _____.   "The Jeffersons. " TV Guide, February 22, 1975,
      p. 1.

1838 _____.   "Julia. " TV Guide, October 12, 1968, p. 52.

1839 _____.   "That's My Mama. " TV Guide, October 12, 1974,
      p. 34.

1840 "'Amos 'N' Andy' at 22. " Newsweek, May 10, 1948, p. 48.

1841 "Amos 'N' Andy. " Newsweek, September 13, 1948, p. 56.

1842 "'Amos 'N' Andy' on Television; Negro Actors Picked for
      Roles in TV Version of Oldest Radio Show after Two-Year
      Search. " Ebony, May 1951, p. 21-22+.

1843 "'Amos 'N' Andy's' Transition." Newsweek, July 9, 1951, p. 57.

1844 Antoine, Roane. "Red Foxx's New Television Series." Sepia, June 1980, p. 40-44.

1845 Bedell, S. "Redd Foxx vs. Farrah Fawcett-Majors." TV Guide, November 12, 1977, p. A-3.

1846 "Benny and Rochester; TV's Hottest Team." Our World, August 1955, p. 51-55.

1847 Berry, William. "TV Sex Rules Changes For 'Room 222' Stars." Jet, October 18, 1973, p. 86-90.

1848 Brown, George. "Race Plus Humor: Winning Formula For TV Success." Jet, December 5, 1974, p. 58-61.

1849 Buck, Jerry. "On 'The Jeffersons,' Florence Plays a Role Naturally Made From Life." New York Post, January 3, 1978, p. 18.

1850 Casper, W. "'Good Times' a Show Accent on Negative." Portland Scribe, July 29, 1978, p. 9.

1851 Collier, Aldore. "'The Jeffersons' Becomes No. 1 TV Show." Jet, August 27, 1981, p. 58-61.

1852 _____. "'The Jeffersons': Secret of Longest Running TV Show with Black Stars." Jet, September 20, 1982, p. 62-65.

1853 "Cos Show Cancelled." Soul, December 6, 1976, p. 1.

1854 "Cosby Show Gets Ax in CBS-TV Revamp." Jet, April 19, 1972, p. 54.

1855 Doan, R. K. "Sonny and Cher, Redd Foxx Peril Own Programs." TV Guide, March 2, 1974, p. A-1.

1856 "Easing the Pressure: 'Amos 'N' Andy.'" Newsweek, September 4, 1961, p. 64.

1857 "Eliminate the Racial Slur: Revival of the 'Amos 'N' Andy' TV Series." Christian Century, June 10, 1964, p. 57.

1858 "Esther Rolle Leaves 'Good Times.'" Pittsburgh Courier, August 27, 1977, p. 3-17.

1859 Finnigan, J. "Pryor Might Quit His New Show." TV Guide, September 24, 1977, p. A-3.

1860 "Foxx Show Criticized." Los Angeles Sentinel, October 13, 1977, p. A-7.

1861   "Getting 'Room 222' on the Road." TV Guide, January 31,
       1970, p. 10-11.

1862   "'Good Times': Male Parent role to be written out of series
       when it returns in fall." Wall Street Journal, June 7,
       1976, p. 59.

1863   "'Grady' To Go Off Air; Other Black Shows Are Southern TV
       Heavyweights." Jet, February 19, 1976, p. 56.

1864   "'Hazel' Crashes TV." Our World, June 1950, p. 60-61.

1865   Hill, Karen. "Who Laughs At Racial Comedies On TV." Es-
       sence, May 1974, p. 8.

1866   "'The Jeffersons' Are In ... But Most Black Shows Are Out
       On TV." Jet, October 12, 1978, p. 27-28.

1867   "'The Jeffersons': TV'S Affluent New Black Family." Sepia,
       February 1975, p. 63-66.

1868   "Joan Pringle Replaces Lynne Moody In 'That's My Mama.'"
       Jet, August 28, 1975, p. 62.

1869   Johnson, Robert E. "'The Jeffersons'; Hottest New TV Fam-
       ily." Jet, March 27, 1975, p. 57-60.

1870   _____. "Marla Gibbs Makes Maid Role Pay Off with Own
       TV Series." Jet, May 21, 1981, p. 58-60.

1871   "'Julia': Breakthrough Or Let Down? First Family Type Sit-
       uation Comedy about Blacks." Saturday Review, April 20,
       1968, p. 49; May 25, 1968, p. 36.

1872   "Julian Bond to Headline NBC's 'Saturday Night.'" Soul, May
       9, 1977, p. 8.

1873   Lane, Bill. "Jeffersons Tell Their Side of the Story." Sepia,
       March 1980, p. 39-42.

1874   Lucas, Bob. "A Salt Pork and Collard Greens TV Show."
       Ebony, June 1974, p. 51.

1875   "New TV Comedy Due--The Show Folks." Soul, June 7, 1976,
       p. 8.

1876   Obatala, J.K. "Blacks On TV: A Reply of 'Amos 'N' Andy?'"
       Los Angeles Times, November 26, 1974, p. 5-5.

1877   O'Daniel, M. "Redd Foxx: An Insider's View." TV Guide,
       February 14, 1976, p. 18-20; February 21, 1976, p. 24-
       26.

1878   O'Hallaren, B.   "NBC Renovates the 'Sanford Arms.'"   TV
        Guide, September 17, 1977, p. 55-60.

1879   Pitts, Leonard.   "'Komedy Tonite' on NBC May 9."   Soul,
        May 15, 1968, p. 9.

1880   "Redd Foxx Returns to 'Sanford & Son.'"   Jet, July 25, 1974,
        p. 56.

1881   "Roll Out: TV Show Gets Booted Out."   Jet, November 29,
        1973, p. 88.

1882   "Ron Glass Envisions Changes in 'New Odd Couple' Show."
        Jet, February 7, 1982, p. 58.

1883   Rose, A.M.   "TV Bumps Into the Negro Problem: A Sociolo-
        gist Looks at the 'Amos 'N' Andy' Controversy."   Printer's
        Ink, July 20, 1951, p. 36-37+.

1884   "Sammy Davis Is Featured in Bob Hope Comedy Salute."
        Cleveland Call & Post, January 7, 1979, p. A-2.

1885   "Sanford Is Choice of Black Viewers."   Los Angeles Times,
        October 7, 1976, p. 4-24.

1886   Schoenstein, R.   "What's Happening."   TV Guide, February
        19, 1977, p. 36.

1887   Shayon, Robert Lewis.   "'Julia' Breakthrough or Letdown."
        Saturday Review, April 20, 1968, p. 49.

1888   Slater, Jack.   "The Real People Behind 'The Jeffersons.'"
        Ebony, September 1980, p. 83-94.

1889   Stone, J.   "A Look at 'Barefoot in the Park.'"   TV Guide,
        October 10, 1970, p. 30-35.

1890   "A Teacher Looks at 'Room 222.'"   TV Guide, September 4,
        1971, p. 36-37.

1891   "'What's Happening'!! ABC's Popular Teen-Age Sitcom Suc-
        ceeds In Spite of Itself."   Ebony, June 1978, p. 74-82.

1892   "'What's Happening' Gets Ax; Jefferson's All Alone."   Jet,
        May 10, 1979, p. 56.

1893   "'What's Happening' Gets Its Share of TV Viewers."   Jet,
        June 23, 1977, p. 57.

1894   Wolcott, James.   "WKRP in Cincinnati."   Village Voice, Jan-
        uary 27, 1982, p. 61.

Programs--Detective

1895 Amory, C. "Get Christie Love!" TV Guide, January 11,
      1975, p. 17.

1896 Antoine, Roane. "Can James Earl Jones Win as a TV Cop?"
      Sepia, January 1980, p. 39-42.

1897 _____. "Ben Vereen; 'Tenspeed and Brownshoe.'" Sepia,
      May 1980, p. 41-46.

1898 "Black Private Eyes On New TV Shows." Sepia, July 1973,
      p. 64-67.

1899 "High Suspense on 'Mod Squad.'" TV Guide, October 17,
      1970, p. 16-17.

1900 Hobson, D. "'I Spy' on Location." TV Guide, March 25,
      1967, p. 15-18.

1901 Karnow, S. "Bill Cosby Variety is the Life of Spies: Co-
      Star of 'I Spy.'" Saturday Evening Post, November 1965,
      p. 283-286+.

1902 Pringle, Beatrice. "Cancellation of 'Paris' Leaves Little
      Hope for Balanced Racial Depiction on Television." Sepia,
      March 1980, p. 3.

1903 "Richard Lawson on 'Chicago Story.'" Jet, May 8, 1982,
      p. 64.

1904 "'Shaft' vs. 'Tenafly.'" Soul, May 24, 1974, p. 2-3.

1905 "Sheila DeWindt of 'McClain's Law.'" Jet, May 3, 1982, p.
      58-60.

Programs--Documentary

1906 "'Black Journal' Eyes Threat to Close Black Colleges." Bal-
      timore Afro American, April 9, 1977, p. I-7.

1907 "Black Muslims in America Today." Los Angeles Sentinel,
      June 30, 1977, p. A-3.

1908 "'Blacks in America: With All Deliberate Speed,' CBS-TV
      Reviewed." Christian Science Monitor, July 23, 1979,
      p. 13.

1909 Brown, Pamela J. "Odyssey in Black--A New Role for ETV."

Education and Industrial Television, November 1972, p. 19-21.

1910 "Convicts Who Fight Crime." Sepia, September 1980, p. 32-38.

1911 "'Crow Dog' Documentary to Air on PBS." Bilalian News, June 29, 1979, p. 24.

1912 "'Freedom Journey' Series Chronicles Blacks." Bilalian News, September 9, 1977, p. I-12.

1913 Hall, J. "A Look at 'Americans All.'" TV Guide, August 17, 1974, p. 28-29.

1914 "Julian Bond To Narrate Black Church TV Series." Jet, December 20, 1973, p. 29.

1915 "'Men of Bronze' Documentary Aired." Bilalian News, November 18, 1977, p. I-29.

1916 "NAACP Is 'Black Journal' Topic." Cleveland Call & Post, April 16, 1977, p. A-1.

1917 "'Operation Meharry'"; TV Documentary Shows How Radioactive Gold Can Be Used to Kill Cancer Cells." Ebony, September 1956, p. 64-67.

1918 "Polaroid Airs UNCF Mini-Documentary of Top Achievers." Jet, January 14, 1971, p. 20.

1919 "The Rafer Johnson Story, September 13, on CBS." Jet, September 21, 1961, p. 66.

1920 "St. Louis Blues; Nat King Cole Plays Lead Role in Biography of W. C. Handy, 'Father of the Blues.'" Ebony, May 1958, p. 27-28+.

1921 "Tony Brown Series Called 'Black and White TV.'" (Editorial). Norfolk Journal & Guide, November 3, 1982, p. 8.

1922 "TV Program 'Scared Straight.'" Bilalian News, May 11, 1979, p. 19.

1923 "Who Speaks for Birmingham?; Narrated by Howard K. Smith; Hour-Long Documentary on CBS-TV; Birmingham, White Publisher and Negro Editor Disagree On Documentary." Jet, July 27, 1961, p. 10-12.

1924 "Who Speaks for the South?; School Integration in Georgia, May 27, 1960, CBS-TV." Jet, June 2, 1960, p. 66.

1925 "'Wilma Rudolph Story' to Be Aired." Cleveland Call & Post, December 10, 1977, p. A-13.

1926 "'Women in Prison' Views Georgia Prisons." Atlanta Daily
       World, March 1, 1977, p. I-5.

Programs--Drama

1927 Arthur, R. A. "Remembering 'Philco Playhouse' with Sidney
       Poitier." TV Guide, March 17, 1973, p. 6-10.

1928 "The Big Tall Wish to Run on 'Twilight Zone' Series, CBS-
       TV." Jet, March 31, 1960, p. 57.

1929 "Black Samson." Our World, March 1954, p. 10+.

1930 Blount, Roy. "Palmerstown, USA." Panorama, December
       1980, p. 50.

1931 Brown, Geoff. "Story Behind Haley and Lear Television
       Team." Jet, April 1980, p. 48-51.

1932 "'Buffalo Soldiers'; A TV Story That Makes Blacks Proud."
       Jet, June 7, 1979, p. 54-56.

1933 Cole, Larry. "Will 'Fame' Pass Its Toughest Test?" TV
       Guide, November 6, 1982, p. 27-32.

1934 Davis, Nolan. "'Harris And Co.' Shifts Gears For TV Prime
       Time." San Diego Union, January 9, 1979.

1935 "'The Day of the Fox' on British TV with Sammy Davis, Jr.
       and Yolande." Jet, December 7, 1961, p. 62.

1936 "Esther Rolle Stars in 'Winners' TV Episode." Baltimore
       Afro American, March 11, 1978, p. I-11.

1937 "Ethel Waters in a Starring Dramatic Role in 'Good Night
       Sweet Blues' on Route 66, October 6, 1961 on CBS-TV."
       Jet, October 12, 1961, p. 66.

1938 "Gold at the End of TV's Rainbow." Ebony, October 1980,
       p. 71-72.

1939 "Harris and Company." (Robertson column). Los Angeles
       Sentinel, June 7, 1979, p. A-6; June 14, 1979, p. A-6;
       May 24, 1979, p. A-6.

1940 "'Harris & Company' On NBC." (Young column). Los An-
       geles Sentinel, March 29, 1979, p. A7.

1941 "'Imitation of Life,' Starring Juanita Moore." Ebony, April
       1959, p. 70-73.

1942 "James Earl Jones Signs to Play Alex Haley." Pittsburgh
      Courier, July 22, 1978, p. 3-18.

1943 "James Earl Jones Stars in 'Paul Robeson.'" Los Angeles
      Sentinel, October 11, 1979, p. B-1A.

1944 "Juano Hernandez in 'Young Man.'" Sepia, March 1962, p.
      16-18.

1944a Kaufman, Bel. "Where Is the ... Smell of Chalk?" (Fame).
      TV Guide, February 26, 1983, p. 15-20.

1945 "LeVar Burton Stars in TV Drama." Norfolk Journal & Guide,
      August 27, 1977, p. B-15.

1946 Levin, E. "Vinnette Carroll Will Impersonate Sojourner
      Truth on an Episode of 'The American Parade.'" TV
      Guide, August 3, 1974, p. 36.

1947 "Lou Gossett in 'Young Rebels at Valley Forge.'" TV Guide,
      July 18, 1970, p. 24-25.

1948 "Lou Gossett, Jr. Stars In 'Lazarus Syndrome' On ABC Tele-
      vision." Grapevine, July/August 1979, p. 17-18.

1949 "Lynn Hamilton and Hal Williams Co-Star on 'The Waltons'
      Program." Los Angeles Sentinel, January 19, 1978, p.
      ENT-1.

1950 McFadden, Cyra. "Up and Coming." Panorama, November
      1980, p. 11.

1951 "Mandrake The Magician;" Muscular Woody Strode Gets Lothar
      Role In New TV Series." Ebony, December 1954, p. 103-
      106.

1952 Margulies, Lee. "Righteous Apples." Emmy, Winter 1980,
      p. 34.

1953 "Playing with Fire--and Not Getting Burned." (Beulah Land).
      TV Guide, May 24, 1980, p. 10-11.

1954 Reney, John. "There's TV Gold at End of 'Righteous' Rain-
      bow." Peoria Journal Star, May 24, 1980, p. 9.

1955 "'The Righteous Apples' Debut on KECT." Los Angeles Sen-
      tinel, May 8, 1980, B-2A.

1956 "'Righteous Apples' Takes A Fresh Look at Everyday Life."
      Scottsdale [AZ] Daily Progress, May 16, 1980, p. 17.

1957 See, C. "Percy Rodriguez on 'Peyton Place' as Census Taker."
      TV Guide, September 28, 1968, p. 24-29.

1958   "Tempest in Watts Over NBC Production of 'Losers Weepers.'"
       Broadcasting, January 9, 1967, p. 70-71.

1959   Terry, Mike. "'White Shadow': Fresh Black Talent." Soul,
       March 5, 1979, p. 8-9.

1960   "Topper Carew's Gold at the End TV's Rainbow; Black Pro-
       ducer for Rainbow TV Works." Ebony, October 1980, p.
       71-72+.

1961   "Topper Carew's 'Righteous Apples' Recent Debut." Black
       Monitor Supplement, June 1980, p. 8.

1962   "The White Shadow." New York Amsterdam News, May 26,
       1979, p. 40.

1963   Wilkinson, Bud. "PBS Series 'Righteous Apples' Addresses
       Racial Issues." Arizona Republic, May 25, 1980, p. 8-10.

1964   "William Marshall Plays 'Othello' on PBS." Los Angeles
       Sentinel, June 7, 1979, p. B-2A.

1965   Wolcott, James. "Righteous Apples." Village Voice, June
       2, 1980, p. 50.

Programs--Game

1966   "Do You Trust Your Wife?" Couple on Edgar Bergen's CBS
       Quiz Show Are Biggest Negro TV Winners." Ebony, Au-
       gust 1956, p. 86+.

1967   "'Mahalia Jackson Sings'; New Half-Hour TV Series Being
       Planned in Hollywood." Jet, April 20, 1961, p. 58.

1968   "Queen for a Day." Our World, October 1952, p. 48.

1969   "$64,000 Kid; Gloria Lockerman Is a Modern Fortune's Child."
       Our World, November 1955, p. 12-15.

1970   "TV Game Shows." Chicago Daily Defender, November 12,
       1977, p. I-12.

1971   "TV Host Adam Wade." Los Angeles Sentinel, January 12,
       1979, p. ENT. 2A.

1972   "TV 'Turnabout' Host." Baltimore Afro American, January
       14, 1979, p. I-12.

Programs--Movies

1973   "Adam Wade in Movie-for-TV 'Street Killing' on ABC." (Bur-
       rell column). Soul, October 25, 1976, p. 14.

1974   "Adam Wade Plays Della Reese's Lover." Jet, August 9,
       1979, p. 61.

1975   "Andrew Young Comments on 'King' Film." Atlanta Daily
       World, January 12, 1979, p. I-6.

1976   Ashley, Franklin. "Grambling's White Tiger." TV Guide,
       September 26, 1981, p. 40+.

1977   "Belafonte To Portray Malcolm X for TV Movie." Jet, June
       23, 1977, p. 59.

1978   "Bernie Casey Portrays Joe Louis in TV Movie." New York
       Amsterdam News, January 7, 1978, p. D-4.

1979   "'Blackboard Jungle'; Sidney Poitier Has Key Role in Brutal
       Film about Teacher, Juvenile Delinquents." Ebony, May
       1955, p. 87-88+.

1980   "Brown Queers WNET and PBS Airing of Harlem Film."
       Broadcasting, May 19, 1975, p. 39-40.

1981   Cassidy, Robert. "Marva Collins Story." TV Guide, Novem-
       ber 28, 1981, p. 15+.

1982   "Cicely Tyson to Portray Mrs. King in TV Movie." Norfolk
       Journal & Guide, May 28, 1977, p. B-18.

1983   "Cicely Tyson's Transformation in the Autobiography." Jet,
       January 3, 1974, p. 56-57.

1984   "'Cooley High': A Trip Back to the 60s." Soul, August 18,
       1975, p. 15.

1985   "'Cooley High' Film Comes to TV." Michigan Chronicle,
       April 2, 1977, p. B-4.

1986   "'Cooley High' Tells it Like it is." Milwaukee Courier, Jan-
       uary 31, 1976, p. 18.

1987   Davidson, M. "Cicely Tyson in 'The Autobiography of Miss
       Jane Pittman.'" TV Guide, January 26, 1974, p. 14-16.

1988   "Esther Rolle Discusses Her Role in ... 'Why the Caged
       Bird Sings.'" Michigan Chronicle, April 28, 1979, p.
       B-4.

1989   "Gilliam Signs for Disney Movie--'The Million Dollar Duck.'"
        Soul, October 5, 1970, p. 9.

1990   Hartman, Hermene. "Color TV Goes Blackened-White:
        'Cindy,' ABC Friday Night Movie." Soul, June 5, 1978,
        p. 40.

1991   "'Island in the Sun'; Dandridge, Belafonte Star." Ebony, July
        1957, p. 32-34+.

1992   Killens, John. "A Woman Called Moses." TV Guide, Decem-
        ber 9, 1978, p. 33+.

1993   "King TV Film Biography Set for 1976-77 Season." Jet, Oc-
        tober 30, 1975, p. 55.

1994   "'King,' TV-Movie Criticized by Family and Friends." Bi-
        lalian News, August 19, 1977, p. I-10.

1995   "LaVar Burton Stars in 'One in a Million.'" Chicago Daily
        Defender, May 13, 1978, p. ENT-13.

1996   "Legal Steps Taken to Block 'King' Film." Michigan Chron-
        icle, August 20, 1977, p. C-9.

1997   "Lou Gossett Stars in 'An Officer and a Gentleman.'" Ebony,
        September 1982, p. 112-116.

1998   "Movie Based on King Scheduled for TV." Bilalian News,
        April 15, 1977, p. I-9.

1999   "Richard Pryor and Pam Grier in 'Greased Lightning.'"
        Right On, August 1977, p. 46-47.

2000   "Richard Pryor's Role in 'California Suite.'" Chicago Daily
        Defender, December 2, 1978, p. I-13.

2001   "Richard Pryor's 'Some Kind of Hero.'" Right On, July 1982,
        p. 60.

2002   "'Rocky II' Described by Carl Weathers." Baltimore Afro
        American, June 9, 1979, p. I-11.

2003   "... 'Scottsboro Boys' Film." Norfolk Journal & Guide, Jan-
        uary 1, 1977, p. B-15.

2004   "Screen Test; Dorothy Dandridge Wins 'Carmen Jones' Title
        Role with Sizzling Performance." Ebony, September 1954,
        p. 37-40+.

2005   "Strode Muscles In; Rugged, Ex-All-American Football End
        Plays African Prince in New 'Mandrake the Magician' TV
        Film." Our World, December 1954/January 1955, p. 34-
        37.

2006   "Tamara Dobson's Role in 'Cleopatra Jones.'" Los Angeles
       Sentinel, August 3, 1978, p. B-2A.

2007   Wickham, P. J.   "Pryor and Cosby: 'California Suite': How
       Sweet It Isn't." Soul, January 22, 1979, p. 12-13.

                         Programs--Music

2008   Akers, Suzanne.   "Don Cornelius: His Train's Dancing on
       the Right Track." Soul, March 14, 1977, p. 15.

2009   Barber, R.   "Duke Ellington: We Love You Madly." TV
       Guide, February 10, 1973, p. 28-30.

2010   _____.   "Right on Time with 'Soul Train.'" TV Guide,
       May 25, 1974, p. 31-33.

2011   "Ben Vereen Signs for 'All That Jazz.'" Los Angeles Sen-
       tinel, November 23, 1978, p. B-3A.

2012   "The Duke on TV." Jet, May 23, 1957, p. 60.

2013   "For Ellington, Cameramen in Cassocks." TV Guide, April
       13, 1968, p. 6-7.

2014   Higgins, R.   "Harry Belafonte and Lena Horne Get Together."
       TV Guide, March 21, 1970, p. 14-17.

2015   Johnson, Connie.   "'An Evening on TV with Diana Ross':
       The First One-Woman 90-Minute Show." Soul, March 14,
       1977, p. 2-3.

2016   "Minstrel Man." Michigan Chronicle, March 5, 1977, p. B-
       4; Pittsburgh Courier, March 5, 1977, p. 3-20; New York
       Amsterdam News, March 5, 1977, p. D-2; Baltimore Afro
       American, February 26, 1977, p. I-11.

2017   "Oscar Brown to Host 'From Jumpstreet'--A Story of Black
       Music." Chicago Daily Defender, June 20, 1979, p. I-20;
       Atlanta Daily World, June 24, 1979, p. 10.

2018   "Patricia Pratt Jennings in Symphony Program." Pittsburgh
       Courier, February 26, 1977, p. 3-18.

2019   Sederberg, Kathryn.   "Syndicated 'Soul Train' Heads Down the
       Track to Young Black Market." Advertising Age, February
       7, 1972, p. 34.

2020   "Soul Train." (A Billboard Spotlight). Billboard, September
       28, 1974, p. ST1-32.

2021 "'Soul Train' All Stars Top J-5 in Charity Basketball Game."
      Soul, April 26, 1976, p. 4.

2022 "'Soul Train' Gang Reveal Thoughts for the New Year." Right
      On, February 1976, p. 43-44.

2023 "'Soul Train' Heads Down the Syndicated TV Track to Young."
      Advertising Age, February 7, 1972, p. 34.

2024 "'Soul Train' Reaches 13th Year." Los Angeles Sentinel,
      April 14, 1983, p. B-7.

2025 "'Soul Train' Rides to RCA." Jet, December 11, 1975, p. 63.

2026 "The 'Soul Train' Story." (Parts 1-6) Arizona Informant,
      (Entertainment page). November 5/December 10, 1980,
      p. 5.

2027 "'Soul Train's' Dance Studios Open." Soul, July 3, 1978,
      p. 24.

2028 "Stan Myles' 'Louis Armstrong' to Air January 25." (Burrell
      column). Soul, January 19, 1976, p. 12.

2029 "'Tony Brown's Journal' Show Looks at Black and White
      Music." New York Amsterdam News, June 30, 1979, p.
      34.

2030 Van Doren, Bill. "Soul Train." Soul, June 20, 1977, p.
      38-40.

                        Programs--News/Talk

2031 "Adam Wade Host of 'Black Journal.'" Jet, April 15, 1976,
      p. 24.

2032 "Amsterdam News Chairman's Appearance on 'Like It Is'
      Protested." New York Amsterdam News, December 11,
      1982, p. 1.

2033 "Ben Jochannan, Sales and Noble Discuss Black History."
      New York Amsterdam News, September 10, 1977, p. D-16.

2034 "Betty Shabazz and Gil Noble Report on Schools." New York
      Amsterdam News, August 27, 1977, p. D-15.

2035 "Black Journal." Bilalian News, February 18, 1977, p. I-9.

2036 "Black Journal." New York Times, May 16, 1975, p. 36.

2037   " 'Black Journal' and Soul TV Shows May Be Cut. "   Jet, January 4, 1973, p. 14.

2038   " 'Black Journal' and Tony Brown. "   New York Amsterdam News, March 26, 1977, p. D-8.

2039   " 'Black Journal' Cancellation Protested By Blacks. "   Jet, January 16, 1973, p. 18.

2040   " 'Black Journal' Charges 'New York Times' With Attempted Assassination. "   Jet, January 27, 1972, p. 44-45.

2041   " 'Black Journal' Funding Favored By Public. "   Jet, February 1, 1973, p. 14.

2042   " 'Black Journal' Gets New Co-Host. "   (Adam Wade).   San Francisco Sun Reporter, May 13, 1976, p. 18.

2043   " 'Black Journal' Goes to New Weekly Format. "   Pittsburgh Courier, October 9, 1971, p. 17.

2044   " 'Black Journal' Looks at the Black Revolution. "   Bilalian News, April 29, 1977, p. I-3.

2045   " 'Black Journal' on PBS. "   Washington Post, April 26, 1971, p. 85.

2046   " 'Black Journal' Premiere Features Nipsey Russell. "   Cleveland Call & Post, January 31, 1976, p. 18.

2047   " 'Black Journal' Sponsored by National, Educational TV, lacks Funds; May Close. "   Jet, June 12, 1964, p. 44.

2048   " 'Black Journal'--What Is A Black Leader? "   Atlanta World, March 17, 1977, p. 1-9; Chicago Defender, March 10, 1977, p. ENT-10.

2049   "Black Perspective. "   Time, October 30, 1972, p. 85.

2050   " 'Black Perspective'--Behind The Scenes. "   Des Moines Iowa Bystander, March 4, 1976, p. 9.

2051   "Black Women's TV Series Debuts in June. "   Pittsburgh Courier, May 28, 1977, p. 2-12.

2052   "Bryant Gumbel to Be Featured on NBC-TV's 'Today Show. ' "   Michigan Chronicle, August 16, 1980, p. B-2.

2053   "CBS-TV's 'Person to Person' Filmed the Show for Later Showing with Ella Fitzgerald in her Home in Los Angeles, California. "   Jet, June 16, 1960, p. 62.

2054   " 'Ebony/Jet Showcase' Airing in DC and Atlanta. "   Jet, October 14, 1982, p. 61.

2055   "'Ebony/Jet TV Celebrity Showcase' Set to Air in Atlanta,
        Washington, D.C." Jet, August 30, 1982, p. 58.

2056   Davis, Curt. "For You ... Black Woman." Encore, July
        18, 1977, p. 33-34.

2057-   "Don Cornelius Prepares Syndicated TV Talk Show, 'Don's
8   Place.'" Jet, May 11, 1978, p. 25.

2059   "'For You ... Black Woman' Begins 3rd Year." Norfolk
        Journal & Guide, September 21, 1979, p. A-5.

2060   "'For You, Black Woman' Continues Production." Pittsburgh
        Courier, September 3, 1977, p. 2-12.

2061   "'For You, Black Woman' Series Debuts." New York Amster-
        dam News, May 21, 1977, p. D-15.

2062   "'For You, Black Woman' to Debut for Black Women." Mich-
        igan Chronicle, June 4, 1977, p. B-4.

2063   "Hadda Brooks; Singer Has New Hit Television Program On
        West Coast." Ebony, April 1951, p. 101-102.

2064   Hickey, N. "PBS Has Two New Series, 'Changing Music' and
        'Black Perspectives on the News.'" TV Guide, June 30,
        1973, p. 42.

2065   "Inner Visions-Beah Richards." Los Angeles Sentinel, Jan-
        uary 12, 1979, p. ENT-1.

2066   "Janet Langhart Co-Host 'Noontime America Live.'" Jet,
        July 27, 1978, p. 18.

2067   "Janet Langhart, Co-Host of 'A.M. New York.'" Bilalian
        News, April 27, 1979, p. 12; New York Amsterdam News,
        May 12, 1979, p. 29.

2068   "Jesse Jackson to Appear on 'Directions' and Discuss Racism."
        Cleveland Call & Post, May 5, 1979, p. B-9.

2069   "Jordan Discusses Social Problems on 'Firing Line.'" Nor-
        folk Journal & Guide, December 17, 1977, p. A-10.

2070   "'Like It Is,' 14 Black Businessmen Will Sponsor WABC-TV
        Program 'Like It Is' For One Year." New York Times,
        October 1, 1975, p. 75.

2071   "'Like It Is' to be Distributed by Central Education Network."
        Michigan Chronicle, September 1, 1979, p. A-6.

2072   "'MacNeil-Lehrer Report' to Carry Essay by C. Hunter-Gault."
        Los Angeles Sentinel, May 17, 1979, p. A-9.

2073   "Michael Jackson Discusses Career on 'Ebony/Jet' Television
        Show." Jet, April 25, 1983, p. 60.

2074   "Muhammad Ali Interviewed on 'For You ... Black Woman.'"
        New York Amsterdam News, November 19, 1977, p. D-18.

2075   "Pepsi-Cola Sponsors 'Tony Brown's Journal.'" New York
        Amsterdam News, November 12, 1977, p. D-2.

2076   "'Person to Person'; Edward R. Murrow Takes Negro Celeb-
        rities into the Homes of 20 Million Television Viewers."
        Ebony, October 1956, p. 51-54+.

2076a   "Ponchitta Pierce Hosts 'Today' in New York." Jet, February
        11, 1982, p. 29.

2077   "Rev. Ike Interviewed on 'For You ... Black Woman.'" New
        York Amsterdam News, December 31, 1977, p. D-14.

2078   Shales, Tom.   "PBS 'Black Journal' May Be Cancelled."
        Los Angeles Times, December 21, 1972, p. CAL. 2.

2079   "Tony Brown's 'Black Journal' Begins 9th Season." Michigan
        Chronicle, February 12, 1977, p. B-4.

2080   "Tony Brown Is Back with 'Black Journal.'" New York Ams-
        terdam News, October 29, 1977, p. A-1.

2081   "Tony Brown's 'Journal' Moves to Commercial Television,"
        Bilalian News, December 30, 1977, p. 29.

2082   "Tony Brown's 'Journal' Show Features WBLS." Atlanta Daily
        World, August 28, 1981, p. 4.

2083   "Tony Brown's 'Journal' Show Looks At Life in the Year 2000."
        New York Amsterdam News, July 12, 1980, p. 37.

2084   "TV Series Addressed to Black Women to Debut." Norfolk
        Journal & Guide, May 21, 1977, p. B-16.

2085   "WTAE-TV Slates 'Black Chronicle.'" Pittsburgh Courier,
        April 17, 1971, p. 12.

                            Programs--Roots

2086   "Alex Haley, Beyond 'Roots.'" Sepia, November 1977, p. 23-
        27.

2087   Ames, K. and R. Menkoff.   "Uprooted." Newsweek, January
        22, 1979, p. 10.

2088 Angelou, Maya. "Haley Shows Us the Truth of Our Conjoined
      Histories. " New York Times, January 23, 1977, p. 2-27.

2089 "Author Haley, Reporter Moore Wins Pulitzer. " Jet, May 5,
      1977, p. 16.

2090 Baker, J. F. "PW Interviews--Alex Haley. " Publishers
      Weekly, September 6, 1976, p. 8-9.

2091 Baldwin, James. "How One Black Man Came to be an Amer-
      ican. " New York Times Book Review, September 26,
      1976, p. 1.

2092 "Benjamin Hooks Reviews 'Roots. '" Michigan Chronicle,
      March 26, 1977, p. B-8.

2093 Berry, Jason. "The Search for 'Roots. '" The Nation, Octo-
      ber 2, 1976, p. 313-315.

2094 Black, Doris. "Television's Most Ambitious Black Program. "
      Sepia, February 1977, p. 36-38+.

2095 "Black Historians Reflect on Criticism of 'Roots. '" Jet,
      April 28, 1977, p. 16-17.

2096 Brown, Les. "ABC Took A Gamble with 'Roots' and is Hit-
      ting Pay Dirt. " New York Times, January 28, 1977, p.
      2-1.

2097 _____. " 'Roots'' Success in South Seen as Sign of Change. "
      New York Times, February 10, 1977, p. 15.

2098 Buck, Jerry. "Making TV History: Viewers Pulled in by
      'Roots. '" Los Angeles Times, January 29, 1977, p. 2-4.

2099 Clayton, M. S. "Interview with Alex Haley. " Today's Edu-
      cation, September 1977, p. 46-47.

2100 Forbes, C. "From these Roots; the Real Significance of
      Haley's Phenomenon. " Christianity Today, May 6, 1977,
      p. 19-21.

2101 Fraser, C. Gerald. "Blacks and Whites Found to Have Mis-
      apprehensions on Impact of 'Roots. '" New York Times,
      June 7, 1977, p. 71.

2102 Greenfield, M. "Uncle Tom's Roots. " Newsweek, February
      14, 1977, p. 100.

2103 Haley, Alex. "My Furthest-Back Person--The African. "
      New York Times Magazine, July 16, 1972, p. 13-16.

2104 _____. " 'Roots': A Black American's Search for his

Ancestral African Roots." Ebony, August 1976, p. 100-107.

2105 _____. "There Are Days When I Wish It Hadn't Happened." Playboy, March 1979, p. 114-119.

2106 _____. "What 'Roots' Means to Me." Reader's Digest, May 1977, p. 73-76.

2107 "Haley Ascribes Success to God." Los Angeles Times, February 2, 1977, p. 4-16.

2108 "Haley's Quest for 'Roots.'" Forbes, February 15, 1977, p. 24.

2109 Hay, Samuel A. "Roots-A-Corrected Image." Media & Methods, April 1977, p. 16-18.

2110 "I Began Weeping Like Some Baby." (Alex Haley) TV Guide, January 22, 1977, p. 6-9.

2111 "I Have Been Gripped and Thrilled: Author of 'Roots' Describes its Astonishing and Exhausting Impact on his Life." TV Guide, January 21, 1978, p. 6-8.

2112 "Impact of 'Roots.'" (Martin column). Pittsburgh Courier, February 15, 1977, p. I-6.

2113 "Impact of 'Roots' Dramatization Surveyed." Bilalian News, March 25, 1977, p. I-7.

2114 "Impact of 'Roots' Earns ABC a Respite from Programming Charges." TV Guide, February 12, 1977, p. A-4.

2115 "Increased Demand for 'Roots.'" (Robertson column). Los Angeles Sentinel, February 17, 1977, p. A-6.

2116 Jackson, James Thomas. "Awakening to a Common Suffering --and Pride." New York Times, February 8, 1977, p. 30.

2117 "James Earl Jones to Play Haley in 'Roots II.'" Atlanta Daily World, July 30, 1978, p. I-3.

2118 Johnson, Thomas A. "80 Million Saw 'Roots' Sunday, Setting Record." New York Times, February 2, 1977, p. 2-16.

2119 _____. "'Roots' has Widespread and Inspiring Influence." New York Times, March 19, 1977, p. 46.

2120 King, Larry L. "From the Seed of Kunta Kinte." Saturday Review, September 18, 1976, p. 20-22.

2121 "Kunta Kinte's Village Today." Sepia, September 1977, p. 35-37.

2122 Lane, Bill. "'Roots I' vs. 'Roots II.'" Sepia, May 1979,
      p. 18-30.

2123 "Leslie Uggams Bruised in Filming of 'Roots.'" Michigan
      Chronicle, April 2, 1977, p. A-1.

2124 "Literacy Message in 'Roots.'" (Martin column). Michigan
      Chronicle, February 12, 1977, p. A-8.

2125 Lloyd, R. G. "'Roots,' The Book; The TV Version; The
      Message." Negro Education Review, April 1977, p. 58-
      62.

2126 Margulies, Lee. "Financial View of 'Roots.'" Los Angeles
      Times, February 19, 1979, p. 4-16.

2127 _____. "Last Episode Garners Largest Audience Ever."
      Los Angeles Times, February 2, 1977, p. 4-1.

2128 Meritt, Carole. "Looking at Afro-American 'Roots.'" Phylon,
      June 1977, p. 211-212.

2129 Michener, James A. "'Roots,' Unique in its Time." New
      York Times, February 27, 1977, p. 7-29.

2130 Nelson, Truman. "Delinquent's Process." Nation, November
      8, 1965, p. 336-338.

2131 O'Connor, John J. "TV Review." New York Times, January
      21, 1977, p. 3-21.

2132 "One 'Roots' Does Not a Medium Make." Soul, October 10,
      1977, p. 2.

2133 Phillips, K. "Distortions of 'Roots' on Television are Inflam-
      matory." TV Guide, February 19, 1977, p. A-5, A-6.

2134 "Political Impact of 'Roots.'" (Payne column). Pittsburgh
      Courier, February 19, 1977, p. I-6.

2135 Reuter, M. "Doubleday Answers Haley: Denies all Charges."
      Publishers Weekly, April 25, 1977, p. 34-35.

2136 _____. "Haley Settles Plagiarism Suit, Concedes Passages."
      Publishers Weekly, December 25, 1978, p. 22.

2137 _____. "Why Alex Haley is Suing Doubleday: An Outline
      of the Complaint." Publishers Weekly, April 4, 1977,
      p. 25.

2138 Rich, Frank. "A Super Sequel to Haley's Comet." Newsweek,
      February 19, 1979, p. 84-88.

2139   "Roots." (Hawkins column). Los Angeles Sentinel, February
       17, 1977, p. A-7. (Hawkins column). Norfolk Journal &
       Guide, February 19, 1977, p. A-11.

2140   "Roots." Michigan Chronicle, February 26, 1977, p. B-8.

2141   "'Roots' Cases." New York Times, November 20, 1978, p.
       126-127.

2142   "'Roots' Fever Grips U. S. After Marathon Telecast." Jet,
       February 24, 1977, p. 60-61.

2143   "'Roots' Reaps Vast Harvest." Los Angeles Times, February
       1, 1977, p. 2-4; p. 4-1.

2144   "'Roots' Rerun Tops On TV, Sequel Cost $18 Million." Jet,
       August 28, 1978, p. 56.

2145   "'Roots' Reviewed & Discussed." (Robertson column). Los
       Angeles Sentinel, March 3, 1977, p. A-6, March 10, 1977,
       p. A-6; (Hooks column). Baltimore Afro American, March
       5, 1977, p. 1-5; Atlanta Daily World, March 10, 1977, p.
       1-4; Norfolk Journal & Guide, March 19, 1977, p. A-9.

2146   "'Roots' Seen As Little Help To Black Actors." Chicago De-
       fender, January 13, 1974, p. 9.

2147   "'Roots' Telecast." (Hooks column). New York Amsterdam
       News, March 12, 1977, p. A-4.

2148   "'Roots' TV Drama Commended." (Editorial). Michigan
       Chronicle, February 12, 1977, p. A-8.

2149   "'Roots II': A Distortion of Our History and Culture." Vol.
       2, No. 3, First World, p. 29-30.

2150   "'Roots II' Sneak Peek." Right On, February 1979, p. 18-19.

2151   "'Roots II': The Next Generations." Soul, October 2, 1978,
       p. 15.

2152   Salaam, Kalamu Ya. "Alex Haley, Root Man: A Black Ge-
       nealogist." Black Collegian, November/December 1976,
       p. 30-33.

2153   Schillaci, P. "'Roots' On TV: It Touched Us All." Media
       & Methods, April 1977, p. 22-23.

2154   Sheppard, R. Z. "African Genesis." Time, October 18, 1976,
       p. 109.

2155   Slaton, Shell. "The Alex Haley Happening." Right On, Sum-
       mer 1978, p. 34-35.

2156 "Slave Literacy Problem in 'Roots.'" (Martin column). Pittsburgh Courier, February 19, 1977, p. I-6.

2157 "Stan Shaw Lands Leading Role in 'Roots II.'" Baltimore Afro American, May 13, 1978, p. I-11.

2158 Swertlow, S. "Ratings Say 'Roots' Is Top Show Ever Created for TV." TV Guide, February 5, 1977, p. A-5.

2159 "Theater Revenues Decline During 'Roots' Telecast." New York Amsterdam News, February 26, 1977, p. D-15.

2160 Topogna, P. "'Roots' Spin Off." Today's Education, September/October 1977, p. 18.

2161 "TV Dramatization of 'Roots.'" Michigan Chronicle, February 5, 1977, p. A-1.

2162 "View from the Whirlpool." Time, February 19, 1979, p. 88.

2163 Waters, H. F. "After Haley's Comet." Newsweek, February 14, 1977, p. 97-98.

2164 Watkins, Mel. "A Talk with Alex Haley." New York Times Book Review, September 26, 1976, p. 2.

2165 Wilkins, Roger. "The Black Ghost of History." New York Times, February 16, 1977, p. 27.

2166 Williford, Stanley O. "The Vulgarization of a Great Book." Los Angeles Times, January 31, 1977, p. 5-3.

2167 Wood, P. H. "Roots of Victory, Roots of Defeat." New Republic, March 12, 1977, p. 27-28.

2168 Woodward, K. L. and A. Collings. "Limits of Faction." Newsweek, April 27, 1977, p. 87.

2169 Zimmerman, P. D. "In Search of a Heritage." Newsweek, September 27, 1976, p. 84-86.

Programs--Specials

2170 "An Evening with Diana Ross." Michigan Chronicle, March 5, 1977, p. B-4.

2171 "Ancient Artistry Discussed on Hill's Focus." Los Angeles Wave, June 23, 1977, p. 10; August 28, 1980, p. 9.

2172 "'And Beautiful,' Black Firm Johnson Products Sponsors

First Hour-Long TV Special. " Jet, September 11, 1969, p. 60-61.

2173 "Count Basie and Joe Williams Tape Special. " Michigan Chronicle, August 27, 1977, p. B-4.

2174 Crail, T. "George Kirby Is Ready. " TV Guide, July 18, 1970, p. 13-15.

2175 "Diahann Carroll Ready for 1st Special. " Soul, August 30, 1976, p. 1.

2176 Diehl, D. "Diana Ross in a Special This Week. " TV Guide, December 7, 1968, p. 14-16.

2177 Green, Maury. "Dick Cochran's Special On Los Angeles Gangs, On KABC. " Los Angeles Times, March 2, 1973, p. CAL-2.

2178 "Lorraine Hansberry Does Civil War Play Script; 'The Drinker's Gourd' to be Shown in 1960 on NBC-TV. " Jet, February 11, 1960, p. 59.

2179 MacDonough, S. "5th Dimension Special. " TV Guide, May 30, 1970, p. A-4.

2180 "Motown Tapes TV Special to Observe 25th Anniversary. " Jet, April 8, 1983, p. 62-64.

2181 "Paul Winfield Talks About Role in TV Special about MLK, 'King. '" Pittsburgh Courier, February 18, 1978, p. 4-26.

2182 "Paula Kelly in 'Four Men and a Girl. '" TV Guide, November 13, 1954, p. 12.

2183 "Richard Pryor at Work on TV Special. " Soul, October 11, 1976, p. 1.

2184 "Richard Pryor Concert. " Michigan Chronicle, November 4, 1978, p. B-6.

2185 "Richard Pryor Featured in TV Special. " Michigan Chronicle, May 7, 1977, p. B-4.

2186 "Richard Pryor Special. " New York Amsterdam News, June 25, 1977, p. D-14.

2187 "Richard Pryor Special. " Norfolk Journal & Guide, May 14, 1977, p. B-15; Michigan Chronicle, May 14, 1977, p. B-4.

2188 "Richard Pryor Special to Be Re-Aired. " Norfolk Journal & Guide, August 27, 1977, p. B-15.

2189 " 'The Smokey Robinson Show' on ABC December 18. " (Bur-
      rell column). Soul, November 30, 1970, p. 6.

2190 "Tribute Set for Nat King Cole March 17. " Soul, March 16,
      1967, p. 8.

2191 "TV Special on Paul Robeson. " (Editorial). Baltimore Afro
      American, April 21, 1979, p. I-4.

                        Programs--Variety

2192 Amory, C. "The Flip Wilson Show. " TV Guide, October 10,
      1970, p. 44.

2193 _____. "The Sammy Davis Jr. Show. " TV Guide, March
      19, 1966, p. 1.

2194 "Bill Cosby Set For CBS-TV Variety Show Series in 1972. "
      Jet, June 10, 1971, p. 59.

2195 "Black Entertainers on O'Connor Show. " Soul, October 7,
      1968, p. 4.

2196 Davidson, B. "Flip Wilson--The Hit of the TV Season. " TV
      Guide, January 23, 1971, p. 20-23.

2197 "Della Reese's TV Show Cancelled After 10 Minutes. " Jet,
      March 19, 1970, p. 56.

2198 "Flip Wilson Sings for TV Specials With CBS. " Jet, April 3,
      1975, p. 57.

2199 "Flip Wilson: Something New for His TV Season. " Jet, Oc-
      tober 25, 1973, p. 88-91.

2200 "Ford Foundation May Refund Black Soul TV Series. " Jet,
      March 26, 1970, p. 59.

2201 "Lack of New Black Shows on TV. " New York Amsterdam
      News, May 21, 1977, p. B-6.

2202 Levin, E. "Ossie Davis' Family All Contribute to 'Today Is
      Ours' Episode of CBS Festival of Lively Arts for Young
      People. " TV Guide, February 2, 1974, p. 26.

2203 "Living Color Comes To TV. " Sepia, June 1971, p. 50-55.

2204 "Miss Black Universe Pageant Gets National TV Coverage. "
      Jet, January 4, 1979, p. 59.

2205 "New Detroit Inc. Funds TV Series." Michigan Chronicle, November 12, 1977, p. C-10.

2206 "New Heights For The Jackson Five." Ebony, September 1971, p. 126-132.

2207 "1982 'Parade of Stars' Generates $1.3 Million for UNCF." Norfolk Journal & Guide, August 18, 1982, p. 9.

2208 "Our Part in Body and Soul." Opportunity, January 1948, p. 21.

2209 "'Positively Black' Program." New York Amsterdam News, November 26, 1977, p. D-8.

2210 "Pryor Contracts for TV Series." Soul, July 4, 1977, p. 11.

2211 Raddatz, L. "A Prize Pupil Hands in Her Report Card." TV Guide, July 1, 1972, p. 28-29.

2212 "Rahway Inmates Show Kids Prison's Harsh Realities." New York Amsterdam News, December 10, 1977, p. D-4.

2213 "Reynelda Muse to Host 'Spoonful of Lovin' Video Series." Jet, December 13, 1982, p. 46.

2214 "Richard Pryor Show." Cleveland Call & Post, October 15, 1977, p. B-3; Michigan Chronicle, October 15, 1977, p. C-10.

2215 "Richard Pryor Show." Soul, November 7, 1977, p. 7.

2216 Rosenberg, Howard. "The Fall TV Schedule--Color It White." Los Angeles Times, September 11, 1978.

2217 "Roy Campanella Starts a New Weekly Program, 'Campy's Corner' January 12, 1960 on WFIX-TV." Jet, January 14, 1960, p. 66.

2218 Slaton, Shell. "This Life--Sidney Poitier's Sizzling Autobiography." Right On, October 1980, p. 26.

2218a "'Soul!' Premiers On National TV This Week." New York Amsterdam News, February 7, 1970, p. 1.

2219 "'Soul TV' Cancellation Termed An Insult." Jet, June 21, 1973, p. 5.

2220 Spiegelman, Judy. "Jackson Five Finish Concert Tour, Begin TV Series." Soul, October 11, 1971, p. 1-3.

2221 "Television Programs." (Williams column). Cleveland Call & Post, October 8, 1977, p. B-3.

2222   "TV Sunday School." Ebony, April 1956, p. 81-84.

2223   "TV Telethon for Congress of Racial Equality." Jet, July 20,
       1961, p. 61.

2224   "TV Challenges Shaping Up in Detroit." Broadcasting, June
       25, 1973, p. 48-49.

2225   "TV's Personality Girl; Ohio Housewife Has Two Shows on
       TV, Three on Radio." Ebony, December 1957, p. 102-
       106.

2226   "TV's Top Goat." TV Guide, May 24, 1975, p. 6-7.

2227   White, A. "From Tom-Toms To Television." Our World,
       February 1951, p. 30-38.

2228   "'Your NAACP Reporter,' Weekly TV Show, Station KTVF,
       Fairbanks, Alaska; 4-year Old Show is Only Regular TV
       Program Among NAACP Branches." Jet, April 14, 1960,
       p. 7.

                          Protest/Controversy

2229   "ACLU Protest Police Image in TV Shows." Bilalian News,
       March 11, 1977, p. I-28.

2230   "Action Against Coonskin Threatened." Black Panther, Au-
       gust 25, 1975, p. 21.

2231   "Alabama ETV's Lose Licenses for Lack of Services to Black
       Audience." Broadcasting, January 13, 1975, p. 23-24.

2232   "'Amos 'N' Andy,' on Television; Negro Actors Picket for
       Roles in TV Version of Oldest Radio Show After Two-Year
       Search." Ebony, May 1951, p. 21-22.

2233   "Ashley, Amelia. "Reed Fights Suspension Over Hair Style."
       San Francisco Reporter, January 29, 1981, p. 3.

2234   "Barbara Payne Returns; Detroit TV Apologizes." Jet, July
       21, 1977, p. 38.

2235   "Battle to Integrate Alabama TV." Encore, March 8, 1976,
       p. 8-9.

2236   "Betty Wright Cancels South African TV Show." Jet, May 22,
       1980, p. 54.

2237   "'Beulah Land' Becomes a Battlefield." Right On, September
       1980, p. 74+.

2238   " 'Beulah Land' Controversy. " <u>New Orleans Times Picayune</u>
       March 2, 1980, p. TVF-3.

2239   " 'Beulah Land' Happy Slave TV Movie Attacked in Hollywood. "
       <u>Jet</u>, April 3, 1980, p. 56.

2240   " 'Beulah Land' Postponed." <u>Washington Post</u>, April 12, 1980,
       p. B4.

2241   " 'Beulah Land' Review. " (Robertson column).   <u>Los Angeles Sen-
       tinel</u>, August 29, 1980, p. A-3.

2242   "Beverly Payne's Protest Against TV-2 Aired. "   <u>Michigan
       Chronicle</u>, May 28, 1977, p. D5.

2243   "Beverly Payne Resigns As TV Anchorwoman. "   <u>Madison
       Chronicle</u>, July 9, 1977, p. 1.

2244   "Beverly Todd Says White Backlash Keeps Blacks Off TV. "
       <u>Jet</u>, April 23, 1970, p. 53.

2245   "Bias Charged in Black TV Programming. "   <u>New York Am-
       sterdam News</u>, October 1, 1977, p. C-9.

2246   "Bias in Motion Picture and TV Industry. "   <u>Bilalian News</u>,
       July 28, 1978, p. I-6.

2247   "Bias Suit Against Film and TV Industry. "   <u>Chicago Daily De-
       fender</u>, December 7, 1981, p. 11.

2248   "Biased Reporting of News Discussed. "   <u>New York Amsterdam
       News</u>, February 12, 1977, p. D-9.

2249   "Black Actors' Support of Screen Actors' Guild Strike. "   <u>Los
       Angeles Sentinel</u>, September 11, 1980, p. A-2.

2250   "Black Anti-Defamation Coalition Eyes TV Programs. "   <u>At-
       lanta Daily World</u>, July 29, 1982, p. B-5.

2251   "Black Caucus Protest of CBS-TV Show." (Deeb column).
       <u>Chicago Tribune</u>, March 12, 1979, p. 2-10.

2252   "Black Caucus Protest of TV Show." (Jarret column).   <u>Chi-
       cago Tribune</u>, March 11, 1979, p. 2-6.

2253   "Black Caucus Strangles 'Mr. Dugan'; Star of Cancelled Show
       Steaming Mad. " <u>Jet</u>, March 29, 1979, p. 58.

2254   "Black Network Rejects NAACP Negotiation Offer in Strike. "
       <u>Atlanta Daily World</u>, March 30, 1979, p. I-6.

2255   "Black Stereotype Characters Appear in Programs. "   <u>Pitts-
       burgh Courier</u>, December 24, 1977, p. 3-17.

2256 "Black Stunt Group Sues Honda Corp. over Discrimination Is-
      sue." Los Angeles Sentinel, April 24, 1980, p. A-5.

2257 "Black Stunt Persons Plan to Picket Honda Headquarters."
      Los Angeles Sentinel, May 1, 1980, p. A-1.

2258 "Black Stuntpersons' Coalition Pickets Honda Co. Headquarters."
      Los Angeles Sentinel, May 8, 1980, p. A-8.

2259 "Black TV Artist Group Criticizes Procter and Gamble Co."
      Los Angeles Sentinel, January 24, 1980, p. A-3.

2260 "Black TV Reporters for ABC Air Grievances." Chicago Daily
      Defender, March 3, 1981, p. 8.

2261 "Blacks and TV Actors' Strike." (Robertson column). Los
      Angeles Sentinel, September 4, 1980, p. A-6.

2262 "Blacks Disagree With Television Portrayals." Cleveland Call
      & Post, October 16, 1976, p. 1.

2263 "Blacks Expect Too Much of Television, Says Diahann Car-
      roll." Soul, October 11, 1976, p. 1.

2264 "Blacks In Film & TV Industries." (Robertson column).
      Los Angeles Sentinel, February 28, 1980, p. A-6; March
      6, 1980, p. A-6; March 13, 1980; p. A-6; March 20, 1980,
      p. A-6.

2265 "Blacks Refuse ABC Program After Black Panel Member De-
      nied." Los Angeles Times, May 22, 1972, p. 21.

2266 "Bock, Hal. "Sammy Davis Jr. Blasts TV Over Black Cast-
      ings." Variety, June 11, 1971, p. 18.

2267 "Boycott in Hollywood." (Porgy and Bess). Time, December
      2, 1959, p. 90.

2268 Brown, Les. "'Good Times' Will Drop Male Parent; Black
      Media Coalition Protest Move." New York Times, June
      7, 1976, p. 18.

2269 Buchanan, P. "Big Brother Pokes His Nose into TV's Tent."
      TV Guide, September 17, 1977, p. A-5. A-6.

2270 "Can Sammy Davis, Jr. Crash Network TV?" Ebony, October
      1954, p. 33-34+.

2271 "Church of Christ Representative Criticizes FCC Deregulation
      Plans." New York Amsterdam News, November 14, 1981,
      p. 5.

2272 "Cicely Tyson Criticizes Media Images of Black Women."
      Baltimore Afro American, June 23, 1979, p. 6.

2273 "Cicely Tyson Views TV Roles for Black People." Los An-
      geles Times, February 11, 1979, p. CAL-5.

2274 Clark, Cedric. "Television and Social Controls: Some Ob-
      servations on the Portrayal of Ethnic Minorities." Tele-
      vision Quarterly, Spring 1969, p. 18-22.

2275 "Clergyman Calls for Boycott of TV." Atlanta Daily World,
      January 6, 1977, p. I-5.

2276 "Comment on Petition Filed by United Church of Christ with
      FCC after Inquiry on Employment of Women and Minorities
      in Mass TV Stations." New York Times, July 2, 1972,
      p. 2-11.

2277 "Congressional Black Caucus Launches War on CBS/TV Com-
      edy Show." Chicago Tribune, March 8, 1979, p. 1-2.

2278 "Controversy Over TV Program 'Beulah Land.'" New Orleans
      Times Picayune, March 2, 1980, p. TVF-3.

2279 "CPB's Alleged EEO Failures Anger Blacks." Jet, April 15,
      1976, p. 24.

2280 "Criticism of ABC Anchorman Robinson." (Washington column).
      Los Angeles Sentinel, May 14, 1981, p. A-6.

2281 "Cross Burns at Nashville TV Station During 'Roots.'" Jet,
      August 28, 1978, p. 56.

2282 Dalron, F. K. "Why Television Is A Wasteland for Negroes."
      Negro Digest, June 1963, p. 27-30.

2283 Davidson, B. "Trouble in Yorkin-Lear's Paradise." TV
      Guide, April 6, 1974, p. 4-8; April 13, 1974, p. 12-17.

2284 "Demise of 'Mister Dugan' TV Program." Los Angeles Times,
      March 25, 1979, p. CAL-103.

2285 "Detroit TV Station Dropped shows on cause of racial problems;
      inter faith group rejected movie out of prime time; switched
      to education UHF channel." Wall Street Journal, June 10,
      1968, p. 8.

2286 "'Dick Gregory Show' Cut Off Station." Jet, January 22, 1970,
      p. 58.

2287 "Discrimination Alleged In TV Productions." Los Angeles
      Sentinel, June 16, 1977, p. A-1.

2288 "Discrimination In TV Industry." Los Angeles Sentinel, Feb-
      ruary 22, 1979, p. A-8.

2289   "Distortions of Blacks, Women and Minorities Studies." Bi-
       lalian News, September 16, 1977, p. I-16.

2290   Doan, R.K.   "FCC Studies Proposals that News, Children's
       and Minority Programming Be Exempted from Prime-Time
       Access Rule." TV Guide, October 20, 1973, p. A-1.

2291   _____. "How TV Covered Dr. King's Death." TV Guide,
       April 13, 1968, p. A-1.

2292   _____. "Network Programming Attempts to Ease Racial
       Tensions." TV Guide, May 25, 1968, p. A-1.

2293   _____. "TV Mirrors Nation's Upheaval--King's Death."
       TV Guide, April 20, 1968, p. A-1.

2294   _____. "WMAA-TV in Jackson, Miss. Revokes Earlier
       Ban on Markedly Integrated 'Sesame Street.'" TV Guide,
       June 13, 1970, p. A-3.

2295   "'Does Busing Work?' Program Generates Debate." New
       York Amsterdam News, August 27, 1977, p. A-3.

2296   "Double Standards of Racism on Television." Norfolk Journal
       & Guide, July 7, 1978, p. A-8.

2297   "EEO for Blacks and Women Affirmed." Atlanta Daily World,
       September 25, 1977, p. I-10.

2298   "EEOC Sex Bias Suit Costs NBC Over $1 Million." Atlanta
       Daily World, September 22, 1977, p. 7.

2299   "Effects of TV Programs Assessed." Bilalian News, Septem-
       ber 16, 1977, p. I-14.

2300   "Efforts to Limit Minority Control of Radio and TV." (Belle
       column). Norfolk Journal & Guide, September 22, 1978,
       p. A-8.

2301   Efron, E.   "After the Blackout: Reverse Racism in New
       York Media." TV Guide, August 20, 1977, p. A-5, A-6.

2302   _____. "Minority Complaints About Television." TV Guide,
       October 27, 1973, p. 6-11.

2303   "Employment Discrimination in Communications." Baltimore
       Afro American, April 2, 1977, p. I-11.

2304   Epstein, B.R.   "Stereotypes." Community, September 1961,
       p. 9-10.

2305   "Eric Monte Seeks Credit for Black TV Hit Programs." Bi-
       lalian News, July 22, 1977, p. 29.

2306 "Ethical Culture's TV Follow-up: Still Deficient in Depicting
      Negroes." Variety, December 9, 1964, p. 1.

2307 "Few Black Actors Benefit from 'Roots' and Other 'Black'
      Shows." Bilalian News, March 17, 1978, p. I-28.

2308 Fife, Marilyn Diane. "Black Image in American TV: The
      First Two Decades." Black Scholar, November 1974, p.
      7-15.

2309 Flander, Judy. "Racial Conflict at Series 'CORE.'" Wash-
      ington Post, June 4, 1980, p. C1-C2.

2310 "Gary Deeb Article on Max Robinson." (Editorial). Norfolk
      Journal & Guide, May 20, 1981, p. 6.

2311 "Gary Deeb Article on Max Robinson." (Evelyn Wall column).
      Norfolk Journal & Guide, May 20, 1981, p. 14.

2312 "Gary Deeb's Criticism of Max Robinson." (Cleaver column).
      Los Angeles Sentinel, May 14, 1981, p. A-7.

2313 Gates, Jr., Henry Lewis. "Portraits in Black: from 'Amos
      'n' Andy' to 'Coonskin.'" Harper, June 1976, p. 16-19+.

2314 "Gehman, Richard. "Black and White Television?" TV Guide,
      June 20 and 26, 1964, p. 15-21.

2315 Gunther, M. "TV Dramas Teach Civil Rights." TV Guide,
      December 18, 1971, p. 6-9.

2316 Harding, H. "1963 Network Civil Rights Coverage." TV
      Guide, August 10, 1963, p. A-1.

2317 "Hollywood NAACP Demands Denial of TV Licenses." Los
      Angeles Herald Dispatch, August 28, 1977, p. 1.

2318 "Hollywood Negroes Upset Over Employment." Broadcasting,
      July 11, 1966, p. 62.

2319 "Hooks Agrees With Civil Rights Commission On TV Race
      Bias." New York Amsterdam News, August 27, 1977, p.
      B8; Chicago Defender, August 27, 1977, p. 1-8; Cleveland
      Call & Post, August 27, 1977, p. 1; Norfolk Journal &
      Guide, September 17, 1977, p. A-8; Bilalian News, Sep-
      tember 23, 1977, p. 29.

2320 "How Linda Darnell Fights Jim Crow." Color, March 1956,
      p. 19-21.

2321 Hule, W. B. "The Fight to Force Alabama Educational TV
      off the Air." TV Guide, February 8, 1975, p. 20-24.

2321a "The Impact of 'Roots.'" (Bremond column). Norfolk Journal & Guide, March 12, 1977, p. A-9.

2322 "Integrated Love Meets Dixie Test; North Raises Greatest
Protest As Leontyne Price Sings Lead Role in TV Opera
Tosca." Ebony, May 1955, p. 32-34+.

2323 "Irresponsible TV Programming Under Fire." Michigan Chronicle, September 3, 1977, p. A-3.

2324 "Jesse Jackson Criticizes Walter Jacobson for Cobbs Funeral
Story." Chicago Daily Defender, July 9, 1979, p. 3.

2325 "John Amos Quits Cast of New Show Before It Airs." Jet,
January 11, 1979, p. 56.

2326 "John Johnson Charges WABC-TV Discriminatory." Washington Post, January 23, 1980, p. E9.

2327 "John Johnson Drops Suit Against ABC." Washington Post,
April 23, 1980, p. D15.

2328 "John J. Johnson, NY Newsman Wins Bias Settlement Pay Hike
Against ABC." Jet, May 15, 1980, p. 26.

2329 Jones, M. "Racism In Television." Black World, March
1971, p. 72-78.

2330 "Judge Cooper's Ruling on TV and Williams Trial." (Editorial). Atlanta Daily World, August 27, 1981, p. 4.

2331 "Judge Horton and the Scottsboro Boys." Baltimore Afro
American, January 15, 1977, p. I-7.

2332 "Judith Jamison and Maurice Hines Sue TV Producers." Jet,
March 29, 1982, p. 57.

2333 "Julian Dixon, California Congressman, Blast Images of Blacks
On TV. Jet, December 20, 1979, p. 59.

2334 Koiner, Richard. "Black Image on TV: Good or Bad?" (Part
I) Los Angeles Herald Dispatch, November 14, 1980, p.
4; (Part II) November 21, 1980, p. 4.

2335 Krupnick, Jerry. "Ditching of 'Dugan' Leaves Many Questions." Newark Star-Ledger, March 14, 1979, p. 27.

2336 "Lack of Black TV Anchors." Michigan Chronicle, June 1977,
p. A-8.

2337 "Lack of Minorities In Television." Los Angeles Times, June
1, 1980, p. CAL-27.

2338 "Late Protest Against Renewals In D. C., W. Va. (WTTG-TV, WHIS-AM-FM-TV)." Broadcasting, September 11, 1972, p. 39-40.

2339 LeBlanc, J. "TV Helps the Army Face Race Problems." TV Guide, December 30, 1972, p. 10-12.

2340 Levin, E. "A Mississippi Station Changes Its Attitude." TV Guide, April 5, 1975, p. 3-5.

2341 "Literacy Problem in 'Roots.'" (Adams column). Michigan Chronicle, February 19, 1977, p. A-8.

2342 "'Little Rascals' Stirs NAACP Protest." Chicago Daily Defender, November 19, 1977, p. I-3.

2343 McCaffrey, J.D. "Uproar Cancels TV Show." Philadelphia Evening Bulletin, March 9, 1979, p. 18.

2344 "Manager of WLBT-TV Testifies In U.S. House On FCC Regulations." Chicago Defender, May 26, 1979, p. 1, 5.

2345 Margulies, Lee. "Blacks Object, Show Canceled." Los Angeles Times, March 9, 1979, p. 1.

2346 Mattox, Michael. "The Day Black Movie Stars Got Militant." Black Creation, Winter 1973, p. 1.

2347 "Mike Wallace Refuses U.S. Information on Panthers." Jet, March 12, 1970, p. 30.

2348 Miller, Mark and Miller, Judith. "Television And The Black Image." Sepia, December 1979, p. 56-62.

2349 Mills, Jon. "Blackness In Televisionland." Essence, April 1976, p. 15.

2350 "Minority Group Opposes NBC's Entry into Low-Power Market." Los Angeles Sentinel, May 7, 1981, p. A-8.

2351 "'Mister Dugan' Is Voted Out." Time, March 19, 1979, p. 85.

2352 "Models Picket CBS Station in Hollywood." Los Angeles Sentinel, April 7, 1977, p. A-3.

2353 Moore, Trudy. "Why 'Sister, Sister' Film Was Kept Off TV for Three Years." Jet, June 21, 1982, p. 58-60.

2354 "Move to Block Showing of 'Beulah Land.'" (Editorial). New Orleans Times Picayune, March 2, 1980, p. TVF-3.

2355 "'Mr. Dugan' Yanked Before Its Debut on CBS." Variety, March 14, 1979, p. 72.

2356 "Must Tell Jury of Visit With Panthers; Judge Orders TV Re-
      porter." Jet, November 5, 1970, p. 24.

2357 "NAACP Confab Authorizes Boycott of White Films." Jet,
      July 19, 1982, p. 64.

2358 "NAACP Files $500 Million Damage Suit Against TV and Radio
      Stations in Southern California." Soul, October 10, 1977,
      p. 2.

2359 "NAACP, Film Industry Reach Temporary Pact." Jet, Feb-
      ruary 11, 1982, p. 59.

2360 "NAACP Opposes Return of 'Amos 'n' Andy.'" Michigan
      Chronicle, October 9, 1982, p. A-2.

2361 "NAACP to Enter Broadcasters Labor Dispute." Atlanta Daily
      World, March 23, 1979, p. I-6.

2362 "NAACP Urges Producers of 'Beulah Land' to Meet With Black
      Group." New Orleans Times Picayune, March 7, 1980, p.
      3-8.

2363 "NAB Raps SBA for Not Helping Blacks Buy Radio-TV Sta-
      tions." Pittsburgh Courier, June 3, 1978, p. 3-22.

2364 "National Association of Broadcasters Seeks to Reduce TV
      Violence." Atlanta Daily World, March 6, 1977, p. I-12.

2365 "National Black Network Ends Strike in New York." Baltimore
      Afro American, June 3, 1978, p. I-3.

2366 Nazel, Joe. "The Black Wasteland." Players, May 1977, p.
      40-41+.

2367 "NBC Delays Showing of Movie 'Beulah Land.'" Los Angeles
      Times, April 7, 1980, p. 4-8.

2368 "NBC-TV Plans For 'Beulah Land.'" New York Amsterdam
      News, July 26, 1980, p. 10.

2369 "Next NAACP Stop New York; Effort to Integrate TV Programs
      and Commercials Will Include Talks with Advertisers and
      Agencies." Broadcasting, July 29, 1963, p. 91.

2370 "'Nigger' Approved for Television by FCC." Bilalian News,
      August 10, 1978, p. I-18.

2371 "Now A Negro Push On Radio-TV: NAACP Opens Campaign
      for Jobs Throughout Broadcast System." Broadcasting,
      July 1, 1963, p. 27-29.

2372 "Number of Blacks in Film and on TV." Los Angeles Sen-
      tinel, April 26, 1979, p. A-1.

2373 "Objections To NBC's 'Beulah Land' Discussed." Baltimore
      Afro American, September 27, 1980, p. 1.

2374 "Old-fashioned Debate on TV between Two Men Holding Views
      On Negro Sit-in Movement in South." Wall Street Journal,
      November 11, 1960, p. 16.

2375 "Ossie Davis Testifies To House Committee On TV & Movie
      Bias." Los Angeles Times, January 23, 1976, p. C-16.

2376 "Otis Young of the 'Outcasts' Talks About the Problems of
      Black Actors." Jet, February 13, 1969, p. 54-56.

2377 "Parker Sees Progress In Hiring Policies (Commercial TV)."
      Broadcasting, October 22, 1973, p. 18.

2378 "Pattern of Bilalian Exclusion from Media Employment Charged."
      Bilalian News, January 5, 1979, p. 12.

2379 Prelutsky, Burt. "Hollywood's Negro Mired in Stereotypes."
      Los Angeles Times, February 19, 1967, p. CAL-1.

2380 "President's TV Interview in L. A." (Cleaver column). Los
      Angeles Sentinel, May 19, 1977, p. A-1.

2381 "Producers Halt Showing of TV Series About Black Congress-
      man." Los Angeles Times, March 9, 1979, p. 1-3.

2382 "Professor Says 'Roots' Shatters Black Family Myth." Michi-
      gan Chronicle, February 19, 1977, p. A-3.

2383 "Project B. A. I. T. Combats Negative Black Images on Radio
      and TV." Michigan Chronicle, August 11, 1979, p. C-9.

2384 "Protest Over Racial Portrayals In NBC's 'Beulah Land.'"
      New Orleans Times Picayune, February 18, 1980, p. 2-5.

2385 "Protesting N. Y. Film Makers Seek Minority Access To Public
      TV." Los Angeles Times, February 26, 1980, p. 4-3.

2385a "The P. T. A. Attacks Violence on TV Programs." Bilalian
      News, February 18, 1977, p. I-19.

2386 "PTA Opposes Violence on TV." Bilalian News, May 13, 1977,
      p. I-3.

2387 "Public Broadcasting Challenged By Black Radio-TV Group."
      Michigan Chronicle, May 28, 1977, p. D-5.

2388 "PUSH Threatens TV 'View-In' by Blacks." Chicago Defender,
      November 17, 1976, p. 1.

2389 "Race Issue Excised From EEOC Suit Against WREC- TV."
      Broadcasting, September 24, 1973, p. 26.

2390 "Race Race"; Black-oriented Series and Specials." Newsweek,
      July 15, 1968, p. 74-75.

2391 "Racial Bias In TV Alleged." Atlanta World, August 26, 1977,
      p. 3.

2392 "Racial News Coverage Is Defended." Editor & Publisher,
      July 11, 1959, p. 69.

2393 "Racism on Television." (Editorial). New York Amsterdam
      News, August 20, 1977, p. A-4.

2394 Ramsey, Alvin. "Through A Glass Whitely: The Television
      Rape of Miss Jane Pittman." Black World, August 1974,
      p. 31-36.

2395 Rankin, Edwina L. "TV's Controversial Interracial Couple."
      Jet, August 18, 1977, p. 60-63.

2396 "Red Jamison Sues Station." New York Times, August 13,
      1977, p. 17.

2397 "Redd Foxx Blasts TV Racism." Black Panther, July 3, 1976,
      p. 1.

2398 "Rev. E. C. Parker Concerned that Commercial Interests
      Will Dominate Cable TV and Deny Access to Medium by
      Minorities and Poor." New York Times, March 30, 1971,
      p. 1.

2399 "Richard Hatcher, Carl Stokes Cancel ABC-TV Appearance;
      No Black Newsman On Panel." Jet, June 8, 1972, p. 27.

2400 "Robert Guillaume Bothered by Lack of Blacks on TV." Jet,
      July 31, 1980, p. 30.

2401 "'Roots' Rerun Tops On TV, Sequel Cost $18 Million." Jet,
      August 28, 1978, p. 56.

2402 "'Roots' Seen as Little Help to Black Actors." Chicago Daily
      Defender, January 13, 1979, p. 9.

2403 Sanders, Charles. "Has TV Written Off Blacks?" Ebony,
      September 1981, p. 114-118.

2404 "Scarcity of Black Television Programs." Los Angeles Times,
      October 28, 1979, p. CAL-47.

2405 "The Scottsboro Case." (Worthy column). Baltimore Afro
      American, February 5, 1977, p. I-5.

2406 "Scottsboro 'Victim' Sues NBC." Atlanta Daily World, July
      12, 1977, p. I-3.

2407 "Screen Actors Guild to Protest Bias in Film and TV Industries." Los Angeles Sentinel, September 27, 1979, p. A-1.

2408 Shayon, Robert L. "The Black Man's Image." Saturday Review, March 22, 1969, p. 25.

2409 Sklar, Robert. "Is Television Taking Blacks Seriously: Impact of 'Roots' Promised An Era of Solid Dramatic Series About Black Life." American Film, September 1978, p. 25+.

2410 "Slow Progress for Negroes On TV." Broadcasting, April 4, 1966, p. 115.

2411 Smith-Hobson, Sheila. "Rise and Fall of the Blacks in Serious Television." Freedomways, November 1974, p. 185-199.

2412 "Some Chicago Blacks Criticize WLS-TV Newsman Joel Daley." Chicago Daily Defender, September 15, 1981, p. 6.

2413 Spiegelman, Judy. "Otis Young Says 'The Outcast' Should Be Off TV." Soul, August 11, 1969, p. 14.

2414 "Stars and All Fall On Alabama (ETV)." Broadcasting, February 14, 1972, p. 39-40.

2415 "Still Another Racial Barrier Comes Tumbling." Sepia, July 1963, p. 26.

2416 Sullivan, E. "Can TV Crack America's Color Line." Ebony, May 1951, p. 58-62+.

2417 Swertlow, Frank. "Black Actors Jobless Despite 'Roots.'" Newark Star-Ledger, February 23, 1979, p. 9.

2418 "Talent Is Color Blind." Ebony, September 1955, p. 41-42.

2419 "Tempest in Watts Over NBC Production of Drama Called 'Losers Weepers.'" Broadcasting, January 9, 1967, p. 70-71.

2420 "Theresa Merritt Denies 'Black Mama' Image On TV." Jet, September 19, 1974, p. 61.

2421 "Tony Brown, 'Black Journal' Producer Blasts Nielsen Ratings." Jet, August 15, 1974, p. 22.

2422 "Trials of A Television Actress." Ebony, September 1955, p. 104+.

2423 "TV & Blacks." Michigan Chronicle, January 13, 1979, p. A6; January 27, 1979, p. A10.

2424 "TV Film of King Provokes Anger of His Top Associates."
      Jet, March 9, 1978, p. 12.

2425 "TV Networks Deny Negro Bias, Rep. Adam Clayton Powell
      Hears Pro and Con Testimony." Broadcasting, November
      5, 1962, p. 68.

2426 "TV Networks Respond to TV Violence Issue." Bilalian News,
      March 4, 1977, p. I-10.

2427 "TV News Bias in Coverage of U.S. Budget Story." Atlanta
      Daily World, May 13, 1982, p. 4.

2428 "TV Puts Damper on Explosive Situation." (Local station ac-
      tions after bombing of Charlotte, NC Negro's home).
      Broadcasting, December 6, 1965, p. 66.

2429 "TV Violence Bows to Pressure." Bilalian News, September
      16, 1977, p. I-6.

2430 "TV Violence Comes Under Fire." Bilalian News, September
      9, 1977, p. I-29.

2431 "TV's Programming to Overcome Prejudice Must Be Intelli-
      gent." TV Guide, August 10, 1968, p. 4.

2432 Unger, Arthur. "Blacks On TV: Dropping the Stereotypes."
      Christian Science Monitor, September 24, 1974, p. 23.

2433 "United Church of Christ Report On Minorities." New York
      Times, January 10, 1977, p. 44.

2434 "United Freedom Association Offers To Fight Cinema & TV
      Industries." Los Angeles Sentinel, January 10, 1979, p.
      A13.

2435 "United Methodist Church Raps 'Soap.'" Michigan Chronicle,
      September 24, 1977, p. B-6.

2436 "US Advisory Unit Urges More Public TV Aimed At Minor-
      ities." Los Angeles Times, August 21, 1972, p. 4-22.

2437 "US Appeals Court Ruling on Black Efforts for 'Soul' in TV
      Petition Nullifies FCC Policy Not To Consider License
      Challenges Against Radio and TV Stations That Have Sub-
      stantially Met Programming Needs of the Community."
      New York Times, June 12, 1971, p. 4.

2438 "U.S. Civil Rights Commission Hits White Male Dominance of
      TV." Chicago Defender, January 17, 1979, p. 4; Atlanta
      Daily World, January 23, 1979, p. 1; New York Amsterdam
      News, January 27, 1979, p. 62.

2439 "U.S. Court of Appeals Holds that FCC's Granting of A License To A Station In Jackson, Miss. Without A Hearing On A Complaint that Station Failed to Give A Balanced Presentation of Issues Concerning Negroes Was An Error. Case Sent Back to FCC For Further Proceeding." Race Relations Review, Winter 1966, p. 1661-1671.

2440 "U.S. Judge Considers Stunt Persons' Suit Against Honda Motors." Los Angeles Sentinel, August 21, 1980, p. A-5.

2441 "U.S. to Probe Black Actors' Claims of TV and Movie Bias." Los Angeles Sentinel, April 2, 1981, p. A-5.

2442 Wareham, R. and Byhoe, P.C. "New Stereotypes Are Not Better Than the Old." Urban Review, November 1972, p. 14-18.

2443 Waters, H.F. "Black Experience; 'Roots.'" Newsweek, January 24, 1977, p. 59.

2444 "WDIV-TV Apparently Demotes Ben Frazier; Protest Launched." Michigan Chronicle, October 17, 1981, p. A-1.

2445 Webb, A. "How TV Is Missing the Boat On Tan Stars." Ebony, May 1960, p. 19-22.

2446 Weisman, J. "NBC's 'King' Attacked by Southern Christian Leadership Conference." TV Guide, August 27, 1977, p. A-1.

2447 "What Blacks Can Do About TV." Ebony, May 1973, p. 166-167.

2448 "What Do Negroes Want From TV?" (Contest for Chicago's UHF Channel 38 at issue)." Broadcasting, April 19, 1965, p. 71.

2449 "Who Gets Tube Time? Black Caucus Asks for Free Network Prime Time." New Republic, February 19, 1972, p. 7.

2450 "Who's To Police Minority Gains In Public TV." Broadcasting, August 16, 1976, p. 28-29.

2451 "Why Not Chance To Tell Black Man's View of Television?" Baltimore Afro American, April 17, 1971, p. 11.

2452 "Why 'Roots' Hit Home." Time, February 14, 1977, p. 68-71.

2453 Wideman, Richard. "Blacks Favor True-to-Life TV." Cleveland Plain Dealer, November 4, 1976, p. 1.

2454 Williams, James D. "Blacks & Public TV: As Squeeze Play

Misfires, Blacks Challenge White Control of Tax-Supported
Medium." Black Enterprise, January 1974, p. 31-33.

2455 Wilson, Reggie. "NAACP vs. Hollywood." Right On-Focus,
      Spring 1983, p. 14-16.

2456 "WLBT: 18-Year Old Dispute Over Control." New York
      Times, November 20, 1978, p. 23.

2457 "WMAL-TV Renewal Appealed By Blacks." Broadcasting,
      March 15, 1971, p. 56.

2458 "WPIX-TV In New York Accused of Racism At Federal Hear-
      ing." Jet, November 11, 1971, p. 48.

                    Religious Broadcasting

2459 "Air Preachers: All Faiths Have Hours for Broadcasting."
      (Solomon Michaux). Newsweek, March 31, 1934, p. 30.

2460 Aversa, Rudy. "Ike: Cash is His Salvation." Los Angeles
      Herald Examiner, August 24, 1974, p. 9.

2461 "Ben Kinchlow Co-Hosts 'The 700 Club' for Christian Network."
      Norfolk Journal & Guide, November 24, 1978, p. B-15.

2462 "Ben Kinchlow Named Vice President of Christian Broadcast-
      ing Network." Norfolk Journal & Guide, December 22,
      1982, p. 10.

2463 "Blacks in the Religious Media--TV." Chicago Daily Defender,
      June 6, 1981, p. 10.

2464 Campbell, C. Clare. "Who Is Rev. Ike?" The Black Church,
      Fall 1974, p. 10-12.

2465 Chander, Russell. "Rev. Ike: He Blesses the Poor With
      Cult Money." Los Angeles Times, February 27, 1976,
      p. 9.

2466 "Church and Television." (Solomon Michaux). Newsweek,
      April 18, 1949, p. 78.

2467 "Cleopus Robinson, Singing TV Minister, Scores Movie." St.
      Louis Post Dispatch, September 25, 1978, p. 9.

2468 Collins, Lisa. "Religious Broadcaster: George Hill, Pro-
      ducer Ecumenical Insights/Interfaith Forum." Sepia,
      November 1980, p. 56-61.

2469   "Elder Michaux." Our World, January 1950, p. 44-47.

2470   "Fellowship and Clay Evan's TV Service Starts 2nd Year." Chi-
       February 25, 1978, p. 9.

2471   "Former FCC Commissioner Brown Speaks to Religious Broad-
       casting Convention." Los Angeles Sentinel, June 4, 1981,
       p. A-2.

2472   "Fred Price TV Program Goes National." Grapevine, Decem-
       ber 1980, p. 13.

2473   No entry.

2474   "Frederick Price: Top TV Minister." Grapevine, January/
       February 1980, p. 48-51.

2475   Garnett, Bernard. "Elder Michaux Called 'Most Unbelievable
       Black Businessman in History.'" Jet, April 24, 1969, p.
       p. 20-25.

2476   Hazard, David. "He Was A Black Bigot--Ben Kinchlow."
       Christian Life, March 1979, p. 30-32+.

2477   Herbut, Paula. "Benjamin Smith's Dream Blossoms In to
       New Spirit." Philadelphia Bulletin, July 18, 1978, p. 13-
       14.

2478   Hill, George. "Dr. Clayton Russell: Los Angeles' Premier
       Black Broadcaster." Los Angeles Sentinel (Sentinel 50
       Supplement), April 14, 1983, p. 97.

2479   "InterFaith Forum Discusses Unity." Carson Courier, October
       13, 1977, p. 2.

2480   Jenkins, Flo. "Rev Frederick K. Price: Top TV Minister."
       Grapevine, February 1980, p. 48-51.

2481   Jones, Howard O. "I Pray For Our Country." Religious
       Broadcasting. February/March 1976, p. 10.

2482   _____. "The Urgency of Broadcasting." Religious Broad-
       casting, February 1981, p. 36-37.

2483   Kinsolving, Lester. "Rev. Ike." Abilene Reporter-News,
       February 26, 1972, p. 1.

2484   "L.S. Michaux." Time, November 1, 1968, p. 98.

2485   Landrum, Phil. "How Are You Going To Teach Them in Sun-
       day School After They've Seen TV?" Christian Life, Oc-
       tober 1974, p. 46+.

2486 Lane, Bill. "Martha Jean Steinberg: Queen of the Evangelists." Sepia, May 1978, p. 20-25.

2487 "Marla Gibbs Aids Minister's TV Ministry." Cleveland Call & Post, July 15, 1978, p. A-9; Los Angeles Sentinel, July 20, 1978, p. C-9.

2488 Murray, Virgie. "Fred Price: Teaching Ministry Draws Young People." Los Angeles Sentinel, June 22, 1978, p. C11.

2489 _____. "Rev. Ike." Sepia, February 1980, pp. 79-82.

2490 "'Odyssey' Features Hill, Collins." Los Angeles Sentinel, July 3, 1980, p. C-10.

2491 "Portrait: Solomon L. Michaux." Saturday Evening Post, June 1938, p. 15.

2492 Ransky, Frank. "Harlem's Religious Zealots." (Solomon Michaux). Negro Digest, March 1950, p. 52-62.

2493 "Rev. Ike--You Can't Lose With the Stuff I Use." Encore, March 17, 1975, p. 21-25.

2494 Rouse, Parke. "Happy Am I." (Solomon Michaux). The Commonwealth, July 1965, p. 30-33.

2495 Sanders, Charles. "Gospel According to Rev. Ike." Ebony, December 1976, p. 148-154.

2496 "Second Front in Harlem; Elder Michaux and His Choir." Time, December 21, 1942, p. 74-76.

2497 Smith, Susan. "Through the Bonds of Devotion: The Ben Kinchlows' Story of Coming Through the Struggle." Black Family, May/June 1983, p. 10-13+.

2498 "Speaking of Pictures; Mass Negro Baptism." (Solomon Michaux). Life, April 4, 1949, p. 24-26.

2499 Stoddard, Maynard G. "CBN's Remarkable Ben Kinchlow." Saturday Evening Post, April 1983, 42-48.

2500 Taylor, Brooke. "Ben Kinchlow--An Unlikely Convert." Newport News Daily Press, June 11, 1978, p. 3.

2501 "This Far by Faith." (Hooks column). Atlanta Daily World, April 8, 1977, p. I-6.

2502 "This Far by Faith." Cleveland Call & Post, February 19, 1977, p. B-11.

2503   "This Far by Faith." Los Angeles Sentinel, June 23, 1977,
       p. B-4A.

2504   "'This Far by Faith' History of the Black Church." New
       York Amsterdam News, February 19, 1977, p. D-16.

2505   "'This Far by Faith' Telecast." Pittsburgh Courier, February
       15, 1977, p. 3-21.

2506   "TV Gospel Time." Sepia, July 1965, pp. 50-54.

2507   "TV Star Aids Rev. Cleophus Robinson's TV Ministry." Aim,
       July/August 1978, p. 9.

2508   Walker, Robert. "Discovery On TV." Christian Life, June
       1970, p. 32+.

2509   _____. "Your Lifestyle and TV." Christian Life, February
       1979, p. 29.

                          Soap Operas

2510   "ABC-TV Hollywood Studios Picketed over No Blacks on Day-
       time TV." Los Angeles Sentinel, March 16, 1978, p. A-
       16.

2511   "Bi-Racial Romance on Soap Opera Written Out." Michigan
       Chronicle, June 18, 1977, p. C-10.

2512   "Antoine, Roane. "Blacks In Daytime Television." Sepia,
       September 1980, p. 76-79.

2513   "Black Soap Stars." Sepia, June 1982, p. 28-31, 69.

2514   "Blacks in the Soaps." Ebony, March 1978, p. 32-36.

2515   "Blacks on the Soaps." Ebony, November 1982, p. 123-128.

2516   Collins, Lisa. "Blacks in Soap Operas." Sepia, July 1976,
       p. 28-32.

2517   Cosby, Corinne and Fuller, Marilyn. "Black Image on Tele-
       vision: Do 'Soapers' Bring Us the Purest Picture?" Soul,
       December 6, 1976, p. 8.

2518   "Darnell Williams' Role on 'All My Children.'" New York
       Amsterdam News, August 21, 1982, p. 24.

2519   Fee, Debi. Diane Sommerfield Is Valerie on 'Days of Our
       Lives.'" Right On, November 1982, p. 46-47.

2520 _____. James Reynolds from 'Days of Our Lives.'" Right
      On, September 1982, p. 50+.

2521 Harney, Almena Ruth. "Irving Allen Lee of 'The Edge of
      Night.'" Right On, December 1981, p. 18-19.

2522 "Irving Allen Gets Role in 'Edge of Night' TV Serial." Atlanta
      Daily World, November 15, 1979, p. 6.

2523 "Margie Hall Has Regular Role as a Nurse in the Daily NBC-
      TV's 'Days of Our Lives.'" Jet, November 27, 1969, p.
      54.

2524 "Pearl Bailey Debuts in 'As the World Turns.'" Jet, April 19,
      1982, p. 60.

2525 Richardson, Diane and Manning, Steve. "Darnell Williams
      Regular on 'All My Children.'" Right On, October 1982,
      p. 26-27.

2526 "Sammy Davis Reported Leaving 'Stop the World' Show." Los
      Angeles Sentinel, June 1, 1978, p. A-1.

2527 See, C. "Ruby Dee: The Census Taker Comes to 'Peyton
      Place.'" TV Guide, September 28, 1968, p. 24-29.

2528 Wilderson, Frank. "Video Tape Soap Opera." The Black
      Collegian, October/November 1980, p. 190-192.

                              Sports

2529 "Actor Satch; Ageless Hurler Plays Cavalry Sergeant." Ebony,
      December 1959, p. 109-110+.

2530 "Ali Is Prime Pick for Prime Time TV." Soul, July 19,
      1976, p. 7.

2531 "Althea's Debut." Ebony, July 1959, p. 73-74+.

2532 "'The American Sportsman' and LeVar Burton Go to Africa."
      Michigan Chronicle, June 18, 1977, p. B-4.

2533 "Article on Jayne Kennedy by Chicago Sun-Times Sports Writer
      Criticized." Chicago Daily Defender, December 9, 1978,
      p. I-4.

2534 "Barbara's Gal Friday." Our World, August 1954, p. 73.

2535 "The Baseball Business." Atlanta Daily World, April 17, 1977,
      p. I-7.

2536 Bedell, S. "CBS Picks up Next Ali Fight." TV Guide, October 29, 1977, p. A-3.

2537 "Ben Hooks Hits TV Sports Coverage." Jet, May 1, 1975, p. 9.

2538 "Bill Russell to Host Washington Talk Show." (Burrell column). Soul, July 5, 1971, p. 6.

2539 "Black and White Athletes Share Emotions Equally on Television." TV Guide, November 14, 1970, p. 4.

2540 "Black Baseball Featured on 'The Way It Was.'" Cleveland Call & Post, April 9, 1977, p. A-13; Michigan Chronicle, April 23, 1977, p. B-2.

2541 "Black Groups File Brief in Suit Over NCAA TV Football Contract." Atlanta Daily World, October 31, 1982, p. 2.

2542 "Black Sportscasters." (H. Evans column). New York Amsterdam News, July 3, 1982, p. 68.

2543 "Blacks in Sportscasting." Michigan Chronicle, March 26, 1977, p. B-3.

2544 "Bryant Gumbel, NBC Sportscaster, Gets Barbs From Blacks, Whites." Jet, July 14, 1980, p. 16.

2545 "Bryant Gumbel Replaces Tom Brokaw as Co-Anchor of NBC-TV's 'Today Show.'" Jet, November 12, 1981, p. 15.

2546 Christmas, Faith. "Scrimmage in the Courtroom: Legal Action Against NBC's 'Sports World.'" Black Enterprise, September 1979, p. 22.

2547 "Don King Stages Boxing Event at Marion, Ohio Prison." Cleveland Call & Post, March 12, 1977, p. A-1.

2548 "Don King Takes Boxing to Ohio Prison." Baltimore Afro American, March 12, 1977, p. I-10.

2549 Durslag, M. "Bill Russell Comes to TV." TV Guide, February 19, 1972, p. 13-14.

2550 _____. "Businessman-Boxer Archie Moore." TV Guide, October 21, 1961, p. 6-7.

2551 _____. "Cassius Marcellus Clay." TV Guide, February 15, 1964, p. 15-17.

2552 _____. "Elgin Baylor." TV Guide, February 9, 1974, p. 31-33.

2553 _____ . "Globetrotters; From Back Alleys to Ballrooms."
TV Guide, January 24, 1970, p. 20-21.

2554 _____ . "Hank Aaron and the Home Run Derby." TV Guide,
April 22, 1972, p. 44-45.

2555 _____ . "Leo Durocher and Jackie Robinson." TV Guide,
July 24, 1965, p. 12-13.

2556 _____ . "Maury Wills' Tough Decision." TV Guide, July
2, 1977, p. 15-16.

2557 _____ . "Maury Wills Would Rather Be in the Dugout."
TV Guide, July 7, 1973, p. 17-18.

2558 _____ . "Muhammad Ali Defends His Title on TV." TV
Guide, May 10, 1975, p. 30-31.

2559 _____ . "No One Pulls for Wilt Chamberlain." TV Guide,
February 22, 1969, p. 24-25.

2560 _____ . "O.J. Simpson Looks at Monday Night Football."
TV Guide, September 14, 1974, p. 26-27.

2561 _____ . "Some Advice from Roosevelt Grier." TV Guide,
May 30, 1970, p. 10-11.

2562 "Eddie Alexander, KDKA TV, Sports Director." Pittsburgh
Courier, March 24, 1979, p. 3-26.

2563 Finnigan, J. "Sugar Ray Robinson in Hollywood." TV Guide,
August 2, 1969, p. 25-26.

2564 "Floyd Patterson Trains to Meet Hurricane Jackson on TV."
TV Guide, July 27, 1957, p. 10-11.

2565 "'Harder They Fall'; Joe Walcott Is Convincing Actor in First
Role." Ebony, May 1956, p. 87-90.

2566 Harding, H. "Archie Moore Changes Boxing Style to Suit TV."
TV Guide, August 12, 1961, p. A-1.

2567 "The Harlem Globetrotters at Sea." TV Guide, January 14,
1967, p. 12-13.

2568 Harris, M. "Jackie Robinson: Major League Baseball's
First Black." TV Guide, August 6, 1977, p. 10-14.

2569 "Herman McKalpain Named WGPR-TV Sports Director."
Michigan Chronicle, November 19, 1977, p. B-2.

2570 "J. Gilbert Named NBC Sports, Olympic Games Administrator." Michigan Chronicle, March 11, 1979, p. B-4.

2571 "Jackie Robinson Predicts the Yanks and the Dodgers." TV
      Guide, April 13, 1957, p. 14-15.

2572 "Jayne Kennedy Becomes First Black Woman in Network
      Sports." Soul, September 4, 1978, p. 2.

2573 "Jayne Kennedy Joins 'NFL Today' Team." Atlanta Daily
      World, August 10, 1978, p. I-6; Los Angeles Sentinel,
      August 10, 1978, p. B-1; Cleveland Call & Post, August
      19, 1978, p. B-18; Chicago Daily Defender, August 19,
      1978, p. I-9.

2574 "Jim Hill, KNXT Sportscaster & Actress Denise Nicholas
      Wed." Los Angeles Sentinel, February 19, 1981, p. 1.

2575 "Jim Mueller Named WKYC-TV Sports Anchorman." Cleveland
      Call & Post, January 30, 1982, p. A-11.

2576 "Joe Wins One for Uncle Sam." Ebony, January 1957, p. 42+.

2577 Levin, E. "Oscar Robertson Replaces Elgin Baylor as CBS's
      Basketball Analyst." TV Guide, November 2, 1974, p. 44.

2578 "Lou Brock Named Sports Director for Telcom Cablevision."
      Atlanta Daily World, January 27, 1980, p. 7.

2579 "Meadowlark Lemon, Basketball Player and Actor." New York
      Amsterdam News, November 10, 1979, p. 68.

2580 "Mean Joe Green Is CBS Broadcaster." Jet, August 30, 1982,
      p. 60.

2581 "Memphis TV Station Wins Renewal Fight (WMC-TV)." Broad-
      casting, October 4, 1971, p. 27.

2582 Moore, Archie. "Why I Played Jim, the Slave." Ebony,
      September 1960, p. 43-44.

2583 "NBA Players Association President Discusses Sports Vision."
      Chicago Daily Defender, October 17, 1981, p. 60.

2584 Ralbovsky, M. "Hank Aaron's Countdown." TV Guide, Au-
      gust 11, 1973, p. 12-13.

2585 "Reggie Jackson's TV Program." (Young column). Los An-
      geles Sentinel, May 19, 1977, p. A-7.

2586 "Ron Vasser, TV Sports Producer-Director." Chicago Daily
      Defender, July 28, 1979, p. 3-19.

2587 Shaun, Jackye. "Tom Hawkins, KNBC-TV." Soul, April 5,
      1971, p. 6.

2588   Smith, R. "Archie Moore Hopes to Put Durelle on Canvas."
       TV Guide, July 11, 1959, p. 6-7.

2589   Smith, Red. "Ezzard Charles." TV Guide, June 4, 1954,
       p. 21.

2590   "Sports Broadcasters." (Peter Harris column). Baltimore
       Afro American, October 30, 1982, p. 9.

2591   "Sportscaster Jay Berry Joins WLS-TV in Chicago." Chicago
       Daily Defender, June 7, 1979, p. 34.

2592   "Sports Vision TV Service." (John Reyes commentary). Chi-
       cago Daily Defender, October 14, 1981, p. 24.

2593   Stevens, Jo Ann." Claudia Polley: Multi-talented TV Sports-
       caster Ever In Search of New Roles." Black Sports, July
       1976, p. 22.

2594   "2 Athletes Appear on 'Phil Donahue Show.'" Chicago Daily
       Defender, August 12, 1982, p. 28.

2595   "What Makes O. J. Simpson Run." Ebony, September 1981,
       p. 106-110.

2596   "Willie Davis; Baseball Star and Natural Actor." Sepia, May
       1970, p. 58-59+.

2597   Young, A. S. "How Jayne Kennedy Lost Her Job on 'NFL
       Today.'" Sepia, October 1980, p. 45-46.

                              Women

2598   "Black Pilots Group Honors Actress Nichelle Nichols." Los
       Angeles Sentinel, June 8, 1978, p. A-11.

2599   "Black Women in Entertainment." Ebony, August 1982, p.
       102-108.

2600   Delaunoy, Didier. "Women in Television: Eleanor Jean Hen-
       dley Speaks Her Mind." Soul, August 28, 1978, p. 18.

2601   Douglas, Pamela. "An Inside Perspective on The Black Woman
       TV Executive." Contract, Spring 1974, p. 46.

2602   "Dr. George Hill's Women's Special." Los Angeles Sentinel,
       August 28, 1980, p. B-8.

2603   "Few Black Women Have Managerial Jobs in TV." Jet, April
       22, 1976, p. 29.

2604   "Image of Black Women on TV Eyed." Los Angeles Sentinel, December 8, 1977, p. A-7.

2605   Jennings, R. M. "Television Station Employment Practices: The Status of Minorities and Women. New York: United Church of Christ, November 1972.

2606   Lucas, Bob. "Pam: Why Are Black Women Fading from Films?" Jet, November 6, 1980, p. 58-61.

2607   Mapp, Edward. "Black Women in Films." Black Scholar, March/April 1973, p. 42-46.

2608   "Minorities and Women Have Few Important Rises on TV." Washington Post, January 17, 1979, p. AII.

2609   "Minority and Women Gain In TV Employment." Washington Post, December 2, 1974, p. B-3.

2610   "Newest Black Women Who Have Won TV and Movie Roles." (Ronalda Douglas, Darcel Wynne, Lydia Nicole, Claudette Wells, Diane Day, Rose Dursy). Ebony, April 1983, p. 63-66.

2611   Shapiro, Marc. "Black Actresses: Are They Getting the Short End of the Stick?" Soul, March 19, 1979, p. 14-15.

2612   Smith, Barbara. "Black Women in Film Symposium." Freedomway, 1974, p. 266-269.

2613   Stewart, Gail. "Black Actress: Just Sleeping on Cold Sheets." Soul, May 24, 1976, p. 15.

2614   Tait, E. V. "Women Behind the Television." Essence, June 1979, p. 37-38.

2615   "Trials of a Television Actress." Ebony, March 1955, p. 104+.

Cable--Ownership

2616   "Black Caucus Hails Adoption of Proposal on Black Media Ownership." Baltimore Afro American, June 10, 1978, p. I-8.

2617   "Black Entrepreneurs Intensify Efforts to Win Cable TV Franchises." Wall Street Journal, August 13, 1971, p. 1.

2618   "Black-Owned Cable System in Columbus, Ohio." Baltimore Afro American, October 28, 1978, p. I-8.

2619 "Black-Owned Cable TV Company Gets Newark, NJ, Franchise." New York Amsterdam News, May 17, 1980, p. 64.

2620 "Black Ownership of Cable TV Franchise Halted by Financing." Pittsburgh Courier, February 11, 1979, p. I-2.

2621 "Blacks Get a Foot In Cable Business." Broadcasting, September 10, 1973, p. 56-58.

2622 "Blacks Get Cable TV Franchise in Columbus, Ohio." Pittsburgh Courier, February 18, 1979, p. I-2.

2623 "Cable Atlanta Moves to New Headquarters." Atlanta Daily World, August 3, 1980, p. 4.

2624 "Cable TV Ownership." Pittsburgh Courier, October 8, 1977, p. I-7.

2625 "CATV Survey Backs Minority Ownership in Pittsburgh." Pittsburgh Courier, April 22, 1978, p. I-1.

2626 "Columbus, Ohio, Gets Minority Cable TV Firm." Cleveland Call & Post, January 14, 1979, p. B-2.

2627 "Compton, California, Council Awards TV Franchise to CATV-West." Los Angeles Sentinel, November 5, 1981, p. A-1.

2628 "Don King's Cable TV Network." Jet, February 15, 1982, p. 14.

2629 "Drive For Black Cable TV Franchise Continues." Pittsburgh Courier, January 8, 1977, p. 1.

2630 Emerson, F. E. "Cable Atlanta; Transfer of Cable Franchise to 20% Minority Owned Cable Atlanta Inc." Black Enterprise, December 1979, p. 25+.

2631 "Executive Plans to Form a Black Cable Television Network." Washington Post, August 30, 1979, p. A-2.

2632 "1st Black Awarded Independent Cable Broadcasting Network." Atlanta Daily World, November 9, 1978, p. I-6.

2633 "Gary Communications Form Cable TV Unit 1st in U.S." Jet, January 11, 1973, p. 15.

2634 "How Minorities Swing A Cable TV Franchise." Business Week, February 18, 1980, p. 70.

2635 "Inner City Broadcasting Buys Apollo Theater for Cable Programs." New York Amsterdam News, November 28, 1981, p. 1.

2636   "Inner City Broadcasting Buys Transponder on RCA Satellite."
       New York Amsterdam News, November 14, 1981, p. 1.

2637   "Inner City Broadcasting Launches Cable TV Project." Nor-
       folk Journal & Guide, January 20, 1981, p. 12.

2638   "Los Angeles Commission Endorses Community TV Inc. for
       Cable Contract." Los Angeles Sentinel, December 24,
       1981, p. A-1.

2639   "Minority Businessmen Seek Chicago Cable TV Franchise."
       Chicago Daily Defender, January 26, 1982, p. 3.

2640   "Minority Cable Television Owner." Amsterdam News, Jan-
       uary 22, 1977, p. A-4; Norfolk Journal & Guide, January
       29, 1977, p. A-9; February 2, 1977, p. 5; Atlanta Daily
       World, February 4, 1977, p. 6; Baltimore Afro American,
       February 5, 1977, p. 5.

2641   "Minority Cable TV Ownership Pushed By New Group." Bal-
       timore Afro American, January 1, 1977, p. 8.

2642   "Nation's Only Black Cable TV Network Marks 1st Anniversary."
       Atlanta Daily World, February 1, 1981, p. 3.

2643   "Ted Turner Launches Cable News Network." Atlanta Daily
       World, June 3, 1980, p. 1-2.

2644   "2 Black Firms Battle for L.A. Cable TV Franchise." Los
       Angeles Sentinel, February 5, 1981, p. A-1.

2645   "Two Black-Owned Cable TV Firms Bid for Los Angeles Fran-
       chise." Los Angeles Sentinel, August 7, 1980, p. A3.

2646   "Two Minority-Owned Firms Submit Bids for Southern Cali-
       fornia Cable TV." Los Angeles Sentinel, May 8, 1980,
       p. A-2.

                        Cable--Programming

2647   Arlen, Gary. "A Good Bet." American Film, July/August
       1980, p. 9.

2648   "Atlanta Council Produces Show for Cable Atlanta TV." Atlanta
       Daily World, July 25, 1980, p. 6.

2649   "BET President Sees Solid Audience for Cable TV." Houston
       Post, July 9, 1982, p. F-5.

2650   "Black Entertainment Network Celebrates Debut." Washington
       Post, January 25, 1980, p. D1.

2651 "Black Entertainment Network to Produce Black College Sports
       for Cable TV." Black Enterprise, August 1980, p. 34.

2652 "Black Entertainment Television Cable Network Head, Bob
       Johnson." Washington Post, November 30, 1979, p. C1.

2653 "Black Entertainment Television Expands Programming Hours."
       Norfolk Journal & Guide, December 16, 1981, p. 15.

2654 "Black Entertainment Television Network." Chicago Daily De-
       fender, October 13, 1979, p. 1-6.

2655 "Black Entertainment Television Network." Los Angeles Times,
       August 31, 1979, p. 4-27.

2656 "Black Entertainment Television Viewed as Job Source for
       Blacks." Los Angeles Times, October 2, 1979, p. 5-14.

2657 "Black Entertainment TV to Broadcast Black College Sports."
       Baltimore Afro American, July 5, 1980, p. 10.

2658 "Cable TV Lobbyist Plans Black Network." Washington Post,
       August 30, 1979, p. A-2.

2650 Christopher, Maurice. "Black Entertainment TV to Debut in
       January." Advertising Age, November 26, 1979, p. 9.

2660 "'Flo's Place,' A New York City Cable TV Show." New York
       Amsterdam News, September 27, 1980, p. 10.

2661 "Gary Cable TV Group Get FCC Ok To Start Programs."
       Jet, October 11, 1973, p. 46.

2662 "HBO Set with Pendergrass Show Filmed in London." Jet,
       August 30, 1982, p. 61.

2663 "Interfaith Forum." South Bay Daily Breeze, October 15,
       1977, p. A-12.

2664 "TCI Purchases Minority Interest in Black Entertainment
       Television." Cablevision, December 17, 1979, p. 164.

2665 Watson, John. "Blacks Place BET on Cable TV." Los An-
       geles Times, October 2, 1979, p. CAL-1.

2666 Weintraub, Boris. "Black Entertainment TV Nibbles at Big
       Networks." Washington Star, May 19, 1980, p. 1.

Cable--General

2667 "Apollo Theater in Harlem to Reopen as Cable TV Facility."
      New York Amsterdam News, May 22, 1982, p. 1.

2668 "Atlanta Merchants' Organization Produces Cable TV Program."
      Atlanta Daily World, August 1, 1982, p. 2.

2669 "Barden Cablevision Company of Michigan." Michigan Chron-
      icle, July 17, 1982, p. D-1.

2670 "Bedford Stuyvesant Restoration Corp. and Cable TV." (Edi-
      torial). New York Amsterdam News, August 9, 1980, p.
      16.

2671 "Bedford Stuyvesant Restoration Corp. and Cable TV Company
      Sign Pact." New York Amsterdam News, July 26, 1980,
      p. 4.

2672 "Black Cable Programmer Signs Up Three MSO's." Broad-
      casting, October 15, 1979, p. 18.

2673 "Black Cable TV Franchise Doubtful." Pittsburgh Courier,
      January 1, 1977, p. 1.

2674 "Black Cable TV: Will It Survive?" Soul, September 1980,
      p. 16-17.

2675 "Black Citizens for Fair Media Organization Fights Bias in
      TV Industry." New York Amsterdam News, November
      22, 1980, p. 6.

2676 "Black Columbus Cable TV Project." (Editorial). Cleveland
      Call & Post, April 1, 1978, p. B-2.

2677 "Black Panthers, NAACP Get Cable TV Rights." Jet, May
      4, 1972, p. 24.

2678 "Blacks and Cable TV." (A.S. Young column). Los Angeles
      Sentinel, May 8, 1980, p. A-7.

2679 "Blacks and Cable TV." Michigan Chronicle, March 21, 1981,
      p. A-3.

2680 Brown, M.D., "Cable TV and the Black Community." Black
      Politician, April 1971, p. 4.

2681 Brown, Nick. "Black Cable Bidders Woo Community." Los
      Angeles Sentinel, February 5, 1971, p. 1.

2682 _____. "Long Beach Black Runs Cable Television." Los
      Angeles Sentinel, September 18, 1980, p. A-3.

2683 _____. "Time is Running Out for Black Cable TV." Los
Angeles Sentinel, August 7, 1980, p. A-3.

2684 _____. "Will Blacks Receive Fair Shake in Cable TV
Pacts?" Los Angeles Sentinel, September 4, 1980, p. 1.

2685 "Cable and Satellite Communications Seminar Held in Los Angeles." Los Angeles Times, May 23, 1980, p. 4-2.

2686 "Cable Atlanta Workers Begin Hanging Cable-Supporting Strand."
Atlanta Daily World, April 18, 1980, p. I-3.

2687 "Cable Franchises in Queens Borough." (Editorial). New
York Amsterdam News, November 28, 1981, p. 16.

2688 "Cable Television." New York Amsterdam News, March 19,
1977, p. D-14.

2689 "Cable Television Organizations." Atlanta Daily World, January 28, 1977, p. 6.

2690 "Cable TV." New York Amsterdam News, February 11, 1978,
p. B-8; February 25, 1978, p. D-7.

2691 "Cable TV." New York Amsterdam News, February 11, 1979,
p. B-8; February 25, 1979, p. D-7.

2692 "Cable TV and Blacks." (Charles Colding commentary).
Michigan Chronicle, February 21, 1981, p. A-6.

2693 "Cable TV and Reopening of Phillips Hospital in St. Louis."
(Editorial). St. Louis Argus, October 15, 1981, p. 2-4.

2694 "Cable TV Installer Training Program in Los Angeles." Los
Angeles Sentinel, April 23, 1981, p. A-10.

2695 "Cable TV as Economic Development Issue for Detroit." Michigan Chronicle, November 28, 1981, p. A-8.

2696 "Cable TV for Black Chicago." (Haywood commentary). Chicago Daily Defender, September 30, 1981, p. 6.

2697 "Cable TV for Chicago." (Will Horton column). Chicago
Daily Defender, February 8, 1982, p. 14.

2698 "Cablevision Training Center Program in Missouri." St.
Louis Argus, November 6, 1980, p. I-2.

2699 "Central Videopath Inc. to Connect All Chicago Cable TV."
Chicago Daily Defender, July 6, 1981, p. 7.

2700 "City Communications Firm Formed to Seek Detroit Cable
TV Job." Michigan Chronicle, May 8, 1982, p. D-1.

2701 "City Government Organizations Oppose Deregulating Cable
      TV Franchises." Atlanta Daily World, July 24, 1980,
      p. 8.

2702 "Clark College Department Surveys Atlantans About Cable TV."
      Atlanta Daily World, July 29, 1979, p. 10.

2703 "Cook County Commissioner Stroger Views Cable TV and
      Minority Groups." Chicago Daily Defender, July 12, 1980,
      p. 19.

2704 "Community Cable Consortium of Chicago Organized." Chi-
      cago Daily Defender, July 17, 1982, p. 13.

2705 "Competition for NYC Cable TV Franchise." (Joe Bragg com-
      mentary). New York Amsterdam News, February 28,
      1981, p. 35.

2706 "Connection Cablevision Wires 12,000 Homes in Newark, New
      Jersey." New York Amsterdam News, June 26, 1982, p.
      46.

2707 "Continental Cable Chicago and Stellar Investors Merge."
      Chicago Daily Defender, August 31, 1982, p. 15.

2708 "Converting Cable into Profits: Satellite Cablevision Equip-
      ment, Inc." Black Enterprise, December 1981, p. 76.

2709 "Cox Cable Firm Sells Equipment to Scientific-Atlanta." At-
      lanta Daily World, June 28, 1979, p. 7.

2710 "DABO Sponsors Discussion on Cable TV in Detroit." Mi-
      chigan Chronicle, August 22, 1981, p. A-5.

2711 "Dispute over Including Cable Network in White House Pool."
      Atlanta Daily World, August 11, 1981, p. 2.

2712 "East Cleveland Commission Seeks Probe of 11-4-80 Cable
      TV Vote." Cleveland Call & Post, February 28, 1981,
      p. A-2.

2713 "Effort to Block Pittsburgh Cable TV Franchise." Pittsburgh
      Courier, March 10, 1977, p. 10.

2714 "Electronic Redlining: Fighting for a Share of Cable TV."
      Black Enterprise, October 1981, p. 87-89.

2715 "Few Minorities and Women Found in Better Jobs of Cable
      Business." Broadcasting, August 9, 1976, p. 45.

2716 "14 Applications for Cable TV Franchises Received by NYC."
      New York Amsterdam News, July 5, 1980, p. 25.

2717   "Franchise Awarded to Barden Cablevision of Inkster, Mich-
       igan." Michigan Chronicle, September 19, 1981, p. D-1.

2718   Gupta, Udayan. "Cable Hums with Black Efforts." Advertis-
       ing Age, November 29, 1982, p. M-19.

2719   _____. "Scandal in Cable Television; The Big Corporations
       Are Muscling Out Blacks Who Hoped to Get A Piece of
       This Booming Industry." Black Enterprise, October 1980,
       p. 65-70.

2720   Huil, Marion Hayes. "Blacks and Cable Television." The
       Black Collegian, October/November 1980, p. 208-209.

2721   "Impact of Cable TV to Blacks." Pittsburgh Courier, April
       8, 1978, p. I-2.

2722   "K-ACE to Provide Music for Los Angeles Cable TV Station."
       Los Angeles Sentinel, November 20, 1980, p. A-12.

2723   "L. A. City Council Adopts New Regulations on Cable TV Bids."
       Los Angeles Sentinel, September 4, 1980, p. A-1.

2724   "Los Angeles Black Community and Cable TV." (Editorial).
       Los Angeles Sentinel, September 24, 1981, p. A-1.

2725   "Members of Committee on Minorities in Cable TV." Chicago
       Daily Defender, November 18, 1981, p. 13.

2726   "Metro Communications Group Seeks Cable Franchise in Chi-
       cago." Jet, February 15, 1982, p. 14.

2727   "Minorities and Pay Cable Television." Washington Post, Au-
       gust 1, 1976, p. H-1.

2728   "Minorities Move Into Cable TV." Communication Today,
       June 23, 1975, p. 17.

2729   "Minority Associations in California to Lease Cable-TV Chan-
       nels: Two Concerns Agree to Setup; Coalition of 16 Groups
       Moves Toward Statewide Network." Wall Street Journal,
       November 30, 1972, p. 18.

2730   "Minority Cable TV Conference." (W. Davis commentary).
       Chicago Daily Defender, July 8, 1981, p. 5.

2731   "Minority Role Foreseen in Cable TV in Los Angeles." Los
       Angeles Sentinel, October 1, 1981, p. A-4.

2732   "NAACP and ACLU Release Joint Statement on Atlanta Cable
       TV." Atlanta Daily World, January 28, 1979, p. 5.

2733   "New York City Cable TV Franchise." (Editorial). New York
       Amsterdam News, December 18, 1982, p. 16.

2734 "New York City Cable TV Franchise." (Percy Sutton commentary). New York Amsterdam News, December 18, 1982, p. 17.

2735 "ON-TV, Subscription Service in Chicago." Chicago Daily Defender, May 4, 1981, p. 3.

2736 "Panel Urges Blacks to Take CATV Role." New York Times, September 15, 1971, p. C-76.

2737 "Pay TV." (Billy Rowe column). New York Amsterdam News, October 18, 1980, p. 29.

2738 "Pitt Councilperson Denies CATV Statement." Pittsburgh Courier, December 3, 1977, p. I-1.

2739 "Pittsburgh Cable TV Board Okays Plan Guaranteeing Minority Share." Pittsburgh Courier, May 19, 1979, p. I-8.

2740 "Pittsburgh Cable TV Fight Continues." Pittsburgh Courier, December 31, 1977, p. I-1.

2741 No entry.

2742 "Pittsburgh Cable TV Franchise." Pittsburgh Courier, March 5, 1977, p. 4.

2743 "Pittsburgh Cable TV Franchise Viewed by Council." Pittsburgh Courier; Atlanta Daily World, January 28, 1977, p. 6.

2744 "Pittsburgh Council Eyes Training Minorities for CATV Jobs." Pittsburgh Courier, March 31, 1979, p. 1-2.

2745 "Pittsburgh Councilperson Denies CATV Statement." Pittsburgh Courier, October 8, 1977, p. 7.

2746 "Pittsburgh NAACP Push for Black Cable TV." Pittsburgh Courier, June 11, 1977, p. 2.

2747 "Pittsburgh OIC to Open Cable TV Technical School." Pittsburgh Courier, May 5, 1979, p. I-1.

2748 "Pittsburgh Opposes Minority Cable TV Franchise." Pittsburgh Courier, September 17, 1977, p. 1-9.

2749 "Pittsburghers Speak Out on Cable TV." Pittsburgh Courier, October 20, 1979, p. 1-7.

2750 "President of City Communications Corp. Eyes Bids on Detroit Cable TV." Michigan Chronicle, December 25, 1982, p. D-1.

2751   "Press Club Asks Georgia Supreme Court for New TV-in-
        Court Rule." Atlanta Daily World, September 3, 1981,
        p. 1.

2752   "Renaissance Broadcasting and Other Black Firms." (Horne
        column). Atlanta Daily World, January 28, 1982, p. 6.

2753   "Renaissance Broadcasting Corp. Folds in NJ, Donald McMears
        Blames Racism." Jet, February 15, 1982, p. 16.

2754   "Satellite Cable Communications Company Seeks Chicago Con-
        tract." Chicago Daily Defender, December 18, 1982, p. 3.

2755   "Satellite Cable TV Network Offers Community Channel." Los
        Angeles Sentinel, August 19, 1982, p. A-3.

2756   "Scientific-Atlanta to Supply Cable for Atlanta Cable TV."
        Atlanta Daily World, January 1, 1980, p. 3.

2757   Shales, Tom. "Beyond 'Benson'; Black-Oriented Channel From
        a Cable Pioneer." Washington Post, November 30, 1979,
        p. AIR-C1.

2758   "St. Louis Mayor's Cable TV/Hospital Idea." (Editorial).
        St. Louis Argus, June 11, 1981, p. I-10.

2759   "Storer Broadcasting Executive Eyes Cable TV and Minorities."
        Atlanta Daily World, March 27, 1980, p. 2.

2760   "Storer Executive Eyes Opportunities for Blacks in Cable TV."
        Baltimore Afro American, March 16, 1980, p. 7; Atlanta
        Daily World, March 3, 1977, p. 2.

2761   "Teleprompter Cable TV Corp. Plans Job Training Centers."
        New York Amsterdam News, September 27, 1980, p. 35.

2762   "Tidewater TV Advisory Council Opens in Norfolk." Norfolk
        Journal & Guide, January 27, 1982, p. 13.

2763   "TV Correspondent Speaks in Detroit About Black Viewer's At-
        titudes." Michigan Chronicle, October 4, 1980, p. A-1.

2764   "2 Detroit-Based Firms Seek City's Cable Communications
        Contract." Michigan Chronicle, September 11, 1982, p.
        D-1.

2765   "Universal Cable to Conduct Forum on Impact of Cable TV."
        Los Angeles Sentinel, January 22, 1981, p. A-5.

2766   "U.S. Rep. Washington Makes Statement on Cable TV and
        Minorities." Chicago Daily Defender, May 6, 1982, p. 12.

2767   "Warrensville Heights, Ohio, Officials Accept Free Cable

TV." Cleveland Call & Post, March 13, 1 82, p. A-1.

2768 "Why Cable TV Is Delayed." (Irvis column). Pittsburgh Courier, October 22, 1977, p. I-6.

2769 "X-Rated Movies on Cable TV." (Lucius Lee column). Cleveland Call & Post, December 19, 1981, p. A-17.

Cable--Personnel and Personalities

2770 "Atlanta Alderman Bond Named to National Cable TV Federation." Atlanta Daily World, July 15, 1979, p. 2.

2771 "Betty Lee, Board Member of American Cablevision." St. Louis Argus, April 22, 1982, p. 2-3.

2772 "Bill Cosby and Joe Zingale Form Cozzin Corporation." Los Angeles Sentinel, March 26, 1 981, p. B-6.

2773 "Cathy Adams and Mattie Majors Promoted by Storer Broadcasting." Cleveland Call & Post, October 23, 1982, p. B-16.

2774 "Charles Eure Runs Cable Station in Long Beach." Los Angeles Sentinel, September 18, 1980, p. A-4.

2775 "Don Haney Leaves WXYZ-TV to Become VP of Detroit Cablevision." Michigan Chronicle, February 21, 1981, p. A-8.

2776 "E. B. Wilson Discusses Likely Impact of Cable TV on Detroit." Michigan Chronicle, May 2, 1981, p. A-1.

2777 "Early Monroe Discusses Vital Role Blacks Can Play in Cable TV." Norfolk Journal & Guide, March 25, 1981, p. 9.

2778 "Emmett Cash 1st Black to Receive Independent Cable Network." Norfolk Journal & Guide, November 10, 1978, p. A-1.

2779 "G. McAdoo Submits Paper to Pittsburgh Cable TV Advisory Committee." Pittsburgh Courier, April 21, 1979, p. I-8.

2780 "Gwen Moore Named to California Assembly Subcommittee on Cable TV." Los Angeles Sentinel, December 24, 1981, p. A-9.

2781 "Howard Rollins Stars in 'Tar Baby' on Cable TV." Jet, June 7, 1982, p. 61.

2782   "Jabari Simama to Direct Public Access for Cable Atlanta."
       Atlanta Daily World, August 26, 1980, p. 3.

2783   "James Williams Says He Owns Pittsburgh CATV Franchise."
       Pittsburgh Courier, August 18, 1979, p. 3-19.

2784   "L. A. Alderman Cunningham Votes No on 2 Black Firms'
       Cable TV Bids." Los Angeles Sentinel, May 27, 1982,
       p. A-2.

2785   "Lou Brock Named Sports Director for Telecom Cablevision."
       Atlanta Daily World, January 27, 1980, p. 27.

2786   "Mitch Martin Named Vice President of Cable Atlanta." At-
       lanta Daily World, October 29, 1981, p. 5.

2787   "NAACP's Robert Pitts Eyes Pittsburgh CATV Committee."
       Pittsburgh Courier, April 14, 1979, p. I-2.

2788   "Paul Brown Joins Cable Atlanta, Inc. as Consultant." At-
       lanta Daily World, December 7, 1979, p. 2.

2789   "Perry Parks, Cable TV Executive." Los Angeles Sentinel,
       November 4, 1982, p. A-8.

2790   "Robert Johnson Resigns as National Cable TV Association
       Vice President; Will Establish Black Entertainment TV,
       Cable Network Providing Programs Featuring Black Per-
       formers." New York Times, August 30, 1979, p. 22.

2791   "Stanley Thomas Promoted to Home Box Office Vice President."
       New York Amsterdam News, January 24, 1981, p. 31.

2792   "W. K. Perry Sues Atlanta Mayor and Cable News Network."
       Atlanta Daily World, June 4, 1981, p. 8.

2793   "Wade Briggs Leaves WCHB-Radio to Join Cable TV Firm."
       Michigan Chronicle, August 21, 1982, p. A-1.

2794   "Warner-Amex Cable TV Personality, Gayle Starling." Cleve-
       land Call & Post, November 29, 1980, p. B-4.

2795   "Will Horton Forms Cable TV Organization." Chicago Daily
       Defender, October 28, 1981, p. 15.

2796   "Will Horton's Views on Cable TV Coming to Chicago." Mi-
       chigan Chronicle, August 29, 1981, p. C-10.

2797   "William Johnson Joins Staff of City Communications Company."
       Michigan Chronicle, December 4, 1982, p. D-1.

2798   "William Johnson Views Cable TV." Pittsburgh Courier,
       March 18, 1979, p. 3-22.

Cable--Bidding and Government

2799 "A. C. C. E. S. S. Bids for South Central Los Angeles Cable Franchise." Los Angeles Sentinel, December 9, 1982, p. A-3.

2800 "Atlanta Alderman Bond Eyes Changes in FCC Regulations on Cable TV." Atlanta Daily World, September 16, 1980, p. 3.

2801 "Atlanta City Council Sets Hearings on Atlanta Cable TV." Atlanta Daily World, January 25, 1979, p. 6.

2802 "Atlanta Council Gets NAACP-ACLU Cable TV Complaint." Atlanta Daily World, February 15, 1979, p. 6.

2802a "Bidding on Detroit Cable TV Contract." (Editorial). Michigan Chronicle, December 18, 1982, p. A-5.

2803 "Black Bid for Queens Cable TV Franchise." (Editorial). New York Amsterdam News, September 13, 1980, p. 18.

2804 "Black Firms Bid for South-Central L. A. Cable TV Franchise." Los Angeles Sentinel, July 24, 1980, p. A-1.

2805 "Black Leaders Bid For Cable TV Franchise in South-Central Los Angeles." Los Angeles Times, May 1, 1980, p. 2-1.

2806 "Blacks Bid for Queens Cable TV Franchise. New York Amsterdam News, September 13, 1980, p. 10.

2807 "Cable TV Bill Held up in Pittsburgh Council." Pittsburgh Courier, January 21, 1979, p. I-1.

2808 "Cable TV Firms Prepare to Bid for Los Angeles Contract." Los Angeles Sentinel, August 26, 1982, p. A-4.

2809 "Cable TV Interest High Despite Court Ruling on FCC Requirements." Pittsburgh Courier, March 11, 1979, p. I-8.

2810 "Cable Veteran To Create Black TV Network." San Francisco Valley News, August 30, 1979, p. 18.

2811 "Cablevision Training Center Opened in St. Louis with Telecom's Bid." St. Louis Argus, August 21, 1980, p. 2-4.

2812 "CATV Executive Forms Blacks TV Network." Pittsburgh Courier, September 15, 1979, p. 1.

2813 Christmas, Faith. "Firm Bids for Cable TV Franchise." Los Angeles Sentinel, May 8, 1980, p. A-2.

2814 "Cleveland Government and Cable Television." (Editorial).
      Cleveland Call & Post, November 20, 1982, p. A-8.

2815 "Community-Based Organization Called 'Access' Bids for L. A.
      Cable Rights." Los Angeles Sentinel, September 23, 1982,
      p. A-1.

2816 "CTI, Black Cable Firm Bidding for L. A. Contract." Los
      Angeles Sentinel, February 19, 1981, p. A-3.

2817 "East Cleveland Comrs. Debate Placing of Ad for Cable TV
      Bids." Cleveland Call & Post, June 21, 1980, p. A-9.

2818 "East Cleveland to Vote on Cable TV Franchise." Cleveland
      Call & Post, October 18, 1980, p. A-1.

2819 "Fourteen Applications for Cable TV Franchises Received by
      New York City." New York Amsterdam News, July 5,
      1980, p. 25.

2820 Karmin, Monroe W. "Piece of the Action: Blacks Seeking
      Control of Big-City Cable TV Face Uphill Struggle." Wall
      Street Journal, December 29, 1971, p. 1.

2821 "Los Angeles and NYC Blacks Bidding on Cable TV Rights."
      (Lane column). Baltimore Afro American, May 17, 1980,
      p. 11.

2822 "NYC Mayor Promises EEO Will Be Issue in Cable TV Con-
      tracts." New York Amsterdam News, January 9, 1982,
      p. 3.

2823 "1 Minority Firm to Re-Bid on Los Angeles Cable TV Con-
      tract." Los Angeles Sentinel, June 10, 1982, p. A-2.

2824 "Pittsburgh Cable Advisory Committee Set to Evaluate Fran-
      chise Bids. Pittsburgh Courier, September 22, 1979, p.
      I-12.

2825 "Pittsburgh Council Committee Amends Cable TV Proposal."
      Pittsburgh Courier, July 7, 1979, p. 3-19.

2826 "Pittsburgh Council Gets Legislation on Cable TV Bonding Re-
      quirements." Pittsburgh Courier, July 28, 1979, p. I-1.

2827 "Pittsburgh Council Presented with Proposals for Cable TV
      System." Pittsburgh Courier, June 30, 1979, p. 12.

2828 "Pittsburgh Council Sustains Mayor's Veto of Cable TV Con-
      tract." Pittsburgh Courier, April 21, 1979, p. I-1.

2829 "St. Louis Mayor Wants to Form Cable TV Corporation to
      Fund Phillips Hospital." St. Louis Argus, June 11, 1981,
      p. I-1.

2830 "3 Minority Firms Bid on Detroit Cable TV Franchise." Michigan Chronicle, December 11, 1982, p. B-5.

2831 "2 Black-Owned Cable TV Firms Bid for Los Angeles Franchise." Los Angeles Sentinel, August 7, 1980, p. A-3.

2832 "2 Minority-Owned Firms Submit Bids for S. California Cable TV." Los Angeles Sentinel, May 6, 1980, p. A-2.

2833 "2 NYC-Based Broadcasters Make Joint Bid for Queens Cable TV." New York Amsterdam News, September 6, 1980, p. 33.

2834 "U.S. Supreme Court Rules on FCC Cable TV Regulations." Chicago Daily Defender, April 3, 1979, p. 5.

WAOE-TV
P.O. Box 858
South Oneida Ave.
Rhinelander, WI 54501

KONG-TV
660 Sacramento, CA
Suite 330
San Francisco, CA 94111

WHCT-TV
555 Asylum St.
Hartford, CT 96105

Channel 50
6507 Chillum Pl. NW
Washington, D.C. 20012

WVII-TV
41 Farm Rd.
Bangor, MI 04401

WGPR-TV
3140 E. Jefferson St.
Detroit, MI 48207

KXLI-TV
P.O. Box 1776
St. Cloud, MN 56302

WHMM-TV (PBS)
Howard University
2600 4th St.
Washington, D.C. 20059

KSTS-TV
2349 Bering Dr.
San Jose, CA 95131

WWLG-TV
P.O. Box 340
Macon, GA 31297

Formerly Black-Owned Stations

WHEC-TV
191 East Ave.
Rochester, NY 14604

KLBK-TV
7400 University Ave.
Lubbock, TX 79408

WBLT-TV
P.O. Box 1712
Jackson, MS 38205

WTXS-TV
P.O. Box 2997
Abilene, TX 79604

WRBV-TV
145 Tyler Dr.
Willingboro, NJ 08046

Barden Cablevision
26380 Michigan Ave.
Inkster, MI 48141

Collier City Cablevision
2114 N. W. 5th St.
Pompano Beach, FL 33060

Connection Communications Corp.
360 Central Ave.
Newark, NJ 07013

Delta Development & Management Corp.
819 Main Street
Greensville, MS 38701

KBLE Ohio, Inc.
124 S. Washington St.
Columbus, OH 43215

Kirksey Enterprises, Inc.
3014 Teton Circle
Huntsville, AL 35810

Queens Inner City Unity Cable System
801 Second Ave.
New York, NY 10017

RUBE Cablevision Co.
P. O. Box 64
Edwards, MS 39066

Small Cities Communications Inc.
102 Walters Rd.
Carrboro, NC 27510

Steller-Continental Cable
5725 E. River Rd. -Suite 525
Chicago, IL 60631

Telecable Broadcasting
15929 Euclid
East Cleveland, OH 44112

Aleutian Cablevision Inc.
P. O. Box 415, Smugglers Cove
Metlakatla, Alaska 99926

Black-Owned Cable Program Suppliers

Apollo Entertainment Network
801 Second Ave.
New York, NY 10017

Black Entertainment Television
1050 31st St., N.W.
Washington, DC 20007

Black Music Network
Inner City Broadcasting
801 Second Ave.
New York, NY 10017

The Channel Black
Diaspora Communications Inc.
225 Central Park West-Suite 1123
New York, NY 10024

The Communication Programming Network
124 S. Washington St.
Columbus, OH 43215

National Jazz Network
P. O. Box 157
Amherst, MA 02004

Drama Winners

Olivia Cole--Roots, Part 8, ABC, 1976/77
    Supporting Actress, Single Performance Comedy or Drama
Gail Fisher--Mannix, CBS, 1969/70
    Supporting Actress, Drama
Al Freeman, Jr.--One Life To Live, CBS, 1978/79
    Actor, Daytime Drama Series
Louis Gossett, Jr.--Roots, Part 2, ABC, 1976/77
    Actor, Single Performance, Drama or Comedy Series
Esther Rolle--Summer Of My German Soldier, NBC, 1978/79
    Supporting Actress in a Limited Series or Special
Cicely Tyson--Autobiography of Miss Jane Pittman, CBS, 1973/74
    Actress Of The Year
    Best Actress In A Drama Special
Darnell Williams--All My Children, 1982/83
    Supporting Actor-Daytime Drama Series

Comedy Winners

Robert Guillaume--Soap, ABC, 1978/79
    Supporting Actor, Comedy or Comedy-Variety or Music Series
Isabel Sanford--The Jeffersons, CBS, 1980/81
    Actress, Comedy Series

Variety and Music Winners

Harry Belafonte--Tonight With Belafonte, (Revlon Review) CBS, 1959/
    60
    Performance In A Variety or Musical Program or Series
Nell Carter--Ain't Misbehavin', NBC, 1982/83
    Individual Achievement, Special Class
Andre DeShields--Ain't Misbehavin', NBC, 1982/83
    Individual Achievement, Special Class
Leontyne Price--Live From Lincoln Center, Leontyne Price, Zubin
    Mehta and The New York Philharmonic, PBS, 1982/83
    Individual Performance in a Variety Show
Sarah Vaughan--Rhapsody & Song--A Tribute To George Gershwin,
    PBS, 1980/81
    Individual Achievement, Special Class

Children's Programming--Individual Achievement Winners

Bill Cosby--"The Secret," The New Fat Albert Show, CBS, 1980/81
Butterfly McQueen--"The Seven Wishes of A Rich Kid," ABC After
    School Special, 1979/80
    Performer, Children's Program

News and Documentary Winners

Max Robinson--"Post-Election Special Edition." Nightline, ABC News,
    1979/80
    Programs & Program Segments
Ed Bradley--"CBS Reports: Miami: The Trail That Sparked The
    Riots," 1979/80
    Programs & Program Segments
    --"Too Little Too Late," Segment: CBS News, 1979/80

Writing Winners

Flip Wilson--The Flip Wilson Show, (with Lena Horne & Tony Ran-
    dall) NBC, 1970/71
    Writer, Variety or Music Series
Richard Pryor--Lily, CBS, 1973/74
    Writer, Comedy, Variety or Music, Special Program

Producing Winner

Charles Floyd Johnson--Rockford Files, NBC, 1977/78
    Producer, Drama Series

Directing Winner

Mark Warren--Rowan and Martin's Laugh-In (with Orson Wells),
    NBC, 1970/71
    Director, Variety or Music

Music Winner

Lionel Hampton--No Maps On My Taps, PBS, 1970/80

Music Composition Winner

Quincy Jones--Roots, Part 1, ABC, 1976/77
    In A Series with dramatic underscore

Choreography Winner

Debbie Allen--Fame, NBC, 1981/82; and 1982/83
    Choreography For A Single Episode, Limited Series or Spe-
    cial

Program Winners

Motown 25: Yesterday, Today, Forever, NBC, 1982/83
    Outstanding Variety, Music or Comedy Program
Room 222, ABC, 1969/70
    Outstanding New Series
Black Journal, NET, 1969/70
    Outstanding Cultural Documentary and Magazine-Type Program
Sickle Cell Disease: Paradox of Neglect, WZZM-TV, Grand Rapids,
    1971/72
    The Station Award
Mission Impossible, CBS, 1966/67
    Dramatic Series
The Bill Cosby Special, NBC, 1968/69
    Variety or Music Program
Roots, ABC, 1976/77
    Limited Series
Leontyne Price At The White House, PBS, 1978/79
    Achievement In Coverage of Special Event

News Winners

Charlayne Hunter-Gault, "The Grenada Coverage," The McNeil/Lehrer
    News Hour, PBS, 1983/84
    Outstanding Coverage of a Single Breaking News Story
Ed Bradley, "Larry," 60 Minutes, CBS, 1983/84
    "Lena," 60 Minutes, CBS, 1981/82
    Outstanding News Segments
Lem Tucker, "Black Family,' CBS Evening News, CBS, 1983/84
    Outstanding Informational, Cultural or Historical Program

Dr. George H. Hill, television and radio producer, lecturer, journalist, is vice president of Nightingale Communications & Media, a TV production company and public relations firm. An instructor of media classes at Southwest College in Los Angeles, Dr. Hill taught the first college course on the subject of blacks and television.

His television credits include executive producer/host of cable show, InterFaith Forum and Get It On in Phoenix with Madison Walker. He served on the initial coordinating committee to produce the Baha'i Faith program, Spiritual Revolution.

Sylvia Saverson Hill, M.A., is a secondary administrator, counselor, and educator. She has been a production coordinator on many of Nightingale television projects including Focus On Baha'i, and InterFaith Forum.

Cynthia Griffin, co-author of "History of Blacks On Television," is a freelance writer and author of Black Spots: Everybody's Guide To Black Los Angeles.

Dr. Hill's other books include: Black Media In America: A Resource Guide & Bibliography, Airwaves To The Soul (R & E Associates, 1983); Religious Broadcasting, 1920-1983: An Annotated Bibliography (Garland Publishing Co., 1984) with Lenwood Davis; Blacks In The Armed Forces, 1886-1983, A Bibliography (Greenwood Press, 1984) with Lenwood Davis; Black Business & Economic Conditions: A Bibliography (Garland Publishing Co., 1984); and Jesse Louis Jackson, Preacher & Politician: A Bibliography, with Janet Sims-Wood (Afro Resources, Inc., 1984).

CONTENTS

791.45
H646b

Library of Congress Cataloging in Publication Data

Hill, George.
    Blacks on television.

    Includes index.
    1. Afro-Americans in the television industry--
Bibliography. 2. Afro-Americans in the performing
arts--Bibliography. I. Hill, Sylvia Saverson.
II. Title.
Z1361.N39H53 1985   791.45'028'08996073   84-23639
[PN1992.8.A34]
ISBN 0-8108-1774-8

For Thomas William Graham Jr. and
Marion Barrows Graham

Contents

Preface

In tackling the project that would result in *Lord Byron*, I was from the first aware of a responsibility to think not just about Byron and his works but also about how both have been understood and interpreted in contemporary culture. Accordingly, it seemed appropriate that the frontispiece and dust jacket present something other than an archival or canonical view of Byron. Instead, what's reproduced here is "Byron East and West," a double portrait by Joni Pienkowski, critically acclaimed for her work in various media and styles, among other things for the "Paint Saints" series into which this diptych might seem to fall. Taken together, the two parts of Pienkowski's boldly eclectic vision call up various truths about Byron's status as icon in his contemporary culture and his standing in our own day.

The "West" view of Byron at first appears to need no introduction. It derives from what is probably the most famous of Thomas Phillips's well-known portraits of Byron, the much-reproduced open-collared likeness painted at the height of Byromania in 1814. This portrait still dominates the Byron room at the Albemarle Street establishment of his publisher John Murray. Pienkowski's homage to Phillips is unmistakable, but her postmodern eye and hand have revised the romantic commonplace. Fidelity to an image that Byron's friend Hobhouse never thought faithful to its original slides into ironic mannerism in this portrait. Pienkowki's Byron-after-Phillips wears his beauty with a difference. Overtly conscious of its theatrical effect, this portrait is caught, as the viewer's eye moves from chiseled features to elegant hand, in the act of becoming self-caricature.

The "East" portion of the diptych is less a portrait than a visually rendered thought experiment. Here, Pienkowski's late-twentieth-century Western sensibility imagines a late-eighteenth-century Eastern sensibility imagining Byron dressed not as Prince Hamlet but as an analogous revenger in Japanese drama. The representation is both an evident fiction and a complex allusion to what Byron would call "things existent." When Sharaku produced his famous series of actors' portraits, Byron was a child of seven. Byron never wore Japanese ceremonial garb to a Holland House rout, a dandies' ball, or a Venetian carnival revel. His personal and poetic fame did not penetrate the closed world of Edo in his lifetime. Indeed, the romantic individualism for which both Byron and the Byronic hero are renowned could be seen as the ethical and aesthetic antithesis to values prevailing in the Japanese culture of Sharaku. But the transcultural visual experiment captures Byron's connection with dark, doomed, highborn heroes, his wish to be seen less a man of words and more a man of action, his literal involvement with drama and the stage. Here we view the essential theatricality of a person and poet whose nature, as Keats would have it, was to "cut a figure."

Why might, should, or do late-twentieth-century readers turn or return to the works of Lord Byron, a poet who died in 1824? The answer lies largely in the works themselves. They speak, though in different ways, to different ages, and in some ways they speak better to our age than to others. Part of the answer lies in the life. Byron has at no time been reduced to his words by his readers—that he proved resistant to such reduction is one reason transcendental and formalist models of romanticism have always had trouble finding a place for him. From 1812 on, Byron's life and works blurred and blended together in a mode of celebrity more frequently encountered in later-twentieth-century culture than in Byron's day. Another part of the answer lies in the afterlife, that form of immortality conferred on poets by readers, editors, biographers, critics—particularly in developments over the last few decades that enable us to see Byron differently, in some ways more clearly, than he was seen before.

This book revisits Lord Byron chiefly through his works but attempts to put them in various contexts: biographical, historical, social. After a brief sketch of the chief events of Byron's life, a series of chapters will consider Byron's major and minor works—the latter grouped according to "kind," or genre. Besides setting Byron's literary works in cultural contexts, I aim to attend to the process of image making, in Britain and abroad, that set up Byron, along with Napoléon Bonaparte, Charles Darwin, and Queen Victoria, as one of the European icons of his century.

In the years since Paul G. Trueblood revised his 1969 *Lord Byron* for the Twayne English Authors Series in 1977, a number of scholarly developments have combined to make a contextualized reading of the sort just described more possible and more necessary. Important primary materials, unavailable or imperfectly available to previous generations of scholars, are now before us. In epic array—12 volumes appearing between 1973 and 1982—Byron's biographer Leslie Marchand assembled, edited, and indexed the complete letters and journals of Byron. Brought out concurrently by John Murray (Byron's publishing house for most of his writing career) in the United Kingdom and by Harvard in the United States, Marchand's meticulous and award-winning edition of *Byron's Letters and Journals* made available a wealth of previously unpublished texts and presented in full, faithful form texts extracted from or altered in earlier editions, the most complete of which was the six-volume Prothero edition of 1891 to 1901. In 1994 Marchand supplemented the collection with *What Comes Uppermost*, a volume containing the letters that had come to light since 1981, published concurrently by Murray and the University of Delaware Press.

If Byron's letters are in better shape than ever before, so are his literary texts. Between 1980 and 1993, Jerome J. McGann brought out Oxford's seven-volume Clarendon Press edition of *Byron's Complete Poetical Works*. Like Marchand's edition of the letters and journals, McGann's *Complete Poetical Works* offers a substantial number of previously unpublished or uncollected works and corrects other texts previously known in corrupt versions. Selections from McGann's complete edition appear in the one-volume Oxford Authors series *Byron* (1986) and in the *New Oxford Book of Romantic Verse* (1993), an anthology that presents a diverse range of works by romantic writers in a chronological arrangement that enables readers to see how Byron's works converse with those of his contemporaries.

Thanks to the editorial labors of Marchand and McGann, critics are able as never before to ground Byron's works in his life and times and to take account of particular circumstances of composition, publication, and reception. And never before has such an approach seemed so desirable. Perhaps the main trend in Byron scholarship in the 1980s and 1990s has been to examine his poems in light of their history (that term being taken in the widest sense), an intellectual project in which McGann's critical work has led the way. Not content with a formalist notion of ideal, unmediated art and unwilling to reduce literary works to pure play of language, as some though not all deconstructionist criticism has done, many of Byron's present readers study his works within their complex circumstances. Among the results have been Marxist and feminist studies exposing repressed or mystified content, books and essays considering the interplay between poetry and politics, reexaminations of what Byron's contemporaries wrote about him and how his works converse with others of the day, and materialist studies showing how the particulars of book production and marketing help create the meaning of a work.

With a strengthened notion of historical context and with previously inaccessible minor works increasingly available, students of romanticism have moved beyond the "Gradus ad Parnassum" that isolated on the canonical summit a double trinity of "first-generation" poets (Wordsworth and Coleridge, with Blake as odd man out) and "second-generation" ones (Shelley and Keats, with Byron not entirely comfortable in the company of poet-idealists). More complex understandings of English romanticism, as a matter of "data not dogma," to use Larry Swingle's trenchant phrase, and attention to a wider range of voices and genres now seem worth readers' attention.[1] Similarly, the focus of Byron studies has widened. Without challenging the preeminence of *Don Juan* and the other ottava rima poems, recognized as his masterpieces by the earlier twentieth-century critics, late-twentieth-century scholarly and general readers alike have discovered or recovered the compelling qualities of other works, such as the plays (now even proven to be stageable), the letters and journals (now recognized as literary works in their own right), and the Eastern tales. Some of Byron's works seem truly to have come into their own in the present day: for instance, the entropic nightmare of "Darkness" has never spoken more movingly, plausibly, maybe even inevitably, than to our age with its fears of nuclear winter or ecological apocalypse.

Acknowledgments

It's well known that we gain perspective by standing on other people's shoulders, and I gratefully acknowledge the many critics and scholars, past and present, who have inspired me to read Byron and have enriched my understanding of him. Several people deserve particular thanks for their help at various points in this project: Jerome J. McGann, J. B. Yount III, Hilbert H. Campbell, Robert M. Brown, and Joni Pienkowski. I also thank the English Department of Virginia Polytechnic Institute and State University for a research leave during which several chapters of *Lord Byron* were completed.

BYRON EAST

From Byron East and West *by Joni Pienkowski. From a private collection.*

BYRON WEST

From Byron East and West *by Joni Pienkowski. From a private collection.*

Chronology

1788   George Gordon Byron born 22 January in London, son of Captain John Byron (nephew of the fifth Baron Byron of Rochdale) and his second wife, Catherine Gordon.

1789   Mrs. Byron and her son move to rented lodgings in Aberdeen.

1791   Captain Byron dies in France.

1794   On the death of a cousin, becomes heir to the title. Attends Aberdeen Grammar School until 1798.

1798   On the death of his great-uncle, becomes the sixth Lord Byron.

1799   Enrolls at Dr. Glennie's preparatory school in Dulwich.

1801   Enters Harrow School.

1803   Romantic attachment to Mary Chaworth.

1804   Begins corresponding with his half-sister, Augusta.

1805   Finishes at Harrow, matriculates at Trinity College, Cambridge. Platonic attachment to John Edleston, a choirboy at Trinity.

1806   *Fugitive Pieces* privately printed.

1807   *Poems on Various Occasions* privately printed. *Hours of Idleness* published. Makes friends at Cambridge with John Cam Hobhouse and C. S. Matthews. Leaves Cambridge for London demimonde.

1808   Anonymous reviewer ridicules *Hours of Idleness* in the *Edinburgh Review*. *Poems Original and Translated* published.

1809   Takes his seat, as a Whig, in the House of Lords. *English Bards and Scotch Reviewers* published. With Hobhouse, leaves to travel widely in Portugal, Spain, Malta, Greece, Albania, and Turkey. Begins *Childe Harold's Pilgrimage*.

1810   Sees Troy and swims the Hellespont. When Hobhouse returns to England, Byron remains in Greece, mostly in Athens. Drafts *Hints from Horace* and writes *The Curse of Minerva*.

1811   Returns, via Malta, to England. Deaths of Mrs. Byron, Matthews, and John Wingfield inspire revision of *Childe Harold*. Learns of Edleston's death. Meets Thomas Moore.

1812   Gives his maiden speech, an attack on the Frame Bill, and a second speech, on Catholic emancipation, in the House of Lords. John Murray publishes *Childe Harold* 1, 2. Lionized in Whig society. Liaisons with Lady Caroline Lamb and Lady Oxford. Unsuccessful proposal to Anne Isabella (Annabella) Milbanke. Thomas Claughton offers £140,000 for Newstead Abbey but delays paying.

1813   *The Giaour* published and reissued. Addresses the House of Lords in support of Major Cartwright's right to petition for parliamentary reform. *The Bride of Abydos* appears. Begins affair with Augusta.

1814   *The Corsair* sells 10,000 copies on the day of publication. Medora Leigh, putative daughter by Augusta, born. Second proposal to Annabella Milbanke, who accepts. *Lara* appears.

1815   Marries Annabella 2 January, in a private ceremony at Seaham. Moves to 13 Piccadilly Terrace, London. Publishes *Hebrew Melodies*. Joins the subcommittee managing Drury Lane Theatre. Annabella gives birth to Augusta Ada in December.

1816   Annabella and Ada depart for Seaham. Annabella asks for a legal separation. *The Siege of Corinth* and *Parisina* published. With Dr. William Polidori, leaves England in April. Travels through Belgium and up the Rhine to Switzerland. Settles at Villa Diodati on Lake Geneva. Spends summer in the company of Percy and Mary Godwin Shelley, and Claire Clairmont. Writes *Childe Harold* 3 and *The Prisoner of Chillon*. With Hobhouse and Scrope Davies, tours Alpine sites. Proceeds with Hobhouse to the Bernese Oberland and Italy. Settles in Venice. Begins an affair with Marianna Segati.

1817   *Manfred* completed. Allegra, his daughter by Claire
       Clairmont, born in England. Leases Villa Foscarini on
       the Brenta at La Mira. Tours Rome with Hobhouse
       and, returning to Venice, starts the fourth canto of
       Childe Harold. Liaison with Margarita Cogni. *Beppo*
       completed.

1818   *Beppo* and *Childe Harold* 4 published. Leases Palazzo
       Mocenigo on the Grand Canal. Shelley and Claire visit
       Venice. Begins *Don Juan*.

1819   Sale of Newstead Abbey to Major Thomas Wildman.
       Becomes lover of Teresa Guiccioli. The first two cantos
       of *Don Juan* appear anonymously. Following the
       Guicciolis, goes to Ravenna, then Bologna. Continues
       Don Juan, completing cantos 3 and 4. Back at Venice
       and La Mira, gives "Memoirs" to Thomas Moore, who
       is visiting from England. Established as Teresa's *cavalier
       servente* in Ravenna.

1820   At Ravenna, translates the first canto of *Morgante
       Maggiore*, finishes *Prophecy of Dante*, writes *Marino
       Faliero*, and completes canto 5 of *Don Juan*. Teresa
       obtains a papal separation from her husband.
       Involvement with the Carbonari.

1821   Writes *Sardanapalus, The Two Foscari, Cain, Heaven and
       Earth*, and *The Vision of Judgment*. Begins "Ravenna
       Journal" and "Detached Thoughts." Leaving Ravenna
       with the Gambas for political reasons, joins the Shelley
       circle at Pisa.

1822   Allegra dies of a fever. Shelley drowns. Writes *Werner,
       The Deformed Transformed*, and cantos 6–12 of *Don
       Juan*. With the Gambas, moves to Genoa. Stops pub-
       lishing with Murray and turns to John Hunt.

1823   Writes *The Island* and cantos 13–16 of *Don Juan*. As
       the London Greek Committee's representative, joins
       the Greek struggle for independence. Established on
       Cephalonia.

1824   Proceeds to Missolonghi on the mainland. Starting in
       February, health deteriorates. Dies on 19 April. Buried
       at Hucknall church near Newstead. "Memoirs"
       bequeathed to Moore are burned.

Chapter One

Byron's Life and Legend

George Gordon Byron's early years were not particularly auspicious. Born in London on 22 January 1788 to Captain John "Mad Jack" Byron, nephew of the fifth Baron Byron of Rochdale, and the captain's second wife, the Scots heiress Catherine Gordon of Gight, George Gordon descended from two noble lineages distinguished for their instability. Shortly after Byron's birth, the profligate captain abandoned his stout, plain, irascible wife, whose fortune he had squandered just as he had his previous wife's. Mrs. Byron returned to Scotland, where she rented lodgings in Aberdeen and devoted herself to rearing the club-footed, high-spirited son she sometimes termed her "little lame brat." Spending his formative years in the coastal city at the edge of the Grampians, he received his early formal education at the Aberdeen Grammar School and domestic instruction in Calvinism—and precocious sensuality—from his nurse May Gray. The child Byron was, as the mature man acknowledged in *Don Juan*, "half a Scot by birth, and bred / A whole one."[1]

But circumstances in the kingdom to the south were to change his fortune. When the debt-ridden Captain Byron died in France in 1791, he left his widow and son in precarious financial circumstances. The situation did not improve when in 1794, on the death of his great-uncle Lord Byron's grandson, George Gordon became heir to the barony. When the "Wicked Lord" himself expired in 1798, Byron succeeded to the title of sixth baron and inherited Newstead Abbey, the picturesque but ramshackle family seat in Nottinghamshire, and Rochdale, a lawsuit-ridden Lancashire property. Neither estate dramatically altered the family finances, but becoming an English peer gave Byron a sense of personal consequence he never ceased to cherish. Although Newstead had to be rented out, the Byrons were able to move south. From 1799 on, Byron spent his school days in England, first at Dr. Glennie's preparatory school in Dulwich, then, starting in 1801, at Harrow School. Mrs. Byron eventually established herself not far from Newstead at Burgage Manor, a spacious house in the small cathedral town of Southwell. From this base, where he eventually formed a circle of friends

1

that included the Pigot family, the adolescent Byron explored his ancestral county and fell in love, with his first cousin Margaret Parker in 1800 and with Mary Chaworth of nearby Annesley Hall in 1803. These idealistic attachments, the latter painfully ignored by the eligible Mary, inspired his early ventures into poetry. In 1804 an important personal and epistolary relationship began, Byron's correspondence with his half-sister, Augusta, daughter of Captain Byron's first wife.

Finishing Harrow in 1805, Byron matriculated at Trinity College, Cambridge, where his eccentricities are still the stuff of undergraduate legend. A lifelong animal lover, he kept a bear in Trinity. As was the custom of his time, place, and class, he sometimes drank heavily. To combat his hereditary tendency toward corpulence, he dieted drastically and exercised prodigiously, playing cricket in "seven waistcoats and a great coat." Newly slim, pale, and handsome, he formed an intense if platonic relationship with the choirboy John Edleston and established man-of-the-world friendships with a set of witty Cambridge men devoted to several of his own preoccupations: classical literature, progressive thought, and Whig politics. But despite more than a few congenial companions, Byron never fell under the spell of Cambridge. The expensive attractions of the London demimonde lured him away from the university. Throughout this rackety, unsettled period, he found release in poetry. The results, sometimes mawkish, sometimes promising, often confessional, and generally imitative, were two privately printed collections, *Fugitive Pieces* (1806) and *Poems on Various Occasions* (1807), followed by his first publication, *Hours of Idleness* (1807), which was anonymously noticed and mockingly dismissed in the *Edinburgh Review*, the most prestigious Whig quarterly of the day.

Writhing under the lash of the *Edinburgh*'s reviewer (who turned out to be Henry Brougham), Byron took what literary comfort he could in the satirist's *saeva indignatio* and published *English Bards and Scotch Reviewers* (1809). The same year, Byron attained his majority and took his seat as a Whig in the House of Lords, though his reception there was lukewarm at best. Finished with Cambridge and less than delighted with the prospects poetry and politics seemed to afford him, Byron left England with his friend John Cam Hobhouse for an early-nineteenth-century version of the grand tour. They traveled widely throughout the portions of the Mediterranean world open to British citizens in the Napoleonic era: Portugal, Spain, Malta, Greece, Albania, and Turkey. En route Byron flirted and dallied with women of diverse nationalities; viewed antiquities and vistas; explored dangerous, bandit-infested Albanian territories hitherto unpenetrated by British travelers, where the despotic Ali Pasha gave him a lavish welcome; came to know and love the subjugated people of Greece; swam the Hellespont (a feat he was to mention for years to come); galloped over the ruins of Troy; and presumably sampled the forbidden pleasures of homoerotic love. On this journey he also began *Childe Harold's Pilgrimage*, the long Spenserian poem that was to make his literary reputation.

In 1811 Byron returned to England, where triple bereavement awaited him. In a matter of weeks, he was devastated to learn of the deaths of his mother, his Cambridge friend C. S. Matthews, and his Harrow schoolfellow John Wingfield. A few months later, he would receive news that Edleston, his protégé from Cambridge days, was dead. But a new phase of life in the "Great World" of Whig society was opening for him. At the house of Samuel Rogers, the rich banker-poet, Byron met, and began mending fences with, Thomas Moore, whose Irish origins had not spared him from being one of Byron's targets in *English Bards*. And when John Murray published the first two cantos of *Childe Harold*, Byron "woke up famous," according to his famous phrase. Lionized in London society, he was a desired guest in the most fashionable drawing rooms and boudoirs. Byron's confidante during his "years of fame" was the urbane, tolerant Whig hostess Lady Melbourne, to whom he transmitted epistolary accounts of his amours, sparkling prose to rival the comedies of his Whig hero Richard Brinsley Sheridan. Among his mistresses were Lady Oxford, the beautiful, free-thinking countess renowned for her intense commitments to radical Whig politics and handsome Whig politicians, and Lady Melbourne's own daughter-in-law Lady Caroline Lamb, a volatile and talented member of the ultrafashionable Devonshire House set and wife to William Lamb, who would later be Queen Victoria's first prime minister. During this hectic time Byron proposed unsuccessfully to Lady Melbourne's niece Annabella Milbanke, the earnest, mathematically inclined heiress he styled his "Princess of Parallelograms." In 1813 he began an affair with his amiable half-sister, Augusta, who in the years since their initial correspondence had married her cousin George Leigh, taken on the duties of lady-in-waiting to Princess Caroline, and become the mother of an impecunious, growing family that, in 1814, was augmented by the birth of Medora, Byron's putative daughter.

Byron's social life during the years of fame was a heady blend of romantic intrigue, party-going, theater, boxing, and revelry at Newstead, which Thomas Claughton had offered to buy for £140,000 but

delayed paying for and finally defaulted upon. For a period of months in
1812 and 1813, Byron's role in Whig politics became more active. His
maiden speech in the House of Lords attacked the Frame Bill and supported the cause of Nottingham weavers. He delivered subsequent
addresses in favor of Catholic emancipation and of Major Cartwright's
right to petition for parliamentary reform. His wildly popular poetic
career continued unabated with a series of Eastern tales, "lava of the
emotions" for the author and hot sensations for a reading public eager to
discern Byronic features in the *homme fatal* of the latest poem, whether it
be *The Giaour* (1813), *The Bride of Abydos* (1813), *The Corsair* (1814),
which sold 10,000 copies on the day of publication, or *Lara* (1814), a
sequel to *The Corsair*.

Jaded, exhausted, in need of relief from creditors, suppliants, and
lovers, Byron thought of again traveling with Hobhouse. Instead of
doing so, he perversely and halfheartedly renewed his epistolary
courtship of Annabella Milbanke, who unfortunately accepted his proposal. Thus the end of 1814 found him embarking on a different kind of
pilgrimage. After a Christmas passed with Augusta and her family at Six
Mile Bottom, Byron, accompanied by faithful Hobhouse to serve as his
best man, journeyed north to Seaham, the Milbankes' estate. "Never
was lover less in haste," Hobhouse's journal darkly observes. Having
delayed his arrival long enough for the wedding cake to become stale,
Byron married Annabella 2 January 1815, in a private ceremony. Their
"treacle-moon" was passed at nearby Halnaby Hall, and Byron's recollections of it were anything but heavenly. Waking in the middle of the
night and becoming aware of firelight shining through the deep crimson
bed curtains, he concluded that he was dead and damned, "fairly in hell
with Proserpine lying beside him!"[2] The Byrons embarked on an expensive, creditor-pressed London life at 13 Piccadilly Terrace, where
Augusta often made an awkward third in their tormented togetherness.
The days in Piccadilly Terrace were not entirely uncongenial or unpro-
ductive—during this time Byron worked on *Hebrew Melodies*, lyrics for
music published by Isaac Nathan, and joined the subcommittee managing Drury Lane Theatre. Generally speaking, however, marriage aggra-
vated rather than assuaged the various pressures on Byron. Lady Byron's
heavy-handed piety brought out the worst in her lord, whose violent
moods shocked and distressed her, as did his drinking, his possession of
such unwholesome phenomena as laudanum and the Marquis de Sade's
scandalous novel *Justine*, and his dark hints at manifold sins and wicked-

nesses. While her husband smashed bottles in the room below, Annabella gave birth to their daughter, Augusta Ada, in December.

Early in 1816, Annabella and Ada departed for a visit to Seaham. There she disclosed some of her matrimonial unhappiness and, urged by her parents, asked for a legal separation, to which Byron eventually agreed. Rumors of unspeakable sexual offenses spread, and the fickle Great World snubbed him as thoroughly as it had before fawned over him. Byron's response was to turn his back on those who had turned their backs on him—to become, like his character Childe Harold, a cosmopolitan wanderer. With Hobhouse and Scrope Davies to wish him well, Dr. William Polidori at his side, and creditors at his heels, Byron left England in April. Traveling through Belgium in a great Napoleonic coach, he visited the battlefield of Waterloo, where relics of carnage yet remained, and made his way up the Rhine to Switzerland, where he settled at Villa Diodati, a pleasant house on the shore of Lake Geneva. There he spent a "haunted summer" noted for its chilly, rainy weather in the company of Percy and Mary Godwin Shelley and Mary's stepsister Claire Clairmont, who had become pregnant by Byron in a brief encounter in London the previous spring. Tongues wagged back in England when travelers carried home tales of Diodati's alleged "league of incest," but the enduring fruits of this association were some of the great works of English romanticism: Mary Shelley's *Frankenstein*, Percy Shelley's "Mont Blanc" and "Hymn to Intellectual Beauty," and Byron's third canto of *Childe Harold* and *The Prisoner of Chillon*, a verse tale springing from the story of François Bonivard. In the company of Hobhouse and Scrope Davies, Byron toured Alpine sites later in the summer. Then he and Hobhouse proceeded to the Bernese Oberland and Italy. Byron established himself in Venice, which he called both a "sea-sodom" and "the greenest island of my imagination." Whatever his degree of levity or sincerity in these terms, Byron found that Venice offered a sophisticated, hedonistic, affordable society in which he could live luxuriously and unjudged. Besides touring in gondolas, frequenting conversazione such as that of the Contessa Albrizzi, and studying Armenian at the island monastery of San Lazzaro, he promptly fell in love with Marianna Segati, the beautiful, black-eyed young wife of "a merchant of Venice," and seduced her. Writing home to his correspondents in the "tight little island" that had spurned him, he took defiant pleasure in stressing that he and Marianna had become "one of the happiest— unlawful couples on this side of the Alps" (*BLJ*, 5:141). This affair was to be only the first of many, but Byron's Venetian life would involve much more than unlawful love.

In 1817 Byron completed *Manfred*, a metaphysical drama begun in Switzerland; but the year was distinguished mostly by beginnings. Allegra, his daughter by Claire Clairmont, was born back in England. To escape the summer heat of Venice, Byron leased a country place, Villa Foscarini on the river Brenta at La Mira. Later in the year, he toured Rome with Hobhouse. On returning to Venice, he started a fourth canto of *Childe Harold* and embarked upon a new liaison with a "splendid animal" named Margarita Cogni. Perhaps most important for his subsequent poetic development, he encountered the Italian form called ottava rima and used it for *Beppo*, his first venture in the comic, improvisational mode that proved ideally suited to his sensibility. The year 1818 brought carnival revelry and an epic catalog of mistresses noble, middling, and low-born, "at least 200 of them." Fully immersed in Venetian life, Byron galloped his horses on the sands of the Lido and swam from its beaches up the Grand Canal. He finally leased a grand house of his own, the Palazzo Mocenigo on the Grand Canal. According to Shelley, who with Claire Clairmont paid a visit to Venice, Byron kept a menagerie that included dogs, monkeys, cats, an eagle, a crow, a falcon, peacocks, guinea hens, and an Egyptian crane at the Palazzo Mocenigo. During this rich and busy period *Beppo* and *Childe Harold* 4 were published, and Byron began what would come to be his ottava rima masterpiece, *Don Juan*.

From 1819 through 1822, Byron's attachment to Italy strengthened as the bonds tying him to his native land continued to weaken. At last the sale of Newstead Abbey, to Major Thomas Wildman, was completed. The resulting funds, combined with the £2,500 a year that constituted his share of the Wentworth estate after the death of Annabella's mother, Lady Noel, made him significantly richer than he had ever been—and the affixing of the Noel arms to his own allowed him to sign himself "N. B.," the initials of his fallen hero and counterpart in exile Napoléon Bonaparte. The year 1819 brought an end to Byron's Don Giovanni days: he became the committed lover of Teresa Guiccioli, the pretty, sentimental, convent-bred 19-year-old bride of a 58-year-old count. Their relationship was to be, if not the ethereal romance she recalled in later years, the most sustained and satisfying affair of Byron's life. Perhaps overstated in his love letters to Teresa, certainly understated or ironized in the missives he sent English friends, Byron's powerful and complicated feelings for the young Italian countess may be most candidly conveyed in his "Stanzas to the Po." Following the Guicciolis,

Byron went to Ravenna, then Bologna. Having resisted the chains of love and wrenched himself back to Venice and La Mira, he gave a manuscript of his memoirs to Thomas Moore, who was visiting from England—and then, after some vacillation, returned to Ravenna to become Teresa's *cavalier servente*, a chivalric role the cant-hating Byron sometimes could not help finding ridiculous. Teresa's father, Count Gamba, had never entirely approved of his daughter's match with Count Guiccioli, and with paternal help Teresa succeeded in obtaining a papal separation from her husband. Byron became closely associated with the Gambas, and through them with the real Italy. As he wrote to Thomas Moore, "Now, I have lived in the heart of their houses, in parts of Italy freshest and least influenced by strangers,—have seen and become (*pars magna fui*) a portion of their hopes, and fears, and passions, and am almost inoculated into a family. This is to see men and things as they are" (*BLJ,* 5:170–71). Among these hopes, fears, and passions was the cause of liberty, a lifelong commitment of Byron's, whatever the nation. Along with Count Gamba and Teresa's idealistic brother Pietro, Byron involved himself in the Carbonari, an association of Italian revolutionaries, and thereby aroused the suspicions of the local minions of the Austrian empire. But though he was committed to the liberation of Italy, Byron put individual humanity ahead of partisan principle. When Luigi Dal Pinto, commandant of the troops at Ravenna, was ambushed in the street, Byron braved Carbonari hostility by having the dying man carried to his house and tended by a surgeon.

The period from 1819 to 1822 was one of intense creativity for Byron. The first two cantos of *Don Juan* appeared anonymously in 1819, and he continued the expandable and congenial epic-with-a-difference, completing cantos 3 and 4. At Ravenna in 1820, he translated the first canto of *Morgante Maggiore* by Pulci, finished *Prophecy of Dante*, wrote a Venetian tragedy, *Marino Faliero*, and completed canto 5 of *Don Juan*. In 1821, with his favored mode of introspection and retrospection silenced by Teresa's disapproval of *Don Juan*, Byron began two prose narratives, the "Ravenna Journal" and "Detached Thoughts." He also turned his attention to drama and wrote *Sardanapalus* and *The Two Foscari,* treating historical subjects, and *Cain* and *Heaven and Earth,* based on biblical sources. Irritated by a series of long-distance attacks and innuendos from his old adversary the poet laureate Robert Southey and disgusted by *A Vision of Judgment,* Southey's fulsome panegyric on the recently deceased George III, Byron replied with his own *Vision of Judgment (The,* not *A*) in ottava rima. His most brilliantly executed satire, the poem had

considerable potential to offend mainstream British sensibilities. John
Murray's reluctance to publish it eventually spurred Byron, who had for
some time been growing weary of Murray's caution, to end their long-
standing arrangement and to publish with the radical John Hunt.

Byron's Ravenna period ended in 1821. Finding the city uncomfortable for political reasons, he, Teresa, and the Gambas joined the Shelleys
and their expatriate set at Pisa. The Pisan circle promised something of
a return to the stimulating summer of 1816 on the shore of Lake
Geneva. There were lively discussions of literature, philosophy, and politics, musical evenings, boating at Genoa on Byron's schooner *Bolivar*
(named for the Latin-American liberator) and Shelley's yacht *Don Juan*.
There were plans for a progressive periodical, *The Liberal*, which
Shelley's friend Leigh Hunt was to edit—a speculative arrangement that
brought Hunt and his ill-regulated family to Italy. But tragedy struck
the group in 1822. Byron and Claire's daughter, Allegra, died of a fever
at her convent school; Percy Shelley and Edward Williams drowned
when a storm on the Bay of Spezia struck the *Don Juan*. With the
Gambas, Byron moved on to Genoa, where he still felt, and shouldered,
some responsibility for the widowed Mary Shelley and the stranded
Hunts. Having broken with Murray, Byron designated as his new publisher Leigh Hunt's brother John, who was prosecuted for publishing
the "gross, impious, and slanderous" *Vision of Judgment*.

Byron's poetic powers were not sleeping from 1822 to 1823. He
wrote *Werner*, *The Deformed Transformed*, *The Island*, and, at intervals over
the period, cantos 6 through 16 of *Don Juan*. But he had never considered poetry his true calling, or even an entirely worthy one. Although
Austrian authorities had thwarted his participation in the Carbonari,
opportunities for aspiring liberators beckoned in the East, where Greek
insurgents were fomenting rebellion against the Ottoman empire.
Philhellenes throughout Europe were attracted by the Greek cause, but
few idealistic admirers of mythic and classical Greece had Byron's capacity to recognize, accept, and deal with the long-enslaved nation's messy
contemporary realities: petty intrigues; self-aggrandizing, unreliable, or
incompetent leaders; mercenary or craven troops; widespread venality.
As the London Greek Committee's official representative, Byron determined to devote his efforts, prestige, and fortune to the Greek struggle
for independence. Accompanied by Pietro Gamba, he first established
himself on the Ionian island of Cephalonia. Though more inclined to
contribute generous amounts of his own money or to involve himself in
military action than to tackle mundane business details or to mediate

the quarrels of the Greek factions, Byron proved himself among the most practical and diplomatic of the Western Europeans on the scene. Not just a friend of freedom, he was, as he had been in Ravenna, an advocate of human decency. He hoped, among other things, to steer Greeks and Turks alike away from the atrocities that sullied conduct on both sides.

On 6 January 1824 Byron crossed to Missolonghi, a marshy, unprepossessing, besieged mainland town he had visited years before. Leading a force of Suliote troops paid entirely out of his pocket, Byron intended to play a soldier's role despite his lack of military training or experience. On arriving at Missolonghi, he wrote, "I take it that a man is on the whole as safe in one place as another—and after all he had better end with a bullet than bark in his body" (*BLJ*, 11:107). His aim was to capture the Turkish-occupied fortress of Lepanto at present-day Nafpaktos, but the arrival of Ottoman naval forces delayed his plan. Starting in February, his health deteriorated. After a rainy ride, he caught a fever, which was followed by fits and intermittent bouts of illness. No friend to medical intervention, the failing Byron prudently kept his doctors at bay until, at last too weak for further resistance, he gave way to their desire to bleed him. A victim of his doctors as well as his disease (the immediate cause of death was probably uremia abetted by bleedings and purgings), Byron died on 19 April 1824. But though he expired in bed rather than in battle, of the dreaded bark rather than the desired bullet, Byron's disinterested death for the Hellenic cause made him a national hero whose memory is still cherished throughout Greece. Few Greek towns are without a commemorative statue, a memorial, or a street called Odos Byronos in his honor; and his viscera were left behind in Missolonghi. His embalmed body was shipped back to England. There, after a funeral procession that drew crowds on its passage north from London, Byron was buried among his ancestors in the family vault at Hucknall church near Newstead. Only in 1969 did the British establishment decide that, whatever his sins, Byron's stature had earned him a tablet in the Poets' Corner of Westminster Abbey. Those other remains of his scandalous and fascinating life, the memoirs bequeathed to Thomas Moore, were after heated discussion among his relations and closest friends burned in John Murray's fireplace at 50 Albemarle Street—the very house from which *Childe Harold* and most of Byron's other published works had issued forth into the world.

Chapter Two
Lyric Poems

Byron's first and last substantiated poetic works—the former, [Then Peace to Thy Spirit], an elegiac piece conjecturally dated 1803, the latter, [Love and Death] and [Last Words on Greece], anguished addresses to a beloved Greek youth, Loukas Chalandritsanos, written during the last weeks of Byron's life in 1824—were lyrics.[1] In the time between, short, occasional verses of diverse sorts punctuated his longer compositions. Some of his lyric poems, among them "She Walks in Beauty," "The Destruction of Semnacherib," and "So We'll Go No More A-roving," are staples of anthologists.

Nonetheless, Byron's poetic reputation has had little to do with his lyrics. Critics concerned with the romantic lyric have tended to ignore or deprecate Byron. M. H. Abrams, for instance, observes that "Only Byron, among the major poets, did not write in this mode at all."[2] Even among Byronists, the consensus traditionally has been that his genius is not lyrical, that, in Andrew Rutherford's words, "his short poems seldom escape the metrical banality and sentimentalism which Moore's works encouraged."[3] The main reason for this neglect, as recent criticism has suggested, is that readers have continued to think of the romantic lyric as a sincere voice heard, or overheard, by a sympathetic audience—a model dictated by the theory and practice of Wordsworth and Coleridge. Byron writing at his best twisted the form into something new. For him romantic sincerity, Wordsworth's "spontaneous overflow of powerful feeling," becomes a dramatic or rhetorical posture— one of the many figures a poet might cut. Thus the instantaneous and personal features associated with lyric also make their way into Byron's longer and more generally admired poems. As Jerome J. McGann puts it, "Byron turns all his subjects into lyric forms."[4]

Needless to say, Byron's lyrics, like those of most poets, are far from consistent in quality or type, and by no means are all of his early lyrics sophisticated exercises in literary dandyism. It's unsurprising that his first attempts, written mostly during his Harrow years, tend to be conventional. Verbal compliments, imitations and translations from classical authors (such exercises were routine at the great public schools in

Byron's day), monuments to passing moods, playful gestures, the earliest poems were written without a particular sense of poetic vocation: composition of a casual sort was a solitary and social pastime for many educated people, and some uneducated ones, in Byron's day. Once he began writing and sharing his effusions, though, the praise and interest his works attracted led him to do more. Byron did not profess particular pride in his poetic achievements: his well-known assertion to Annabella Milbanke that "I by no means rank poetry or poets high in the scale of intellect— . . . it is the lava of the imagination whose eruption prevents an earth-quake" reflected an attitude he expressed intermittently throughout his life.[5] Nevertheless, Byron was happy enough that his works were admired by others. The first such admiring audience was the circle of Southwell friends for whom his first volume, *Fugitive Pieces,* was printed privately in the fall of 1806.

In a number of ways, the situation surrounding *Fugitive Pieces* is proleptic of Byron's whole career in writing and circulating poetry. Having consigned his manuscript to the printer Ridge, he left Southwell and while away relied on friends, Elizabeth and John Pigot, to midwife the manuscript. The collection is long on what would come to be recognized as characteristically Byronic moods and gestures—elegy, love-longing, melancholy, the backward glance and the inward one. It also displays the equally Byronic antidotes to such romantic states—humor, irony, common sense. One lyric, "To a Lady, Who Presented to the Author a Lock of Hair, Braided with his Own, and Appointed a Night, in December, to Meet Him in the Garden," offers both—a romantic lady-addressee, a realistic author-narrator—and articulates the first of Byron's many cultural contrasts of love in the sunny South and the frozen North. The rational narrator inquires,

> Why should you weep, like Lydia Languish,
> And fret with self-created anguish?
> Or doom the lover you have chosen,
> On winter nights, to sigh half frozen;
> In leafless shades, to sue for pardon,
> Only because the scene's a garden?

Shakespeare's Juliet may have set a precedent for love alfresco, but literary Italy is one thing and real Britain another. "Oh! would some modern muse inspire, / And seat her by a sea-coal fire," wishes this speaker with more sense than sensibility, before urging his lady to "Think on our chilly situation, / And curb this rage for imitation" (*CPW,* 1:140).

Also present in a number of the poems in *Fugitive Pieces*, most notably the amatory verses "To Mary," is frank eroticism of a sort that gave the gentle readers of Byron's private volume pause:

> Now, by my soul, 'tis most delight
> To view each other panting, dying,
> In love's *extatic posture* lying,
> Grateful to *feeling*, as to *sight*.
>   (*CPW,* 1:134)

As would happen on a bigger stage in later days, the canting Southwell public, especially the Reverend J. T. Becher, cried out. This time at least, Byron went along with his friends' advice. He suppressed the volume (only four copies survive), issued a "miraculously chaste" revision titled *Poems on Various Occasions* (1807), and vented his spleen at his censors in a series of satirical verses: "An Answer to Some Elegant Verses," "To a Knot of Ungenerous Critics," "Soliloquy of a Bard in the Country," "Egotism." What was liveliest had been skimmed off the adolescent effusion; what was blandest remained for general circulation when the poet-peer made his bow to the reading public beyond Southwell. Calling his first published collection *Hours of Idleness*, offering prefatory deprecation of the verses as "fruits of the lighter hours of a young man, who has lately completed his nineteenth year," and announcing that poetry is not his "primary vocation" (*CPW* 1:32, 33), Byron displays the complex attitude toward authorship that would characterize him throughout life. He affects to toss off mere trifles, yet by publishing the verses under his name solicits attention from a wider world than his coterie.

Hours of Idleness came out with Ridge's imprint in June 1807. Deriving from that transitional phase between childhood and adulthood, it is best characterized as a collection of schoolboy verse. The chief subjects are people, places, or incidents from Byron's personal past, both immediate and more remote. The prevailing tone is nostalgia, which, though it might strike adult readers as inappropriate for the promise-filled age of 18, seems natural to the late adolescent, who clearly sees what's past but can only guess at what lies ahead. Byron's Scottish childhood is evoked in "Lachin Y Gair," "Song," and "Stanzas." The last, with its lines "Fortune! take back these cultur'd lands, / Take back this name of splendid sound!"

(*CPW,* 1:121), would be a sitting duck for any advocate of romantic sincerity willing to take potshots at the poet elsewhere inclined to cherish Newstead Abbey and the noble Byrons of days past, subjects of the collection's leadoff lyric, "On Leaving Newstead Abbey," as well as "A Fragment" and "Elegy on Newstead Abbey." We glimpse Harrow (its hill sometimes classicized as "Ida"), Cambridge (or "Granta"), and, part paraded and part veiled through the coy devices of initials and dashes, Byron's well-born friends at those places: the Duke of D[orset], the Earls of [Clare] and D[elawarr], E[dward] N[oel] L[ong], Esq. In "To E.—" and "The Cornelian," in which a heart-shaped pledge of friendship "blushes modest as the giver," Edleston, the Cambridge choirboy whose comradeship Byron enjoyed on terms less equal than those prevailing in his schoolboy friendships, is commemorated with more condescension than appears in the later "Thyrza" lyrics written after his death. Remaining from the privately printed collections are the chaster love lyrics to nymphs pursued—pseudonymous "Mary," "Caroline," "Marion," "Ellen," "Emma," and "Lesbia." There are expressions of more substantial regard for more readily identifiable females: Margaret Parker, the "Young Lady, Cousin to the Author, and Very Dear to Him" whose death, Byron claimed, inspired his first (now lost) poem, and Miss E[lizabeth] P[igot], Byron's literary ally and neighbor across the green at Southwell. There are many translations, imitations, and literary echoes: of Catullus, Anacreon, Virgil, Euripides, Tibullus, and Horace among the classical dead; Gray, Macpherson, Chatterton, Pope, and others among the previous century's voices; Moore, Rogers, Scott, Strangford, perhaps even Wordsworth and Coleridge from the living generation.

Much of the collection is very literary, and so it appeared to Hewson Clark of the *Satirist* and to Henry Brougham, writing anonymously in the illustrious *Edinburgh Review,* whose negative opinions among otherwise positive notices wounded the young author. Clark's scurrilous remarks were annoying, but a thrashing in his culture's preeminent quarterly bothered Byron far more—particularly because it was the literary organ of the political party he intended to join on attaining his majority, the Whigs. Brougham's review has been termed cruel, brutal, inappropriately personal—but it's no harsher than Byron's own critical response to Wordsworth was to be years later, in his preface to *Don Juan.* As Byron would later do (perhaps having learned the trick from his *Edinburgh* reviewer), the anonymous Brougham adopts a down-to-earth tone and allows the poet's own prefatory and poetic words to damn him: not an especially difficult task.

Having claimed in his preface to have crossed his poetic Rubicon, Byron declares that now that he's on the public (that is, published) side of the river he will "submit without a murmur" if the critical verdict goes against him (*CPW,* 1:32). Then he proceeds to special pleading. These are the poems of youth—furthermore, a youth of rank wrote them. Byron reminds his readers of Dr. Johnson's pronouncement that highborn writers' effusions should be "handsomely acknowledged" and, having done so, renounces the privilege he's claimed: he'd rather "incur the bitterest censure of anonymous criticism, than triumph in honours granted solely to a title" (1:34). He loftily announces the volume a "first, and last attempt," for "[i]t is highly improbable, from my situation, and pursuits hereafter, that I should ever obtrude myself a second time on the Public." Brougham subjected the poems so introduced to cool scrutiny, juxtaposed some of Byron's imitations with superior originals ("On a Distant Prospect of Harrow" to Gay's "Ode on Eton College," "The Tear" to Rogers's "On a Tear"), undermined the 18-year-old's claim of tender years with "alas, we all remember the poetry of Cowley at ten, and Pope at twelve," and made an ironic, dismissive bow to the peer-poet: "We are well off to have got so much from a man of this Lord's station, who does not live in a garret but 'has the sway' of Newstead Abbey."[6]

Byron was not the only poet to be caught, in his first published volume, in embarrassing self-revelation and to writhe when a reviewer lashed his thin skin: Browning, a generation later, would suffer a similar fate with *Pauline* (1833). Like Browning, Byron learned from humiliation, and his poetical career changed because of it. Most immediately, the work then in progress, his Horatian satire *British Bards,* took a tack toward the Juvenalian and became *English Bards and Scotch Reviewers*— but that is the subject for another chapter. As a lyric poet Byron learned several lessons. He came to distinguish private poems, the occasional verses sent to friends or circulated in a coterie, from candidates for publication. Later, his published lyrics tended to appear strategically, whether anonymous or acknowledged, independent or accompanied, and they often served some conscious, larger purpose. Even when sounding confessional, they tended to be verbal masquerades—"ludic lyrics," to use James Soderholm's phrase—involving manipulation of both speaker and audience.[7]

Byron had already recognized the advantages of indirection in *Hours of Idleness*, where what would seem to have started out as self-revelation, "My Character," turns to a Theocritan "translation" when published under the title "Damaetas":

> In law an infant, and in years a boy,
> In mind a slave to every vicious joy,
> From every sense of shame and virtue wean'd
> In lies an adept, in deceit a fiend;
>
> . . . .
>
> Damaetas ran through all the maze of sin,
> And found the goal, when others just begin:
> Ev'n still conflicting passions shake his soul,
> And bid him drain the dregs of pleasure's bowl;
> But pall'd with vice, he breaks his former chain,
> And, what was once his bliss, appears his bane.
>
> *(CPW,* 1:51–52)

Here is a precocious portrait of dissipated youth to rival Childe Harold and the protagonists of the Eastern tales—even to out-Glenarvon Glenarvon, the half-real hero of Lady Caroline Lamb's Byronic roman à clef. The truths of "Damaetas," formerly "My Character," are told slant.[8] But determining the nature and extent of the slant truths is no simple matter. A reader's awareness of the title change does not turn fictive translation into oblique self-revelation any more than the author's changing the title could make translation out of confession. Whatever the lyric is called, the incremental effect of its insistently absolute rhetoric is self-subversion. Damaetas, or Byron, can't be as bad as the words paint him, just as Donna Inez in *Don Juan* can't possess all the learning and virtue the narrator heaps upon her. The consequence of *Don Juan*'s overblown praise is that readers think Inez stupid and vicious: do the verbal excesses of "Damaetas" work in a similar way but an opposite direction, to raise readers' opinions of the indicted protagonist, whoever he may be? If so, what does one call the strategy of defending a reputation by attacking it in words patently worse than warranted? When hypocrisy dramatizes rather than conceals itself, can it still be hypocrisy?

After *Hours of Idleness,* Byron deployed the lyric—indeed, his poetry in general—in a much more deliberate way. He continued to use lyrics for personal communication, whether facetious ("Farewell Petition to J[ohn] C[am] H[obhouse] Esq.," 1810) or poignantly serious ([Epistle to Augusta], 1816), topical commemoration ("Inscription on the Monument of a Newfoundland Dog," 1808, or the less flattering "Lines on

Hearing that Lady Byron was Ill," 1816), verbal game-playing ([Bouts-rimés from Seaham], 1815; the "versicles" on his reading of 1817), or self-administered catharsis ("Thyrza," 1811; "Remember Thee, Remember Thee!," 1813). Most such poems were not intended for the general public and were published without his authorization or after his death, the first important gathering of his unpublished short poems being in Thomas Moore's *Letters and Journals of Lord Byron: With Notices of His Life* (1830).

When he did again publish a collection of lyrics, the circumstances minimized the risks of being charged with egoizing. In June 1814 the composer Isaac Nathan had proposed that Byron write lyrics to be set to Hebrew music. Byron took up this project some months later, in October, when his friend Douglas Kinnaird intervened on its behalf. A further reason for taking on the *Hebrew Melodies* may have been to please Annabella Milbanke, to whom he had just become engaged. Desire to ingratiate himself with Annabella is certainly evident in Byron's description of the project in the postscript of a letter to his pious fiancée dated 20 October 1814: Nathan, Byron relates, "is going to publish the *real old undisputed Hebrew melodies* which are beautiful & to which David & the prophets actually sang 'the songs of Zion'—& I have done nine or ten—on the sacred model—partly from Job &c. & partly my own imagination. . . . it is odd enough that this should fall to my lot—who have been abused as 'an infidel' " (*BLJ,* 4:220). Such a project provided a shared concern in the ill-suited lovers' awkward engagement and painful marriage—most of the fair copies of *Hebrew Melodies* are in Annabella's hand. But sacred songs pure and simple are in short supply in the collection, which starts with the completely secular "She Walks in Beauty," Byron's lyric response to glimpsing his cousin Anne Wilmot at a Lansdowne House entertainment:

> She walks in beauty, like the night
> Of cloudless climes and starry skies;
> And all that's best of dark and bright
> Meet in her aspect and her eyes:
> Thus mellow'd to that tender light
> Which heaven to gaudy day denies.
> (*CPW,* 3:288)

Some of the poems, among them "Jeptha's Daughter" and the cluster of poems on King Saul, offer distinctively Byronic projections into the minds of biblical characters. Others, such as "Oh! Snatched Away in Beauty's Bloom," "Thy Days Are Done," and "Sun of the Sleepless!," are secular meditations. Still others are political poems—biblical in their details but relevant by inference to Napoleonic Europe ("Vision of Belshazzar," "The Destruction of Semnacherib") or Regency England ("Herod's Lament for Mariamne"). Throughout, Byron appropriates passages of Scripture as texts for his own speculations, interjects echoes of Old Testament verses, and explores contemporary preoccupations in terms of ancient analogues. In a literally etymological sense, the lyrics in *Hebrew Melodies* are "translations." As Thomas L. Ashton rightly observes, "Generally biblical tales and Jewish history are made to serve as the basis of *dramatic* lyrics."[9] These lyrics carry ancient Hebrew themes, characters, and phrases across the abyss of time to readers in 1815, and they provide a means through which Byron can connect his subjectivity and the particulars of his day with a larger cultural heritage.

The partnership with Nathan offered a good reason to produce a volume of lyric verses, but throughout his career Byron was far likelier to fit lyrics in with his longer poems. He appended lyric dedications and epigraphs to long poems—for instance, "To Ianthe," addressed to Lady Charlotte Harley, precedes *Childe Harold* 1 and 2. Such positioning enriches both the short poem and the long one. The dedicatory lyric to the pure "Young Peri of the West" contrasts neatly with the narrative poem's opening stanzas on Childe Harold's precocious libertinism. The poet connects with the young beauty he christens "I-and-thee" through language, not love, in what Jerome Christensen calls an intimacy "not promiscuous but tactical . . . not bookish but textual."[10] Together the lyric dedication and the narrative's opening stanzas set what is to be the poem's prevailing pattern: romantic illusion succeeded by realistic disillusion. This literary contextualizing also downplays the ironies of the lyric's real-life context: Lady Charlotte, the daughter of Byron's current mistress, Lady Oxford, was one of the beautiful, diversely fathered brood called the "Harleian Miscellany" in allusion to the Oxford family's collection of manuscripts and their mother's collection of radical Whig lovers.

Byron also inscribed lyrics within long poems: "Childe Harold's Good Night!," "To Inez," a Suliote war-song, and an effusion, "The castled crag of Drachenfels," enrich the travelogue, and vary the Spenserian stanzas, of *Childe Harold's Pilgrimage*. In *Don Juan,* the two inscribed lyrics are yet more important to the long work containing them. "The Isles of Greece!," one of Byron's best-known short poems, is a drinking song contrasting the glorious Hellenic past with a debased Romaic present:

> The isles of Greece, the isles of Greece!
> Where burning Sappho loved and sung,
> Where grew the arts of war and peace,—
> Where Delos rose, and Phoebus sprung!
> Eternal summer gilds them yet,
> But all, except their sun, is set.
>   (*CPW,* 5:188)

The ballad of the Black Friar, a gothic ghost story, also has to do with profanation, the transformation of a Dominican monastery to an aristocratic family seat in the reign of Henry VIII:

> Beware! beware! of the Black Friar,
>   Who sitteth by Norman stone,
> For he mutters his prayer in the midnight air,
>   And his mass of the days that are gone.
> When the Lord of the Hill, Amundeville,
>   Made Norman Church his prey,
> And expelled the friars, one friar still
>   Would not be driven away.
>   (*CPW,* 5:630–31)

Freestanding, these lyrics would be engaging, but contextualized within the long poem, they gain great richness. Inscribed within the longer work, each has the advantage of a highly specified dramatic situation: the first is sung at Don Juan and Haidée's banquet on the pirate Lambro's Cycladic island, the second at an electioneering dinner whose host and hostess are Lord Henry and Lady Adeline Amundeville of Norman Abbey. The singer-composers of these lyrics are also presented in considerable detail. The nameless, opportunistic poet of "The Isles of Greece!" is a "sad trimmer," a man "who had seen many changes, / and always changed, as true as any needle," a traveling versifier whose muse "made increment of any thing / From the high lyric down to the low rational." The brilliant and beautiful Lady Adeline, who nonchalantly sings the ballad of the Black Friar to display her talents as poet and musician, is, like the Greek poet, an artistic cosmopolitan and a mobile improviser. "Watching, witching, condescending" in her "grand role" as society hostess, Lady Adeline performs to entertain the many—and to seduce the one, by suggesting her sympathy for Juan and her disaffection for her husband. Both Lady Adeline and the unnamed Greek are lyricists in the strict sense: solo poet-singers accompanying themselves on the harp. They are also creatures of mobility, liars with lyres. This status connects them with the only other poet granted a lyre in *Don Juan*, the ever-variable narrator, himself the improviser of the very long ottava rima song whose great topic is modern corruption. The association of the Greek lyricist and Lady Adeline with the *Don Juan* narrator brings the reader back to Byron, the slippery ventriloquist who speaks through, and masks himself behind, all three.[11]

Besides tying lyrics into his long poems, Byron composed and published lyric pieces together with longer works, such as tales. After he turned his back on England, his long-distance involvement with the details of publishing was intermittent and inconsistently motivated. Sometimes in his epistolary transmission of manuscripts to Murray, Byron would throw in shorter works as a sort of ballast to the bargain (or the book binding). At other times he would be peremptory in his publishing instructions for a particular lyric. With short poems as well as the long ones, he was capable of changing his mind. It would be false to an antisystematic poet to find consistent, overarching purpose in his gatherings, but those groupings, purposeful or casual, do create intertextual conversations worth following.

A case in point might be the lyrics published in *The Prisoner of Chillon and Other Poems*.[12] The narrative title poem of this 1816 collection, Byron's first verse tale to feature a historical person as its subject, derived from Byron and Shelley's visit to the Castle of Chillon, with its subaqueous dungeon where the Genevese partisan François Bonivard was imprisoned. The lyrics published with *The Prisoner of Chillon* are, like the title poem, products of Byron's Swiss summer, an unusually dark, cold season spent surrounded by the Alps and the Shelley circle at the lakefront Villa Diodati. Two of the lyrics, "Sonnet on Chillon" and "Prometheus," treat abstractly or mythically the subject—a freedom fighter imprisoned—presented palpably and psychologically in *Prisoner of Chillon*. But the lyrics contradict the narrative rather than confirming it. Titanic Prometheus, unyielding in his resistance to despotic authority, is "a symbol and a sign / To Mortals of their fate and force."

If humanity's fate is "wretchedness," its force, in this lyric, is an opposing will "equal to all woes." As symbol and sign of this spirit "Triumphant where it dares defy, / And making Death a Victory" (*CPW,* 4:32), Prometheus stands in sharp contrast with Byron's compassionately drawn Bonnivard. Brave but believably human, Bonnivard (who derives more from Byron's imagination than from the historical Bonivard's circumstances), is mentally subject to his physical circumstances and unavoidably shaped by them over time, as his story reveals, even in its closing words:

> My very chains and I grew friends,
> So much a long communion tends
> To make us what we are:—even I
> Regain'd my freedom with a sigh.
>   (*CPW,* 4:16)

These mortal truths are far from being a Promethean triumph. They are also far from the pronouncements of the "Sonnet on Chillon," which invokes the "Eternal Spirit of the chainless Mind / Brightest in dungeons, Liberty!" (*CPW,* 4:3). Prefacing *The Prisoner of Chillon* with the sonnet and its appended biographical note on Bonivard, Byron aimed to correct historical inaccuracy. When he composed the narrative poem, subtitled "A Fable," he had not been "sufficiently aware of the history of Bonnivard, or I should have endeavoured to dignify the subject by an attempt to celebrate his courage and his virtues" (4:453). Paradoxically, the imagined narrative rings truer to the ear of human experience than does the informed sonnet. It is interesting and characteristic that Byron, having learned about Bonivard's life, chose not to revise his original narrative in light of historical information but instead to respect its integrity as fable and to voice his new thoughts in a contratext.

Very different from all these poems are the 1816 personal retrospections composed around the time of *The Prisoner of Chillon.* "The Dream" transparently fictionalizes Byron's life up to the present, and in so doing implicitly provides a sort of rationale for Byron's travels and Childe Harold's pilgrimage. The dream moves through seven changes: youthful love like Byron's for Mary Chaworth at Annesley Hall, the lady's recognition of that tormented passion, the "wretched" youth's wanderings in "fiery climes," the lady's marriage to "One / Who did not love her better," his equally unfortunate wedding to another, the beloved lady's descent into madness, and his renewed wanderings as a solitary outcast, "compass'd round / With Hatred and Contention" (*CPW,* 4:22–29). With still less attempt at self-concealment, "Stanzas to [Augusta]" speaks from a vantage point Byron's public might well have imagined him to occupy in 1816: "the day of my destiny's over. . . . the star of my fate hath declined"—and addresses someone very like Augusta, if not explicitly identified with her:

> Though human, thou didst not deceive me,
>
> Though woman, thou didst not forsake,
>
> Though loved, thou forborest to grieve me,
>
> Though slander'd, thou never could'st shake.—
>
> (*CPW,* 4:33–34)

"[Epistle to Augusta]" begins and continues on a yet more identifiably personal note:

> My Sister—my sweet Sister—if a name
>
> Dearer and purer were—it should be thine.
>
> Mountains and Seas divide us—but I claim
>
> No tears—but tenderness to answer mine.
>
> (*CPW,* 4:35)

That Byron sent these personal lyrics to Murray for possible publication, pending Augusta's approval (she allowed the former to appear in print but not the latter), shows how uncharacteristically confessional his lyric muse was in the months immediately following his legal separation from Annabella and his self-imposed exile from England.

The 1816 muse's penchant for nihilism appears in "Darkness," a lyric that magnificently opposes the Prometheus myth of a male benefactor bringing the gift of fire that allows human progress and civilization. Byron's vision may have sprung from any or all of an exceptionally wide range of sources. Among the likely candidates: Old and New Testament biblical passages that make "Darkness" a kind of postscript to the *Hebrew Melodies;* contemporary scientific theories advanced by Buffon, Cuvier, Fontenelle, or Fourier; romantic literature's interest in the "last man" motif; "Monk" Lewis's visit, which turned the Diodati circle's attention toward the gothic; the unprecedentedly gloomy weather of

July and August in what would come to be known worldwide as "The Year without a Summer."[13]

"I had a dream, which was not all a dream," this apocalyptic lyric begins, its relative clause seeming especially appropriate given the poem's multiple inspirations.

> The bright sun was extinguish'd, and the stars
> Did wander darkling in the eternal space,
> Rayless, and pathless, and the icy earth
> Swung blind and blackening in the moonless air.

In response to this phenomenon, which late-twentieth-century readers can readily imagine as nuclear winter, all desires and aspirations condense to one, "a selfish prayer for light." Desperate humanity makes a truly democratic burnt offering: thrones, palaces, huts, cities, forests, vanities and necessities, culture and nature, all go up in bonfires. Terrified wild beasts and vipers, "tame and tremulous" in a terrible parody of the Peaceable Kingdom, are slain for food. Humans turn on one another. Even dogs assail their masters. Negation at all levels, from the semantic to the cosmic, overwhelms the poem, until

> The world was void,
> The populous and the powerful—was a lump,
> Seasonless, herbless, treeless, manless, lifeless—
> A lump of death, a chaos of hard clay.

Entropy prevails, or almost does. What endures to the end is the poetic meter (blank verse, appropriately), which has slowed and faltered on occasion but never broken down, and the hope or curse of rebirth implied by female gender: "Darkness had no need / Of aid from them— she was the universe" (*CPW,* 4:40–43).

Whether, where, and how to publish a lyric and the aftereffects of such a decision sometimes proved very complicated, as the contrasting cases of "To the Po" and "Lines to a Lady Weeping" suggest—the former is a poem Byron backed out of publishing, the latter one he edged into acknowledging. "Lines to a Lady Weeping" was written after Byron heard news of a Carlton House banquet on 22 February 1812, at which the Prince Regent abused his former allies the Whigs and thereby distressed his daughter Princess Charlotte, who remained true to principles and friendships her father had found it convenient to abandon.

> Weep, daughter of a royal line,
> A Sire's disgrace, a realm's decay;
> Ah, happy! if each tear of thine
> Could wash a father's fault away!
>
> Weep—for thy tears are Virtue's tears—
> Auspicious to these suffering isles;
> And be each drop in future years
> Repaid thee by thy people's smiles!
> (*CPW,* 3:10)

The lyric, which brilliantly lays a personal and emotive text over a highly specified political subtext, first appeared anonymously in the Whig *Morning Chronicle* of 7 March. Its provenance became known two years later when Byron had it published with *The Corsair*—a highly appropriate literary gesture, given that the Eastern tale features female loyalty (Medora's) and resistance to tyranny (Gulnare's), and implicitly links Turkey's repression of Greece with Britain's of Ireland.[14] The result of the republication was a controversy that, like the lyric and its mode of circulation, offers insights on the relation of private and public spheres, the permeable realms of feeling and action, the disgrace of betraying once-cherished principles. When his authorship of "Lines to a Lady Weeping" became known, Byron was ferociously attacked in the Tory *Courier,* which condemned the verses as "insolent doggerel" and charged their author with disloyalty. Two direct effects of the *Courier's* explicating the lyric's implied insolence, as Byron clearly recognized, were heightened public awareness of his Whig sentiments and increased sales of *The Corsair:* "The occasional propensity of mankind to be curious when their attention is awakened has led to a more extensive circulation of the obnoxious verses than they might otherwise have obtained" (*BLJ,* 4:42). The case of "Lines to a Lady Weeping" also shows how a single lyric and its attendant circumstances of composition, publication, and reception might affect Byron's subsequent writing. An indirect and belated literary consequence of the events linking *Corsair* with *Courier* in Byron's retentive mind may have been the couplet concluding one of *Don Juan*'s raciest passages, the fifth canto's brilliantly witty conflation of the "calumniated Queen Semiramis" of Assyria with Princess Charlotte's mother, the uncrowned Queen Caroline, around whom the Whigs were rallying in 1820:

> That injured Queen, by Chroniclers so coarse,
>   Has been accused (I doubt not by conspiracy)
> Of an improper friendship for her horse,
>   (Love like religion sometimes runs to heresy);
> This monstrous tale had probably its source
>   (For such exaggerations here and there I see)
> In printing "Courser" by mistake for "Courier":
> I wish the case would come before a jury here.
>   (*CPW,* 5:260)

At the beginning of June 1819, Byron explored a far commoner form of heretical love in "To the Po," one of his most sincerely self-revealing poems. A lyric that has come into its own in the later twentieth century, "To the Po" had been published in a highly corrupt form until its appearance in the Oxford *Complete Poetical Works*. As McGann points out, the poem's previous publications all derived from its first printing, in Thomas Medwin's *Journal of the Conversations of Lord Byron* (1824). Based on a series of inferior transcripts, the Medwin printing also introduced a number of unauthorized changes into Byron's poem (*CPW,* 4:496–97). That the text of "To the Po" should have been in such poor shape for a century and a half is due, at least in part, to Byron's eventual decision not to publish it in his own day.

His tentative plan, announced to Murray in letters of 15 March and 4 May 1822 (*BLJ,* 9:125, 155), had been to publish the lyric together with the plays *Heaven and Earth* and *Werner* and a translation of the Francesca da Rimini episode from Dante. But on 6 June 1822 Byron wrote to Murray, "With regard to the lines to the 'Po'—perhaps you had better put them quietly in a second edition (if you reach one—that is to say) than in the first—because though they have been reckoned fine—and I wish them to be preserved—I do not wish them to attract IMMEDIATE observation—on account of the relationship of the Lady to whom they are addrest with the first families in Romagna and the Marches——"

(9:167). He reiterated this preference for nonpublication on 26 June and 8 July, also excluding from the volume the Francesca da Rimini translation: the Dante interlude portrays an adulterous situation too closely resembling Italian life as Byron then was living it (9:178, 182).

"To the Po" is a rarity among Byron's lyrics: lava of the emotions spewed forth "in *red-hot Earnest*" rather than vented in an ironizing or attitudinizing way (*BLJ*, 7:115). Written when travel with her husband took Teresa Guiccioli away from Byron only a few weeks after their liaison had begun at Venice, "To the Po" is based in the facts of the lovers' separation as Byron understood them at the time. While he passes near the source of the Po en route to Bologna, Byron imagines Teresa at Count Guiccioli's house, Ca' Zen, near the Po's entry to the Adriatic Sea. In this poem, far more than in the famously Wordsworthian and Shelleyan alpine passages of *Childe Harold* 3, Byron truly discerns and presents "congeniality" between himself and a force of nature. His lines flow like the river; its current surges like his passions:

> River! that rollest by the antient walls
>   Where dwells the Lady of my Love, when she
> Walks by thy brink and there perchance recalls
>   A faint and fleeting memory of me,
> What if thy deep and ample stream should be
>   A mirror of my heart, where she may read
> The thousand thoughts I now betray to thee
>   Wild as thy wave and headlong as thy speed?
>   (*CPW,* 4:210)

Byron's lyric, as Soderholm has observed, is the sort we call a "reflection"; its romantic relationship may be seen as a reworking of the Narcissus myth, with a "far-flung" Echo (750). But the Po, unlike Narcissus's pool, is no mere reflector. Its "sweeping, dark, and strong" waters dynamically substantiate their observer's emotional turbulence: "Borne on our old career unchanged we move, / Thou tendest wildly to the wilder main / And I to loving one I should not love" (*CPW,* 4:210–11).

Byron's attention now turns to his lady, whom he imagines looking on the Po in summer twilight, her eyes reflected in the very wave that carries the salt-water expression of his love seaward.

The wave that bears my tear returns no more
    Will She return by whom that wave shall sweep?
Both tread thy bank, both wander by thy shore,
    I near thy source, and She by the blue deep.
But that which keepeth us apart, is not
    Distance, nor depth of wave, nor space of earth,
But the distractions of a various lot,
    Ah! various as the climates of our birth!
                                                    (*CPW,* 4:211–12)

Alas, love in a warm climate is not love beyond the perplexing constraints of social mores and manners—and like the ironically detached
Beppo and *Don Juan,* "To the Po" meditates on cultural contrast as well as
love. Byron wrote regularly (in Italian prose, not English verse) to Teresa
around the time when he composed "To the Po." The letters show that
though much of his emotional disturbance during the separation came
from Teresa's physical absence and from his anxiety over her illness,
some derived from his uncertainty about the Guicciolis' movements and
whereabouts and some resulted from the mixed tedium and confusion of
being a stranger loitering around Italy while waiting to resume an affair
whose etiquette he understood imperfectly. Byron's cultural uncertainty
is evident in a letter written nine days after he drafted "To the Po": "You
are so surrounded: I am a foreigner in Italy—and still more a foreigner
in Ravenna—and naturally little versed in the customs of the country—
I am afraid of compromising you" (*BLJ,* 6:154). The P.S. to another letter implores, "Forgive me if my answer has been *too English* in the first
lines of this note—but I have not come to Italy to speak of myself and
my own doings—but rather to forget my life of *beyond the mountains*—
and above all, to love you—*you,* my only and last delight" (6:159).

Despite having been born in that chill north beyond the Alps, Byron
admits in "To the Po" that his "heart is all meridian"; here in Italy, he
finds himself the "Slave again" of love. To acknowledge this condition is
not the same as to desire it. The foe of tyranny in all forms, Byron never
accepted the sway of love, though he never escaped from it. Wryly recognized as the *Don Juan* narrator's "constant guest," love figures in the
last lines of "To the Po" as a cruel visitor not unlike the eagle of Jove,
come to torture a Prometheus bound by his passions:

'Tis vain to struggle, I have struggled long
To love again no more as once I loved.
Oh! Time! why leave this earliest Passion strong?
To tear a heart which pants to be unmoved?
(*CPW*, 4:212)

Affirming an emotional commitment while clearly recognizing practical, principled, and also heartfelt reservations about that commitment, "To the Po" takes no refuge in subterfuge or pseudotranslation. It sincerely reveals its author's deep love and deep ambivalence. Instructing Murray not to publish, Byron chose to be discreet in both his love and his ambivalence.

As I hope some of the excerpted passages have shown, reading Byron's lyrics against one another is profitable. An obvious and useful strategy is to examine lyrics connected by time of composition or publication, or by a common subject: for instance, the lyrics centering on romantic love, or those devoted to male friendship, or those to be discussed here, the lyrics addressing Napoléon, both the most important and fascinating political personage of the day and, for Byron, something of a self-construed alter ego in verse and in life. Byron's considered thoughts on Napoléon and his career appear in passages from the long poems published after the Battle of Waterloo and the Congress of Vienna: the third and fourth cantos of *Childe Harold's Pilgrimage, Don Juan,* and *The Age of Bronze.* In contrast, the Napoleonic lyrics display intermittent, emotional responses to the conqueror, as his fortunes were very much in flux. Like Hobhouse and many of his other friends in Whig society, Byron cherished considerable but not unmixed admiration for Napoléon, who had toppled corrupt monarchies on the continent only to crown himself, his family, and his friends. For such liberals as Byron, Napoléon's abdication was really a second fall: making himself emperor had been the first.

Thus Byron and those like him saw the events of 1814 and 1815 as an unedifying spectacle of new despot giving way to old despots. But Byron's lyrics on the man he persistently dubbed his "little pagod" were neither merely contemporary nor merely political. Like many other classically nurtured persons of his day, Byron persistently read the present in light of the past—the French dictator against Greek tyrants, France's empire against Rome's. Byron also read the public in light of the personal. In *Don Juan* he styled himself "grand Napoleon of the realms of rhyme," and he delighted in writing the initials "N.B." after the terms of his mother-in-law's will had him affix the Noel arms to his own. Although self-conscious mockery was part of both gestures, Byron's ambitions were, like Napoléon's, grandiose. It is particularly relevant to a study of the Napoleonic lyrics that the dates 1814 to 1816 span crucial and parallel periods in the lives of Napoléon (from surrender and exile to Elba to escape, the Hundred Days, defeat at Waterloo, and banishment to St. Helena) and of Byron (his years of fame and marriage, followed by separation and self-exile from England).

The first and longest of Byron's Napoleonic lyrics is "Ode to Napoleon Buonaparte," written a few days after Byron heard the news of abdication. His 1814 journal records specific impressions and mentions historical and mythic analogues that would make their way into the poem. The 8 April entry reads, "Out of town six days. On my return, found my poor little pagod, Napoleon, pushed off his pedestal;—the thieves are in Paris. It is his own fault. Like Milo, he would rend the oak; but it closed again, wedged his hands, and now the beasts—lion, bear, down to the dirtiest jackall—may all tear him" (*BLJ*, 3:256). The entry for 9 April amplifies: "I mark this day! Napoleon Buonaparte has abdicated the throne of the world." Byron goes on to list abdicators who did a better job of ceding power—Sulla, Dioclesian, Amurath, even Charles the Fifth of Spain. Despite finding it hard to believe that Napoléon could submit to banishment on Elba, Byron reflects, "But, after all, a crown may not be worthy dying for. Yet to outlive *Lodi* for this!!!" He continues to lament, "Alas, this imperial diamond hath a flaw in it, and is now hardly fit to stick in a glazier's pencil:—the pen of the historian won't rate it worth a ducat." The entry concludes less negatively, on a barding note: "But I won't give him up even now; though all his admirers have, 'like the Thanes, fallen from him' " (*BLJ*, 3:256–57).

Characteristically associated with lofty subjects and extensive enough to encompass a range of shifting moods, the ode is probably the lyric form best suited for feelings and opinions as complex as Byron's about the abdicating Napoléon. The theme first struck is fallen greatness:

> 'Tis done—but yesterday a King!
> And arm'd with Kings to strive—

> And now thou art a nameless thing
>> So abject—yet alive!
> Is this the man of thousand thrones,
> Who strew'd our earth with hostile bones,
>> And can he thus survive?
> Since he, miscall'd the Morning Star,
> Nor man nor fiend hath fall'n so far.
>> *(CPW,* 3:259)

Subsequent stanzas sarcastically thank the deposed emperor for his exemplary lesson in the folly of hero worship and deplore, as the journals do, Napoléon's willingness to survive his reign:

> Is it some yet imperial hope
> That with such change can calmly cope?
>> Or dread of death alone?
> To die a prince—or live a slave—
> Thy choice is most ignobly brave!
>> *(CPW,* 3:261)

Then follow comparisons with legendary and actual heroes and rulers whose careers offered similar yet significantly different cases: Milo trapped by the rent oak, the dictator Sulla, who abandoned power while he still held it, Charles the Fifth, who "cast crowns for rosaries away." Napoléon, from whose "reluctant hand / The thunderbolt is wrung," is contemptible in contrast, but his fall may be fortunate for the world:

> If thou hadst died as honour dies,
> Some new Napoleon might arise
>> To shame the world again—
> But who would soar the solar height,
> To set in such a starless night?
>> *(CPW,* 3:263)

Byron eventually wrote several additional stanzas that, against his intentions, posthumously became part of the ode;[15] but as he first envisioned and published it, the conclusion dismisses Napoléon to his isle of exile and contrasts him unfavorably with the liberator Prometheus, foe to the king of Olympus as Napoléon had been to the crowned heads of Europe: "He in his fall preserv'd his pride, / And, if a mortal, had as proudly died!" (*CPW,* 3:265).

The rhetorical intensity of the ode suggests the world-changing, and Byron-changing, nature of Napoléon's ignoble abdication; but a man of the world does not live by politics alone. Byron's journal entry for 10 April 1814 sets the ode in context: "To-day I have boxed one hour— written an ode to Napoleon Buonaparte—copied it—eaten six bis- cuits—drunk four bottles of soda water—redde away the rest of my time—besides giving poor * * a world of advice about this mistress of his" (*BLJ,* 4:257). Thus poetry and politics take the places allotted them in Byron's modus vivendi. And yet Byron was more serious about the ode than his rather dismissive prose attitude would suggest. His episto- lary instructions to Murray, who published the poem independently in pamphlet form, show considerable concern for the specifics of the poem and his own degree of association with it. Having written extra stanzas, he decides to keep them out of the published text. "Let it be *without* a name—though I have no objection to it's being *said* to be mine," he writes on the day of composition (*BLJ,* 4:94). A day later he tells Murray, "[Y]ou may *say* openly as you like that it is mine—& I can inscribe it to Mr. Hobhouse from ye. *Author* which will mark it suffi- ciently" (*BLJ,* 4:94). By the 10th edition of the ode (1814), Byron was ready to have his name added (*CPW,* 3:456).

Although he had affixed his name to the disdain and disillusion expressed in the ode, Byron changed his mind about his erstwhile hero after hearing of Napoléon's escape from Elba. Writing to Thomas Moore on 27 March 1815, a week after Napoléon's reentry into Paris, Byron observes, "It is impossible not to be dazzled and overwhelmed by his character and career. Nothing ever so disappointed me as his abdication, and nothing could have reconciled me to him but some such revival as his recent exploit; though no one could anticipate such a complete and brilliant renovation" (*BLJ,* 4:284–85). As he had during the eventful spring of 1814, Byron received detailed firsthand bulletins of events in Paris from his fellow liberal constitutionalist Hobhouse, who had made his way there and sent full accounts of Napoléon's triumphant return, along with acute analysis of French politics and national psychology. Hobhouse remained on the scene until the summer of 1815, thus wit- nessing and recording for Byron the consequences of Waterloo, which he called "the most wicked cause for which brave men have ever died"—an opinion Byron shared.[16]

Byron voiced his own sympathies supplemented with firsthand information from Hobhouse in a series of lyrics presenting Napoléon's defeat from various viewpoints, all purportedly Gallic: "Napoléon's Farewell (From the French)," "From the French," "On the Star of the 'Legion of Honour' (From the French)," and "Ode (From the French)." "From the French" and "On the Star of the 'Legion of Honour' " both speak from the perspective of Napoléon's comrades in arms. The first, beginning "Must thou go, my glorious Chief, / Severed from thy faithful few?" (*CPW,* 3:314) offers a simple soldier's profession of undying loyalty to his chief, king, and friend. The second, inspired by Lady Caroline Lamb's sending from Paris a Legion of Honour cross by way of a souvenir, has a more sophisticated political vantage point. This tribute is not to Napoléon the emperor but to Napoléon the liberator, whose starlike ascent carried with it the tricolor of a free France:

> Before thee rose, and with thee grew,
> A rainbow of the loveliest hue
> Of three bright colours, each divine,
> And fit for that celestial sign;
> For Freedom's hand had blended them,
> Like tints in an immortal gem.
> (*CPW,* 3:317)

The ostensibly French premise of this lyric is one shared by Byron, Hobhouse, and a number of other Whigs—that, if not threatened by the Holy Alliance, France under a returned Napoléon could have become a constitutional monarchy like the one ushered in by Britain's bloodless revolution of 1688 and the accession of William and Mary.

Byron's headnote to the "Ode (From the French)" as it appeared in the Whig *Morning Chronicle* disingenuously associates the poem with one of Byron's literary counterparts across the channel: "The French have their *Poems* and *Odes* on the famous Battle of Waterloo as well as ourselves.— . . . We have received the following poetical version of a poem, the original of which is circulating in Paris—and which is ascribed (we know not with what justice) to the muse of M. de Chateaubriand" (*CPW,* 3:492). More intensely topical than the two lyrics mentioned above, the ode offers a cosmopolitan view of Napoléon. Though ascribed to

Chateaubriand, the feelings are equally those of the friends of freedom outside France: "The Chief has fallen, but not by you, / Vanquishers of Waterloo!" Here, Napoléon's succumbing to the age-old urge for absolute power is what's lamentable:

> Who could boast o'er France defeated,
> Till lone tyranny commanded?
> Till, goaded by ambition's sting,
> The Hero sunk into the King?
> Then he fell;—So perish all
> Who would men by man enthral!
>   (*CPW,* 3:376)

In "Napoleon's Farewell" the imagined speaker is of course the deposed emperor himself. But the sentiments involve, as Byron's feelings for Napoléon often do, a good deal of self-projection. Indeed, the first few lines of the lyric are uncannily appropriate for the melodramatic role of exile Byron would find himself playing the following spring:

> Farewell to the Land, where the gloom of my Glory
> Arose and o'ershadowed the earth with her name—
> She abandons me now—but the page of her story,
> The brightest or blackest, is filled with my fame.
> I have warred with a world which vanquished me only
> When the meteor of Conquest allured me too far . . .
>   (*CPW,* 3:312)

In an ingenious discussion of "the uncanny power of Romantic art to fulfill its wishes," Jerome Christensen points out the interplay between Byronic literature and Napoleonic history: "Waterloo extends in a neatly analogical manner the series *Corsair*— abdication— *Lara*. Waterloo revises the first abdication on the model of *Lara*'s revision of *The Corsair*. Napoleon's life imitates Byron's art" (131). Similarly, in the months after Waterloo Byron's life and art would imitate, parallel, and invert Napoléon's career in life and as rendered in the Napoleonic lyrics, which Annabella ironically enough had copied for him.

Allured too far by conquest of various kinds in his years of fame (1812–1816), Byron alienated some readers with his Napoleonic sentiments, still others after the breakup of his marriage in January 1816. Lady Byron whispered dark words about the separation's causes. Its eventual great effect was to make Byron, a Napoléon in reverse, leave his island for the Continent. Before doing so, he wrote and had printed his notorious "Fare Thee Well!" to Annabella, a domestic variation on the *Et tu, Brute* theme:

> Fare thee well! and if for ever—
> Still for ever, fare *thee well*—
> Even though unforgiving, never
> 'Gainst thee shall my heart rebel.
> . . . .
> Though my many faults defaced me,
> Could no other arm be found
> Than the one which once embraced me,
> To inflict a cureless wound!
> (*CPW,* 3:380–81)

Around the time that the agreement of separation became final, a copy of the lyric went to Lady Byron, with (if Byron's recollection and Hobhouse's record are reliable) this dramatic introduction: "Dearest Bell—I send you the first verses that ever I attempted to write on you, and perhaps the last that I may ever write at all. This at such a moment may look like affectation, but it is not so. The language of all nations nearest to a state of nature is said be Poetry" (*BLJ,* 5:51–52).

The next step in the circulation of "Fare Thee Well!" was its unauthorized publication in the *Champion* through the agency of Byron's anonymous reviewer from *Hours of Idleness* days, the lawyer Henry Brougham, who was ostensibly serving as legal mediator between the Byrons at the time. This publication proved to be the first step in an anti-Byron campaign, engineered by Brougham and the *Champion*'s editor, John Scott, that linked attack on his politics, especially as expressed in "Ode (From the French)" with critical denunciation of "Fare Thee Well!" and its companion domestic piece, "A Sketch from Private Life," bitter satire against Annabella's personal maid, Mary Anne Clermont. The *Champion* pieces, linking poetry, politics, and private life, had much to do with the downfall of Byron's reputation in England. Waterloo had found its way into his lyrics, and his lyrics played their part in his Waterloo.

From 1816 on, with England behind him, Byron had compelling reason for using lyric poetry in one of the ways he had employed it earlier: as a means of enriching letters and conveying, when prose proved less congenial, moods or thoughts to absent people important to him. Not surprisingly, Augusta Leigh and John Cam Hobhouse were among the recipients of these long-distance lyrics. So were Byron's friend and financial adviser Douglas Kinnaird, his publisher John Murray, and his fellow poet Thomas Moore. Just as these correspondents received different kinds of letters from the adaptable pen of Byron, so they tended to be addressed in different strains of lyric. To Augusta he sent heartfelt effusions, poems sometimes too personal for publishing, as earlier discussion of the 1816 lyrics associated with *The Prisoner of Chillon* has shown. Man-of-the-world wit was more the rule in what Byron dispatched to Hobhouse, Kinnaird, and especially Murray, who could be counted on to show the latest squib or parody to the literary comers and goers at his publishing house on Albemarle Street. Indeed, one of the worst breaches in Byron and Hobhouse's lifelong friendship occurred in 1820 after Hobhouse, consigned to Newgate Prison for some inflammatory passages he had written in a political tract, saw for the first time, and in no less public a place than the pages of the *Morning Post*, a lampoon ballad Byron had sent Murray on the unfortunate incarceration. The teasing "New Song" to the tune of "Whare hae ye been a' day, / My boy Tammy O?" begins this way:

> How came you in Hob's pound to cool
>   My boy Hobbie O?
> Because I bade the people pull
>   The house into the Lobby O.
>   (*CPW,* 4:287)

But of all Byron's correspondents, Moore received the most letter-enriching lyrics, some of them poems sent to other correspondents as well, some of which he was the unique recipient. This situation calls for some explaining. Moore, an Irishman eight years senior to Byron, was not his longest-standing attachment, not his closest confidant, not the likeliest expediter of his literary, financial, or personal errands. He was, however, the friend who most closely matched Byron in lyric sensibility—in fact, his poems had served as models for some of Byron's juvenile imitations. Nonetheless, as Thérèse Tessier has acutely observed, Byron recognized that Moore was no literary rival but a man of letters who had "a peculiarity of talent, or rather talents—poetry, music, voice—all his own" (*BLJ*, 3:215), and Moore also both saw and accepted the difference in their powers.[17] Moore, who after meeting and liking the younger poet at Samuel Rogers's house did much to pave his way in Whig society, matched Byron in his political sentiments and in his regard for Napoléon. As good an audience as he was a performer, Moore proved a discriminating but undemanding friend whom Byron once characterized as "the best-hearted, the only *hearted* being I have ever encountered; and then his talents are equal to his feelings" (*BLJ*, 3:236).

This high estimate, combined with the good-natured wish to help a much less prosperous fellow poet, probably accounts for Byron's otherwise somewhat puzzling choice during this period of their friendship of the significantly older Moore as his editor-and-biographer-to-be. "Remember you must edite [*sic*] my posthumous works, with a Life of the Author, for which I shall send you some Confessions, dated 'Lazaretto,' Smyrna, Malta, or Palermo—one can die any where" (*BLJ*, 3:75), Byron wrote—rather presciently, as it would turn out—in July 1813. Among the "confessions" he put while living into Moore's hands are the journal of 1813 to 1814, some of his finest travel letters from Venice, and the famous memoir presented during Moore's 1819 visit to Venice and burned in Murray's fireplace after Byron's death. It might be said that the lyrics addressed to Moore could be similarly construed as material for the posthumous life, letters, and literary remains.

Byron's inclination to make Moore his lyric audience seems to have begun on his first embarking from Dover and to have continued well into his Italian period, though this tendency, along with the letters to Moore, faded in the last years of Byron's life when the English cantos of *Don Juan* offered a natural vent for his retrospections and the immediacies of Italian love and politics or, later, Greek revolutionary matters filled his present. The first of Byron's exile lyrics, [To Thomas Moore], presents itself as an extempore improvisation whose moment seems to coincide with the start of Byron's voyage:

> My boat is on the shore,
> And my bark is on the sea;

But, before I go, Tom Moore,
Here's a double health to thee!

Here's a sigh to those who love me,
And a smile to those who hate;
And, whatever sky's above me,
Here's a heart for every fate.
(*CPW,* 4:125)

In fact Byron composed only the initial stanza in 1816. The remaining
five apparently issued from his pen under circumstances vividly conjured
up in the paragraph following the lyric in Byron's 10 July 1817 letter to
Moore: "This should have been written fifteen moons ago—the first
stanza was. I am just come out from an hour's swim in the Adriatic; and
I write to you with a black-eyed Venetian girl before me, reading
Boccac[c]io." (*BLJ,* 5:251). Considered in isolation, the lyric's pose of
spontaneity and optimism seems duplicitous: not even an inveterate
traveler of Byron's stamp could be expected to start out in such good
spirits when he's just been abandoned by wife, child, his fickle admirers
in the Great World, everyone but a few loyal friends and some persistent
creditors. Framed within Byron's letter to Moore and directed from his
summer villa at La Mira rather than from a lurching ship, the lyric's
cheerful equanimity seems more natural. Byron has found a fate to his
liking under the Venetian sky, and immediate events—the arrival of
extracts from Moore's *Lalla Rookh,* sent by Murray, and a visit from
Monk Lewis—bring England back to a mind that can now imagine the
setting forth from Dover more auspiciously than must have been possible at the actual time of embarkation.

Here Byron's lyric sincerity lies in the lapse his prose openly acknowledges. This short poem was completed when its mood was natural, not
forced. Moore, as Byron's future editor-biographer, had a choice to make
on receiving the text: should he present it as a pure lyrical moment,
which would involve silently passing over the clearly avowed circumstances of composition, or should he acknowledge the historical situation, which would subvert the poetical illusion? It turned out that the
stanzas first were printed as a song with sheet music, " '*My Boat Is on the
Shore*': Written and Addressed to Thomas Moore Esq. by Lord Byron.
The Music by Henry R. Bishop. Published by J. Power, 34, Strand
[1818]." McGann characterizes variants introduced when the lyric

appeared in Moore's *Life* of 1831 and preserved in later editions as "almost certainly later alterations introduced by Moore to 'clean up' the poem" (*CPW,* 4:480). Cleaning up, to the nineteenth-century editor or biographer, often meant detaching "timeless" art from its temporal contingencies. Such excision can strike the late-twentieth-century reader as analogous to Lord Elgin's removal of marbles from the Parthenon, an intervention causing more harm than good.

Whatever meanings we derive or construct, we are less likely to understand Byron's letter-framed lyrics as he meant them when we read them out of context. For instance, two untitled lyrics addressed to Moore in Byron's 1816 Christmas Eve letter from Venice, [Song for the Luddites] and [To Thomas Moore], are richest when pieced back together as Byron presented them. This specimen of Byronic "garrulity" describes his Venetian way of life—mornings of Armenian lessons at the monastery of St. Lazarus, evenings of theater- and conversazione-going, nights of love. Lest earlier letters have miscarried, Byron reiterates his description of his current "Donna," Marianna Segati:

I will merely repeat, that she is a Venetian, two-and-twenty years old, married to a merchant well to do in the world, and that she has great black oriental eyes, and all the qualities which her eyes promise. . . . And now, what art *thou* doing?

What are you doing now,
Oh Thomas Moore?
What are you doing now,
Oh Thomas Moore?
Sighing or suing now,
Rhyming or wooing now,
Billing or cooing now,
Which, Thomas Moore?

Are you not near the Luddites? By the Lord! if there's a row, but I'll be among ye! How go on the weavers—the breakers of frames—the Lutherans of politics—the reformers?

As the Liberty lads o'er the sea
Bought their freedom, and cheaply, with blood,

> So we, boys, we
> Will *die* fighting, or *live* free,
> And down with all kings but King Ludd!

The remaining two stanzas of the Luddite song follow, and then comes
Byron's gloss on this lyric that returns to old preoccupations from the
days when he flirted with a political future in the House of Lords:
"There's an amiable *chanson* for you—all impromptu. I have written it
principally to shock your neighbour * * [Hodgson?], who is all clergy
and loyalty—mirth and innocence—milk and water." The allusion to
English clerical innocence and sobriety leads Byron back to the first and
interrupted lyric, which now turns to the dissipated Italian things Byron
is about to be doing:

> But the Carnival's coming,
>   Oh Thomas Moore,
> The Carnival's coming,
>   Oh Thomas Moore,
>
> Masking and humming,
> Fifing and drumming,
> Guitarring and strumming,
>   Oh Thomas Moore.
>   (*BLJ,* 5:148–49)

Fractured by poetry and prose as the song of embarkation [To Thomas
Moore] was interrupted by time, the Carnival stanzas lose self-contain-
ment. But they gain a psychological and intellectual integrity different
from and more important than the formal integrity that is sacrificed.

Even the lyric some readers have called Byron's best and most beautiful, [So We'll Go No More A-Roving], is more resonant when resituated
in the letter where Byron placed it. The wistful world-weariness, though
a generally recognizable emotion, is more precisely understood when the
lyric is recognized for what it is, a Lenten reverie after Byron's first
Venetian carnival. On 28 February 1817, Byron writes to Moore,

> The Carnival—that is, the latter part of it—and sitting up late o'nights,
> had knocked me up a little. But it is over,—and it is now Lent, with all
> its abstinence and Sacred Music.

The mumming closed with a masked ball at the Fenice, where I went, as also to most of the ridottos, etc. etc.; and, though I did not dissipate much upon the whole, yet I find "the sword wearing out the scabbard," though I have but just turned the corner of twenty-nine.

> So we'll go no more a roving
>> So late into the night,
> Though the heart be still as loving,
>> And the moon be still as bright.
>
> For the sword outwears its sheath,
>> And the soul wears out the breast,
> And the heart must pause to breathe,
>> And love itself have rest.
>
> Though the night was made for loving,
>> And the day returns too soon,
> Yet we'll go no more a roving
>> By the light of the moon.
>>> (*BLJ*, 5:176)

It might seem that if ever there were a lyric to let be timeless and placeless, this would be it. Byron's stanzas on *Carnevale* do have a depth and economy unavailable to prose, but his prosaic contingencies reinforce his poetic eternities. The poem's images of satiety are for the most part temporary. Except to believers in transmigrating souls, an outworn body is permanent; but swords can be resheathed, night continues to alternate with day, the moon waxes after it wanes, inhaling follows exhaling. The heart must "pause," not "stop," here; love requires "rest," not "end"; the brilliantly concise lyric circles back, with variation, to its incipient moment. The cycles of the poem have their equivalent in the ebb and flow of sacred and profane, feast and fast, in Venetian life. Passing his first February in Catholic Italy, Byron is sharply aware of contrast as the weeks of Carnival give way to the weeks of Lent, which itself will end in the Easter feast. Sending expatriate thoughts and feelings from the "greenest isle" of his imagination to the "tight little island" where the Irish expatriate Moore resides, Byron needs both prose and poetry to help his friend, correspondent, biographer, and editor understand all he is trying to convey.

When in July 1823 Byron sailed for Greece, he left behind not only his love Teresa Guiccioli but also many of the poetic genres that had been important in his life. He had finished his last satire, *The Age of Bronze*, in December 1822. The first months of 1823 saw him complete his last verse tale, *The Island*. Back in England Thomas Moore heard rumors that Byron was ensconced in a delightful Ionian villa and continuing *Don Juan*, but the epic masterpiece languished fragmentary, 16 cantos completed and a few stanzas of a 17th written. At his first Greek base on the island of Cephalonia, and still more so on the mainland at Missolonghi, Byron found himself beset by a wide range of problems—diplomatic, political, military, economic, personal—that called upon his energies and talents in ways they had not before been tested. What poetry he wrote in the last months of his life was lyric, and he transmitted it to no absent friends or biographers in waiting. Several fragments survive, along with a Suliote war song, but more than incidental interest resides only in the three surviving poems of 1824, all of them concerned with Byron's feelings for the handsome Greek boy whose heart he could not move, Loukas Chalandritsanos.[18]

The most publicly presented of Byron's last lyrics was the birthday verse popularly known as "On this day I complete my thirty sixth year," though as McGann points out in his textual notes this phrase appears below the date and place "January 22nd 1824. Messalonghi": a choice subordinating the personal to the historical (*CPW*, 7:152). Teresa's brother Pietro Gamba, who had accompanied Byron to Greece, describes the circumstances of composition and delivery this way: "January 22.—This morning Lord Byron came from his bedroom into the apartment where Colonel Stanhope and some friends were assembled, and said, with a smile, 'You were complaining, the other day, that I never write any poetry now:—this is my birthday, and I have just finished something, which, I think, is better than what I usually write.' "[19] Byron's word "better" seems apter in an existential sense than in an aesthetic one. The lyric expresses an intent to turn from unworthy private feeling to worthy public action—to trample "reviving passions" and, soldierlike, embrace heroic death in a just war. It begins with love, though, and the tone is autumnally Shakespearean:

1.
'Tis time this heart should be unmoved
Since others it hath ceased to move,

> Yet though I cannot be beloved
>> Still let me love.

> 2.
> My days are in the yellow leaf
>> The flowers and fruits of love are gone—
> The worm, the canker and the grief
>>> Are mine alone.
>>>> (*CPW,* 7:79)

Such familiar poetic accessories as volcano, pyre, and chains are then invoked. The tired imagery is, I think, entirely deliberate: Byron as poet and lover finds himself left like the old Yeats of "The Circus Animals' Desertion" in "The foul rag and bone shop of the heart."

In its fifth stanza, the lyric wrenches away from love. Its last half resolutely turns, with something of the rhetorical flourish and ancestral pride characterizing Byron's juvenilia, to the just cause and the public good: "The Sword—the Banner—and the Field / Glory and Greece around us see!" But Greece, with the Greek love it might afford, is no country for old men. Therefore,

> 9.
> If thou regret'st thy youth, *why live?*
>> The Land of honourable Death
> Is here—up to the Field! and give
>>> Away thy Breath.

> 10.
> Seek out—less often sought than found,
>> A Soldier's Grave—for thee the best,
> Then look around and choose thy ground
>>> And take thy Rest.
>>>> (*CPW,* 7:81)

This is the final figure Lord Byron might have wished to cut if he, like Yeats, were writing his bardic last words. But there was a bit more to

come, two anguished love lyrics giving the lie to the insistent turn
toward heroism. [Love and Death] lists, in five successive stanzas almost
entirely true to actual chronology, Byron's evidences of selfless but fruitless attachment: he has watched and tended Loukas "when the foe was
at our side," "in the breakers," amidst fever, during earthquake. His
spirit turned to the beloved even "when convulsive throes denied my
breath" in the strong fit of February 15. This devotion gains no reward
beyond grim recognition of the truth:

> Thus much and more—and yet thou lov'st me not,
> And never wilt—Love dwells not in our will—
> Nor can I blame thee—though it be my lot
> To strongly—wrongly—vainly—love thee still.
>   (*CPW,* 7:82)

[Last Words on Greece] is the countertext to Byron's verses on his
36th birthday. Attempted stoicism gives way to confessional pathos; the
friend of liberty's dream of "Glory and Greece" cannot console the slave
of love:

> What are to me those honours or renown
>   Past or to come, a new-born people's cry
> Albeit for such I could despise a crown
>   Of aught save Laurel, or for such could die;
> I am the fool of passion—and a frown
>   Of thine to me is as an Adder's eye
> To the poor bird whose pinion fluttering down
>   Wafts unto death the breast it bore so high—
> Such is this maddening fascination grown—
>   So strong thy Magic—or so weak am I.
>   (*CPW,* 7:83)

We grant last words extra meaning because they are last—or because
we imagine them to be. It would be easy to do that with this lyric,
which rings true to the facts of Byron's final days as we understand
them. But we should be wary of the itch for endings, as in its way the
lyric might imply. A syntactically complete unit ending in a period, the

poem reaches a kind of closure, but it closes with two alternatives (not mutually exclusive ones) held in suspension. Its form remains similarly ajar. No sonnet, no ottava rima or Spenserian stanza, this sequence of alternating a-b rhymes has no formal reason to stop at 10. Thus, two final thoughts on Byron's last surviving poem: the poet's last word is "I." And there is no last word.

Chapter Three

Satires

The satire, like the lyric, is a genre Byron explored early and one to which he returned throughout his life. Nature and nurture combined to make satire a congenial form of expression for him. Byron's temperament included the satirist's ruling traits—skepticism, a sharp sense of the ridiculous, and the inclination to denounce those wrongs and absurdities he detected. The classics-based education he received, like most others of his sex and class, exposed him to the Roman satirists at an early age and, more important, trained him in the skill of *imitatio* that, by giving contemporary observers not just the philosophical stance but also the rhetorical posture of another (better) time, lets them speak for other ages and to their own. From first to last, Byron's satirical poems depend on *imitatio*. To the extent that they do, they involve self-suppression as much as self-expression. Because the satiric mode, like the lyric one, appears intermittently in Byron's long works, the following pages will take brief account of portions from *Childe Harold* and *Don Juan,* the satirical interjections that punctuate his letters, and his short occasional pieces, along with the more substantial satires: *English Bards and Scotch Reviewers, Hints from Horace, The Curse of Minerva, Waltz, The Blues, The Irish Avatar, The Age of Bronze,* and his satirical masterpiece, *The Vision of Judgment.*[1]

The satirist's penchant for mockery is evident in the poem Thomas Moore identified as Byron's first, a 10-year-old's observations on an adult visitor who had offended him:

> In Nottingham county there lives at Swine Green,
> As curst an old lady as ever was seen;
> And when she does die, which I hope will be soon,
> She firmly believes she will go to the moon.
>
> *(CPW,* 1:1)

Only 13 days before he died at Missolonghi, the arrest of his politically influential landlord's father-in-law had Byron satirically dissecting Greek factionalism in terms of musical theater in a letter to Samuel Barff:

> The row has had one good effect—it has put them on the alert. What is to become of the father-in-law, I do not know: nor what he has done, exactly: but
>
> " 'Tis a very fine thing to be father-in-law
> To a very magnificent three-tail'd bashaw,"
>
> as the man in *Bluebeard* says and sings.
>
> (BLJ, 11:151)

Satire served Byron as a lifelong comfort and an amusement, a means of responding to personal and public events and of displaying his responses to friends. For instance, writing to his confidante the political hostess Lady Melbourne, Byron lets satirical verses—[Politics in 1813. To Lady Melbourne], uncollected until the McGann edition of 1981— both explain and compensate for his relative disengagement from the Whig cause:

> 'Tis said *Indifference* marks the present time,
> Then hear the reason—though 'tis told in rhyme—
> A King who *can't*—a Prince of Wales who *don't*—
> Patriots who *shan't*, and Ministers who *won't*—
> What matters who are *in* or *out* of place
> The *Mad*—the *Bad*—the *Useless*—or the *Base*?
>
> (CPW, 3:91)

Similarly, when in 1813 it was discovered that Charles I was buried in Henry VIII's vault at Windsor, the Prince Regent's presence at the opening of Charles's coffin struck Byron's satirical eye as a political and moral tableau verging on allegory. This event inspired him to write, refine upon, and disseminate among his friends the verses traditionally called "Windsor Poetics." The variant first published appeared in an unauthorized Paris collection of 1818, Galignani's *English Bards and Scotch Reviewers . . . etc.: Suppressed Pieces* (*CPW*, 3:424–25):

Famed for contemptuous breach of sacred ties,
By headless Charles, see heartless Henry lies;
Between them stands another Sceptered thing,
It moves, it reigns, in all but name—a King:
Charles to his People, Henry to his Wife,
—In him the double Tyrant starts to Life:
Justice and Death have mixed their dust in vain,
Each Royal Vampyre wakes to life again;
Ah! What can tombs avail—since these disgorge
The blood and dust of both—to mould a G[eor]ge.
                                                        (3:86)

Distance from his native land did not silence Byron's topical vein of satire. In 1821, on learning of the outpouring of British popular support when Queen Caroline was acquitted of adultery charges, Byron put one guild's demonstration of loyalty into an epigram:

It seems that the Braziers propose soon to pass
An Address and to bear it themselves *all* in *brass*,
A Superfluous Pageant, for by the Lord Harry!
They'll *find*, where they're going, much *more* than they carry.
                                                        (*BLJ*, 8:58)

Though Byron was himself a Whig partisan of "poor Queeney," his satirical eye could not help seeing the tradesmen's elaborate armored deputation to congratulate her as a laughable redundancy. Nor could he resist sharing his articulation of the irony in letters to his friends at home in England. A few months later, he combined false tales of his drama *Marino Faliero* being hissed when staged and true reports of his mother-in-law's recovery from illness in a satirical couplet also shared with his correspondents: "Behold the blessings of a luck lot / *My play is damned*, and *Lady Noel* not" (*BLJ*, 8:128).

When Byron used his satirical gifts on so personal a subject as Lady Noel's convalescence, he wrote for catharsis and for the amusement of a friendly coterie, not for the faceless reading public—and, as was the case with his lyrics, trouble could arise when a private poem was carried into the public sphere. The most notorious such instance involves

"A Sketch from Private Life," his bitter denunciation of Lady Byron's former governess Mary Anne Clermont, who had lived in their household and whose meddling he believed a catalyst of their breakup. In a letter to his estranged wife dated 10 April 1814, Byron wrote of Mrs. Clermont, "She came as a guest—she remained as a spy—she departed as an informer—& reappeared as an evidence—if false—she belied—if true—she betrayed me—the worst of treacheries—a 'bread and salt traitress' she ate & drank & slept & awoke to sting me.—— The curse of my Soul light upon her & hers forever!" (*BLJ,* 5:63). To his loyal friends, however, he distributed 50 copies of "A Sketch from Private Life" printed and privately circulated by Murray, then given unauthorized publication in various newspapers and piratical editions (*CPW,* 3:495). This publication, far more than "Fare Thee Well!," with which it became linked in the press, went far toward turning popular opinion against Byron in the days just following his legal separation from Annabella.

The sketch's "Honest Iago!" epigraph from *Othello* signals Byron's literary strategy. His satire offers the central situation of Shakespeare's tragedy with the genders reversed: Annabella is counterpart to noble, misled Othello, Byron is Desdemona with a difference, traduced but far from smothered. Clermont of course is a female Iago, a malignant, envious being who has risen through the ranks to destroy the marital happiness of her superiors:

> Born in the garret, in the kitchen bred,
> Promoted thence to deck her mistress' head;
> Next—for some gracious service unexprest,
> And from its wages only to be guess'd—
> Rais'd from the toilet to the table,—where
> Her wondering betters wait behind her chair.
> (*CPW,* 3:382)

This treacherous servant, who is "[q]uick with the tale, and ready with the lie— / The genial confidante, and general spy," next becomes "an only infant's earliest governess." Her unnamed charge's "high Soul," however, proves incorruptible, and a digression presents the pupil as possessing virtues and talents that make her the antithesis of her teacher:

> Foil'd was perversion by that youthful mind,
> Which Flattery fool'd not—Baseness could not blind,
> Deceit infect not—near Contagion soil—
> Indulgence weaken—nor Example spoil—.
>
>   (3:383)

Turning from the vision of past youthful innocence, the narrator now resumes the "baleful burthen of this honest song" and laments that the hateful domestic's venom has succeeded in poisoning her mistress's adult, married life: "Though all her former functions are no more, / She rules the circle which she served before." Unfettered invective constitutes this section of the satire. "Viper," "snake," "hag of hatred," "Hecate of domestic Hells," the serving-woman blends "truth with falsehood—sneers with smiles— / A thread of candour with a web of wiles" to blight all within her sphere. At once potent and contemptible, she is a monster part Fate and part bitch: "This female dog-star of her little sky, / Where all beneath her influence droop or die" (*CPW,* 3:384–85).

Like the letter to Annabella, the sketch ends with a formal curse— but one that lacks a crucial part, the accursed one's name:

> But for the love I bore, and still must bear
> To her thy malice from all ties would tear
> Thy name—thy human name—to every eye
> The climax of all scorn should hang on high,
> Exalted o'er thy less abhorred compeers—
> And festering in the infamy of years.
>
>   (*CPW,* 3:385–86)

Mary Anne Clermont's name appears nowhere in "A Sketch from Private Life," nor does Annabella's or Byron's. But readers have never doubted that the poem is a personal one. The friends for whom it was written needed no names to get its *ad mulieram* point. When its unintended readership the general public saw it, first in the Tory *Champion* of 14 April 1816 and then elsewhere, the satire had passed beyond its author's control. It had become an unseemly companion to "Fare Thee Well!," published simultaneously, and both poems constituted evidence of Byron's hypocrisy and wickedness, as pointed out by the newspaper's commentator.

The personal element that "A Sketch from Private Life" never transcends, despite its Shakespearean analogue, played a part in Byron's longer satires, though never such a large one. It was the personal details of *Don Juan*'s dedication and first canto—the satiric allusions to Lady Byron, Castlereagh, and the Lake poets—that, above all things, caused Hobhouse and Byron's other literary advisers back in England to argue against publication of the manuscript.[2] Years earlier, personal grievance had transformed Byron's first long satire and first mature poem from the amiably Horatian *British Bards* to the sharply Juvenalian *English Bards and Scotch Reviewers,* a work containing some biting assessments Byron would come to regret once acquainted with the men whose literary or critical powers he pillories in the satire.

Having finished with Cambridge and gone up to London in 1807, the young author of *Hours of Idleness* was occupied with a piece that could have served as complement to his friend Hobhouse's sociopolitical imitation of Juvenal's 11th satire. Writing in the manner of Lady Anne Hamilton's recently published *Epics of the Ton*, Byron took for topic the misguided literary talents of his day. As he was making efforts to have his and Hobhouse's short satires published together, the *Edinburgh Review*'s wounding review of *Hours of Idleness* reached him. In response Byron amplified his rather mild poem with comments on additional poets and, more important, on the critical establishment—especially Francis Jeffrey, editor of the preeminent *Edinburgh,* whom Byron mistakenly supposed was his hostile reviewer. The poem, augmented with some Hobhouse lines on William Lisle Bowles, appeared anonymously from the publishing house of Cawthorn in the spring of 1809. *English Bards* sold well and was favorably noticed—particularly by Tory and English readers for the attacks on Whigs and Scots—as a worthy successor to the *Baviad* and *Maeviad* of William Gifford, whose praise of his satire Byron particularly cherished.

Encouraged by the work's success, Byron quickly prepared an augmented and unrepentantly vitriolic second edition, enlarged from 696 lines to 1,050 (including replacement of Hobhouse's comments on Bowles with his own) and published under his name just as he was embarking on his Eastern tour with Hobhouse. In response to continued favorable sales while Byron was traveling, Cawthorn brought out third and fourth editions that were reprints of the second. After returning to England in 1811, Byron emended his poem for a second issue of the fourth edition and prepared a fifth edition, which he ultimately suppressed—chiefly out of consideration for the wishes of Lord Holland, whose political and intellectual circle Byron had attacked in *English Bards* but then entered, as celebrated author of *Childe Harold* and rising Whig peer, in 1812.

English Bards and Scotch Reviewers is today best known for its pithy and memorable denunciations of the early-nineteenth-century poets and critics remembered in our time. Aware of Byron's hostility to the Lake poets, twentieth-century anthologists, editors, and scholars focus on Byron's denunciation of "Ballad-monger Southey" as base aspirant to the epic heroism of Camoens, Milton, and Tasso; his mockery of Wordsworth, "that mild apostate from poetic rule" whose psychological and poetic experiments in *Lyrical Ballads* Byron deftly deploys to make a case against him so "[t]hat all who view 'the idiot in his glory,' / Conceive the Bard the hero of the story"; and his ridicule of Coleridge, whose "Lines to a Young Ass" gain the memorable tribute "[s]o well the subject suits his noble mind, / He brays the Laureat of the long-ear'd kind" (*CPW,* 1:235–37).

Nearly as famous is Byron's witty conflation of Francis Jeffrey and the infamous seventeenth-century lord chief justice George Jeffreys of the Bloody Assizes:

> Health to immortal JEFFREY! once, in name,
> England could boast a judge almost the same:
> In soul so like, so merciful, yet just,
> Some think that Satan has resigned his trust,
> And given the Spirit to the world again,
> To sentence Letters, as he sentenced men.

The narrator amuses himself in mock-epic fashion by imagining the Hanging Judge's shade rising, executioner's rope in hand, from the underworld and greeting his near-namesake:

> "Heir to my virtues! Man of equal mind!
> Skilled to condemn as to traduce mankind,
> This cord receive! For thee reserv'd with care,
> To wield in judgment, and at length to wear."
> (*CPW,* 1:242–43)

Directly after comes the mock-heroic account of Jeffrey's duel with Thomas Moore, a passage that spurred Moore to demand satisfaction of

Byron. The abortive encounter between Jeffrey and Moore was reported to have involved unloaded pistols, and in Byron's Homeric burlesque of the situation, Jeffrey is saved by his patroness-mother, the muse of Scotland:

> But Caledonia's Goddess hovered o'er
> The field, and saved him from the wrath of MOORE;
> From either pistol snatched the vengeful lead,
> And strait restored it to her favourite's head.
>
> (1:244)

Though remembered in extracts, *English Bards* is a comprehensive satire that gives those who read it in full a vivid survey of early-nineteenth-century writers and their deficiencies. It attacks the absurdities of nearly all Byron's poetic contemporaries, from Walter Scott, who by popular and critical acclamation wears the "hallow'd bays" that Byron thinks properly belong to Milton, Dryden, and Pope, down to "grovelling Stott," a writer of verses under the name Hafiz whose beginning lines on the Portuguese royal family's departure Byron reported in his notes to *English Bards:* " 'Princely offspring of Braganza / Erin greets thee with a stanza' etc. etc." (*CPW,* 1:402). Setting himself up as a "country practitioner" who aims to cure moral ills among the talented and the untalented alike, Byron exempts from his compendium of offenders only writers who have stayed true to earlier values: Gifford, Campbell, Rogers, Crabbe, Shee. In mastering the heroic couplet and voicing the neglected standards of neoclassic poets and critics, Byron did more than polish his schoolboy talent for imitating Horatian and Juvenalian tropes. He also developed what would come to be a lifelong admiration for his English predecessor Pope, who explicitly identified with the Roman satirists and renovated those writers for the eighteenth-century Augustans. As Frederick Beaty aptly puts it, "Pope's success in playing off imitation against original pointed the way to what Byron might accomplish within the same tradition."[3]

The revelation of originality through imitation is one of the surprises *English Bards and Scotch Reviewers* offers readers interested in the development of Byron's poetic career. The poem accurately foreshadows Byron's lifelong values. In it we see the earliest sustained evidence of his hatred of tyranny. "Each brute hath its nature, a King's is to *reign,*" he was to write years later in *The Irish Avatar* (*CPW,* 6:9), and in *English Bards* the

reigning powers under attack are self-enthroned critics and their debased subjects the poets. As the national adjectives of its title suggest,
English Bards and Scotch Reviewers offers the first major literary evidence
of Byron's characteristic dislike of self-serving provinciality, whether the
tradition-denying narrowness of his fellow poets or the critical smugness
of such north-of-the-Tweed reviewers as Jeffrey. In this satire Byron
takes advantage of what later would be a habitual gambit—strengthen-
ing his position as moral critic by candidly avowing his status as sinner:

> E'en I must raise my voice, e'en I must feel
> Such scenes, such men destroy the public weal:
> Altho' some kind, censorious friend will say,
> 'What art thou better, meddling fool, than they?'
> And every Brother Rake will smile to see
> That miracle, a Moralist in me!
>   (1:251)

The less than discriminating nature of the critique in *English Bards
and Scotch Reviewers* and the personal origins of its revised form are evident in a passage added to the second edition:

> Laugh when I laugh, I seek no other fame,
> The cry is up, and scribblers are my game:
> Speed, Pegasus!—ye strains of great and small,
> Ode! Epic! Elegy!—have at you all!
> I, too, can scrawl, and once upon a time
> I poured along the town a flood of rhyme,
> A school-boy freak, unworthy praise or blame;
> I printed—older children do the same.
>   (*CPW,* 1:230)

Not surprisingly, once Byron was established in Britain's highest social
and literary circles, he came to regret some of the barbs he had hurled
when young, wounded, and on the way out of his country. Notable
among his regrets—not least because it pained his half-sister,
Augusta—was the couplet on his guardian: "No Muse will cheer with
renovating smile, / The paralytic puling of CARLISLE" (1:252). This

attack resulted from Lord Carlisle's failure to introduce 21-year-old Byron at his investiture in the House of Lords, and "the provocation was not sufficient to justify such acerbity," Byron conceded in 1816 (1:413). Similarly, on making friends with Thomas Moore, a poet well connected in Whig society, the lionized author of *Childe Harold* had to do some fence mending for the offended author of *English Bards:* "Why do you say that I dislike your poesy? I have expressed no such opinion, either in *print* or elsewhere. In scribbling myself, it was necessary for me to find fault, and I fixed upon the trite charge of immorality, because I could discover no other" (*BLJ,* 2:160).

In the same vein, Byron let Lord Holland know that the satire's strictures on Holland House and innuendos concerning its patroness, Lady Holland, were the "boyish rashness of my misplaced resentment" (BLJ, 2:168). Walter Scott, whom Byron came to know, respect, and like, received an even more explicit apology: "The satire was written when I was very young & very angry, & fully bent on displaying my wrath & my wit, & now I am haunted by the ghosts of my wholesale assertions" (2:182). Byron even made his peace with Francis Jeffrey, who, he came to learn, was not the author of the hostile review of *Hours of Idleness* and who favorably reviewed *The Giaour* in 1813. Byron's poetic peace offering to Jeffrey, whom he had never met, appears in *Don Juan:*

> Here's a health to "Auld Lang Syne!"
> I do not know you, and may never know
> Your face—but you have acted on the whole
> Most nobly, and I own it from my soul.
> (*CPW,* 5:44)

It is amusing to note that this handsome atonement for the offenses of *English Bards and Scotch Reviewers* appears in the English cantos of *Don Juan* and that it is followed, a stanza later, by Byron's admission that "I am half a Scot by birth, and bred / A whole one" (*CPW,* 5:442; *DJ,* 10:17).

The circumstances surrounding Byron's second long attempt at classical satiric *imitatio* contrast tellingly with those of his first. Whereas *English Bards and Scotch Reviewers* was rapidly published and republished, generally admired by readers, and ultimately regretted by Byron, *Hints from Horace,* drafted in 1811 but then put aside until revised from 1820 to

1821, remained unpublished during his lifetime and has never attracted much popular or critical attention, though Byron persisted in valuing it highly. In a letter to Murray dated 1 March 1821, when he was writing *Don Juan*, Byron went so far as to say of *Hints from Horace,* "I look upon it and my Pulci as by far the best things of my doing" (*BLJ,* 8:88). Byron's pronouncements should not always be taken at face value, but the wide gap between his claim and most everyone else's sense of the satire's comparative worth warrants comment. The true value of *Hints from Horace* may lie less in what it achieves than in what it set Byron up to achieve. Writing it enabled him to clarify and articulate his literary standards, and the relaxed Horatian style first allowed him the freedom to range widely and eclectically over topics (Beaty, 59). *Hints from Horace* earned him the literary license he would exploit more brilliantly in *Beppo, Don Juan,* and *The Vision of Judgment.*

Although it is now a critical commonplace to see Byron and Hobhouse's association as involving poetic genius on the one side and prosaic competence on the other, Byron highly esteemed his friend's talent and literary judgment, particularly during their Cambridge days and joint Eastern tour. This regard is nowhere more evident than in the composition of *Hints from Horace,* begun at Athens, where Byron lived after his traveling companion had returned to England. Byron turned up a copy of Horace in the Capuchin convent and began an exercise along the lines of the Horatian pieces in Hobhouse's *Imitations and Translations,* published by Longman in 1809: "I have just finished an imitation in English verse (rhyme of course) of Horace's 'Art of Poetry' which I intend as a sequel to my 'E[nglish] Bards,' as I have adapted it entirely to our new school of Poetry, though always keeping pretty close to the original.— This poem I have addressed, & shall dedicate to you, in it you fill the same part that the 'Pisones' do in Horace, & if published it must be with the Latin subjoined.—I am now at the 'Limae[?] Labor' though I shant keep my piece nine years, indeed I question if Horace himself kept to his precept" (*BLJ,* 2:43).

According to Robert Dallas's report, Byron "believed Satire to be his *forte*" on returning to England.[4] He was much prouder of *Hints from Horace* than he was of the Spenserian poem written on his travels—so much so that it took considerable persuasion to turn his attention toward publishing *Childe Harold.* Continuing to emend *Hints from Horace,* Byron decided to bring it out along with the fifth edition of *English Bards* and with his third satire, *The Curse of Minerva.* Then on becoming famous for *Childe Harold* and deciding to suppress *English*

Bards, he put *Hints from Horace* away until 1820, thus fulfilling the Horatian recommendation of delay that his letter to Hobhouse had mentioned breaching.

Byron's renewed interest in *Hints from Horace* derived from his involvement in a partly personal and partly literary controversy over the character of Alexander Pope, that English Horace assailed by William Lisle Bowles, who had edited his works. Supporting the case advanced by his fellow neoclassicist Thomas Campbell, Byron prepared an epistolary defense of Pope, *Letter to ********** {John Murray}, on the Rev. W. L. Bowles' Strictures on the Life and Writings of Pope*. Simultaneously he reviewed the manuscript of his Horatian satire and was greatly pleased by it. "I wrote better then than now—but that comes from my having fallen into the atrocious bad taste of the times—partly," he observed (*BLJ*, 7:179). This might seem an odd announcement from the poet engaged in writing *Don Juan*, but *Hints from Horace* offered as clear a statement of Byron's poetic precepts as *Ars Poetica* did of Horace's, or *Essay on Criticism* and *Imitations of Horace* did of Pope's (Beaty, 51).

The highly derivative form and content of Byron's satire implicitly demonstrate its key principle—the wisdom of *imitatio* when one's models are the Worthies—and therein lies one of the reasons for the poem's limited appeal. In a romantic age valuing individuality and innovation, Byron supports the Augustan ideals of community and tradition—a kind of apostolic succession of poets through the ages. As heir of Horace and his imitators and translators, among them Pope, Byron carries the Augustan's precepts into his own age. For instance, Horace's goals of *prodesse et delectare* become "[t]wo objects always should the poet move, / Or one, or both, to please, or to improve" (*CPW*, 1:308), and *ut pictura poesis* is rendered "[a]s Pictures so shall Poems be" (1:310). Horace's accurately rendered literary standards are made relevant to an early-nineteenth-century readership thanks to pertinent contemporary illustrations, milder versions of those displayed in *English Bards*. Southey still is mocked, here for potboilers rushed into print:

> And print not piping hot from Southey's school,
> Who, ere another Thalaba appears,
> I trust will spare us for at least nine years;
> And, harkee, Southey! Pray—but don't be vext—
> Burn all your last three works—and half the next.
>
> (1:311)

Wordsworth is teased, as he will be in *Don Juan*, for his Lakeland provinciality:

> Write but like Wordsworth,—live beside a lake
> And keep your bushy locks a year from Blake,
> Then print your book, once more return to Town,
> And boys shall hunt your Bardship up and down.
>   (1:306)

In contrast, Byron looks more kindly on the works of Scott than he had previously, as evidenced by these comments on the contemporary English ode:

> Yet Scott has shown our wondering isle of late
> This measure shrinks not from a theme of weight,
> And varied skilfully, surpasses far
> Heroic rhyme, but most in Love and War.
>   (*CPW*, 1:304)

Even Horace's engagingly personal references are appropriately updated. *Ars Poetica*'s epistolary relation between Horace and the Pisos finds a counterpart in Byron's friendship with Hobhouse, alias

> Moschus, with whom once more I hope to sit
> And smile at Folly, if we can't at Wit,
> Yes, Friend! For thee I'll quit my Cynic cell,
> And bear Swift's motto "Vive la Bagatelle!"
> Which charmed our days in each Aegean clime,
> As oft at home, with Revelry—and Rhyme.
>   (1:301–2)

And the satire's initial assessment of the gap between aspiration and accomplishment endemic to the age ends with a bit of genial Horatian self-deprecation clearly applicable to Byron himself. Here at last the author of *Hours of Idleness* seems to have gained enough personal and poetic maturity to put that juvenile publication and its *Edinburgh* review behind him:

Thus many a bard describes in pompous strain
The clear brook babbling through the goodly plain;
The groves of Granta, and her gothic halls—
King's Coll.—Cam's streams—stain'd windows, and old walls:
Or, in adventurous numbers neatly aims
To paint a rainbow, or—the river Thames.

You sketch a tree, and so perhaps may shine
But daub a shipwreck like an ale-house sign;
You plan a vase—it dwindles to a pot—
Then glide down Grub-street—fasting, and forgot;
Laughed into Lethe by some quaint Review,
Whose wit is never troublesome, till true.
In fine, to whatsoever you aspire,
Let it at least be simple and entire.

                                                    (1:290)

Not surprisingly given that he started writing *Hints from Horace* at Athens, Byron's advice to his contemporaries includes the quintessentially Horatian prescription "Ye who seek finished models, never cease / By day and night, to read the works of Greece" (*CPW,* 1:304). His philhellenism takes center stage in *The Curse of Minerva*, a satire also begun at the Capuchin convent. During Byron's residence there, Lord Elgin's agent, Lusieri, was readying the last consignments of Parthenon marbles for transport to London. Byron himself was to sail for Malta on a ship that also carried Lusieri and some cases of the marbles.

By the time of this satire's inception, the nature of Byron's hostility to Elgin had undergone something of a metamorphosis. In *English Bards* Elgin and his fellow Scots peer Lord Aberdeen are mocked for their dubious taste and for the debated provenance of what had been carried home from the Acropolis:

Let ABERDEEN and ELGIN still pursue
The shade of fame through regions of Virtu;
Waste useless thousands on their Phidian freaks,
Mis-shapen monuments, and maimed antiques.
                                        (*CPW,* 1:261)

Once Byron was on the spot to observe Elgin's ongoing stripping of the Parthenon, aesthetic concerns gave way to political and moral ones. Musing on the series of barbarians who had plundered the Acropolis, *Childe Harold*'s narrator asks, "The last, the worst, dull spoiler, who was he?" The answer: Elgin; precisely speaking, a son of Scotland, not England, is the one

> To rive what Goth, and Turk, and Time hath spar'd:
> Cold as the crags upon his native coast,
> His mind as barren and his heart as hard,
> Is he whose head conceiv'd, whose hand prepar'd
> Aught to displace Athena's poor remains.
> (2:47–48)

The digression concludes with a malediction on the "British hands" that carried off relics better guarded on their sacred spot: "Curst be the hour when from their isle they rov'd, / And once again thy hapless bosom gor'd / And snatch'd thy shrinking Gods to northern climes abhorr'd!" (2:49).

William St. Clair's *Lord Elgin and the Marbles* shows that Byron's personal understanding of the situation permanently changed the international debate over the Parthenon relics: "The Elgin Marbles had now become a symbol—of Greece's ignominious slavery, of Europe's failure to help her, and of Britain's overweening pride."[5] Appropriately then, Minerva's curse, addressed to an English tourist dreaming at the Acropolis, personally denounces Elgin but spends most of its force on his nation:

> So let him stand through ages yet unborn,
> Fix'd statue on the pedestal of Scorn,
> Though not for him alone revenge shall wait,
> But fits thy country for her coming fate.
> (*CPW*, 1:327)

Britannia may rule the waves, but nevertheless the national arrogance of which Elgin's despoiling venture is but a small particular manifestation will provoke hostility abroad and at home:

Look to the Baltic—blazing from afar,
Your old ally yet mourns perfidious war:
. . . .
Look to the East, where Ganges' swarthy race
Shall shake your tyrant empire to its base;
. . . .
Look on your Spain, she clasps the hand she hates,
But coldly clasps, and thrusts you from her gates.
. . . .
Look last at home, ye love not to look there
On the grim smile of comfortless despair:
Your city saddens, loud though revel howls,
Here Famine faints, and yonder Rapine prowls.
(1:327–28)

In short, the substance of Minerva's satiric curse is the political argument a Whig outsider or *Childe Harold*'s narrator might advance in other genres.

Though begun in March 1811 at Athens, *The Curse of Minerva* was mostly written months later on Byron's return to England. Plans to publish it fell through with the suppression of *English Bards*, but Byron had Murray print eight copies for private circulation in 1812 (*CPW,* 1:446). A series of pirated texts, extracted and complete, appeared in the following years, and in 1814 Byron himself appropriated the poem's first 54 lines, an atmospheric description of Greek sunset and moonrise, to introduce the third canto of *The Corsair:*

Slow sinks, more lovely ere his race be run,
Along Morea's hills the setting Sun;
Not as in Northern climes obscurely bright,
But one unclouded blaze of living light.
. . . .
But lo! From high Hymettus to the plain
The Queen of Night asserts her silent reign:
No murky vapour, herald of the storm,
Hides her fair face, or girds her glowing form.
(1:320–21)

It seems both ironic and oddly appropriate that *The Curse of Minerva* should suffer pillaging of the very sort it deplores.

The fads and extravagances of the Regency microcosm called the Great World furnished rich material for literary and visual satirists alike. Byron knew the absurdities of this fashionable realm from the inside. Although he made rich use of its denizens and practices in the English cantos of *Don Juan*, only two of his satires, *Waltz* and *The Blues*, focus exclusively on the social ways of the Great World as he experienced it during his "Years of Fame." The latter of these is a minor work at best, a retrospective literary eclogue written in 1821 and consisting of two dramatic sketches. The first, set outside a lecture hall, is a dialogue between Inkel and Tracy, two men of the world who, much in the manner of Byron and Moore or Hobhouse, discuss intellectuals and literati drawn from Byron's usual targets: the poets Mouthey and Wordswords, the heiress Miss Lilac (Annabella Milbanke), and so on. The second eclogue features a gathering of Bluestockings and their hangers-on at the salon of Lady Bluebottle. Byron's model is a Holland House gathering, where the scene includes Miss Lilac, Lady Bluemont (Beaumont), Botherby (William Sotheby), and the lecturer Scamp (Coleridge or Hazlitt). As the scene opens, Sir Richard Bluebottle (Lord Holland) offers a soliloquy voicing sentiments that, as it turned out, contemporary readers of *The Blues* tended to share:

> No pleasure! No leisure! No thought for my pains,
> But to hear a vile jargon which addles my brains;
> A smatter and chatter, gleaned out of reviews,
> By the rag, tag, and bobtail, of those they call "Blues."
> (*CPW*, 6:302)

The satire's mockery seemed dated and out of touch in 1823, when Leigh and John Hunt published *The Blues* in the third issue of the *Liberal*, the radical journal that Shelley had involved Byron in planning and that Byron somewhat grudgingly continued to support after Shelley's death. As Frederick Beaty has pointed out, when *The Blues* appeared anonymously none of its reviewers suspected its authorship (Beaty, 178). They thought it too silly, inept, and harmless to have issued from Byron's pen.

There was nothing outdated or out of touch about *Waltz*, published without either Byron's name or John Murray's imprint in 1813—and as this double anonymity might suggest, the satire could be construed as far from harmless. Byron wrote it in 1812 while staying at the fashionable spa Cheltenham in the company of such Whig aristocrats as the Melbournes, Hollands, and Jerseys. Its primary subject is the waltzing craze that, about a decade after being imported from Germany, had ascended to the highest circles of society, largely due to the patronage of the Prince of Wales. This royal sponsorship, and Byron's anticipation of Yeats's inability or unwillingness to "tell the dancer from the dance," made the satire potentially dangerous. Although lame Byron certainly had personal reasons to dislike the fluid gyrations of the dance that had become so popular with his mistress Lady Caroline Lamb and other fashionables, he also could attack waltzing in a principled argument particularly congenial to the Whigs. His strategy: emphasizing the shared German origins, and the contemporaneous rise, of the wanton dance and the dissolute, treacherous regent who, on coming to power in 1811, had bitterly disappointed the Whigs, his political allies and social companions prior to his ascendancy. The link is made explicit in a note to the poem signed "PRINTER'S DEVIL": "Waltz was not so much in vogue till the R——t attained the acme of his popularity. Waltz, the Comet, Whiskers, and the new Government illuminated heaven and earth, in all their glory, much about the same time" (*CPW,* 3:401).

The stance Byron takes is socially conservative, a John Bullish endorsement of old England and its values in the face of foreign novelties, whether a popular entertainment or a ruling family and the financial entanglements that survive its post-Napoleonic severance from Continental territory:

> O Germany! How much to thee we owe,
> As heaven-born Pitt can testify below;
> Ere curs'd Confederation made thee France's,
> And only left us thy d——d debts and dances;
> Of subsidies and Hanover bereft,
> We bless thee still—for George the Third is left!
> Of kings the best—and last, not least in worth,
> For graciously begetting George the Fourth.
> To Germany, and Highnesses serene,

Who owe us millions—don't we owe the Queen?
To Germany, what owe we not besides?
So oft bestowing Brunswickers and brides;
Who paid for vulgar with her royal blood,
Drawn from the stem of each Teutonic stud;
Who sent us—so be pardoned all her faults,
A dozen Dukes—some Kings—a Queen—and "Waltz."
                                                            (*CPW,* 3:25)

Byron strategically or ineptly problematizes the point of this satire, subtitled "An Apostrophic Hymn," by prefacing it with a letter asserting
that its mingled praise and condemnation come from the pen of a solid
country squire whose identity is not integrated into the poetic lines
themselves. As his letter "To the Publisher" reveals, "Horace Hornem,
Esq.," is far from being a single-minded satirist. The symbolic resonances of this name include classicism, vernacular traditionalism, cuckoldry, and prurience. Similarly, Hornem's letter blends rustic outrage
with faddish delight. When at a London rout where he is "expecting to
see a country-dance," he instead confronts "poor dear Mrs. Hornem
with her arms half round the loins of a huge hussar-looking gentleman"
who has his arms "rather more than half round her waist" as they "turn
round, and round, and round, to a d——d seesaw up and down sort of
tune." This indignation is neither righteous nor long lived, for he concludes his letter by saying, "Now that I know what it is, I like it of all
things"—this despite having broken his shins waltzing. Perhaps the liking arises from his having "four times overturned Mrs. Hornem's maid
in practising" (3:23).

   Though Hornem's letter claims that he has "a turn for rhyme," we see
none of his other traits or personal circumstances inscribed within the
poem itself. Yet because his letter encloses the satire, readers are left per-
plexed as to what moral sense is to be made of the poem's self-refutation.
Is the double-mindedness of *Waltz* meant to be resolved by readers attentive to the nuances of deliberate contradiction? Or dismissed as the dramatized incompetence of a hypocritical, lecherous versifier? When the
penultimate stanza lurches from swooning praise (mock or straight) to
forthright interrogation, what are we to conclude? Can the speaker ask,

      But ye—who never felt a single thought
      For what our morals are to be, or ought;

> Who wisely wish the charms you view to reap,
> Say—would you make those beauties quite so cheap?
> (*CPW,* 3:30)

and also mean what he says a stanza later: "Voluptuous Waltz! And dare I thus blaspheme? / Thy bard forgot thy praises were his theme" (3:31)? *Waltz* is a satirical dance that leaves us unsure of our moral footing, but is this unsteadiness the effect of a failed classical satire or of a successful precociously postmodern one?

Byron's Whiggish antipathy to monarchs in general and to Hanoverians in specific resulted in a pair of satires composed in 1821 that directly or indirectly derived from specific incidents in the royal family: the 1820 death of George III and the 1821 visit of George IV to Ireland only days after the death of his estranged wife, Queen Caroline. The satires' titles suggest something of their complementary subjects. *The Irish Avatar* sarcastically presents a god incarnate, George IV on his state visit to abject Ireland, whereas *The Vision of Judgment* portrays an earthly king stripped to spirit, pitiful George III waiting for admittance at the gates of heaven. Interestingly, neither poem employs Byron's usual satiric form, the Augustan couplets of Pope. *The Irish Avatar* is written in anapestic quatrains, *The Vision of Judgment* in ottava rima. Both metrical choices are significant. As Beaty points out, anapestic quatrains were favored by Thomas Moore, the Irish poet praised in the satire's last line and the friend whom Byron entrusted with a fair copy for the earliest publication (Beaty, 166). Byron's poetic Other of *The Vision of Judgment* is an enemy, not a friend: the poet laureate Robert Southey, whose eulogy of George III, *A Vision of Judgment,* furnished Byron with title and subject but definitely not attitude or meter. In fact, the dactylic hexameters of Southey's *Vision* are pointedly rejected as "spavin'd" and "gouty"—apt adjectives for lame poetic feet—in Byron's. The metrical form this rejection takes is the nimble ottava rima that *Don Juan* had already established as Byron's happiest medium for mocking the laureate.

Living abroad at Ravenna, Byron followed news of the English royals through newspaper accounts, which had reported that Queen Caroline had died on 7 August 1821. Although her body, which was to be buried in her native soil of Brunswick, was still in transit to Germany, George IV saw no reason to delay plans for embarking in the opposite direction, to his "other island," on 11 August. For the next few weeks the popular papers made a point of juxtaposing the two royal progresses, a device Byron seizes upon to begin his poem:

> ERE the Daughter of BRUNSWICK is cold in her grave,
>   And her ashes still float to their home o'er the tide,
> Lo! George the Triumphant speeds over the wave,
>   To the long-cherish'd Isle which he loved like his—bride.
>   (*CPW,* 6:6)

The satiric purposes of the ensuing verses are threefold: to attack the incorrigibly faithless George IV, to denounce and correct the Irish crowds who had fawningly welcomed their despot and his entourage, and to bolster a particular embattled Irishman, Thomas Moore. Long established as a writer of antimonarchical poetry, Moore was in Parisian exile for debt and had suffered recent attack in the Tory press.[6]

*The Irish Avatar'*s sarcastic praise of George IV, who after years of long-distance oppression and exploitation had turned on his charm for the public visit to Ireland, breaks no new ground for Byron but is remarkable for the intensity of its tone, characterized by Goethe as "the sublime of hatred."[7] As he and others of his party had done before, Byron mocks the bloated former "Prince of Whales" for his size: "But he comes! the Messiah of Royalty comes; / Like a goodly Leviathan rolled from the waves!" (*CPW,* 6:7). The new-crowned king's hypocrisy in sporting an Irish shamrock also evokes sarcastic contempt: "But long live the Shamrock which shadows him o'er! / Could the green in his *hat* be transferr'd to his *heart!*" (6:7). But from Byron's perspective greed and insincerity are instinctive traits of the royal beast. Thus he reserves his truly savage indignation for less natural vices. The lavish welcome extended to George IV by the Irish receives the sort of scorn accorded the modern Greeks in *Childe Harold* and in *Don Juan'*s "The Isles of Greece!":[8]

> Let the poor squalid splendour thy wreck can afford
>   (As the bankrupt's profusion his ruin would hide)
> Gild over the Palace—Lo! Erin, thy Lord!
>   Kiss his foot with thy blessing for blessings denied!
>   (6:9)

Even harsher words denounce King George's "Sejanus," the Anglo-Irish peer and politician Castlereagh, foreign secretary since 1812, who as chief secretary for Ireland (1799–1801) had secured the Irish Parliament's passage of the Act of Union with Britain. Playing off the myth of St. Patrick driving all snakes from Ireland, Byron labels Castlereagh a "cold-blooded Serpent, with venom full-flush'd, / Still warming its folds in the breast of a King!" (*CPW,* 6:11). The Irish throng "[s]eems proud of the Reptile which crawl'd from her earth! And for murder repays him with shouts and a smile!" (6:11). Such welcome of a turncoat son is yet worse than groveling to King George, but amid the national obsequiousness that extends all the way up to such Irish leaders as Daniel O'Connell and Lord Fingal, Byron recognizes a few exceptions, most of them deceased. Henry Grattan, John Curran, and Richard Brinsley Sheridan all fought for Irish freedoms in the British Parliament—and Byron ironically points out that, buried on English soil, they are blessedly spared the sight of their homeland's self-humiliation. As if determined to end on a positive note, the poem concludes with the invocation of these glorious dead and one living expatriate. What quenches the narrator's contempt for "a nation so servile though sore" is "the glory of GRATTAN and genius of MOORE!" (6:13).

As was the case with *Waltz,* Byron's framing of *The Irish Avatar* perplexes rather than clarifies the satire. The meter reminiscent of Moore, the tribute to his talent in the poem's final phrase, and his involvement in the poem's first publication all seem to suggest Byron's sense that he and Moore shared similar if not identical feelings on the subject, though as Beaty points out Moore agreed with Byron's assessment of the Irish but differed in thinking that George IV had behaved "well and wisely" (Beaty, 170).[9] Invoking and involving Moore, whom Byron liked and admired, implies the sincerity and seriousness of the political critique. But the poem's signature line reads "(Signed) W.L.B.**, M.A., and written with a view to a Bishoprick." Ascribing *The Irish Avatar* to the parson-poet Byron despised undermines the potential import of the satire, as does the other possible attribution mentioned whimsically in his 9 October 1821 letter enclosing a draft of the manuscript to Murray: "It is doubtful whether the poem was written by Felicia Hemans for the prize of the Dartmoor Academy—or by the Rev. W. L. Bowles with a view to a bishopric—your own great discernment will decide between them" (*BLJ,* 8:236). Byron's playful obfuscation of the satire's authorship and his casualness about its circulation both suggest some truth in the report that Byron had called the poem " 'a silly thing written in a moment of ill nature' " (CPW, 6:600).

In the same letter sending Murray *The Irish Avatar* and asking him to choose between Bowles and Hemans as its putative author, Byron mentions his other pseudonymous satire of 1821: "By last post I sent the 'Vision of Judgment by Quevedo Redivivus'—I just piddle a little with these trifles to keep my hand in for the New 'English Bards &c.' which I perceive some of your people are in want of" (*BLJ*, 8:236–37). Such self-belittling noises might be seen as preemptive, given that Byron knew his poem would cause great unease for the Tory publisher with his Admiralty contracts and suspected that contemporary readers' and critics' reactions to the poem would vary widely.[10] Writing to Murray only three days later, on 12 October 1821, Byron characterized *The Vision of Judgment* more grandly. He described the satire, with its suspension of diverse, unreconciled opposites constituting a kind of poetic chiaroscuro, as being "in my finest ferocious Caravaggio style" (*CPW*, 8:240). Posterity remembers the phrase and rates the poem highly. Andrew Rutherford, who voices an opinion shared by many critics when he argues that the poem has all *Don Juan*'s excellences and none of its faults, pronounces *The Vision of Judgment* "Byron's masterpiece, aesthetically perfect, intellectually consistent, highly entertaining, and morally profound—the supreme example of satire as it could be written by an English poet-aristocrat" (Rutherford, 237).

The catalyst of this satire was a personal insult: Southey's published attack on Byron as unnamed but obvious leader of "the Satanic school" in the preface to *A Vision of Judgment*, his fulsome panegyric on George III's entry into paradise. This attack was but the latest salvo in a series that extended back to 1816, when Southey had taken home to England gossipy reports of the Byron-Shelley circle at Diodati as a "league of incest." The subsequent exchange of paper bullets included various published and suppressed writings: letters to newspapers and journals, a challenge undelivered by Byron's second Douglas Kinnaird, the unpublished (but publicized) dedication to *Don Juan*.

The dedication itself is a superb miniature satire economically denouncing its two chief targets, Southey and Castlereagh, for an Orwellian blend of bad politics and bad use of the English language, with sexual inadequacy thrown in. Freshly stung by the self-righteous smugness of Southey's preface to *A Vision of Judgment*, offended in all sorts of ways by the poem itself, and inspired by Southey's taunt that the satanic school's intemperate leader would be wiser to attack him in poetry (where metrical rules would rein his temper in) than in prose, Byron set out to destroy his opponent's credibility in *The Vision of Judgment*. Over time, the destruction succeeded so completely that most readers nowadays know Southey only as the asinine rhymester of Byron's attacks and read from Southey's voluminous corpus only the immortal quatrain that Byron stole for *Don Juan* and then damned with the acknowledgment "The first four rhymes are Southey's every line: / For God's sake, reader! take them not for mine" (*CPW,* 5:80). But *The Vision of Judgment* achieves its "finest ferocious Caravaggio style" by superbly transcending the personal. In the laureate and his official *Vision* Byron found concentrated what he most despised in his homeland: cant in all its varieties. Ironically, Southey contributed greatly to literature by offending all Byron's principles—those of the aristocratic friend of liberty, the Augustan literary traditionalist, the freethinking religious skeptic, the humanely tolerant moralist. *The Vision of Judgment* burns so brilliantly because Southey and his *Vision* furnished the perfect kindling.

The *Vision of Judgment* draws eclectically on a wide range of precursors, from St. John's apocalyptic vision in Revelations to Milton's *Paradise Lost*, Pope's *Dunciad*, Sheridan's play *The Critic*, Southey's epic *The Curse of Kehama*, and parliamentary details from Byron's brief involvement in House of Lords debates (*CPW,* 6:672). But its most evident brilliance lies in now following, now departing from the pattern of Southey's *Vision*, so a brief synopsis of that despised yet crucial pretext might be in order. Southey's panegyric is a dream vision. Entranced as the bell tolls for George III's passing, the poet laureate sees his monarch's spirit rise to the portal of paradise. There the regal soul shames its base accusers, notably Wilkes and Junius, who reappear in Byron's poem, into respectful silence. The devil and the damned are hurled down to hell; George III is escorted into heaven by the blessed multitude, which includes English monarchs, from Saxon Alfred down to the houses of Stuart and Orange, virtuous men who were republicans on earth such as George Washington, ancient and modern British worthies including Shakespeare and even the antimonarchical Milton (having repented, one presumes) but not Pope, and the members of the royal family who preceded him in death. As the crowd surges into heaven, Southey falls to earth. He awakens in the Lake District, by the shore of Derwentwater, with George III's passing bell still tolling.

Personal grudges aside, Southey's *Vision* offended Byron's principles in many ways.[11] A declared foe to system in all forms and particularly to theory-based innovations tried out by the Lake poets, Byron found Southey's experimental unrhymed hexameters awkward to the point of lameness: "spavin'd dactyls," "gouty feet," "founder'd verses." The politics seemed just as bad. Paid kowtowing to a repressive establishment would strike a Popean gentleman-poet of Byron's sort as disgusting, whoever the hired pen might be. But Southey had cherished and published radical views in his youth. Indeed, one ghostly text, a pirated reprint of *Wat Tyler*, had come back to haunt the laureate in 1817: how could he now have the nerve to trumpet forth Tory pieties? Moving to the theological level, how could any mortal have the arrogance to portion out eternal rewards and damnation—especially on the basis of a political litmus test? Byron had teased Murray, "God will not always be a Tory—though Johnson says the first Whig was the Devil" (*BLJ*, 8:74): in *The Vision of Judgment* he sets up a thought experiment that turns Southey's presumptuous piety on its head. If Southey presents Britain's Tory monarchy as acting out heaven's principles on earth, Byron reverses the glass and satirizes an Anglomorphic heaven where providence works—or fails to work—by British parliamentary procedure.

Malcolm Kelsall has rightly discerned that Southey's *Vision of Judgment* may be a ridiculous poem, but it does not necessarily follow that its ideology is ridiculous.[12] Accordingly, the Whig poet-narrator's rhetoric must ingratiate him with the reader and establish his case as fair and reasonable. Byron settles on several means to achieve these ends. His narrator is quick to display courtesy, humility, good humor, and apparent objectivity. He admits his own sinful nature:

> God help us all! God help me too! I am,
>   God knows, as helpless as the devil can wish
> And not a whit more difficult to damn
>   Than is to bring to land a late-hook'd fish.
>   (*CPW*, 6:317)

This confession forges a sympathetic bond between the narrator and all readers unable or unwilling to claim priggish self-certainty for themselves. The narrator acknowledges the best (minor) attributes of his opponents before deploring their worst (major) ones. Of George III, "although no tyrant, one / Who shielded tyrants," he pronounces "[a] better farmer ne'er brushed dew from lawn, / A weaker king ne'er left a realm undone!" (6:314–15). Even Southey is admitted to be "not an ill-favour'd knave," with a hawklike visage "by no means so ugly as his case" (6:341). In such passages the balance is exquisitely calculated: the praise could not be fainter without ceasing to be praise, and its counterpoising presence serves to make readers feel the justice of the censure that follows. Byron avoids seeming personally churlish and unpatriotic by presenting the trial of King George dramatically and putting the formal charges against him into the mouth of Satan (whose name Byron spells "Sathan" throughout *The Vision of Judgment*). Even arraigning an old, blind madman of George's ilk would have the potential to seem brutal, but Byron shrewdly minimizes appearances of inhumanity. The present action of the poem is set in 1820 (obliquely referred to as "the first year of freedom's second dawn" in allusion to revolutions in Greece, Spain, and Portugal), but the case assembled against George III is drawn from before "the Gallic era eighty-eight." 1788 was the year of George's first attack of insanity, which precipitated the first Regency crisis (Kelsall, 128); and it precedes the start of the French Revolution by one year. This strategy of historical displacement permits the monarch to be judged for what happened when he was sane enough to rule, and it allows for the advancement of a Whig argument whose classical principles had not yet been muddled and modified by political contingencies across the English Channel.

The mise-en-scène of Byron's satire is a heaven that is obviously constructed rather than immanent, a mundane, humanized place where

> Saint Peter sat by the celestial gate,
> His keys were rusty, and the lock was dull,
> So little trouble had been given of late;
> Not that the place by any means was full.
> (*CPW*, 6:312)

But if new residents of paradise have proven scarce, the recording angel and his clerks ("six angels and twelve saints") have been busy accounting for the dead in the era of the Napoleonic wars:

> So many conquerors' cars were daily driven,
> So many kingdoms fitted up anew;
> Each day too slew its thousands six or seven,
> Till at the crowning carnage, Waterloo,

They threw their pens down in divine disgust—
The page was so besmear'd with blood and dust.
(6:313–14)

After "a few short years of hollow peace," we come to 1820 and George III's death. The king's funeral, majestic in Southey's *Vision*, is in Byron's reduced to "a sepulchral melo-drame" at which "[i]t seemed the mockery of hell to fold / The rottenness of eighty years in gold" (6:315).

Byron's specific parody of Southey picks up at the "Gate of Heaven" and "Accusers" episodes of the poet laureate's 12-part panegyric (Rutherford, 226). In Southey's hierarchical paradise, the arrival of George's royal soul is a momentous occasion. In Byron's heaven Christian equality before God seems to prevail, and St. Peter is unimpressed with a cherub's announcement that George III is dead: " 'And who *is* George the Third?' replied the Apostle; / 'What George? what Third?' " (*CPW,* 6:318). Byron does not so much deflate the great opponents of the heavenly war, the Archangel Michael and Sathan, as humanize their manner of greeting: "though they did not kiss / Yet still between his Darkness and his Brightness / There passed a mutual glance of great politeness" (6:323). Following the glance is a bow—more effusive from the Archangel, who has the luxury of being on the side of government. As Leader of the Opposition, "Sathan met his ancient friend / With more hauteur, as might an old Castilian / Poor noble meet a mushroom rich civilian" (6:323).

Then begins the argument over George's soul, presented as if it were a case in the House of Lords. Sathan, like Byron's narrator, willingly concedes George's "neutral virtues, which most monarchs want": "I know he was a constant consort; own / He was a decent sire, and middling lord. / All this is much, and most upon a throne" (*CPW,* 6:326). Furthermore, Sathan acknowledges that George III was not personally responsible for the crimes of his reign: "'Tis true, he was a tool from first to last; / (I have the workmen safe); but as a tool / So let him be consumed!" (6:326). Ultimately, however, a public figure must bear responsibility for public acts done in his name:

The new world shook him off; the old yet groans
Beneath what he and his prepared, if not
Completed: he leaves heirs on many thrones

> To all his vices, without what begot
> Compassion for him—his tame virtues.
> (6:326–27)

The call for prosecution evidence produces a proverbial cloud of witnesses—an international throng clamoring to testify. From this babel, Sathan calls forth the two eighteenth-century Whigs shamed into silence in Southey's *Vision:* the demagogue John Wilkes, known to the populace as "the Friend of Liberty" and to George III as "that Devil Wilkes," and Junius, the pseudonymous author of journalistic attacks on the Tory government and by dint of those attacks a pillar of freedom of the press and freedom of speech (*CPW,* 6:676). As in Southey's *Vision,* the Whig testimony fails to injure George, but for a different reason. The cheery, voluble Wilkes proves reluctant to "turn evidence" against his old adversary's mundane transgressions: "in the sky / I don't like ripping up old stories, since / His conduct was but natural in a prince" (6:334). Shape-shifting Junius is willing, but because he has no personal identity, his testimony must be the text of pseudonymous letters—hardly convicting evidence. Before Sathan can summon more plausible witnesses, enter Robert Southey carried by the devil Asmodeus, who complains, " 'Confound the Renegado! I have sprain'd / My left wing, he's so heavy; one would think / Some of his works about his neck were chain'd' " (6:339).

Allowed a forum as George III's official poet, Southey pleads "his own bad cause," not his king's—and unwittingly convicts himself of opportunism, hypocrisy, and stupidity. The brilliance of Byron's satire lies in letting the juxtaposition of facts do much of the work—as, for instance, by selectively citing a few Southey titles veering from radical insurgency to patriot jingoism: "Wat Tyler—Rhymes on Blenheim—Waterloo."

> He had written praises of a regicide;
>   He had written praises of all kings whatever;
> He had written for republics far and wide,
>   And then against them bitterer than ever;
> For pantisocracy he once had cried
>   Aloud, a scheme less moral than 'twas clever;

Then grew a hearty antijacobin—
Had turn'd his coat—and would have turn'd his skin.
(*CPW,* 6:342)

The devastating portrayal of this turncoat versatility continues:

He had sung against all battles, and again
    In their high praise and glory; he had call'd
Reviewing "the ungentle craft," and then
    Become as base a critic as ere crawl'd—.
(6:342–43)

Having written John Wesley's biography, Southey offers to write
Sathan's or Michael's with his promiscuous "pen of all work." But he
finally goes too far by drawing out the manuscript of his *Vision* and
promising to make all clear by reading aloud from it:

"Now you shall judge, all people; yes, you shall
Judge with my judgment! and by my decision
    Be guided who shall enter heaven or fall!
I settle all these things by intuition,
    Times present, past, to come, heaven, hell, and all,
Like King Alfonso! When I thus see double,
I save the Deity some worlds of trouble."
(6:344)

No need here for Byron to fabricate, or even to exaggerate much: what
suffices is to voice the silent assumptions underlying Southey's poem
and thus to unmask his boorish arrogance.

Rutherford points out that Byron faced a serious technical problem in
ending his satire. If Sathan's case against George III is sound—and it is
meant to seem so—how can the king enter paradise? But if he's dispatched to hell, Byron becomes the presumptuous arbiter Southey was
in his *Vision* (Rutherford, 235–36). Byron's means of escaping this
dilemma is truly inspired. The cream of the jest is that with Southey's
poetic interruption the trial ceases. The judgment finally rendered in

Byron's poem is literary, not political or theological. George III is not judged—Southey is. The sacred text invoked by Michael—"*Non Di, non homines,*" which translates as "Neither gods nor men [will stomach bad poetry]"—comes from Horace, not the Old or New Testament. When the poor mad king, mute throughout his trial, finally speaks, it is to make a literary pronouncement, confused as to details but correct in its discernment: " 'What! What! / *Pye* come again? No more—no more of that!' " (*CPW,* 6:341). And so the poem ends in a complex array of literary, not political, allusions. Five lines into Southey's recitation of his *Vision,* apocalyptic chaos breaks loose, though the Byronic narrator remains in control to the extent that he is still refusing to render eternal judgment on fellow mortals:

> The angels stopp'd their ears and plied their pinions;
> The devils ran howling, deafen'd, down to hell;
> The hosts fled, gibbering, for their own dominions—
> (For 'tis not yet decided where they dwell,
> And I leave every man to his opinions;).
>
> (6:344)

Southey, the particulars of his fate suggested by the end of his own poem, is knocked out of heaven by St. Peter's keys and falls "like Phaeton, but more at ease, / Into his lake," (*CPW,* 6:344), which also means falling like Satan in *Paradise Lost,* or sinking and rising like dull Colley Cibber mocked by Pope. Only with Southey's literary exorcism can Byron's *Vision* end on a note of divine grace rather than heavenly justice, with a final allusion that is biblical:

> King George slipp'd into heaven for one;
> And when the tumult dwindled to a calm,
> I left him practising the hundredth psalm.
>
> (6:345)

Byron means us readers to supply the relevant verses: "Enter into his gates with thanksgiving, and into his courts with praise: be thankful unto him and bless his name. For the Lord is good; his mercy is everlasting; and his truth endureth to all generations."[13]

The "New 'English Bards &c.' " imagined in Byron's 1821 letter to
Murray turned out to be *The Age of Bronze*. Disgusted by the reactionary decisions of the Congress of Verona, which by December 1822
had finished its business of restoring European monarchs to the
thrones from which Napoléon had toppled them, Byron described the
completed poem to Leigh Hunt as "a review of the day in general—in
my early English Bards style—but a little more stilted and somewhat
too full of 'epithets of war' and classical & historical allusions" (*BLJ*,
10:81). Critics responded to the satire's publication along predictably
divided party lines in 1823, but most twentieth-century readers find
the ingeniously topical satire too dense to decipher without footnotes.
Knowing about Byron's private life does not give a reader much help
with *The Age of Bronze*. Unique among Byron's satires, it remains
almost entirely impersonal.

Titling his poem *The Age of Bronze*, subtitling it "Carmen Seculare et
Annus Haud Mirabilis" (a two-directional nod to Horace's *Carmen
Saeculare* and Dryden's *Annus Mirabilis*), and giving it the punning
Virgilian epigraph " 'Impar *Congressus* Achilli' " (accurately translated as
"unequally matched with Achilles" or freely botched as "The Congress
doesn't equal Achilles"), Byron allusively implies that modern degener-
acy will be his satirical preoccupation. The opening couplet states this
theme directly: "The 'good old times'—all times when old are good— /
Are gone; the present might be if they would" (*CPW*, 7:1). Both the
form and the content of *The Age of Bronze* overwhelmingly demonstrate
Byron's literary skill at putting conventions from the "good old times"
to present use and his intellectual penchant for seeing the mythic or historical past's situations and personages represented, whether straight-
forwardly or ironically, in current deeds and their doers. For instance,
when the Duke of Wellington appears at Verona with Marie Louise of
France, the ex-wife as apparently indifferent to Napoléon's recent death
as George IV had been to Caroline's, Byron views the real people as
debased modern variants on epic and tragic models:

> She comes!—the Andromache (not Racine's
> Nor Homer's) Lo! On Pyrrhus' arm she leans!
> Yes! The right arm, yet red from Waterloo,
> Which cut her lord's half shattered sceptre through,
> Is offered and accepted!
>   (7:24)

In this dramatized allusion the role of Hector falls to Napoléon. The differences between the two—Hector fighting in a defensive war and Napoléon waging offensive campaigns, Hector dying nobly in battle, Napoléon surviving to accept exile—show the modern hero, like the modern heroine, woefully shrunken. But for Byron, Napoléon's great sin was political rather than military. When he might have been a liberator, he yielded to the selfish temptation to supplant, rather than abolish, the tyranny of kings:

> A single step into the right had made
> This man the Washington of worlds betrayed;
> A single step into the wrong has given
> His name a doubt to all the winds of heaven;
> The reed of Fortune and of thrones the rod,
> Of Fame the Moloch or the demigod;
> His country's Caesar, Europe's Hannibal,
> Without their decent dignity of fall.
>
> (*CPW,* 7:8)

Even worse than Napoléon are the lesser despots who have resumed their places now that he is out of the way. The three monarchs of the so-called Holy Alliance are brilliantly mocked as

> An earthly Trinity! which wears the shape
> Of heaven's, as man is mimicked by the ape.
> A pious unity! in purpose one—
> To melt three fools to a Napoleon.
>
> (7:13)

Mere fools cannot be the real villains of the Congress of Verona. Propping up the titular rulers—or pulling their strings, depending on whether one prefers the metaphor of dummies or marionettes—are the reactionary foreign ministers representing their countries at the congress: Wellington, Metternich, Chateaubriand, Montmorency.

In phrases such as "melt three fools to a Napoleon" and "I speak not of the Sovereigns—they're alike, / A common coin as ever mint could strike," (*CPW,* 7:23), Byron puns on the palpable connection between rulers and currencies, power and wealth. Along with monarchs and ministers, his satire indicts the less conspicuous but far more numerous profiteers enriched by decades of Continental warfare, especially international moneylenders and English landowners. Of the latter, Byron asks, "For what were all these country patriots born? / To hunt, and vote, and raise the price of corn?" (8:18). Perhaps the best-known passage of the poem, Byron's bravura ringing of changes on the rhyme of "Rent," refers to the gains reaped and garnered by these "inglorious Cincinnati," these "Farmers of war" (7:20):

> Safe in their barns, these Sabine tillers sent
> Their brethren out to battle—why? For Rent!
> Year after year they voted cent. per cent.
> Blood, sweat, and tear-wrung millions—why? For Rent!
> They roared, they dined, they drank, they swore they meant
> To die for England—why then live? For Rent!
>
> (7:20)

Although the intricacies of nineteenth-century historical details, classical allusions, and witty interweavings of past and present may perplex twentieth-century readers, Byron's denunciation of his era's sordid marriage of money and power, as dramatic as Ezra Pound's tirades against twentieth-century *usura* in the *Cantos*, gives *The Age of Bronze* striking relevance in the Age of Plastic. As far as Byron's published satires go, *The Age of Bronze* brings things full circle. "Tired of foreign follies," the aristocrat who began his satiric career with a denunciation of Scottish critical tyranny over English literature ends *The Age of Bronze* with a homeward glance. There his muse sees "Sir William Curtis in a kilt!" With this mock-epiphany, incipient political tragedy veers off into social comedy. The sight of so consummate a bourgeois as the ex-Lord Mayor of London accompanying George IV north to Scotland offers Byron's satiric muse a small, 14-years-belated revenge on the land of mists, oats, and reviewers:

> To see proud Albyn's Tartans as a belt
> Gird the gross sirloin of a City Celt,
> She burst into a laughter so extreme,
> That I awoke—and lo! It was *no* dream!
> (*CPW,* 7:25)

As the immoderate tone of these lines suggests, a real alliance between royalty and commerce must ultimately seem as bitter as it does laughable to an aristocratic "friend of the people." During an age when such forces join, the hopes of the poem's second couplet—"Great things have been, and are, and greater still / Want little of mere mortals but their will" (7:1)—must be at best a dream deferred. Perhaps what remains for the frustrated satirist is to give over satire—and go to Greece.

Chapter Four
Tales

The generic term *tale* casts a wide net that holds all narratives with simple plots. Tales can be true or imaginary, exemplary or amoral, prose or verse. Here, "tale" will serve as the category to contain Byron's nondramatic narratives, poems he wrote intermittently from 1812 onward. Tale telling was a literary preoccupation characteristic of the poets writing during Byron's time: as Caroline Franklin explains, *romantic,* deriving from *romance,* suggests the influence of narrative on poetry. The practitioners of the Regency verse tale (notable among Byron's predecessors in this vein were Robert Southey and Walter Scott) brought the elements of conventionally feminine romance—geographical or historical exoticism, pathos, sensation, imagination—into the poetic realm. As if to compensate for the origins of romance, these writers of tales characteristically downplayed the poetic productions themselves, emphasized the learned accuracy of the background details, located the obligatory feminine topos of romantic love within situations involving virile adventure, and enveloped the poetic tales aimed at a largely female and middle-class readership in elaborate prose paraphernalia: dedications, prefaces, and notes validating their writers as literati in the eyes of the elite (mostly male and ruling-class) readership.[1] Byron's tales were by far the most popular of the period. Nonetheless, as we shall see, they consistently display a family resemblance to such other romantic tales as Southey's *Thalaba the Destroyer* (1801) or *The Curse of Kehana* (1810), Scott's *The Lay of the Last Minstrel* (1805) or *The Lady of the Lake* (1810), Campbell's *Gertrude of Wyoming* (1809), Rogers's *Jacqueline* (1814), or Moore's *Lalla Rookh* (1817).

The six poems termed the Eastern, Oriental, or Turkish tales comprise a natural group. Byron wrote these works rapidly, though sometimes recursively, in the years of fame following the publication of *Childe Harold's Pilgrimage: The Giaour* and *The Bride of Abydos* appeared in 1813, *The Corsair* and *Lara* in 1814, *The Siege of Corinth* and *Parisina* in 1816. Characteristically deprecating the tales as mere effusions, he

emphasized the negligence of works that were often rapidly and sometimes carelessly composed. A 10 November 1813 letter describing *The
Bride of Abydos* to Annabella Milbanke strikes his habitual pose: "I have
been scribbling another poem—as it is called—Turkish as before—for I
can't empty my head of the East" (*BLJ*, 2:160). Though professing
indifference to the art of the tales, he admitted to a classically educated,
well-traveled gentlemanly concern over matters of Eastern fact in proof-
revising instructions dispatched to Murray four days later: "I send you a
note for the *ignorant*—but I really wonder at finding *you* among
them.—I don't care one lump of Sugar for my *poetry*—but for my *cos-
tume*—and my *correctness* on those points (of which I think the *funeral* was
a proof) I will combat lustily—" (*BLJ*, 3:165).

   Authorial noises notwithstanding, the tales were more than versified
lava of the emotions. Byron's apt choice of subject matter allowed him
to play to his strong suit, the field of readerly interest in which he had
established preeminence with the success of *Childe Harold*. He explained
the strategy to Thomas Moore, then at work on an Oriental narrative
poem of his own: "Stick to the East;—the oracle, Staël, told me it was
the only poetical policy. The North, South, and West, have all been
exhausted; but from the East, we have nothing but S**'s [Southey's]
unsaleables" (*BLJ*, 3:101). Unlike Southey's second- or thirdhand literary Orientalia, Byron's Eastern tales, though invented, spring from history, firsthand experience, and anecdote or legend gathered on the spot.
The firmly grounded tales offer more than exotic adventure: they are, as
McGann has observed, "a series of symbolic historical and political meditations on current European ideology in the context of the relations
between East and West after the break-up of the Roman Empire and the
emergence of Islam."[2] Further, in their role as souvenirs the Oriental
tales demonstrate Byron's nostalgia for a place and mode of living
unlike London and its fashionable round, as the retrospective "Lines
Associated with *The Siege of Corinth*" makes plain:

> We were a gallant company,
> Riding o'er land, and sailing o'er sea.
> . . . .
> All our thoughts and words had scope,
> We had health, and we had hope,
> Toil and travel but no sorrow.
>   (*CPW,* 3:356)

Amid the hectic monotony of his lionized existence in the English Great
World, Byron much fancied "doing a Levant" and rejoining that "blithe
and motley crew" of his Eastern travels in 1810, thereby escaping the
social strictures, political skirmishes, overheated amours, and ever-
increasing debts of a life lived beyond his emotional and financial means.
But profitable though the Eastern tales proved to their publisher,
Murray, and to Dallas, designated holder of the earlier copyrights, the
widely purchased poems did not prevent Byron from "doing a Levant"
in the figurative sense of the phrase: that is, borrowing at ruinous rates
from moneylenders. As aristocratic amateur, he still refused to be paid
for writing, though he displayed considerable interest in how much
money the tales earned. Although they are distinct poems separately
published, the Eastern tales can be seen as a poetic equivalent to musical
variations on a theme. Like musical variations, their recurrences and
innovations bear discussion in relation to one another. In this chapter,
information on the individual publication and content of the six tales
will precede consideration of their shared themes and preoccupations.

The Giaour, whose title is a Turkish pejorative for a non-Muslim infidel, relates the consequences of love between the unnamed Christian
protagonist and Leila, an enslaved Islamic woman unfaithful to her lord,
Hassan, who has her sewn up in a sack and drowned at sea for her infidelity. The giaour avenges Leila by killing Hassan, to which he confesses
on his deathbed as he tells a Greek monk of the hot-blooded life whose
particulars, save one, he proudly refuses to regret:

> I die—but first I have possest,
> And come what may, I *have been* blest;
> Shall I the doom I sought upbraid?
> No—reft of all—yet undismay'd
> But for the thought of Leila slain,
> Give me the pleasure with the pain,
> So would I live and love again.
>   (*CPW,* 3:75)

Byron fashioned this tale from recycled materials: the remnants of an
envisioned "poem of 6 Cantos" along the line of *Childe Harold's* published two. The central incident came from his stay in Greece, where at
Piraeus he rescued a young woman on the point of suffering Leila's

mode of death—the Ottoman penalty for Muslim women guilty of adultery with infidels. Though rumors and hypotheses have abounded, Byron's personal relationship with the girl rescued remains unproven but plausible.[3] Evolving over six months (September 1812 to March 1813) and through 7 of the 14 editions that preceded its incorporation in the first collected edition of Byron's poems (1815), the poem grew by accretion. Writing on 26 August 1813—between the appearance of the fourth and fifth editions—Byron accurately termed *The Giaour* "this snake of a poem—which has been lengthening its rattles every month" (*BLJ,* 3:100).

Subtitled *A Fragment of a Turkish Tale, The Giaour* is in fact a collection of fragments: disconnected bits of direct or indirect narration from the multiple vantage points of Leila's lover, her master, the Turkish fisherman who saw her execution, the Greek Orthodox monk who heard the giaour's confession, the Turkish bard who relayed the tale, and the Western poet or editor who juxtaposes the fragments. Strikingly absent are the words or perspective of Leila herself, a passive heroine completely objectified and disposed of as chattel. *The Giaour*'s fragmented, multiple point of view derives from *The Voyage of Columbus* (1812) by Samuel Rogers, to whom the poem is dedicated. Caroline Franklin argues that this form, unique among the Eastern tales, serves technically to mystify the events and to distance the reader from the shocking central act of the poem (Franklin, 39–40). Within the text, the multiple perspective is necessary, the incompletion inevitable, and Leila's inaccessibility brilliantly calculated. Her silence and absence constitute an eloquent and present indictment of a world where female autonomy is so completely repressed.

Like *The Giaour, The Bride of Abydos* centers on violation of a cultural taboo. This time the betrayed-engagement theme involves, or borders on, incest. As Marchand has noted, Byron's relations with Augusta and his "platonic" skirmishing with the Lady Frances Wedderburn Webster—the latter romantic situation resembling the story of Potiphar's wife, from which Byron takes his heroine's name Zuleika—were much on his mind during the time of composition.[4] Byron's journal of 1813–1814 discreetly avows the poem's therapeutic importance:

Let me see—last night I finished "Zuleika," my second Turkish Tale. I believe the composition of it kept me alive—for it was written to drive my thoughts from the recollection of—

"Dear sacred name, rest ever unreveal'd."
At least, even here, my hand would tremble to write it.

(*BLJ,* 3:205)

Writing to the Eastern traveler E. D. Clarke, who had praised the work
for its faithfully rendered Oriental details, Byron offers another credible
explanation for making his hero and heroine relatives: "[N]one else
could there obtain that degree of intercourse leading to genuine affec-
tion—I had nearly made them rather too much akin to each other—&
though the wild passions of the East . . . might have pleaded in favour of
a copyist—yet the times and the *North* . . . induced me to alter their
consanguinity and confine them to cousinship" (*BLJ,* 3:199). But as
Daniel Watkins has pointed out, more than personal ambivalences and
recollections of exotic travels find their way into the tale. Although
Byron was wrestling with private entanglements, he was concurrently
coming to terms with his waning commitment to Whig public life, and
The Bride of Abydos is the richer for tracing the interconnections between
personal and public life.[5]
     In *The Bride of Abydos,* Zuleika, daughter of the pasha Giaffir, is des-
tined for an arranged marriage with Osman, Bey of Carasman, a powerful prospective ally. Reluctant to wed the stranger and join his harem,
Zuleika shares her sadness with her beloved brother Selim, who, on
arguing her case to the pasha, is informed of his true status. Selim is
"son of a slave" by Giaffir's brother, long since a victim of fratricide.
Denounced by the pasha as "Greek in soul, if not in creed" (*CPW,*
3:110), Selim meets Zuleika in a seaside cave, where he reveals his true
identity and avows his intention of joining a waiting band of pirates,
with whose aid he intends to avenge his slain father. Selim begs his erstwhile sister, "Oh! never wed another— / Zuleika! I am not thy brother!"
(3:128). Giaffir discovers the cousins together and shoots the fleeing
Selim, who has turned for one last "fatal gaze" backward. But Zuleika
has preceded him in death: her "heart grew chill" on Selim's flight,
"[a]nd that last thought on him thou could'st not save / Sufficed to
kill— / Burst forth in one wild cry—and all was still" (3:144). Byron
returns to this tableau of futility involving a father, a daughter, and her
lover in *Don Juan,* in which the unfired pistol of the pirate Lambro parts
Juan and Haidée.
     The Bride of Abydos proved yet more popular than *The Giaour* and
went through 11 editions between 1813 and 1815. Even as his second
tale was published, Byron was writing a third, *The Corsair,* completed

between 18 December 1813 and 16 or 17 January 1814 (*CPW,* 3:444). The title character is Conrad, a mysterious Aegean pirate whose disappearance at the poem's end tantalizingly "left a Corsair's name to other times, / Linked with one virtue, and a thousand crimes" (3:214). As the tale begins, Conrad has received word that Turkish fleet of the pasha Seyd is about to attack his island. To forestall the invasion, Conrad takes leave of his love, Medora, and disguised as a dervish penetrates Seyd's stronghold at night. Because the pirates begin burning the Turkish ships ahead of schedule, Conrad's intended preemptive strike is not a complete success. He rescues Gulnare, the pasha's favorite odalisque, from imminent execution but is himself wounded, captured, and sentenced to die. Gulnare falls in love with her rescuer, obtains a stay of execution, and smuggles Conrad a weapon with which he can murder the sleeping pasha. When he recoils from this unmanly act, Gulnare herself kills Seyd and thereby purchases their opportunity for escape, though at the high price of becoming loathsome to Conrad. Accompanied by Gulnare, Conrad arrives at the pirate island to find that Medora, on receiving a false report of Conrad's death, has perished of grief. The bereaved pirate disappears: "Nor trace, nor tidings of his doom declare / Where lives his grief, or perished his despair!" (3:214).

In *The Corsair*'s dedicatory epistle to Thomas Moore, Byron announces the tale as "the last production with which I shall trespass on public patience, and your indulgence, for some years" (*CPW,* 3:148). Nonetheless, 15 May 1814 found him continuing Conrad's story in *Lara,* which he finished drafting on 12 June. Described in its advertisement as "a sequel to a poem that recently appeared," *The Corsair* was, for the first three of its five editions, published anonymously along with Samuel Rogers's *Jacqueline.* Byron's name first appeared on the fourth edition. The enigmatic, brooding count Lara, alias Conrad, returns home, accompanied by his page Kaled, who in fact is Gulnare disguised as a boy. Back in his native Spain—and as Byron explained to Murray, "the name only is Spanish—the country is not Spain but the Moon" (*BLJ,* 4:146)—Lara becomes embroiled in a feud, his principal foes being Ezzelin, a knight who apparently recognizes him from his piratical days, and Otho, chieftain of the lands adjoining Lara's. Wounded in the strife, Lara dies in Kaled's arms. Then an indirectly narrated scene, with obliqueness and uncertainty equal to the cryptic report of Hassan's drowning of Leila in *The Giaour,* goes back to the disappearance of Ezzelin, possibly murdered by Lara or the vengeful Kaled. As in earlier tales, the conclusion announces the obliteration of all but the names of the principals: "And Kaled—Lara—Ezzelin—are gone, / Alike without their monumental stone!" (*CPW,* 3:255).

If Byron's first Eastern tale was an accretive snake, his last two, *The Siege of Corinth* and *Parisina*, are patchworks. As McGann's textual scholarship has shown, these concurrently published tales resulted from Byron's intermittent but persistent attempts to salvage materials from a tale probably begun before *The Giaour* in 1812 but abandoned, as were two other Eastern narrative fragments of the period, "Il Diavolo Inamorato" and "The Monk of Athos." Resumed and dropped again in 1813 and at least once in 1814, the material was divided between *The Siege of Corinth* and *Parisina* in 1815. Most of Byron's narrative went into the former tale, and he grafted the remaining passages onto another story found in Gibbon (*CPW,* 3:479–80, 489–90). Murray brought out three editions of the jointly published tales in 1816.

As its advertisement makes plain, *The Siege of Corinth* rises out of a historical incident from the long struggle between Venice and the Ottoman Empire for control of the Greek Morea. In 1715 a Turkish army moved to regain Corinth, strategic port of the Peloponnisos. The badly outnumbered defenders of Corinth, commanded by Giacomo Minotto (or Minotti, in Byron's tale), were besieged from 28 June until early August, when Minotto surrendered the indefensible city. Then the Venetian magazine mysteriously exploded, killing a number of Turks and precipitating a Turkish massacre of the garrison, enslavement of the Greek survivors, and imprisonment of some 180 Venetian soldiers, including Minotto, though the *History of the Turks* from which Byron's advertisement quotes claims that Minotto died in the massacre. Against this historical situation, the details of which were not widely available until the middle of the nineteenth century, Byron presents an imagined love, the tale of Francesca, daughter to the Venetian commandant Minotti, and Alp, a Venetian renegade in the service of the Turks.

Here the variant on the triangular relation characteristic of the Eastern tales involves a daughter who chooses patriarchal and patriotic loyalty over romantic love, a Byronic hero acting against both his native culture and his beloved's wishes, and a father whose power directly destroys neither daughter nor lover (Franklin, 70). Francesca has died before the Turks penetrate Corinth, Alp perishes by a bullet as the invasion begins, and Minotti's final act is to annihilate attackers and defenders alike as he explodes the magazine concealed in the vaults beneath a church's altar. A hellish multicultural inferno of Turks, Venetians, and

Greeks ends the tale in a horrific literalizing of the Anglican prayerbook phrase "ashes to ashes": "Some fell on the shore, but, far away, / Scattered o'er the isthmus lay; / Christian or Moslem, which be they? / Let their mothers see and say!" (*CPW,* 3:354). Only startled birds and beasts remain behind to share with readers the narrator's laconic summation: "Thus was Corinth lost and won!" (3:356).

Some material from the tale that finally became *The Siege of Corinth* yet remained, and Byron discovered the historical incident onto which he could splice this remnant in a new 1814 edition of Gibbons's *Miscellaneous Works.* His intent, as McGann puts it, was not "to versify history so much as to use history as a vehicle for treating some subjects nearer to home" (*CPW,* 3:490)—whether his own perplexing infidelities or the endemic licentiousness of contemporary London society. *Parisina* presents a domestic and dynastic tragedy from fifteenth-century Ferrara, where Azo Prince of Este (Byron's version of Niccolò III) discovers the adultery of his second wife, Parisina, and his illegitimate son Hugo and punishes the guilty lovers. The story of incest and intergenerational conflict closely resembles the situation of *The Bride of Abydos.* Again Byron, engaged and then married to Annabella but unable to sever his liaison with Augusta, displaces his personal conflicts of the here-and-now into a tale of the there-and-then. This literary strategy of simultaneous veiling and venting spilled back over into life: Byron had his bride, Annabella, prepare the fair copy of the manuscript and then boasted to Murray, "[M]y copyist would write out anything I desired in all the ignorance of innocence" (*BLJ,* 5:13).

Within the tale, the bastard son Hugo, on trial for his life, concisely voices the intergenerational ironies of his situation: "Begot in sin, to die in shame, / My life begun and ends the same: / As erred the sire, so erred the son— / And thou must punish both in one" (*CPW,* 3:367). Handsome, valiant, and noble in nature though illegitimate in birth, Hugo has been barred from marrying Parisina by dint of the bastard status to which he is condemned as offspring of Azo's profligacy. Worse, Hugo has had to watch his beloved wed his father. Now Azo must endure being cuckolded and, through the instrument of his own vengeful justice, deprived of a fine son and a fair wife alike. Hugo dies piously and bravely on the executioner's block, but the tale leaves the fates of Parisina and Azo somewhat uncertain. The adulteress disappears from the hour of Hugo's execution—whether executed, imprisoned, dead of love, or alive in a convent. Azo lives to take another wife and beget other sons, "But none so lovely and so brave / As him who withered in the grave; / Or if they were—on his cold eye / Their growth but glanced unheeded by" (*CPW,* 3:374).

The Eastern tales are technically independent of one another. But the rapidity with which they succeeded one another, the mutability and interrelatedness of the separate texts (*The Giaour*'s successive expansions, *Lara*'s continuation of *The Corsair*, the common origin of *The Siege of Corinth* and *Parisina*) and the recurrence of themes, backdrops, character types, and situations all made it inevitable for contemporary readers to think categorically of the six poems. Such an approach can be repaying, for certain general features hold true, with variation, throughout the sequence. Most famously, the Eastern tales incrementally fostered the fame of that character type now called the "Byronic hero," a potentially noble yet blighted man of action, part individualist and part anarchist, aptly described by Andrew Rutherford as "a glorification of the outlaw, the rebel, the renegade, the Ishmaelite, the bold bad man."[6] In most of the tales, Byron devotes considerable attention to the spiritual anatomizing of these glorious outlaws, who come across as far more vital and attractive than his first such creation, Childe Harold, had done. The portrayal of Lara can stand as representative of the Byronic hero of the Eastern tales: "In him inexplicably mix'd appeared / Much to be loved and hated, sought, and feared" (*CPW,* 3:224). Although the proportions of these antithetical qualities may vary considerably, the mixture (explicable or not) appears in the giaour, Selim, Alp, and Hugo. Whether the cause be the stain of illegitimacy or the marginality of the cultural outsider, each of these heroes exhibits an alienation that becomes fascinating because it is linked with an intense if thwarted need for personal attachment:

> There was in him a vital scorn of all:
> As if the worst had fall'n which could befall
> He stood a stranger in this breathing world,
> An erring spirit from another hurled;
>
> . . . .
>
> With more capacity for love than earth
> Bestows on most of mortal mould and birth,
> His early dreams of good outstripp'd the truth,
> And troubled manhood follow'd baffled youth.
>   (*CPW,* 3:225)

In each tale, as in *Lara*, disappointed idealism makes the protagonist a rebel without a cause, or a rebel who champions a cause for personal and not entirely commendable motives:

> Too high for common selfishness, he could
> At times resign his own for others' good,
> But not in pity, not because he ought,
> But in some strange perversity of thought,
> . . . .
> And this same impulse would in tempting time
> Mislead his spirit equally to crime;
> So much he soared beyond, or sunk beneath
> The men with whom he felt condemned to breathe.
> (*CPW,* 3:225–26)

The extraordinary nature of such a hero suggests that he is not to be judged by the mundane moral standards prevailing either in his milieu (which is manifestly a troubled realm anyway) or in that of the reader. The consequence, *Lara*'s narrator claims, is irresistibility:

> You could not penetrate his soul, but found,
> Despite your wonder, to your own he wound;
> His presence haunted still; and from the breast
> He forced an all unwilling interest;
> Vain was the struggle in that mental net,
> His spirit seemed to dare you to forget!
> (*CPW,* 3:227)

With the publication of each new Eastern tale, Byron's enthralled contemporary readers proved that what *Lara*'s narrator says of the protagonist is equally applicable to the author.

Paired with these irresistibly and unforgettably bold, bad men are beautiful women (Leila, Zuleika, Medora, Francesca, Parisina) distinguished less for their virtue than for their passivity. For these heroines, action is limited to choosing between loyalty, which reduces the woman to a pawn in the patriarchal game of dynasty building, and love, which makes her a different sort of object, the goal in what Caroline Franklin describes as the Western lover's "internalized individualistic quest for self-completion" (Franklin, 38). Whichever her choice, the heroine suffers the fate of sexualized women in conventional romance: she dies, sometimes even before the present action of the poem has commenced. Standing in notable contrast to these lovely and beloved objects is the harem slave Gulnare, who rejects the alternatives available to women and wins her freedom with a knife. Her transgressive act simultaneously cuts off the chance of gaining the Byronic hero Conrad's love, however, and her continued association with Conrad/Lara depends on renouncing her femininity and putting on the masculinity of Kaled the page, a disguise Lara never penetrates.

The romantic triangle that recurs, with variation, throughout the Eastern tales has a significance beyond the discreet or indiscreet venting of Byron's romantic perplexities and the exploration of women's rights and choices in love, a matter in which Byron's own inconsistencies accurately reflected the ambivalence of Regency society. The beautiful female body guarded by father (or fiancé or owner) and desired by lover can serve as metonym for land long disputed by political and religious rivals. Not without reason did Byron begin canto 3 of *The Corsair*, which ends with Conrad's grief over the beautiful corpse of Medora. In lines describing sunset and moonrise over the landscape of enslaved Greece, the well-known passage begins, "Slow sinks, more lovely ere his race be run, / Along Morea's hills the setting sun" (*CPW,* 4:190). Appropriately enough, he extracted and resituated these lines from *The Curse of Minerva,* his savage satire against Lord Elgin's dilapidation of the Parthenon in particular and against British imperialist ventures in general. In the double light of their original context and their eventual one, the lines suggest that the Eastern tales are as political as they are personal, that the politics appraised are as Western as they are Eastern, and that the resonances of those appraisals are contemporary even when the situations are historical. The Eastern tales may have been Byron's "lava of the emotions," but they also record the social eruptions and tremors he detected at home and abroad.[7]

Making historical incident the point of departure for an imagined tale, as he had done in *The Siege of Corinth* and in *Parisina,* proved useful to Byron in a number of tales and related narrative poems written after his departure from England. Four such works, *The Prisoner of Chillon* (1816), *The Lament of Tasso* (1817), *Mazeppa* (1818), and *The Prophecy of Dante* (1819), resemble *The Giaour* in being exclusively or predominantly told from a first-person point of view. Like the Eastern tales that recurrently embodied the perplexities and pressures Byron faced from 1812 to 1816, these four poems from the early years of his self-exile can be profitably read as a group. *The Prisoner of Chillon* and its three successors all examine, from inside, the various sufferings of confined or banished protagonists who, as historical personages imaginatively presented, offer Byron a way to explore his own situation and to cloak the personal nature of that exploratory enterprise.

Not surprisingly, *The Prisoner of Chillon*, written while Byron's wounds of separation and exile were fresh, is the darkest of the four poems. The inspiration for the tale was Byron and Shelley's visit to the chateau of Chillon during their sailing tour of Lac Leman in June 1816. Picturesquely rising out of a rocky islet just off the northwest shore of the lake and strategically dominating the important trade route to the Alpine pass Grand-St.-Bernard, Chillon was built as a stronghold by the noble house of Savoy. Exploring the towers and subterranean passages of the fortress-residence-prison, Byron and Shelley heard of its most famous prisoner, the Savoyard François Bonivard (spelled "Bonnivard" by Byron and some of his sources), who supported Protestant Geneva against Catholic Savoy. For his partisanship, Bonivard suffered confinement in Chillon's dungeon between 1530 and 1536, when he was released by Geneva's Bernese allies, who seized Chillon and there imprisoned Catholics who opposed the Reformation. Wrenched out of this complicated historical context, Bonivard became commemorated as a champion of liberty in the face of oppression—and so Byron presents him in the "Sonnet on Chillon" (written after the tale but published as a sort of epigraph to it), which he wrote, as his appended note states, "to dignify the subject by an attempt to celebrate his courage and his virtues" (*CPW,* 4:453). But when he drafted *The Prisoner of Chillon* Byron was "not sufficiently aware" of Bonivard's history. Accordingly, his tale is a thought experiment rather than a commemoration, and its protagonist is not a Promethean rebel but a completely human prisoner, a damaged man whose years of physical imprisonment have left behind a narrowed mind and a broken spirit: "It was at length the same to me, / Fettered or fetterless to be" (4:16).

Distinctive among Byron's tales for its antiheroism, *The Prisoner of Chillon* is also unique for its womanless scenario. In this story of the clash between the Bonnivards (a father martyred for his faith and his seven sons, among them the narrator-protagonist François) and their persecutors, the closest approximation to the feminine is found in the youngest brother, "the favorite and the flower, / Most cherish'd since his natal hour, / His mother's image in fair face" (*CPW,* 4:9). In the tale's first section, its prematurely aged protagonist, whose "hair is grey, but not with years," quickly sketches the particulars of his family's persecution. The father "perish'd at the stake / For tenets he would not forsake," and of his six sons, "[o]ne in fire and two in field, / Their belief with blood have seal'd." The surviving "[t]hree were in a dungeon cast, / Of whom this wreck is left the last" (4:4–5).

The bulk of his tale subjectively represents the debilitating consequences of this unjust imprisonment. Even in the early days, when the confined and shackled brothers could comfort one another through speech and song, their voices took on a dungeon resonance: "A grating sound—not full and free, / As they of yore were wont to be: / It might be fancy—but to me / They never sounded like our own" (*CPW,* 4:6). Next come the decline and death of the two younger Bonnivard brothers, who have contrasting characters but equally pure minds: the youngest is beautiful, gay, and kind, the other strong, assertive, and independent. Their deaths deprive François of human companionship but also, by implication, drain him of the virtues they possessed. He is left to hopelessness, then unconsciousness, then a sort of death-in-life comparable to what Coleridge's horrifying late lyric "Limbo" calls "positive negation":[8]

> It was not night—it was not day,
> It was not even the dungeon-light,
> So hateful to my heavy sight,
> But vacancy absorbing space,
> And fixedness—without a place;
> There were no stars—no earth—no time—
> No check—no change—no good—no crime—
> But silence, and a stirless breath
> Which neither was of life nor death;
> A sea of stagnant idleness, .
> Blind, boundless, mute, and motionless!
>   (*CPW,* 4:11–12)

In prototypical romantic fashion, the ministering power of nature, in the form of a caroling azure bird, calls Bonnivard back to the world. But he returns a changed and broken man. Whether out of compassion or out of recognition that their prisoner has internalized his prison, Bonnivard's keepers unfasten his chains. He finds it "liberty to stride / Along my cell from side to side" (*CPW,* 4:13): bitter demonstration of the relativity of human perceptions. To such a diminished man, glimpses of the world outside—the snowy Alps, the "blue Rhone in fullest flow," the "white walled distant town. / And whiter sails"—are too intense to bear. Bonnivard retreats from his window with a sense that his dungeon is "as a new-dug grave" but also with a recognition that he is no longer fit for that external world. His striking reversal of language casts liberty as tyrannical, imprisonment as restorative: "And yet my glance, too much opprest, / Had almost need of such a rest" (*CPW,* 4:15). As years go by, Bonnivard becomes so habituated to his dungeon that

> when they appear'd at last
> And all my bonds aside were cast,
> These heavy walls to me had grown
> A hermitage—and all my own!
> And half I felt as they were come
> To tear me from a second home.
> (*CPW,* 4:16)

So much for the "[e]ternal spirit of the chainless mind! / Brightest in dungeons, Liberty!," bravely apostrophized in the "Sonnet on Chillon" (*CPW,* 4:3). As would later so often be the case in *Don Juan,* Byron's candid exploration of concrete particulars ends up revealing the hollowness of abstract generalities.

The antithesis to the aged and melancholy Bonnivard, who ends by admitting that after years of imprisonment "[m]y very chains and I grew friends" (*CPW,* 4:16), is Mazeppa, toughened by his sufferings, vigorous in old age, still cheerful in the aftermath of battle when he has just fought on the losing side. Byron's chief source for this tale was Voltaire's *History of Charles XII,* which relates the story of Mazeppa, a Polish page in the court of King John Casimir V. Banished in a distinctively barbaric fashion for being caught in adultery with a nobleman's wife, Mazeppa rose to become Hetman of the Ukraine under Peter the Great but later defected from the Russian monarch to Charles XII of Sweden, under whom he was serving when Russia defeated Sweden at the Battle of Pultowa in 1709. Byron frames the first-person narrative by having

Mazeppa tell his tale in the aftermath of Pultowa, where the fleeing
Charles has had one horse slain under him and its successor sink "after
many a league / Of well sustain'd, but vain fatigue" (4:174). When
Mazeppa exclaims, " 'Ill betide / The school wherein I learn'd to ride!' "
Charles XII, hoping to gain "the boon of sleep" rather than enlighten-
ment from the story, asks " 'Old Hetman, wherefore so, / Since thou
hast learn'd the art so well?' " (4:177). That Mazeppa should offer his
retrospective account of heroic endurance in the present context of a
bloody defeat and exhausting retreat enhances the tale's relevance, but
this effect is undercut by the poem's last line: "The king had been an
hour asleep" (4:200).

Casting his memory back half a century, Mazeppa recalls being
caught in flagrante with his married mistress, stripped naked, and tied
to the back of an unbroken Tartar horse that was then set loose "with a
sudden lash— / Away!—away!—and on we dash!— / Torrents less
rapid and less rash" (*CPW,* 4:185). What follows for Mazeppa, as the
horse races back from Poland to its native steppes, is the worst possible
blend of bondage and banishment. His punishment is set in motion by
human tyranny but continued by the natural elements. Starving,
thirsty, chilled and burned, chafed by rawhide, soaked by rivers, scarred
by branches, Mazeppa suffers after the fashion of an equestrian
Prometheus until at last the exhausted horse drops dead. Still bound to
its corpse, Mazeppa loses consciousness—then wakes to find himself
tended by a Cossack maid. He recovers and eventually becomes the
leader of his rescuers. From this position, he is able "[w]ith twice five
thousand horse, to thank / The Count for his uncourteous ride"
(4:186). This lesson of endurance and revenge, his concluding general-
ization implies, is something Charles XII should keep in mind after
Pultowa:

> Thus the vain fool who strove to glut
> His rage, refining on my pain,
> Sent me forth to the wilderness,
> Bound, naked, bleeding, and alone,
> To pass the desert to a throne,—
> What mortal his own doom may guess?—
> Let none despond, let none despair!
>   (4:199–200)

The Lament of Tasso and *The Prophecy of Dante* are, precisely speaking, monologues rather than tales. In the former, Byron incorporates sentiments from the Italian poet Tasso's works into his own verses and then puts those verses into the mouth of Tasso, whom Alphonso II, Marquess of Este (great-great-grandson of Niccolò III, husband of Parisina), imprisoned for madness in the Hospital of Sant'Anna. In Byron's account, Tasso's confinement rises from two further reasons: the poet's libertarian spirit and his presumptuous, unreciprocated love for Alphonso's sister Leonora. Byron knew that the latter claim had been disproven but believed the former, which since his day has also been discredited (*CPW*, 4:479). Presenting Tasso as persecuted for resisting authority in politics and defying convention in love, Byron can make use of the Italian story to comment indirectly on his own exile from England. Tasso's address to Leonora might, at times, be Byron speaking to Augusta: "That thou wert beautiful, and I not blind, / Hath been the sin which shuts me from mankind; / But let them go, or torture as they will, / My heart can multiply thy image still" (4:118). Similarly, toward the end of Tasso's lament to Leonora comes a prediction that could with equal accuracy be applied to Byron and Augusta or, in rather a different vein, Annabella: "No power in death can tear our names apart, / As none in life could rend thee from my heart" (4:124).

Byron composed *The Prophecy of Dante* with another beloved in mind: the Beatrice to his Dante was Teresa Guiccioli, at whose behest the poem was written. Here, Byron appropriates not merely the persona of the older poet but also the verse form he used in the *Divinia Commedia*, terza rima. Byron had gained more than a reader's familiarity with Dante's rhyme by translating the Francesca da Rimini episode from the *Inferno* section of the *Commedia,* and he was proud of his four-canto impersonative prophecy, which he cagily characterized to Murray as "the best thing I ever wrote if it be not *unintelligible*" (*BLJ,* 7:59). It was a project he thought worthy of continuation: "[I]f approved I will go on like Isaiah" (7:57). His pride partly rose from a sense that the poem could help the then-promising cause of Italian nationalism by foreshadowing the liberation of Italy from Austria. But like imprisoned Tasso's lament, exiled Dante's prophecy also permits Byron to offer a veiled criticism of the British culture that drove him away:

> The day may come when she will cease to err,
> The day may come when she would be proud to have

The dust she dooms to scatter, and transfer
Of him, whom she denied a home, the grave.
                                            (*CPW,* 4:218)

Dante, as presented in the first-person prophecy, has gained through
banishment an independence to be cherished, notwithstanding its high
price. Like Byron, he has learned "[a] bitter lesson; but it leaves me free:
/ I have not vilely found, nor basely sought, / They made an Exile—not
a slave of me" (4:221).

Beppo (1817) is something of an anomaly in this chapter. Based on a
comic anecdote Byron heard at La Mira, it is obviously a tale—one
deriving from gossip, not history or legend. Further, as English appropriation of Italian ottava rima, it clearly belongs in the company of the
various "translations"—a word we can use literally to mean putting particular works from other languages into English (such as the Armenian
"Pleasures of the Summer Houses of Byzantium" or the first canto of
Pulci's *Morgante Maggiore*)—occupying Byron at this stage of his career.
More loosely, the term can also be used to indicate his tales' use of verse
forms, characters, voices, and situations from another language, culture,
or poet's oeuvre (as in *Mazeppa, The Lament of Tasso,* and *The Prophecy of
Dante,* discussed earlier). But despite its status as tale, *Beppo* is a narrative whose characters and story are incidental, far less interesting than
are its narrator and his digressions. And despite being based on trivial
material, *Beppo* has received a high degree of critical attention—principally for the way it goes against the spirit of Byron's other tales and
anticipates in miniature the brilliance of *Don Juan.* Jerome McGann and
Peter Manning voice critical consensus when they respectively characterize *Beppo* as "probably the most crucial single work in the entire canon"
and "the pivot in Byron's turn on the Romantic excesses of his generation."[9]

   Beppo's reputation has not always been so high. On 29 August 1817
Byron heard from Pietro Segati, husband of his mistress Marianna, the
droll story of another amorous triangle: a Venetian woman whose spouse
had for years been presumed lost at sea, her lover, and a Turk who, on
taking lodgings at her inn, revealed himself as the long-absent husband.
In September Byron came across the immediate poetic model for his
telling of this tale, John Hookham Frere's English use of ottava rima in
Prospectus and Specimen of an Intended National Work, by William and Robert

Whistlecraft (first installment of *The Monks and the Giants*, popularly known as "*Whistlecraft*"), published by Murray in 1817 and brought to Byron by either Rose or the Kinnairds. Apparently written in two days, October 9 and 10, *Beppo* went off to Murray with instructions that "it won't do for your journal [i.e., the Tory *Quarterly Review*] being full of political allusions—*print alone—without name*" (*BLJ*, 6:7).

Beppo appeared in late February 1818, and Francis Jeffrey, anonymously appraising the anonymous poem in the *Edinburgh Review*, struck the keynote for those reviewers who were amused by its liveliness if not edified by its moral stance: "It is, in itself, absolutely a thing of nothing—without story, characters, sentiments, or intelligible object—a mere piece of lively and loquacious prattling."[10] Other reviewers were less tolerant. In the recently founded *Blackwood's Magazine*, for instance, "Presbyter Anglicanus" addresses a "Letter to the Author of *Beppo*" (which carried its author's name starting with the fifth edition of late April) denouncing all Byron's works on account of "how little there is whose object it is to make us reverence virtue or love our country!"[11] In *Childe Harold* and the Oriental tales, "[i]f you were an immoral and an unchristian, you were at least a serious, poet." But now in *Beppo*, "We see you in a shape less sentimental and mysterious. We look below the disguise which has once been lifted, and claim acquaintance, not with the sadness of the princely masque, but with the scoffing and sardonic merriment of the ill-dissembling reveller beneath it. In an evil hour did you step from your vantage-ground and teach us that Harold, Byron, and the Count of Beppo were the same."[12] The crude conflation of author and characters by the Presbyter may seem naive, but what Byron's contemporary reviewers either deprecated or denounced in *Beppo* resembles what present-day readers value, whether they share McGann's view that *Beppo* is Byron's means of "transmitting what is essentially a very personal poem" or Manning's sense that the Byronic self fashions its image, rather than reflecting its essence, through such tales that "navigate impersonal structures."[13]

The self expressed or constructed through *Beppo* was saner and happier than Byron had been during his last year in England and his first year abroad. In Italy—especially at Venice, "very agreeable for Gentlemen of desultory habits" (*BLJ*, 4:44)—he had settled comfortably into a milieu that cared nothing for the scandal of his domestic discords and nothing for the canting rules that governed English liaisons, though to be sure a different set of hypocritical conventions defined Italian love as he was experiencing it. A further reason for Byron's new tack in *Beppo* is his sense, alluded to above, that the British poets of his age were getting things badly wrong, an argument he had earlier made in *English Bards* but largely retracted in his years of fame. Writing to Murray around the time he would have read Frere's *Whistlecraft,* Byron says, "I am convinced the more I think of it—that he [Moore] and *all* of us . . . are upon a wrong revolutionary poetical system—or systems—not worth a damn in itself" *(BLJ,* 6:265). This letter signals the rebirth of Byron's fervent partisanship for "the little Queen Anne's Man" Alexander Pope, but fortunately for *Beppo,* rekindled veneration did not push Byron back into quasi-Augustan verse. As Andrew Rutherford has shrewdly pointed out, "It is one thing to admire a writer—quite another to succeed in imitating his style" (Rutherford, 109). Whatever a backward glance at Pope might do for Byron's poetic theory, recognizing the potential of Frere's charming ottava rima experiment and then absorbing the "meridian" tone of the Italian masters whose meter Frere had appropriated (Pulci, Casti) gave a fruitful new direction to his poetic practice.

Beppo sets its tale of triangular love in the context of Venetian Carnival, that season replete "[w]ith fiddling, feasting, dancing, drinking, masking, / And other things which may be had for asking" *(CPW,* 4:129). Here we encounter a heroine the narrator claims to have arbitrarily named (though we need not believe him): "And so we'll call her Laura, if you please, / Because it slips into my verse with ease" (4:136). She is the "still blooming" wife of a shipping merchant, "[h]is name Giuseppe, called more briefly, Beppo," whose failure to return from a voyage has left Laura alone in Venice for several years. Bereft of her husband, this "Adriatic Ariadne"

> waited long, and wept a little,
>   And thought of wearing weeds, as well she might;
> She almost lost all appetite for victual,
>   And could not sleep with ease alone at night,
> She deemed the window-frames and shutters brittle,
>   Against a daring house-breaker or sprite,
> And so she thought it prudent to connect her
> With a vice-husband, *chiefly* to *protect her.*
>   *(CPW,* 4:138)

The man she chooses is a count, accomplished, tasteful, "a perfect cavaliero": "He was a lover of the good old school, / Who still become more constant as they cool" (*CPW,* 4:140). Half a dozen years pass smoothly in the Count and Laura's urbane "new arrangement," and one evening of Carnival finds them at the Ridotto for a masked ball, where Laura, as worldly wise as Petrarch's lady was rarefied, deftly navigates through the throng:

> To some she whispers, others speaks aloud,
>> To some she curtsies, and to some she dips,
> Complains of warmth, and this complaint avow'd,
>> Her lover brings the lemonade, she sips;
> She then surveys, condemns, but pities still
> Her dearest friends for being drest so ill.
>> (4:149)

Before her appears a Turk, "the colour of mahogany," who later on is waiting as Laura and the Count's gondola glides up to their palace stairs. " 'That lady is *my wife!* ' " the Mussulman exclaims—and at the point where a passionate duel would ensue in one of Byron's Eastern tales, the three enter the palace, call for coffee ("[a] beverage for Turks and Christians both"), and amicably sort things out.

In these negotiations, Laura seizes and keeps the initiative by posing a barrage of questions salted with exclamations:

> 'Beppo! what's your pagan name?
>> Bless me! your beard is of amazing growth!
> And how came you to keep away so long?
>> Are you not sensible 'twas very wrong?
>
> 'And are you *really, truly,* now a Turk?
>> With any other women did you wive?
> Is't true they use their fingers for a fork?
>> Well, that's the prettiest shawl—as I'm alive!
> You'll give it me? They say you eat no pork.
>> And how so many years did you contrive
> To—Bless me! did I ever? No, I never
> Saw a man grown so yellow! How's your liver?'
>> (*CPW,* 4:157–58)

It turns out that Beppo was cast away near the ruins of Troy and enslaved until he escaped to a career of piracy and thereby enriched himself until he felt inclined to come home with his ill-gotten gains, passed off as the profits of "a true Turkey-merchant" as he reclaims "[h]is wife, religion, house, and Christian name" (4:159). Totally unlike the returning Ulysses, Beppo by no means avenges himself against the suitor he has caught in residence. In fact the narrator informs us that in Beppo's rich and sociable retirement, "[t]hough Laura sometimes put him in a rage, / I've heard the Count and he were always friends" (4:160).

The Venice preserved in *Beppo* is home to a cheerful amorality quite unlike the tormented intensity generally prevailing in Byron's Eastern tales, or for that matter in the imagined Venice of Shakespeare. *Beppo*'s narrator observes that since Desdemona's time no woman of the Veneto has encountered a

> [h]usband whom mere suspicion could inflame
>   To suffocate a wife no more than twenty,
> Because she had a "cavalier servente."
>
> Their jealousy (if they are ever jealous)
>   Is of a fair complexion altogether,
> Not like that sooty devil of Othello's
>   Which smothers women in a bed of feather,
> But worthier of these much more jolly fellows;
>   When weary of the matrimonial tether
> His head for such a wife no mortal bothers,
> But takes at once another, or another's.
>   (4:134)

As the contriver of this intertextual and intercultural comparison, which juxtaposes Shakespeare's fiction with Byron's and also by inference the island world of Venice with that of England, the raconteur provides a degree of fascination not intrinsic to his tale. It is his words the reader hangs on, whether they recount the dietary hypocrisies of an Italian Lent, the absurdity of English authors who are *"all author"*—notably "Botherby" (William Sotheby) and company—or the comparative delights of Italy's "soft" language, weather, and women to those of England:

> "England! with all thy faults I love thee still,"
>   I said at Calais, and have not forgot it;
> I like to speak and lucubrate my fill;
>   I like the government (but that is not it);
> I like the freedom of the press and quill;
>   I like the Habeas Corpus (when we've got it);
> I like a parliamentary debate,
> Particularly when 'tis not too late.

It seems something less than fair for the Whig Jeffrey to have character-ized a poem containing lines so concise, amusing, and trenchant in their attack on repressive Tory politics in the Napoleonic era as "a thing of nothing." Yet we begin to see why Jeffrey does so as the narrator's ironic catalog of admiration continues:

> I like the taxes, when they're not too many;
>   I like a seacoal fire, when not too dear;
> I like a beef-steak, too, as well as any;
>   Have no objection to a pot of beer;
> I like the weather, when it is not rainy,
>   That is, I like two months of every year.
> And so God save the Regent, Church, and King!
> Which means that I like all and every thing.
>   (*CPW,* 4:144)

Obviously Byron did not like "all and every thing" about his native country—and his well-modulated nuances of praise make that plain to all readers but the obtuse. Nonetheless, the easy ethos of Venice has maneuvered him into an odd corner for a satirist to occupy. His narrator can only imply a critique of the homeland whose climate (political, moral, actual) chilled Byron to the bone. Within the Italian stanzas of *Beppo* he must practice Venetian tolerance. To turn judgmental would be to embody the English moralizing he mocks. The resulting good-humored amorality may be paradoxical for a satirist, but it seems the right keynote for the "broken Dandy lately on his travels" set up as *Beppo*'s narrator, that "nameless sort of person" who can simultaneously disavow and invoke Byron's tale-telling past and present:

Oh that I had the art of easy writing
    What should be easy reading! could I scale
Parnassus, where the Muses sit inditing
    Those pretty poems never known to fail,
How quickly would I print (the world delighting)
    A Grecian, Syrian, or *Assyrian* tale;
And sell you, mix'd with western sentimentalism,
Some samples of the finest Orientalism.
                                                      (4:144)

We encounter just that mixture in Byron's last tale, *The Island* (1823), which is based on the famous *Bounty* mutiny of 1789. Most of Byron's information derives from William Bligh's *A Voyage to the South Sea for the purpose of conveying the Bread-Fruit Tree to the West Indies in his Majesty's Ship Bounty . . . including the Narrative of the Mutiny* (1792) and John Martin's *An Account of the Natives of the Tonga Islands* (1817), a two-volume compilation of William Mariner's observations. Writing to Leigh Hunt, Byron defined his tale in terms of the two things he meant to avoid: "[T]he first that of running foul of my own 'Corsair' and style—so as to produce repetition and monotony—the other *not* to run counter to the reigning stupidity altogether—otherwise they will say that I am eulogizing *Mutiny*" (*BLJ*, 10:90). To further these objectives, his tale marginalizes the mutiny's leader, Christian, last in the long gallery of Byronic heroes, and highlights the courage rather than the tyranny of Bligh, who appears only in the first of the poem's four cantos. Both strategies place Byron's version of the mutiny at odds with the prevailing myth that made its way into nineteenth- and twentieth-century popular culture—and also at apparent variance with the values characteristically embodied in his works, in which no one fares worse than the regents and agents of despotic regimes. (In this regard it is worth remembering that Bligh, quite apart from being a harsh captain to his own crew, was transporting a new food source to nourish the slave economies of the West Indies.)

As had been his way in the Eastern tales, Byron submerges historical contexts and emphasizes personal relationships in *The Island*, which centers on the love of Neuha, the highborn "sun-flower of the Island daughters" of Toobonai, and "A blooming boy, a truant mutineer, / The fair-haired Torquil" (*CPW*, 7:42), a Hebridean sailor based on midshipman George Stewart, who was taken into custody on Tahiti when the

British ship *Pandora* came in pursuit of the *Bounty* mutineers. Caroline Franklin acutely points out that in Byron's version of the *Bounty* mutiny, as in modern feminism, the personal is the political. This assumption explains why Byron used Bligh's narrative, in which the sailors' revolt stems from the attractions of life and love on Tahiti rather than from shipboard tyranny, instead of other accounts more sympathetic to the mutineers (Franklin, 91). But historicized politics are present, if peripheral, in the tale. As epithet, *The Island* might be applied with equal pertinence to Great Britain and to Toobonai, and the cultural comparisons played out in the tale show imperialist Britain, rather than the Edenic South Sea island, as lacking in civilization. The pleasures of natural love in a landscape rich with "[t]he unreaped harvest of unfurrowed fields" and "unpurchased groves" together with

> the luxuries of seas and woods,
> The airy joys of social solitudes,
> Tamed each rude wanderer to the sympathies
> Of those who were more happy, if less wise,
> Did more than Europe's discipline had done,
> And civilized civilization's son!
>
> (7:43 – 44)

To put it another way, the isle of ease—Circe's realm in reverse—makes men of the shipboard beasts called "tars." Bounty humanizes what *Bounty* brutalized.

Canto 1 of *The Island* presents the mutiny, the dispatch of "bold Bligh" and his few adherents, in a minimally equipped craft reminiscent of the longboat in *Don Juan*, and the mutineers' return to "happy shores without a law," where Nature and "Nature's Goddess—Woman" await them and where "all partake the earth without dispute" (*CPW,* 7:33). Canto 2 centers on the love of Neuha and Torquil, perhaps the purest Byron ever brought himself to describe in a narrative poem:

> The love which maketh all things fond and fair,
> The youth which makes one rainbow of the air,
> The dangers past, that make even man enjoy
> The pause in which he ceases to destroy,
> The mutual beauty, which the sternest feel

Strike to their hearts like lightning to the steel,
United the half savage and the whole,
The maid and boy, in one absorbing soul.
                                                    (7:45)

Their seaside idyll, like Juan's and Haidée's, ends at sundown, as the
comic mutineer Ben Bunting comes to warn Torquil that he has sighted
"a wicked-looking craft." At the start of canto 3, the battle is already
over, and all the rebels except a "little remnant" including the wounded
Torquil, Bunting, and their leader, Christian, are dead or captured.
"Silent, and sad, and savage," the Byronic hero Christian resembles his
old adversary Bligh in being a bold and noble specimen of European
manliness. He wishes he could send his injured comrade to safety but
asserts that " '[f]or me, my lot is what I sought; to be, / In life or death,
the fearless and the free' " (7:58). But Neuha, who has arrived with fellow islanders and a pair of "light canoes," takes control and coordinates
a wholesale escape from rapidly approaching armed boats. She places
Christian and the other two sailors in one vessel, herself and Torquil in
the other. They embark and take separate routes to baffle pursuit: "And
now the refuge and the foe are nigh— / Yet, yet a moment! Fly, thou
light Ark, fly!" (7:60).

As the biblical connotation of canto 3's final line implies, Neuha's
canoe carries the lovers to a new life together in canto 4. They paddle to
a black rock not far from the shore of Toobonai where, as the British
approach, Neuha cries, " 'Torquil, follow me, and fearless follow!' "
(*CPW,* 7:63) and dives headlong into the sea. "And where was he, the
Pilgrim of the Deep? / Following the Nereid?" (7:64). After plunging
deep into the sea, the lovers come up into a spacious undersea cave that,
illuminated by "a sobered ray" of penetrating sunlight and the pine
torch resourceful Neuha has carried along, is revealed as a "chapel of the
Seas" complete in all its features with "self-born Gothic canopy," "arch
upreared by nature's architect," "architrave some earthquake might
erect," "buttress from some mountain's bosom hurled," "fretted pinna-
cle," aisle, and nave (7:65–66). As if it were a manmade Christian
church, this natural grotto offers sanctuary for the fleeing outlaw. Here
he and Neuha subsist on the stores she providentially brought there,
while in the world above the waves the other mutineers, civilized by
island life, are hunted down like beasts by their British brothers. Christian dies last, twice wounded but killing one final foe (rather comically

shot with a button, as Christian is out of ammunition) before shaking his fist in a "last rage 'gainst the earth which he forsook" (7:71) and plunging off a high rock. The narrator refrains from judging this end: "The rest was nothing—save a life mis-spent, / And soul—but who shall answer where it went? / 'Tis ours to bear, not judge the dead" (7:72). When the British ship sails off with its captives, Neuha and Torquil return to Toobonai, where their escape at once becomes the tale of "Neuha's Cave." Unique among the lovers of Byron's tales, they return "[t]o Peace and Pleasure, perilously earned; / A night succeeded by such happy days / As only the yet infant world displays" (7:74).

Though at first glance they might seem antithetical works, *The Island* and *Beppo* resemble one another and differ from the rest of Byron's tales in two important ways. As tales of tolerance, both offer their lovers (young or no longer young, couple or triangle) happy endings, and both present women whose powers make them fully and undisguisedly equal to men and whose candid sexuality is rewarded rather than punished. In each case, the tale's mise-en-scène is central to the tolerant outcome. As we have seen, the supercivilized amorality of Venice allows the principal characters of *Beppo* to resolve their potential differences by drinking coffee rather than by shedding blood. In a different way, the "infant world" of Toobonai permits the endurance of romantic bliss and the equality of women and men because it is a primitive paradise. Significantly, in both tales the island values prevailing and the British values contrasted with them come into contact only obliquely. Venice and Britain or Toobonai and Britain are juxtaposed realms rather than rival powers disputing territory, as, for instance, the Ottoman and Venetian Empires did over Corinth. *The Island* and *Beppo* demonstrate more clearly than do any of the other tales Byron's ambivalent or relativist sense of different codes for different places—but also his concurrent understanding that some human truths transcend, or underlie, all such local differences.

Chapter Five

Dramatic Poems

Byron was a keenly interested patron of the theater and a persistent writer of dramatic works, but he claimed that these two roles were not to overlap. His involvement with the theatrical world of Regency England dovetailed with his highly dramatic presence in Whig society following the debut of *Childe Harold*. In 1812 London's Theatre Royal, Drury Lane, which had burned in 1809, was due to reopen. Lord Holland, a member of the special committee for Drury Lane, asked Byron to enter a competition to write the opening-night address. Byron declined and confided his reasons to Lady Melbourne: "I never risk *rivalry* in anything." (*BLJ*, 2:193). After the committee rejected all submissions, Holland asked Byron to write the address. Gratified, Byron labored to produce occasional verses that proved serviceable and tame at best.[1]

With Thomas Moore, Byron saw the renowned tragedian Edmund Kean's first performance as Iago in *Othello*. In Hobhouse's company, he later met, dined, and chatted with the actor so highly admired for this and other Shakespearean roles. Through his friendship with Douglas Kinnaird, Byron was appointed in 1815 to the Sub-Committee of Management of Drury Lane Theatre. He became deeply involved in recruiting actors and acquiring dramatic works. For help with the latter, he turned to fellow poets—most successfully to Walter Scott, on whose recommendation he gained Charles Maturin's tragedy *Bertram*. From his exile abroad Byron sent Kinnaird a "Monody on the Death of the Right Hon. R. B. Sheridan," to be read at Drury Lane, formerly owned by Sheridan and, through its burning, the cause of his financial ruin. Like Byron's address, this topical piece did not come to life in spite of his heartfelt regard for its subject.

The limited success of Byron's ventures into the Regency theatrical world caused him to remark in a letter to Kinnaird, "As to tragedy, I may try one day—but *never* for the *stage*—don't you see I have no luck there?—my two addresses were not liked—& my Committee-ship did but get me into scrapes—no—no—I shall not tempt the Fates that way—besides I should risk more than I could gain—I have no right to encroach on other men's ground—even if I could maintain my own. . . . Unless I could beat them all—it would be nothing—& who could do that? nor I nor any man—the Drama is complete already—there can be nothing like what has been" (*BLJ,* 5:196). The problems: Byron admired stage drama too fervently to settle for anything less than the highest accomplishment, and he knew the fickle insolence of playgoers too well to subject one of his works to the risk of being hissed. Thus when Byron turned his hand to playwriting, as he first did with *Manfred* (1817), he explicitly and repeatedly indicated that his works were not meant for staging—and he lashed out when *Marino Faliero* was put on the boards against his expressed wishes. Despite his fears of onstage failure, though, dramatic poetry suited his sensibility. His ottava rima poems *Beppo* and *Don Juan,* written in the spontaneously conversational mode of an Italian *improvisatore,* set up an essentially theatrical relationship between the tale's contriver and his audience. Especially at times when the composition of *Don Juan* languished, Byron displayed this theatrical penchant in poetic dramas based on stories from diverse sources. *Marino Faliero* (1820), *Sardanapalus* (1821), and *The Two Foscari* (1821) have historical origins. *Cain* (1821) and *Heaven and Earth* (1821) derive from the Bible. *Werner* (1822) and *The Deformed Transformed* (1822) draw eclectically from German and English literary sources, as does *Manfred.*[2]

Byron began writing *Manfred* during his summer of 1816 in Switzerland and completed it in Venice in the winter of 1817. The drama sprang from three sources: the August 1816 visit of "Monk" Lewis, who came to Villa Diodati trailing clouds of gothicism and who orally translated *Faust* for Byron and his circle; Byron and Hobhouse's September tour of the high Bernese Alps; and what Byron evasively termed "something else," presumably his remorse and retrospection in the first year of exile. Byron composed the first two of the dramatic poem's three acts while at his zenith of romantic sublimity. He wrote and revised the last act in another, more skeptical mood, and it is in this latter vein that he characterizes the piece in a letter to Kinnaird, his former colleague on the Drury Lane subcommittee. *Manfred,* Byron explains, is a sort of metaphysical drama "which is the very Antipodes of the stage and is meant to be so—it is all in the Alps & the other world—and as mad as Bedlam—I do not know that it is even fit for publication—the persons are all magicians—ghosts—& the evil principle—with a mixed mythology of my own—which you may suppose is somewhat of the strangest.———" (*BLJ,* 5:194–95). Although the drama's blend of literary sources has proved too subtle for some readers—notably those who saw *Manfred* as plagiarism without recognizing, as Goethe himself did, that it offers the Faust motif in an altogether different key³—Byron's "mixed mythology" proves a larger stumbling block. Just as the drama's doomed yet intractable protagonist, part Faust and part Hamlet but all Byronic hero, goes through natural and supernatural realms refusing to genuflect to any authority—whether nature, society, God, or "the evil principle"—so the perennially skeptical Byron was unwilling or unable to put his serious metaphysical speculations into a systematic form that would permit them to be followed to an unambiguous conclusion. As a result, the dramatic poem can repel readers who lack a taste for philosophy and frustrate those who have one.

The play begins with "MANFRED *alone—Scene, a Gothic gallery—Time, midnight.*" After a monologue acknowledging the "fatal truth, / The Tree of Knowledge is not that of Life" (*CPW,* 4:53), the magelike protagonist calls up a succession of elemental spirits, the seventh and most powerful governing "[t]he star which rules thy destiny." When this spirit appears in beauteous female shape and then vanishes, Manfred falls senseless. In his swoon he hears an incantation issuing from external nature or from his own depths. Whatever its source, the import is romantic solipsism: "I call upon thee! and compel / Thyself to be thy proper Hell!" (4:61). The nature of the curse becomes clearer in the next scene, which finds Manfred alone on the cliffs of the Jungfrau at morning. His brain reels on the edge of the abyss, yet his foot is firm and he does not plunge. It is his "fatality to live"—but not to live either as simple creature or as pure spirit. Manfred, Hamletlike at this point, identifies the fatal blend of "low wants and lofty will" as the universal human condition:

> Beautiful!
> How beautiful is all this visible world!
> How glorious in its action and itself;
> But we, who name ourselves its sovereigns, we,
> Half dust, half deity, alike unfit
> To sink or soar, with our mix'd essence make
> A conflict of its elements.
>
> (4:63)

Though all humanity may share this mixed essence, not all humans think alike. Poised on the cliff's edge, Manfred reaches a self-absorbed, suicidal conclusion: "Earth! take these atoms!" But a chamois hunter providentially or fortuitously arrives on the scene in time to stop his plunge, and the hunter's perspective takes account of human interconnectedness: "though aweary of thy life, / Stain not our pure vales with thy guilty blood" (4:66).

Act 2 discloses more a personal reason for Manfred's alienation. Having taken leave of the hunter, he encounters the Witch of the Alps, presumably a representation of natural beauty, who rises up beneath the sunbow shimmering on an alpine cataract. Manfred will not subjugate himself to her will, but he does provide her with a detailed account of his development as an extraordinary being whose "spirit walk'd not with the souls of men, / Nor look'd upon the earth with human eyes" (*CPW*, 4:72). His tragedy on this lonely path has been to lose the one person capable of sympathizing with him: Astarte, a sister, lover, anima, or all three, a being Manfred reads as himself "soften'd all, and temper'd into beauty." "Her faults were mine—her virtues were her own— / I loved her and destroy'd her!" (4:74). As Manfred believes, the means of Astarte's destruction was not his hand but his heart, "which broke her heart— / It gazed on mine, and withered" (4:74). Perhaps because Astarte died a suicide, Manfred's wanderings next take him to the underworld, where a motley throng of spirits and destinies who have been celebrating on the Jungfrau in the preceding scene now gather in the Hall of Arimanes, prince of darkness. Again Manfred will not be cowed by supernatural presences, and the impressed Arimanes has Nemesis conjure up the phantom of Astarte, who tells Manfred his earthly ills will end the next day, then disappears with only a "Farewell!"

Act 3 returns the action of Manfred's metaphysical drama to the physical world and human society. The abbot of St. Maurice has come to Manfred's castle in hopes of helping him "to reconcile thyself with thy own soul, / And thy own soul with heaven" (*CPW*, 4:91). Courteous but self-reliant, Manfred dismisses the priest, and instead of making peace with his heavenly father addresses the setting sun as its last rays fall on him and he looks his last on it: "As my first glance / Of love and wonder was for thee, then take / My latest look: thou wilt not beam on one / To whom the gifts of life and warmth have been / Of a more fatal nature" (4:94). After some conventionally comic relief involving Manfred's retainers, the abbot returns to find their master still communing by moonlight with nature from his tower: "I linger yet with Nature, for the night / Hath been to me a more familiar face / than that of man" (4:97). Manfred again resists the abbot's evangelism. When infernal spirits rise

up to claim him, Manfred banishes them not with God's name but with
a self-sufficiency reminiscent of Milton's Satan in *Paradise Lost:*

> —Back to thy hell!
> Thou hast no power upon me, *that* I feel;
> Thou never shalt possess me, *that* I know:
> What I have done is done; I bear within
> A torture which could nothing gain from thine."
>   (4:101)

As the demons disappear, Manfred feels death upon him and says to the
abbot, "Fare thee well— / Give me thy hand."

> ABBOT.   Cold—cold even to the heart—
>   But yet one prayer—alas! how fares it with thee?—
> MAN.   Old man! 'tis not so difficult to die.
>   [MANFRED *expires*]
> ABBOT.   He's gone—his soul hath ta'en its earthless flight—
>   Whither? I dread to think—but he is gone.
>   (6:102)

The drama ends with this irony of the young, skeptical, alienated
man comforting the old, pious, connected one. It did not so end when
first published, because of Byron's decision to dispense with seeing final
proofs. At the advice of Gifford, who corrected those proofs at Byron's
direction, Murray left out Manfred's last speech. With this small but
crucial omission, Byron observed, Murray "destroyed the whole effect &
moral of the poem" (*BLJ,* 5:257). The line was replaced in 1818—but
that was not to be the end of Byron's trouble with his publisher over
matters of faith and doubt in drama.

Although the loosely structured *Manfred* is exactly what Byron termed
it, a "dramatic poem" rather than a drama, his next theatrical efforts,
Marino Faliero, Sardanapalus, and *The Two Foscari,* follow the model of
neoclassical five-act tragedy. Byron even goes so unfashionably far as to
observe or approximate the traditional unities of action, time, and place
in these historically grounded plays, a strategy he defends in the preface

to *Sardanapalus, The Two Foscari,* and *Cain* by "conceiving that with any very distant departure from them, there may be poetry, but can be no drama" (*CPW,* 6:16). At the same time, Byron claims in this preface that the plays "were not composed with the most remote view to the stage," words echoing the preface to *Marino Faliero,* which asserts, "Were I capable of writing a play which could be deemed stageworthy, success would give me no pleasure, and failure great pain. . . . I never made the attempt, and never will" (4:305). The potentially contradictory nature of Byron's statements and practices seemed evident to a good many of his contemporaries, among them William Elliston of Drury Lane, who produced *Faliero* despite Byron's objections, and Francis Jeffrey, whose review of *The Two Foscari, Sardanapalus,* and *Cain* poses the reasonable question, "Why, then, should he affect the form, without the power of tragedy?"[4]

Writing elsewhere, Jeffrey labels *Marino Faliero* "merely another *Venice Preserved*" and deprecates Byron's tragedy as "continually recalling, though certainly without eclipsing," Otway's drama.[5] Byron had read and admired *Venice Preserved,* but his inspiration was more than Otway—and more than literary.[6] The still-visible signs of Faliero's conspiracy against the oligarchy powerfully moved Byron in 1817, when he was becoming acquainted with Venice and its history: "There is still, in the Doge's palace the black veil painted over Falieri's picture & the staircase where he was first crowned Doge, & subsequently decapitated.—This was the thing that most struck my imagination in Venice" (*BLJ,* 5:203). Imaginatively engaged, Byron read widely of Faliero in accounts ancient and modern, up through Antoine Daru's *Histoire de la République de Venise* (1819). He learned from these sources that Marino Faliero (1270–1355) was a distinguished military and diplomatic leader appointed doge in 1354. Enraged when a young patrician named Steno, tried for defiling the ducal chair with graffiti alluding to the infidelity of Faliero's wife, received only a light punishment from the governing Council of Forty, Faliero joined forces with a group of plebeian revolutionaries plotting to overturn the patrician oligarchy. At the discovery of the plot, Faliero and the other conspirators were executed.

As John Spalding Gatton points out, Byron's changes to Faliero's story—compressing two weeks of action into a single day, moving portions of the story from their actual sites of occurrence, making the tale hinge on the aged Faliero's volatile temper, foiling the old, irascible doge with a young, steady wife (the well-named Angiolina), having the outraged Faliero approached by an already formed band of conspirators

with whom he agrees to fight "this o'ergrown aristocratic Hydra" the
Venetian oligarchy, ascribing Faliero's downfall to classical tragedy's fate
and fortune rather than Christian sin and punishment—all serve to
respect the three dramatic unities.[7] Most of these innovations also
enhance the personal and political resonances of the drama, written in
Ravenna during spring and summer of 1820, the early days of Byron's
official *serventismo* and of his involvement in the cause of Italian liberation. Faliero's alienation from a society that once fawned upon but now
insults him and his ambivalence as a well-born "friend of the people"
opposed to an authoritarian regime but nevertheless uncomfortable
with the populace he befriends can be seen as parallel to Byron's personal and political feelings about England or, in rather a different way,
Italy. The fourteenth-century Venetian republic of *Marino Faliero* proves
analogous to both post-Napoleonic Italy (where with the aristocratic
Gambas Byron was supporting the revolutionary Carbonari movement)
and late Regency England (where Byron deplored the repressive Tory
government only somewhat more than he deprecated Hobhouse's con-
sorting with Radical reformers). It may be that the analogical reverbera-
tions of Faliero's dramatized story suffice to answer Jeffrey's question of
"Why, then, should he affect the form?" Perhaps the power of a tragedy
with such a blend of political and personal overtones need not be
invoked onstage.

In his study *Byron's Politics,* Malcolm Kelsall argues that *Marino Faliero*
and *The Two Foscari,* which was written after *Sardanapalus* in June and
July of 1821, "form a mutually commenting pair."[8] Byron took the
account of the fifteenth-century Venetian doge Francesco Foscari, like
that of Faliero, from historical reading, especially in Daru and Sismondi.
Beaten down by the grief and insult of having his only living son, Jacopo,
repeatedly tried and banished for personal and political crimes, Foscari
withdrew from state responsibilities but refused to abdicate. Deposed by
the Council of Ten, Foscari died two days later, on 1 November 1457—
about 10 months after Jacopo had died in exile on Crete. In his tragedy's
account of father and son, Byron again manipulates history in order to
preserve the dramatic unities. He eliminates Francesco's wife but gives
her name, Marina, to Jacopo's wife, whom he presents as a fearless, vocif-
erous foil to both male Foscaris. He replaces potentially dramatic incident (such as Jacopo's crimes, trials, banishments, and unauthorized
return to Venice) with exposition to unify the tragedy's action within a
day. He brings the two Foscaris' deaths together in time, place, and
mode—the son expires on departing for Cretan exile, the father on hear-

ing the bell that tolls him out of office (Gatton, 65 – 67). Such innovations reduce or eliminate the chances for a dynamic piece of theater. As a stage play *The Two Foscari* may be, in Jeffrey's appraisal, "wanting in interest, character, and action."[9] But as a piece of closet political theater, it effectively complements *Marino Faliero*. If the Aristotelian fatal flaw in the former play is violent resistance to the state's injustice, the cause of tragedy in the latter is passive obedience, which brings both the doge and his son to their deaths. In the Venetian republic and in the British constitutional monarchy that the two historical tragedies shadow forth, neither resistance nor obedience leads to political progress. "Taken together," says Kelsall, "the two plays are indicative of a total impasse producing, in Venice, decline and eventual extinction. What moral might that offer for Britain?" (Kelsall, 91).

Between January and late May of 1821, Byron wrote *Sardanapalus,* a tragedy freely adapted from Diodorus Siculus's and William Mitford's accounts of the last king of Assyria. Bracketed by the two Venetian plays, *Sardanapalus* is, despite the obvious differences of period and locale, like *The Two Foscari* something of a pendant to *Marino Faliero*. As Richard Lansdown points out, Sardanapalus falls victim to just the sort of rebellion that Faliero joins.[10] Byron presents Sardanapalus as a man of *mobilité* trapped in the role of absolute monarch: hedonistic yet courageous, humane, ironic, self-dramatizing, separated from his wife and engrossed in his mistress, more lovable than respectable, he might be compared to a number of real or fictive prototypes, alone or in combination. Sardanapalus resembles the Mark Antony of Shakespeare or Dryden (torn between Egyptian and Roman worlds and values), Byron himself (divided, in his Italian life, between private indulgence and public activism), George IV (another unfaithful husband who as Prince Regent decreed for himself at Brighton a spacious seaside pleasure dome not unlike Sardanapalus's pavilion over the Euphrates), the impulsive Don Juan blended with the cynical, witty *Don Juan* narrator.

In his effort to "approach the unities," Byron condenses the rebellion that brought down the royal Assyrian line of Nimrod to less than one day's incident. The play begins at evening in a hall of the palace, with the luxury-loving Sardanapalus *"effeminately dressed, his Head crowned with Flowers, and his Robe negligently flowing"* (*CPW,* 6:20), decreeing the night's revels. The tragedy ends in the hall where it began, after daybreak the next morning, as Sardanapalus, now dressed in battle gear and weary from war rather than revelry, enthrones himself on his funeral pyre. At his side in both scenes is his favorite concubine, Myrrha, a freethinking if enslaved Ionian who reluctantly "loves / Her master and would free him from his vices" (6:44). In the hours spanned by the drama, we see the self-indulgent man play the king—indeed, we come to realize that his degree of self-indulgence is, like that of a Louis XIV, possible only for someone thoroughly confident in his royal prerogatives. Warned by his brother-in-law Salemenes of incipient revolution among the Medes and Chaldeans, Sardanapalus parties on, having pardoned the two chief fomenters of rebellion when they were caught conspiring in the palace. The midpoint of the play brings tidings of revolution to the royal feast, and before his sycophantic guests' eyes, the "she-king" turns heroic. He arms, hurries to the front, and leads his troops in a battle that eventually goes against him—partly due to the treachery of allies but ultimately because of natural disaster, as the flooding Euphrates sweeps away a great section of the unassailable palace wall.

Throughout, Byron proves much less involved with the historical particulars of ancient Assyria than he was with the accurate representation of fourteenth- and fifteenth-century Venice in *Marino Faliero* and *The Two Foscari*. In *Sardanapalus*, as in Shakespeare's *Antony and Cleopatra* and Dryden's *All for Love,* the ancient world of the Near East provides an exotic backdrop against which to play out questions of conduct and loyalty, valor and effeminacy, and cross-cultural love, dilemmas whose often paradoxical resolutions transcend the fictive milieu in which they are situated. Discussing the influence of *All for Love* on *Sardanapalus,* Michael G. Cooke identifies a "restoration ethos" in Byron's play.[11] One might go yet further and, tying in the many allusions to and departures from Shakespeare's *Antony and Cleopatra*, see Byron's tragedy as a sort of ethical palimpsest, on which we discern superimposed layers of timeless and contingent values and behaviors.

The chief supporting characters in this tragedy exist almost entirely in relation to Sardanapalus—a state of affairs that may say as much about the literary status of a tragic protagonist as it does about the political privilege of a god-king. Conspiring against Sardanapalus are the Mede soldier Arbaces, aspirant to the throne, and the Chaldean soothsayer Beleses, a subtle blend of priest-warrior—the former inclined to underestimate the king but then to admire his honor when Sardanapalus rashly but nobly spares the plotters, the latter able to recognize the king's dormant power from the start but, when spared, unable to see the transparently noble act for what it is. Always aiming to rouse the king from hedonism to heroism is his brother-in-law Salemenes, whom

Sardanapalus identifies as his polar opposite, a man "hard but as lofty as the rock" in contrast with the king's "softer clay, impregnated with flowers" (*CPW,* 6:65). Two very different but equally dignified women vie for Sardanapalus's love in the last hours of his life. The slave-concubine Myrrha despises herself, a freeborn Greek, for loving her barbarian captor and living a harem life centered on unworthy love—but like Salemenes, she wishes Sardanapalus to vindicate his heritage through martial action and the public exercise of kingship. Salemenes's sister Zarina, Sardanapalus's spurned queen, is equally loyal to her lord, despite his infidelity and long-standing neglect. In contrast to Myrrha, however, the queen urges Sardanapalus to abdicate his royal responsibilities and flee with her into the realm of the purely personal: "Assyria is not all the earth—we'll find / A world out of our own" (6:99–100).

The extraordinary generosity of these two women—the wife unwilling to reproach her manifestly guilty husband, the slave willing to die with her master—apparently rose out of a quarrel between Teresa Guiccioli and Byron, in which she defended love as the loftiest theme for tragedy. He later wrote, "I believe she was right. I must put more love into 'Sardanapalus' than I intended" (*BLJ,* 8:26). But foregrounding of woman's capacity to love may not have the personal significance Byron implied and Teresa inferred. As McGann has observed, Byron's first intention was to call the Ionian slave Byblis, a name Ovid gives to a sister incestuously enamored of her brother, and the high-minded and gracious final interview between Sardanapalus and Zarina may enact a fantasy revision of Byron's parting from his wife (*CPW,* 6:611).

But whether we see Myrrha as more like Teresa Guiccioli or Augusta Leigh, and whether we conceive of Zarina as a pure invention or a vastly improved Lady Byron, an autobiographical reading certainly finds support in the paradoxical blend of poses and values evident in Sardanapalus himself. Like Byron, the Assyrian king is an unapologetic worldling caught up in the passing pleasures of bodily existence, a self-deprecator who (being an epigram writer like Byron) can say of his greatest accomplishment, " 'Sardanapalus / The king, and son of Anacyndaraxes, / In one day built Anchialus and Tarsus. / Eat, drink, and love; the rest's not worth a fillip' " (*CPW* 6:29–30). Like Byron, he is troubled by the call to public and personal duty even in the midst of his dissipations, and when he turns to action, friends and foes alike discover that "the king fights as he revels" (6:77). But there is as much dandyism as valor in his war making. Arming himself, the king rejects a heavy and serviceable helmet—"Wear Caucasus! why, 'tis / A mountain on my temples" (6:74)—and lacking his preferred royal helm with its gem-encrusted diadem, he goes forth bareheaded. The act is in equal propor-tions a fashion statement, a strategic encouragement for his troops, and a brazen provocation for the enemy. "I go forth to be recognized," says Sardanapalus, who though no warrior in the past instantly knows how a king should conduct himself in battle (6:74). The dandy-hero's orna-mental fillet ends up bandaging his arm, wounded in combat. But even though Salemenes and Myrrha praise him for demonstrating his worth as scion of the warrior race of Nimrod and Semiramis, Sardanapalus believes after his testing as he had before that a banquet-giving king of peace is better for his people than a conqueror, a despotic law giver, or an exploitative deviser of "pyramids, or Babylonian walls." Christlike yet lightly mocking, Sardanapalus observes to one of his imminent betray-ers,

> I pray you note,
> That there are worse things betwixt earth and heaven
> Than he who ruleth many and slays none;
> And, hating not himself, yet loves his fellows
> Enough to spare even those who would not spare him
> Were they once masters—.
>
> (6:57)

When Sardanapalus must yield to the battle cry in his blood (an acquiescence given brilliant shape in his Act 4 dream of a hellish feast with his ancestors, prominently including Nimrod and Semiramis) and shed the blood of others, he realizes, as Byron did—and as most rulers of the early nineteenth century did not—that war is more brutality than valor. Temporarily out of combat, he heatedly exclaims to Salemenes, "Let me then charge!"

> SALEMENES.   You talk like a young soldier.
> SARDANAPALUS.   I am no soldier, but a man: speak not
>   Of soldiership, I loathe the word, and those
>   Who pride themselves upon it; but direct me
>   Where I may pour upon them.
>
> (CPW, 6:107–8)

Profligate and profound, this king of peace has discovered his natural penchant for war, then found through the rapier-play of wit a way to recapture on the field the humanity he lost in yielding to heroism.

Byron's Ravenna Journal of January and February 1821 discloses his first thoughts of writing a tragedy with Adam and Eve's firstborn as its protagonist: "Cain, a metaphysical subject, something in the style of Manfred, but in five *acts*, perhaps, with the chorus" (*BLJ,* 8:36–37). In fact, *Cain* turned out to resemble *Manfred* in shape as well as style, with three acts rather than the formulaic five of neoclassical tragedy and of Byron's history plays. Byron subtitled *Cain* "A Mystery," a term he claimed to mean "a tragedy on a sacred subject" (8:205), though Philip W. Martin has argued convincingly that such a designation would have seemed deliberately inflammatory to 1820s readers, who would have associated "mystery" with an indecorous, or downright obscene, treatment of scripture.[12] A letter to Thomas Moore indicates in considerable detail what Byron put into this drama:

> It is in the Manfred, metaphysical style, and full of some Titanic declamation;—Lucifer being one of the dram. pers., who takes Cain a voyage among the stars, and, afterwards, to "Hades," where he shows him the phantoms of a former world, and its inhabitants. I have gone upon the notion of Cuvier, that the world has been destroyed three or four times, and was inhabited by mammoths, behemoths, and what not; but *not* by man until the Mosaic period, as, indeed, it [*sic*] proved by the strata of bones found;—those of all unknown animals, and known, being dug out, but none of mankind. I have, therefore, supposed Cain to be shown, in the *rational* Preadamites, beings endowed with a higher intelligence than man, but totally unlike him in form, and with much greater strength of mind and person. You may suppose the small talk which takes place between him and Lucifer upon these matters is not quite canonical.
>
> The consequence is, that Cain comes back and kills Abel in a fit of dissatisfaction, partly with the politics of Paradise, which had driven them all out of it, and partly because (as it is written in Genesis) Abel's sacrifice was the more acceptable to the Deity. (8:215–16)

Byron's preface to the mystery takes pains to stress his fidelity to Old Testament sources, and his inscription of the play to a respected and conservative fellow author, Sir Walter Scott (who admired *Cain*'s beauty and strength), seems calculated to soothe the reading public. But in spite of these explanatory and conciliatory gestures, *Cain* is in fact a provocative work, as was recognized prior to its publication by both the right-wing Murray and the left-wing Hobhouse, with both of whom Byron quarreled over the play. A subversive note sounds in the first speeches of the first act, which presents morning prayers at Adam and Eve's new home, ambiguously labeled *"The Land without Paradise."* While Adam, Eve, their younger son, Abel, and their daughters, Adah (Cain's wife) and Zillah (Abel's wife), praise God in sequence, only Cain remains silent, irritated by the style or substance of their worship. His first verbal gesture in the play is an act of patriarchal disrespect that foreshadows later, graver offenses:

> ADAM.   Son Cain, my first-born, wherefore art thou silent?
>
> CAIN.   Why should I speak?
>
> ADAM.   To pray.
>
> CAIN.   Have ye not pray'd?
>
> ADAM.   We have, most fervently.
>
> CAIN.   And loudly: I
>   Have heard you.
>
> (*CPW,* 6:232)

Once the other characters have gone off "each to his task of toil," Cain reveals in monologue the deeper source of his grievance: "Toil! and wherefore should I toil?—because / My father could not keep his place in Eden. / What had *I* done in this?" (6:234). Enter Lucifer, sympathetically conjured up, as it were, by Cain's dissatisfaction, which might be seen as the primordial complaint of firstborn sons whose feckless fathers have lost the ancestral estate. Lucifer may be a spirit second only to God in consequence, but his presence does not awe Cain, who, though naive about the nature of things, has Manfred's stubborn unwillingness to bend the knee. Desiring knowledge like his mother, Eve—"Let me but / Be taught the mystery of my being" (6:243)—Cain is about to follow where Lucifer leads, when Adah returns. What ensues might at first seem to be Lucifer's tempting of both Cain and Adah. But Adah has two things Cain lacks, simple faith and contentment with human life shared with those dear to her, Cain and their children dearest of all—and the end of the act presents Cain caught between her persuasions and Lucifer's, love and knowledge. Sinfully proud, Cain resists Adah's argument that their domestic joys are enough: "Be thou happy then alone— / I will have nought to do with happiness, / Which humbles me and mine" (6:248). He does not understand that Lucifer's words "[f]ollow me," blasphemously proleptic of Christ calling the apostles, demand his allegiance rather than merely offer him an hour's guided tour of "things of many days." Cain signals his sympathies by leaving with the tempting spirit rather than staying with the loving woman.

If the Old Testament ethos laid down by Jehovah dominates *Cain*'s first and final acts, Lucifer presides over what Edward Bostetter calls "the cosmos of nineteenth-century scientific speculation" in Act 2,[13] which unlike the others is divided into two scenes, the first set in the Abyss of Space, the second in Hades. Unfortunately for Cain, his newfound knowledge of natural law proves just as alienating as God's commands have been. Lucifer asks Cain, "Thou hast seen both worms and worlds / Each bright and sparkling—what dost think of them?" (*CPW,* 6:256). Cain's response is to cherish both as "beautiful in their own sphere"—but with this affirmation of beauty comes awareness that the earth on which his family toils is only a small part of creation. A similar lesson comes from seeing in Hades the phantoms of beings that "have an aspect, which, though not / Of men nor angels, looks like something, which, / If not the last, rose higher than the first, / Haughty, and high, and beautiful, and full / Of seeming strength" (6:261). The Preadamite shapes confirm Lucifer's previous assertion that "mightier things have been extinct / To make way for much meaner than we can / Surmise" (6:257).

In defending the morality of *Cain* to John Murray, Byron explained that Lucifer's object with Cain is "to *depress* him still further in his own estimation than he was before—by showing him infinite things—& his own abasement—till he falls into the frame of mind—that leads to the Catastrophe—from mere *internal* irritation" (*BLJ,* 9:53). As Act 3 opens, newfound awareness of humanity's inconsequential position in the expanse of space and the continuum of time has injured Cain without killing his sense that all life is sacred. Thus when he returns to what is now called "*The Earth near Eden*," the sight of his peacefully slumbering son Enoch occasions as much pain as joy. He tells the deeply concerned Adah, " 'Twere better that he ceased to live, than give / Life to so much of sorrow as he must / Endure, and, harder still, bequeath" (*CPW,* 6:280). Despite Adah's maternal fears, Cain's wish that his dear "disinherited boy" might escape the suffering of life in the postlapsarian world is quite another thing from being able to dispatch Enoch from that world. In fact, Cain's outrage at the unwarranted pain that he now knows to be the shared lot of all sentient creatures is broad and deep enough to include the lower animals. When Abel arrives at the appointed hour for them to sacrifice to Jehovah, Cain the farmer is infuriated not by God's preference of Abel the shepherd but by his cruel-seeming pleasure in animal, rather than vegetable, offerings. Irritated past endurance at the imminent suffering and death of an innocent lamb, Cain interrupts Abel's piety. When opposed with Abel's martyr-like "I love God far more / than life," Cain snatches a brand from the altar and strikes down his brother, uttering as he does so the obvious rejoinder to Abel's provocative testimonial: "Then take thy life unto thy God, / Since he loves lives" (6:286–87).

What may be most shocking about this romantic revision of biblical narrative is that its central crime is, in effect, the offense of the Ancient Mariner in reverse. The second, and graver, fall of humanity—murder or manslaughter rather than the eating of a forbidden fruit—comes about through sympathy rather than insensibility. In Byron's works, as in much romantic poetry, sympathy entails commitment to the mortal world of fellow sufferers rather than to transcendent abstraction, and the play ends with its most engaging character, Adah, acting out this ethos. The circumstances of her enactment lend themselves, as is so often the case in Byron's dramas, to being interpreted as containing veiled autobiographical relevance. Unlike either Augusta Leigh or Lady Byron (herself mother of an Ada), Cain's sister-wife keeps company with the outcast she loves as he, like Byron in 1816, sets a course "[e]astward from Eden."

The completed part of Byron's other mystery, *Heaven and Earth*, draws to its close with descendants of Cain and Adah expressing similar loyalty, though in very different circumstances. These two women are true to angel lovers, with whom they go forth into the unknown heavens as the deluge covers earth. As with *Cain,* Byron drew upon the Book of Genesis for the great flood survived only by Noah and his fellow denizens of the Ark, but he also consulted the apocryphal Book of Enoch for his account of love between angels and mortal women. If we are to believe Lady Byron, the motif and its possible personal application had been in his mind for some years. She wrote in 1817 that "His Imagination dwelt so much upon the idea that he was *a fallen angel* that I thought it amounted nearly to derangement, and the tradition that Angels, having fallen from Heaven, had become enamored of mortal women, struck him particularly, and he said he should compose upon it, and that *I* should be the woman, who was all perfection."[14] Be this as it may, one of Byron's acutest contemporary readers, William Hazlitt, admired the drama above all Byron's other plays for its transcendence, rather than expression, of authorial personality: "We prefer it even to *Manfred*. *Manfred* is merely himself with a fancy-drapery on. But, in the dramatic fragment published in the *Liberal*, the space between Heaven and earth, the stage on which his characters have to pass to and fro, seems to fill his Lordship's imagination; and the Deluge, which he has so finely described, may be said to have drowned all his own idle humours."[15]

Heaven and Earth, which Byron characterized as "a lyrical drama (entitled a Mystery from it's [*sic*] subject)," was written in October and November of 1821 and sent to Murray on 14 November. Byron specified, "I wish the first part to be published before the second—because if it don't succeed—it is better to stop there—than to go on in a fruitless experiment" (*BLJ*, 10:58–59). Denunciations of *Cain*'s sacrilege made the prudent Murray, fearful of jeopardizing his connections to what Byron scorned as "the Parsondom—or your Admiralty patrons—or your Quarter*lyers*" (*BLJ*, 10:22), wary of publishing yet another scandalous work on a biblical theme. Eventually the proofs of *Heaven and Earth* went at Byron's instructions to the radical John Hunt for publication in *The Liberal*. If in fact there is scandal in the play, it derives less from the mutual attachment of the angels and their women than from the detachment of a Creator who, having filled a world with thinking, feeling creatures, can sweep them away in the sort of catastrophe that is common ground between Genesis and Cuvier's geological theories.

The play opens at midnight near Mount Ararat, where Noah's Ark will eventually come to rest after the deluge. Two daughters of the race of Cain and Adah, the gentle Anah (whose nature, like her name, resembles her foremother's) and the proud Aholibamah (who seems to have inherited Cain's stiff-necked defiance), invoke their angel lovers, Azaziel and Samiasa. The next scene discloses a pair of spurned men who love these women: Irad, who has managed to put his love of Aholibamah behind him, and Japhet, a son of Noah still persisting in his devotion to Anah. Japhet seeks Anah at a cavern in the Caucasus as a chorus of malevolent spirits, rejoicing at the coming destruction, mock him, "remnant of Seth's seed" destined to live while the whole race of Cain, including his beloved Anah, perishes:

> Go, wretch! and give
> A life like thine to other wretches—live!

And when the annihilating waters roar
Above what they have done,
Envy the Giant Patriarchs then no more,
And scorn thy sire as the surviving one!
Thyself for being his son!
(*CPW,* 6:359)

When the archangel Raphael comes to warn Azaziel and Samiasa that in
staying on doomed earth they are condemning themselves, the daughters of Cain vow their willingness to face death alone: Aholibamah out
of courage ("Let us resign even what we have adored, / And meet the
wave, as we would meet the sword, / If not unmoved, yet undismay'd"),
Anah out of concern for her beloved ("My pangs can be but brief; but
thine would be / Eternal, if repulsed from heaven for me"; 6:372–73).

The center of emotional interest, however, is not the beautiful
descendants of Cain, or the angel lovers who do not abandon them, or
Noah, who, having come to collect his errant son before the heavens
open, preaches acceptance of God's catastrophic will in a tone of grim
satisfaction Byron may have recalled from his Calvinist youth. Byron's
most brilliant stroke is his depiction of Japhet. Though only a peripheral
character in both the biblical narrative and Byron's revisionist account,
Japhet articulates a sympathetic agony for dying humanity that undercuts orthodox acceptance of divine justice far more compellingly than do
the words and deeds of the rebellious lovers, who fly off as the deluge
begins. Japhet, standing in for Byron's readers, remains onstage while
mortals fleeing their inevitable destruction without the aid of angels'
wings express the widest range of feelings: panic, piety, curses. The last
voice, that of a woman whose "valley is no more," might speak for all
humanity in the drowning world:

When to the mountain cliff I climb'd this morn,
 I turn'd to bless the spot,
And not a leaf appear'd to fall;—
 And now they are not!—
Why was I born?
JAPH.   To die! in youth to die;
And happier in that doom
Than to behold the universal tomb

> Which I
> Am thus condemn'd to weep above in vain.
> Why, when all perish, why must I remain?
>
> (*CPW,* 6:380–81)

Byron had told Thomas Medwin of his idea for the end of *Heaven and Earth*. The four lovers were to proceed on an "aerial voyage" until, denied admittance by the guardian-spirits of all the planets, they would at last be obliged to alight on the only peak of earth still above the flood. Here the lovers would part: the angels called to judgment, the sisters drowning as they lived, one boldly, one piteously, as the Ark floated by with Japhet in despair. But perhaps like some other romantic works the play is best in its fragmentary form. What final speech could improve upon Japhet's question, unaskable from the standpoint of faith, unanswerable from the perspective of doubt?

Byron wrote one act of *Werner* in 1815, soon after completing *The Siege of Corinth*. But he put aside the idea until 1821, when he asked Hobhouse to send what he described as "the first act of a thing begun in 1815,— called 'Werner' " (*BLJ,* 9:81). Hobhouse did not transmit the manuscript—now housed in the John Murray archives and published in the commentary of McGann's edition of the *Complete Poetical Works* (*CPW,* 6:698–712)—and Byron eventually wrote to his friend, "I have not been able to hold out till you fished up the first act of 'Werner'—but have written *four new* acts (and am in labour with the fifth) of the same drama" (*BLJ,* 9:88). Byron's preface acknowledges that the drama "is taken entirely from the '*German's Tale, Kruitzner,*' published many years ago in '*Lee's Canterbury Tales*' " (*CPW,* 6:384). Byron has been criticized for this appropriation, less often for plagiarism than for putting Harriet Lee's prose so directly into the generally flat, unpoetic blank verse of his five-act play. But if *Werner* is arguably the least poetic of Byron's dramas, it is certainly his most effective deployment of contemporary theatrical conventions, perhaps because he conceived of the project during his period of direct involvement with Drury Lane Theatre. Barry Weller's account of the stage history of Byron's plays shows *Werner* by far the most successful with nineteenth-century audiences. It was a staple of the London stage from 1830, and the title role was generally considered one of the finest in the repertory of the great tragedian William Charles Macready (6:586–88).

Byron subtitled his drama "The Inheritance," a theme that echoes literally and figuratively throughout the play. Set on the Silesian frontier
and near Prague during the Thirty Years' War, the plot involves the succession to the lands and castle of Siegendorf. Count Siegendorf has banished his son, now living impoverished in hiding under the name
Werner, for the sins of "o'er-fervent youth." The chief o'er-fervency
seems to have involved attaching himself (like Byron) to an Italian
woman, Josephine. The couple have given up their only son, Ulric, to
Siegendorf on the condition that the old count's wrath "stop short / Of
the third generation"; but Ulric has mysteriously disappeared from his
grandfather's domain, leaving Werner to observe, prophetically as it
turns out, that "[h]eaven seems / To claim her stern prerogative, and
visit / Upon my boy his father's faults and follies" (*CPW,* 6:390). As the
play opens, the old baron has died, leaving the path of inheritance open,
apart from a "cold and creeping kinsman" and persecutor, Count Stralenheim, next in line after Werner and Ulric. A stormy night brings to
the "decayed Palace" occupied by Werner and Josephine assorted
strangers: most momentously, Stralenheim and two rescuers.

An intricately plotted sequence of imagined and enacted vengeance,
pursuit, concealment, and disclosure ensues. Stralenheim silently suspects Werner to be Siegendorf's heir but does not recognize that one of
his rescuers is a Hungarian enemy, Gabor, and that the other is Ulric,
who now leads a band of soldiers or brigands. Making his way to
Stralenheim's room through a concealed passage, Werner steals some of
his rich kinsman's gold. Once aware of his loss, Stralenheim suspects
Gabor of the theft. Guilty Werner, acting to save the innocent
Hungarian from his pursuers, shows Gabor the secret panel, giving him
access to the hidden passage leading to Stralenheim's chamber. Soon
after, Ulric discloses himself to his father. Joyful and abashed to be
reunited with his son at such a time, Werner confesses his petty crime,
an act soon eclipsed by the news that Stralenheim lies murdered, presumably by Gabor, who has fled. With the connivance of Ulric, Werner
and Josephine (who have the most to gain from Stralenheim's death)
escape from this potentially compromising situation.

When we next encounter Werner's family, in Act 4, they have inherited Siegendorf. Further improvements in the dynastic fortunes seem
imminent. The Treaty of Prague has brought peace to eastern Europe.
Ida, daughter and heiress of Count Stralenheim, is betrothed to Ulric.
Siegendorf, who donates Stralenheim's stolen gold to a monastery, at
last sheds the burden of secret guilt for his petty crime and for his unin-

tended complicity in the still-mysterious circumstances surrounding Stralenheim's death. But as was the case in Byron's tale *Lara*, a figure from the past rises up to change things for the lord returned to his lands. Gabor appears in Prague at the public festivities celebrating peace. Summoned to Castle Siegendorf, he reveals himself as no murderer but as an eyewitness to the aftermath of crime. From the secret passage, he saw the corpse of Stralenheim and the blood-stained killer: none other than Ulric.

Self-justifying situational ethics have hitherto calmed the conscience of Werner/Siegendorf, but he cannot go so far as to rationalize his son's act or to acquiesce to Ulric's plan to silence the witness by killing him. As Ulric explains it, however, his transgressive code of conduct is only natural for his father's son:

> The man who is
> At once both warm and weak, invites to deeds
> He longs to do, but dare not. Is it strange
> That I should *act* what you could *think*? We have done
> With right and wrong; and now must only ponder
> Upon effects, not causes.
>
> (*CPW,* 6:506)

Fatally ambivalent where his son is criminally single-minded, Siegendorf strips off his jewels and presses them as bribe or guilt money on Gabor, whom he helps to escape. Ulric, declaring, "Henceforth you have no son!" (*CPW,* 6:509), rushes off to rejoin his marauding band. As he leaves, he warns those left behind to "look well to Prague; / Their feast of peace was early for the Times" (6:510), and he brutally informs Ida (who would otherwise be as loyal to him as her near-namesake Adah is to Cain) that her father's blood is on his hand. As Ida falls senseless and Josephine stands speechless, Siegendorf is left to feel and invoke his true inheritance: "Now open wide, my sire, thy grave; / Thy curse hath dug it deeper for thy son / In mine!—The race of Siegendorf is past!" (6:510).

The shadow of Goethe lies over Byron's entire dramatic career. As mentioned earlier, Goethe's *Faust,* orally translated by "Monk" Lewis, was the partial inspiration for *Manfred.* Byron first meant to dedicate *Marino Faliero* to Goethe, and did ultimately offer him the dedicatory honors of *Sardanapalus* and *Werner.* With Byron's last drama, *The*

Deformed Transformed, the situation has come full circle. Byron draws his *"Faustish* kind of drama" (*CPW,* 6:725), an unfinished sequence of blank-verse episodes varied by lyric interludes, from part 1 of Goethe's master-piece and from Joshua Pickersgill's novel *The Three Brothers* (1803), which had previously inspired Lewis's play *The Wood Demon* (1807). The premise of *The Deformed Transformed* is the familiar Faustian deal with the devil, who, as Charles Robinson points out, serves as a second self for the protagonist, Arnold.[16] Given that Goethe had been the second self of Byron's dramatic career, this convergence of dramatic theme and dra-maturgical circumstance seems highly appropriate.

The play opens with an act of rejection as Bertha cries, "Out, hunch-back!" to her limping, misshapen son Arnold, "[o]f seven sons / The sole abortion!" (*CPW,* 6:519). Left alone to cut firewood in the forest, Arnold wounds one of his hands and, as he cleans it in a spring, laments the sight of his "horrid shadow—like a demon placed / Deep in the foun-tain" (6:521). As Arnold is about to hurl himself on his blade, a cloud rises from the spring and a tall black man materializes from the cloud. This sardonic Stranger offers Arnold, in exchange for "no bond / But your own will, no contract save your deeds" (6:524), his choice of shapes. Arnold selects the form and face of Achilles. The Stranger in turn assumes the "abandoned garment, / Yon hump, and lump, and clod of ugliness" (6:534) that recently were Arnold's body and takes the name Caesar, choices that will prevent the transformed Arnold from escaping his old deformity or from forgetting to whom he must render the things that are not God's. Thus accompanied, the newly minted hero sets forth to "where the world is thickest," meaning "where there is War / And Woman in activity" (6:537). On coal-black horses, Arnold and Caesar head for Rome, then under siege by Charles Duc de Bourbon and his troops.

War as depicted in part 2 of *The Deformed Transformed* is as bad as in *The Siege of Corinth,* worse than in *Don Juan,* in which the general car-nage at Ismail is now and then relieved by isolated acts of selfless hero-ism. Heroic Bourbon dies early in the assault on Rome, and the cos-mopolitan sack of the city reveals humanity at its greedy, lustful, fanatical, violent, cowardly worst. Though venerated as the seat of Christianity, with its "[a]bode of the true God, and his true Saint, / Saint Peter" (*CPW,* 6:541), Rome arose, as Caesar reminds Arnold, out of an act of fratricide reminiscent of Cain's killing of Abel: "I saw your Romu-lus (simple as I am) / Slay his own twin, quick-born of the same womb, / Because he leapt a ditch ('twas then no wall, / Whate'er it now be;) and

Rome's earliest cement / Was brother's blood" (6:542–43). No better than his fellow sackers of St. Peter's, Arnold saves the bold and beautiful Olimpia, who has killed a soldier with a crucifix and hurled herself from the altar. His motives are less than disinterested: "there is a woman / Worthy a brave man's liking" (6:565). But as the drama breaks off, in the aftermath of Rome's fall, Arnold is lamenting that the worthy woman does not love him. Embracing a wretchedness his beauty and valor cannot relieve, Arnold moans that "I would not quit / My unrequited love for all that's happy—

> CAESAR.   You have possessed the woman—still possess—
> What need you more?—
> ARNOLD.   To be myself possest—
> To be her heart as she is mine.—
>   (6:577)

Thus *The Deformed Transformed* breaks off where *Manfred* began. Byron's drama writing ends where it started—in the personal hell of a man who has partly gained the beloved object but who longs for what still eludes him.

Chapter Six

Childe Harold's Pilgrimage and Don Juan

Distinguished though Byron's poetic achievements in lyric, satire, tale, and drama may be, his reputation rests mainly on his two ostensibly narrative long poems. *Childe Harold's Pilgrimage*, a meditation in the loco-descriptive tradition, made him famous in his time. *Don Juan*, a self-ironizing epic, ensured his fame in times to come.[1] Beginning with Byron's nineteenth-century readership, it became commonplace to dwell on what distinguishes the two long poems from one another. *Childe Harold* (so goes the familiar contrast) displays Byron's dark, melancholy, alienated side, whereas *Don Juan* offers his lively, witty, cosmopolitan side; the former poem appealed to an elite and the latter to the populace; respectable women adored the one and avoided the other. But in fact what *Childe Harold* and *Don Juan* share is considerable. Both are divided into cantos. Both employ couplet-capped stanzaic structures (nine-line Spenserian in *Childe Harold*'s case, ottava rima in *Don Juan*'s) that ground them in literary traditions to which they sometimes adhere and from which they sometimes depart. The forms chosen lend themselves to loosely structured, expandable narrative that can be interspersed with commentary.

In *Childe Harold* and *Don Juan* alike, Byron took full advantage of this expandability. He wrote both poems in fits and starts that extended their periods of composition over years. *Childe Harold* rose out of three separate periods of foreign travel and sojourn. The first two cantos, composed from 1809 to 1811, reflect his Mediterranean tour with Hobhouse; the third presents his Rhine journey and Swiss summer of 1816; and the fourth records an 1817 trip from Venice to Rome. Similarly, Byron produced cantos 1 through 5 of *Don Juan* between 1818 and 1821—then dropped the poem for months. He picked it up again in 1822 to complete cantos 6 through 16 and to write a few stanzas of 17 before leaving *Don Juan* and Italy behind for Greece and revolutionary action in 1823. In both cases, the interludes between periods of composition allowed for the transformation or redefinition of the recursive literary projects. In both cases, the publishing choices Byron made—who brought out the cantos, what pieces of poetry or prose were published along with them, what associated writings were suppressed—made each volume something more than a mere installment of its long poem.

Byron titled both long poems for their gentlemanly protagonists. Both Harold and Juan began with something of a connection to the author. Childe Harold started out as "Childe Burun," and Don Juan was a role Byron played with conscious relish in Venice, as is signaled by his epistolary catalog of mistresses, a piece of rhetoric he patterned explicitly on the list of romantic conquests in Mozart's *Don Giovanni* and fancied sufficiently to include in letters to several of his correspondents.[2] In different ways the worlds of the two poems are contemporary with their author's life. Beginning *Childe Harold* in 1809, the 21-year-old Byron, having recently taken his degree at Cambridge and his seat in the House of Lords, is, like his protagonist, a highborn young wanderer leaving behind dilapidated Gothic cloisters to travel in equally dilapidated Mediterranean lands. Beginning *Don Juan* at 30, Byron is the age of the poem's narrator rather than of its 16-year-old protagonist. But *Don Juan* is a sort of Bakhtinian chronotope or "time-place," a narrative blending three historical periods that also constitute three separate eras in Byron's life. Added together, these times roughly overlap the span of his existence: the French revolutionary era of about 1787 through 1792 or 1793 (when Don Juan's adventures take place), the Napoleonic era of 1808 to 1816 (Byron's years of fame in English society and the era from which most of the narrator's Byronic recollections are drawn), and the post-Napoleonic restoration of 1818 to 1823 (the poem's years of composition, and the narrator's present).[3]

Despite certain resemblances to the protagonists, Byron allies himself more closely with the narrators of *Childe Harold* and *Don Juan*. Wishing to maintain a distinction between the narrator and himself, Byron allows his distance from each poem's persona to vary, from complete detachment to apparent congruence, with all their intermediate gradations. The poems' narrators embody values and attitudes different from the protagonists'—and perhaps closer to what Byron would like his readers to imagine his own attitudes to be. If Harold is a moody, self-indulgent wanderer and Don Juan a changeable naïf, the narrator of each poem has the worldly wisdom, balance, and detachment to mock gently, and correct implicitly, the protagonists' youthful excesses. Describing young gentlemen on their travels, both narrators make use of the freely associative poetic forms in which they are speaking to meditate on historical and philosophical preoccupations they share with Byron himself: European culture from the classical age on, European politics in the age of Napoleon, the place of humanity in nature and in the cosmos.

In both *Childe Harold* and *Don Juan*, the subjectivity of the protagonist, a being ostensibly distinct from Byron, is generally remote, while that of the narrator, a personage seemingly connected to Byron, is engaging. Because the inner workings of the narrators' minds seemed clear and accessible, readers naturally identified their thoughts and attendant qualities as Byron's. Because the fictive motivations and opinions of Harold and Juan remained sketchy or inaccessible, readers had license to speculate on them—and, without specific reasons to think otherwise, tended to assume that Harold and Juan too were reflections of Byron. In this paradoxical double way the two long poems spawned a variety of images that stuck to the poet: the highborn, melancholy, vaguely wicked wanderer, the cheerful, sophisticated Epicurean, the doubter, the doer of deeds, the freedom fighter. He then tended to live up to those images. Thus the attitudes Byron struck in *Childe Harold* and *Don Juan* shaped his future as much as or more than they rose out of his past. Only when Byron "woke up famous" as the author of *Childe Harold* did he have a chance to become the fashionable *homme fatal* the poem had caused his readers to imagine him, and only when the first installment of *Don Juan* had flouted the conventions of his native land was Byron spurred (or freed) to be the licentious expatriate candid or artful enough to put anything and everything into his evolving, idiosyncratic epic.

For gentry and nobles on the Grand Tour, writing travelogues was as habitual as buying souvenirs. As Byron and Hobhouse proceeded through the ports of call and landlocked venues accessible to journeying Englishmen in the age of Napoléon, they recorded their impressions. Hobhouse, a scholarly, indefatigable sightseer and lifelong diarist, put his thoughts down in prose. Some of his liveliest passages remain as yet unpublished, but other observations filled the learned travel book he published in 1813, *Journey through Albania*. Meanwhile, Byron was trying his hand at the Augustan genre of travel-poem, the most recently published of his inspirations in this vein being *Horae Ionicae* of Waller Rodwell Wright, who had received four favorable verses and an equally benign prose note in *English Bards*. For his poetic form, Byron chose Spenserian verse of the self-consciously archaic sort he had encountered in James Beattie's *The Minstrel,* among other works. In the preface to *Childe Harold's Pilgrimage,* Byron claims to have selected Spenserian verse because it "admits of every variety," and in deploying it he aimed to give full scope to his range of moods and free rein to his own distinctive tastes. "If I ever did anything original, it was in *Childe Harold,*" he wrote in 1814 (when much of his literary originality still lay ahead). But if Byron had declared his freedom from literary conventions and public decorums, he respected the constraints of itinerary. Unlike religious pilgrims, Harold follows no established route to a sacred shrine, but his footsteps are no less prescribed in that they unerringly trace Byron and Hobhouse's route through Portugal, Spain, Malta, Albania, and Greece. This journey in its turn was not capricious wandering but a cultural pilgrim's progress through the interesting places idle, educated, adventurous, well-funded Britons were permitted to visit during the era of Napoléon's European dominance.

The immediate catalysts of *Childe Harold's Pilgrimage* seem to have been a shipboard suggestion from John Galt, a fellow passenger bound for Malta, and Byron's reading in Spenser's *Faerie Queene* when he and Hobhouse had reached Albanian terra firma and made their way to Janina.[4] The substance of the meditative poem was of course to be Byron's immediate travel experiences, but when he began writing at Janina in September 1809, his understanding of the authorial pain that can come from inadequately veiled personal writing was still fresh. The despised reviewers whose critical mockery he had avenged in *English Bards* had taught him a valuable lesson about the need to mystify the relation of his "real" self to his poetry. So as he made Spenserian stanzas on the sights and situations of his 1809 to 1811 travels—Mount Cintra and Mount Parnassus, Spanish beauties, romance with "fair Florence" (Constance Spencer Smith) on Malta, the exotic blend of sublimity, barbarism, and luxury that was Ali Pasha's Albania and the "sad relic of departed worth" that was occupied Greece—Byron filtered his own experiences through the persona of Harold, a melancholy, sated ex-reveler whose presence enabled him to objectify some of his moods and responses without risking direct self-implication. In this way, as Jerome McGann puts it, Byron "presents his access to self-consciousness in a significant form—in a 'story' that gives a meaningful 'plot' to the detailed facts of his poetic life."[5] Harold represents what Byron could imagine being but refuses to be. The first sentences of the "motto" Byron selected for his poem, a cynical extract from Monbron's *Le Cosmopolite,* aptly indicate how the world serves the jaded pilgrim Harold:

"L'univers est une espèce de livre, dont on n'a lu que la première page quand on n'a vu que son pays. J'en ai feuilleté un assez grand nombre, que j'ai trouvé également mauvaises" [The universe is a book of sorts, and he who has seen only his native land has read only the first page. I've skimmed quite a few pages, which I have found equally bad] (*CPW,* 2:3). For the pilgrim Byron, however, there is a further twist: whereas page-turning Harold experiences the world as a bad book, page-filling Byron finds it promising material to put into a better book, his poem.

Not that the poem is without problems of its own. Harold, whom the retrospective eye discerns as the pasteboard prototype for a gallery of Byronic heroes, is unconvincing from the outset, partly on account of the arch Spenserian imitation that introduces and intermittently contin- ues to characterize him:

> Whilome in Albion's isle there dwelt a youth,
> Who ne in virtue's ways did take delight;
> But spent his days in riot most uncouth,
> And vex'd with mirth the drowsy ear of Night.
> Ah, me! In sooth he was a shameless wight,
> Sore given to revel and ungodly glee;
> Few earthly things found favour in his sight
> Save concubines and carnal companie,
> And flaunting wassailers of high and low degree.
>   (*CPW,* 2:9)

Unsurprisingly, Harold feels "the fulness of satiety" and like Byron departs from his ancestral home, a "vast and venerable pile," and from a society where "none did love him—though to hall and bower / He gather'd revellers from far and near" (*CPW,* 2:11). By setting up this patently literary libertine as fictive traveler on his own actual route, Byron avoided confessionalism but offended some discerning readers another way. "Vice ought to be a little more modest," Walter Scott pointed out, recognizing the impudence and conceit in Byron's partly sympathetic, partly ironic depiction of Harold, who offered an oblique way of "informing the inferior part of the world that their little old-fash- ioned scruples and limitation are not worthy of his regard while his for- tunes and possessions are such as have put all sorts of gratifications too much in his power to afford him any pleasure."[6] The jaded, melancholy protagonist sometimes successfully sets a screen for Byron the person but sometimes poses problems for the poet or gets in the way of the narrator. For instance, in canto 1, "The Girl of Cadiz," an interjected love lyric that on consideration struck Byron as too cheerful for Harold's lyre, had to be replaced by "To Inez," the morbid song of a doomed world-roamer avowing that "Still, still pursues, where-e'er I be, / The blight of life—the demon, Thought" (*CPW,* 2:40). And when canto 2 brings Harold to the Balkans and Greece, he is in great measure redundant. The Byronic narrator is there before him, seated on "The marble column's yet unshaken base" (2:47), sincerely commenting, "Cold is the heart, fair Greece! That looks on thee, / Nor feels as lovers o'er the dust they lov'd," then in the next stanza cutting his meditation short with necessary but flat-footed artifice: "But where is Harold? shall I then forget / To urge the gloomy wanderer o'er the wave?" (2:49).

Despite occasional infelicities, in contriving the situation of *Childe Harold* Byron hit upon a strategy that would serve him well later on. In M. K. Joseph's words, he was "already moving towards the separation of hero and narrator which was to become, later, the master-device of *Don Juan.*"[7] The route quasi-Spenserian Harold follows and the sights he sees are highly interesting because they, unlike him, are real and immediate— where Byron has been and what he has seen—and because of how keenly the narrator appraises them. Such appraisal involves cultural contrast, evident throughout the poem and customary in the models from which *Childe Harold* derives, though seldom done so well as in Byron's stanzas. We are shown the difference between the London Sabbath, when "spruce citizen, wash'd artizan, / And smug apprentice gulp their weekly air" (*CPW,* 2:34) and the Cadiz Sabbath, with its brutal but engrossing bullfight:

> Foil'd, bleeding, breathless, furious to the last,
> Full in the centre stands the bull at bay,
> Mid wounds, and clinging darts, and lances brast,
> And foes disabled in the brutal fray:
> And now the Matadores around him play,
> Shake the red cloak, and poise the ready brand:
> Once more through all he burst his thundering way—
> Vain rage! The mantle quits the conynge hand,
> Wraps his fierce eye—'tis past—he sinks upon the sand!
>   (2:37)

Sometimes the exercise in cultural contrast helps define a complex attitude. For instance the cynical narrator, crossing Portugal and Spain even
as the Peninsular Wars are being waged, notes the paradox of Britain's
Spanish allies fighting Napoléon when their Bourbon monarchs, Charles
IV and his son and successor, Ferdinand, have abdicated in his favor:

> Such be the sons of Spain, and strange her fate!
> They fight for freedom who were never free,
> A Kingless people for a nerveless state;
> Her vassals combat when their chieftains flee,
> True to the veriest slaves of Treachery.
>
> (2:41)

Later, in canto 2, he voices sad scorn for the present-day Greeks. But
this time the deplored collective deficiency is of an opposite kind. The
Greeks, unlike the Spaniards, do not confront their imperial oppressors
the Ottomans: "Hereditary bondsmen! Know ye not / Who would be
free themselves must strike the blow? / By their right arms the conquest
must be wrought?" (2:69). Some stanzas later, the narrator senses the
heroic, timeless quality of the plain where democratic Athenian soldiers
led by Miltaides defeated imperial Persian forces in 490 B.C.:

> The Battle-field, where Persia's victim horde
> First bowed beneath the brunt of Hellas' sword
> As on the morn to distant Glory dear,
> When Marathon became a magic word.
>
> (2:73)

This romantic appreciation contrasts with an earlier perspective on
another field, the one disputed in the Battle of Talaverra on 27–28 July
1809. Meditating on this battle, which occurred during Byron's time in
Spain and only weeks before he began writing *Childe Harold*, the narrator
perceives meaningless mortal loss rather than eternal glory—perhaps
because the sacrifices are so recent, perhaps because none of the contend-
ing parties can offer a political ideal he considers worthy, and certainly
because recently contended Talaverra lacks what Byron later describes in
the notes to canto 3 as "that undefinable but impressive halo which the
lapse of ages throws around a celebrated spot" (*CPW,* 2:303):

> Three hosts combine to offer sacrifice;
> Three tongues prefer strange orisons on high;
> Three gaudy standards flout the pale blue skies;
> The shouts are France, Spain, Albion, Victory!
> The foe, the victim, and the fond ally
> That fights for all, but ever fights in vain,
> Are met—as if at home they could not die—
> To feed the crow on Talavera's plain,
> And fertilize the field that each pretends to gain.
> (2:25)

Byron's prose comments on the battle, transmitted in an 11 August letter to his mother, strike a note close to the narrator's sour sense of human waste: "I like the Spaniards much, you have heard of the battle near Madrid, & in England they will call it a victory, a pretty victory! two hundred officers and 5000 men killed all English, and the French in as great force as ever" (*BLJ,* 1:221). The narrator's cultural, historical, and moral attitudes incrementally revealed by these quoted passages and others unquoted are complex but not necessarily self-contradictory. They accurately correspond to Byron's sense that all human life is precious, too valuable to give except in a worthy cause. Such worthy causes include defensive wars, not wars of conquest. Only free societies are worth fighting for—patriotic sacrifice for an authoritarian regime is an absurd gesture.

Travelogues were generally popular in the early nineteenth century. From the earliest drafts, Byron's had many particular attractions to recommend it: widely esteemed Mediterranean beauty spots and fresh Albanian sights (which Byron and Hobhouse were among the first English to visit), a tantalizingly misanthropic protagonist, a humanely intelligent narrator. But these ingredients coalesced and changed into something that transcended the genre only after Byron's 14 July 1811 return to England, where a devastating series of bereavements darkened his homecoming. Mrs. Byron died unexpectedly on 1 August, before he had traveled north to see her. His and Hobhouse's friend the witty and promising C. S. Matthews drowned in the Cam on 3 August. On 10 August Byron received news that a beloved Harrow schoolfellow, John Wingfield, was dead. The repeated shock of loss without the solace of parting found its way into verses for the end of *Childe Harold'*s second

canto, in which Byron voices authentic grief nothing like Harold's
melancholy attitudinizing:

> All thou could'st have of mine, stern Death! Thou hast;
> The parent, friend, and now the more than friend:
> Ne'er yet for one thine arrows flew so fast,
> And grief with grief continuing still to blend,
> Hath snatch'd the little joy that life had yet to lend.
> *(CPW,* 2:75)

Sobered by his losses, Byron embarked on a revision that radically
altered his poem. He removed many of the Spenserian burlesques,
added somber meditative passages, rearranged existing material to
transform *Childe Harold's Pilgrimage* from a loose, variable travelogue in
which the geographical itinerary dominated to a psychodrama in which
the Mediterranean world figures as a backdrop or an objective correla-
tive, to borrow T. S. Eliot's term. The poem's sights, scenes, cultures,
people, situations, and varying moods are subordinated to a different
subject: the development of the traveler's (and poet's) mind *(CPW,*
2:271). And that mind ends confronting the very situation from which
Harold fled:

> Then must I plunge again into the crowd,
> And follow all that Peace disdains to seek?
> Where Revel calls, and Laughter, vainly loud,
> False to the heart, distorts the hollow cheek. (2:76)

Back in his own milieu as the canto ends, the narrator, whose voice now
sounds much like Harold's but is that of the bereaved poet, asks, "What is
the worst of woes that wait on age?" His answer: "To view each lov'd one
blotted from life's page, / And be alone on earth, as I am now" (2:76).

This solitude would not last. The promotion and publication of
Childe Harold's Pilgrimage by the rising house of John Murray was an
early and shrewd instance of celebrity making.[8] After the awaited book
appeared on 10 March 1812, fascinated purchasers and readers wanted
the acquaintance of its author. If Byron hoped to hide behind the mask
of Harold, his poetic strategy backfired. He claimed, "I by no means
intend to identify myself with *Harold,* but to *deny* all connexion with

him" (*BLJ,* 2:122). Nevertheless, the public sensed the poet within the poem and easily slid into associating him with his protagonist. Despite Byron's professions to the contrary, such a fate was not at first entirely unwelcome to a bereaved young man who, though talented and well born, stood outside the inner circle of British fashion and power.

The Childe Harold myth of madness, badness, and danger may not have been much of a burden to Byron in March 1812—but being spurned as an abusive husband and a committer of unspeakable offenses in the same salons where dark mystery had earlier proven so magnetic was not to be suffered in April 1816. A few months after his separation from Annabella, Byron the man turned his back on the society that had turned its back on him and once again became a pilgrim. Again *Childe Harold* proved a congenial medium for Byron the poet, who resumed its writing as he started his journey: his holograph manuscript indicates that the new canto was "[b]egun at Sea" on 25 April (*CPW,* 2:297–98).

How Byron will use *Childe Harold* becomes evident in the sea-born (and seabourne) second stanza, in which, after having invoked his daughter Ada as muse to the canto, he echoes Shakespeare's Henry V at Harfleur and hurls himself into the breach of his broken life, with the English Channel as his warhorse or Pegasus: "Once more upon the waters! Yet once more! / And the waves bound beneath me as a steed / That knows his rider." This heroic attitude tries to transform retreat from England to an advance on the Continent, but Byron is too honest to hold the pose. Further into the stanza he says that the waves guide him rather than the other way around: "I am as a weed, / Flung from the rock, on Ocean's foam, to sail / Where'er the surge may sweep, or tempest's breath prevail" (*CPW,* 2:77). This existential confusion, or mobility, will be the keynote of the third canto. Nature is sometimes a sublime and indifferent power, sometimes a sympathetic companion to human nature, sometimes a perception or creation of the human mind. Byron is both a bereaved sufferer, as he seemed at canto 2's conclusion—though this time he has lost the living—and a freed explorer who, having left a small, unsatisfying place behind, finds the world all before him.

Traveling across the Channel to the battlefield of Waterloo, through the Low Countries to the Rhine, Lac Leman, and the Alps, gave Byron a distraction from his personal troubles back in England. Such a tour of picturesque and historically evocative spots also afforded him the occasional chance to escape his immediate past. But finally the canto is "a personal self-examination and a public justification" (*CPW,* 2:300). Scru-

tinizing imaginary Harold and, far more repayingly, explaining the
great men associated with his sites of Continental pilgrimage—
Napoléon, Voltaire, Gibbon, Rousseau—Byron can assess himself by
indirection. In this canto the distinctions between protagonist, narrator,
and poet dissolve, as critics from Francis Jeffrey on have noticed.[9]
Having spoken first of his biological child Ada, then of his imaginative
child Harold, Byron meditates on the creative act that diffuses the self
beyond its solitary limits:

> 'Tis to create, and in creating live
> A being more intense, that we endow
> With form our fancy, gaining as we give
> The life we image, even as I do now.
> What am I? Nothing; but not so art thou,
> Soul of my thought!
>
> (2:78)

   After landing at Ostend, Byron rattled across the Low Countries in
his coach patterned on Napoléon's—a gesture as politically charged as it
was extravagant. Early in the canto Harold's melancholy misanthropy
converges with the narrator's intelligent historical curiosity and Byron's
personal identification with Napoléon to produce an intense, transfor-
mative reading of Waterloo nearly a year after the battle. The canto's
vividly rendered imaginative account has replaced historical fact in some
readers' understanding of the conflict. Thanks to Byron's canto, many
believe that the "revelry by night" at the Duchess of Richmond's glitter-
ing Brussels ball preceded Waterloo rather than Quatre Bras, a preliminary battle three days earlier, and that Wellington's forces were summoned from the ball by "the cannon's opening roar" rather than by the
more prosaic means of military intelligence from Blucher, the comman-
der of Prussia's forces (*CPW,* 2:302). The verdict pronounced on
Napoléon, admirable as liberator of France but despicable as self-
crowned emperor, generalizes from the contingencies of his career a
timeless exemplary warning against classical hubris or Christian pride:

> There sunk the greatest, nor the worst of men
> Whose spirit antithetically mixt

One moment of the mightiest, and again
On little objects with like firmness fixt,
Extreme in all things! Hadst thou been betwixt,
Thy throne had still been thine, or never been;
For daring made thy rise as fall: thou seek'st
Even now to re-assume the imperial mien,
And shake again the world, the Thunderer of the scene!
                                                            (2:89)

"Conqueror and captive of the earth," the vanquished and exiled
Napoléon as he seemed to humane liberals of Byron's stamp is accurately depicted in the Waterloo stanzas. Yet the portrait is also a looking
glass in which Byron discerns the features of his own fatal excesses, the
deeds that brought on his comparable displacement.

Later in the canto, Byron considers Jean-Jacques Rousseau, whose
philosophic ideas brought about "the wreck of old opinions" and
thereby began the revolutionary era that Napoléon's military deeds
closed. As was the case at Waterloo, place spurs the meditation as
Harold and the narrator see, just as Byron and Shelley did in June 1816,
Clarens and other sites at the eastern end of Lac Leman associated with
Rousseau and with the characters of his novel *Julie, ou la nouvelle Heloise.*
As in the Napoléon stanzas, Byron's assessment is relevant to both
Rousseau and himself. Rousseau is not reduced to a stand-in for Byron,
but appraising the other writer's attributes helps Byron, and thus his
readers, toward an understanding of his own inner torment:

Here the self-torturing sophist, wild Rousseau,
The apostle of affliction, he who threw
Enchantment over passion, and from woe
Wrung overwhelming eloquence, first drew
The breath which made him wretched; yet he knew
How to make madness beautiful, and cast
O'er erring deeds and thoughts, a heavenly hue
Of words, like sunbeams, dazzling as they past
The eyes, which o'er them shed tears feelingly and fast.
                                                            (*CPW,* 2:105)

The next lines on Rousseau particularly illuminate Byron's state of mind
in the stormy summer of 1816: "His love was passion's essence—as a
tree / On fire by lightning." Lightning, nature's potent, sympathetic-
seeming enactment of an elemental human feeling that both kindles
and blasts, manifests itself in other writings that rose out of or reflected
Byron's turbulent feelings of the time: his letters, lyrics, and dramatic
poem *Manfred*, Mary Shelley's *Frankenstein*. More than a connection
between Rousseau and Byron, lightning is also the most powerful
instance of canto 3's persistent Wordsworthian or Shelleyan sense that
nature and human nature (especially a poet's human nature) essentially
correspond to one another. Thus within the poem an actual summer
thunderstorm that swamped Byron and Shelley's sailboat on Lac Leman
seems both to echo a literary precursor in Rousseau's *Julie* and to exter-
nalize the tempest raging in Byron's heart:

> Could I embody and unbosom now
> That which is most within me,—could I wreak
> My thoughts upon expression, and thus throw
> Soul, heart, mind, passions, feelings, strong or weak,
> All that I would have sought, and all I seek,
> Bear, know, feel, and yet breathe—into *one* word,
> And that one word were Lightning, I would speak;
> But as it is, I live and die unheard,
> With a most voiceless thought, sheathing it as a sword.
>   (2:112)

Conditional clause on conditional clause, nouns in sequence, verbs com-
pounded, seven lines of verse until the logical and grammatical unit is
complete: the lines are literally hard to voice, as any untrained reciter
who reads them aloud will breathlessly understand. At the level of
meaning, what's hard to voice becomes unvoiceable because that "one
word . . . Lightning" is an utterance beyond human linguistic possibilities. What rejoinder to a thunderbolt? In *Childe Harold* words follow the
lament of boltlessness—words that describe Byron's Haroldlike misanthropy but then assert a belief in some things as yet unencountered in
Harold's journeyings or Byron's pilgrimage through life:

> I have not loved the world, nor the world me,—
> But let us part fair foes; I do believe,
> Though I have found them not, that there may be
> Words which are things,—hopes which will not deceive,
> And virtues which are merciful.
>
> (2:118)

The hope or faith in "words which are things" is necessary to Byron. Words must constitute his presence for the daughter he reinvokes as canto 3 ends. The exile's words claim her as his child in blood. Though she will grow up without knowing his nurture, she shares his nature, and the words of this canto are not just Byron's self-explanation but also his bond to Ada,

> The child of love,—though born in bitterness,
> And nurtured in convulsion—of thy sire
> These were the elements,—and thine no less.
>
> (2:119)

Despite such oft-quoted lines as "I live not in myself, but I become / Portion of that around me" (2:103), *Childe Harold* 3 has rightly been recognized as a tour de force of the egotistical sublime. As such, it has provoked a wide range of reactions from its readers.[10] Byron himself was ambivalent, as his artful acknowledgment of Thomas Moore's praise for the canto indicates: "I am glad you like it; it is a fine indistinct piece of poetical desolation, and my favourite. I was half mad during the time of its composition, between metaphysics, mountains, lakes, love unextinguishable, thoughts inutterable, and the nightmare of my own delinquencies" (*BLJ,* 5:165). The letter's man-of-the-world mockery contradicts the poem's self-dramatized world-shunning and brings its transcendental aspirations down to earth. But for Byron the creature of mobility, all is true.

Only fairly recently have readers been able to understand canto 3 as it evolved and as Byron intended it to be. The holograph copy of the manuscript, dispatched to England with the returning Scrope Davies in Sep-

tember 1816, languished unknown in a trunk in Barclays' Bank until
1975.[11] Yet more relevant to contextualized perceptions of the work,
Byron did not see proofs for the first edition. Because Murray persuaded
him to allow editing by the conservative Gifford rather than by the radical Shelley, to whom Byron had originally entrusted the task, a good
many potentially inflammatory political observations were excised from
the prose notes, to be restored only in the McGann edition of 1980. If
Shelley was the *fidus Achates* whose companionship crucially influenced
the shape of Byron's thoughts in canto 3, Hobhouse played the part in
canto 4, which is appropriately dedicated to him. Not merely the
author's literary representative in London, Hobhouse accompanied
Byron through the Italian cities and landscapes commemorated in the
stanzas, provided some of the prose notes appended to the canto, and
published a weighty prose companion, *Historical Illustrations to the Fourth
Canto of Childe Harold*. As with canto 3, Gifford advised Murray and
Byron on the publication of canto 4 in 1818, but Hobhouse, whose radical sympathies exceeded Byron's, was also involved in the editorial
process. The republican sentiments of the work remain unmistakable.

Hobhouse's presence on the Italian journey and his pervasive involvement in canto 4's composition and publication may have enhanced its
attunement to the political, historical, and literary associations of place.
But because Hobhouse had been best man at Byron's ill-fated wedding,
his presence in Italy also constituted a personal link to the family and
society Byron had left behind. Thus Hobhouse can be seen as a catalyst
for the confluence that is a particular strength of the canto: the flowing
together of Italy's history and Byron's, of political struggles and psychological ones. In canto 4, finally "weary of drawing a line which every one
seemed determined not to perceive," as his dedicatory epistle says (*CPW,*
2:122), Byron drops the device of Harold and chronicles his own
unmediated Italian pilgrimage. "A ruin amidst ruins," he reflects on the
fall of empires and the decay of past generations and their monuments.
Decadent but reviving Italy offers an actual context but also an analogue to the blight and the willed renewal of Byron's own life.

Though much amplified over months of writing, from 126 stanzas to
186, *Childe Harold* 4 displays a clear two-part structure: first a journey
from Venice to Rome, then wanderings in Rome itself. Culminating the
canto and the poem as a whole, an address to the sea brings the pilgrimage back to the element, if not the geographical place, where it started.
Canto 4 begins dramatically in the sea-built city of Venice, as the poet-

protagonist locates himself in a setting simultaneously architectural, political, and psychological:

> I stood in Venice, on the Bridge of Sighs;
> A palace and a prison on each hand:
> I saw from out the wave her structures rise
> As from the stroke of the enchanter's wand.
>   (*CPW,* 2:124)

The Bridge of Sighs is at once literal and figurative. The palace and prison it links are palpable structures with historical contexts, emblems for political practices the freedom-loving Byron deplored, expressions of his elegiac state of mind, and creations of the "enchanter's wand" we call a pen, which here describes itself in a scene both reflective and reflexive. So Venice remains throughout the early stanzas: decadent republic and "fairy city of the heart" peopled by the imagined beings of "Otway, Radcliffe, Schiller, Shakspeare's art" (2:130). If the literary Venice is as she ever was, the historical city, like the actual Byron, has suffered a sea change for the worse. Now subservient to the Austrian empire, Venice no longer elects doges to wed the sea with rings, and the lapse of those symbolic vows calls to mind the separation of Byron and his lady:

> The spouseless Adriatic mourns her lord;
> And, annual marriage now no more renewed,
> The Bucentaur lies rotting unrestored,
> Neglected garment of her widowhood!
>   (2:128)

Journeying southwest toward Rome, Byron proceeds through countryside and cities associated with his literary predecessors. He passes and meditates on the eternal resting places of Petrarch and Boccaccio, who repose in their "parent earth," and the contrasting situation of Italy's greatest poet, Dante, who, an exile like Byron, is buried at Ravenna "[w]hile Florence vainly begs her banish'd dead and weeps" (*CPW,* 2:144). The road's repeated lesson is partly consoling and partly lamentable: writing persists, though writers and their societies vanish. The most complex meditation on history's still-legible palimpsest comes in stanzas 64–66, devoted to Cicero's friend and correspondent Servius Sulpicius. Sulpicius sailed from Asia Minor, saw the ruins of Megara, Aegina, and Corinth, and recorded what he saw. On his own Eastern tour Byron "traced the path" of Sulpicius, viewed the same "sepulchres of cities," and put his thoughts into *Childe Harold II.* Now an older, terrestrial pilgrim in Italy, Byron discerns further strata of ruin. The Italy of Sulpicius has gone the way of Megara, Corinth, and Aegina. So has the youthful Byron who sailed the Mediterranean. What endures amid the wreckage is the written word, Sulpicius's "yet surviving page" and Byron's still growing poem: "That page is now before me, and on mine / *His* country's ruin added to the mass / Of perish'd states he mourn'd in their decline, / And I in desolation; all that *was* / Of then destruction *is*" (2:139).

When Byron reaches Rome, collective loss and personal bereavement converge in images previously associated with Venice: "Oh, Rome! my country! city of the soul! / The orphans of the heart must turn to thee, / lone mother of dead empires!" (*CPW,* 2:150). When Byron saw it in the second decade of the nineteenth century, the former imperial city seemed one vast graveyard, its monuments being reclaimed by nature, much as is the case in Wordsworth's "Tintern Abbey." Depicting sight after sight, Byron shows how imperfectly the attempt at human commemoration is realized. A tourist at the tomb of Cecelia Metella, he knows nothing of the matron but her name. Trajan's and Titus's columns have no names to distinguish them and bear "apostolic statues" instead of imperial effigies. Only in St. Peter's, built to the glory of God, not man, does the oppressive burden of being a mortal among relics lighten:

> Enter: its grandeur overwhelms thee not;
> And why? It is not lessened; but thy mind,
> Expanded by the genius of the spot,
> Has grown colossal, and can only find
> A fit abode wherein appear enshrined
> Thy hopes of immortality.
>
> (2:176)

With expanded soul, Byron turns away from the ruins of Rome and toward the sea for the famous apostrophe that culminates *Childe Harold's Pilgrimage:* "Roll on, thou deep and dark blue ocean—roll! / Ten thousand fleets sweep over thee in vain" (*CPW,* 2:184). Here at the poem's and the pilgrimage's end, Byron's cautionary verses may address humankind in general—but the lines are specifically relevant to the current self-styled ruler of the waves, Britannia, in whose realm the recent death of Princess Charlotte has united everyone from her father the Prince Regent to his humblest subject in "the electric chain of that despair, / Whose shock was as an earthquake" (2:182). If St. Peter's grandeur nourishes "hopes of immortality," the ocean, "boundless, endless, and sublime— / The image of Eternity" (2:185), offers proof of human transience—a natural law to which the British Empire, like its predecessors, must submit:

> Thy shores are empires, changed in all save thee—
> Assyria, Greece, Rome, Carthage, what are they?
> Thy waters washed them power while they were free,
> And many a tyrant since; their shores obey
> The stranger, slave, or savage; their decay
> Has dried up realms to desarts:—not so thou,
> Unchangeable save to thy wild waves' play—
> Time writes no wrinkle on thine azure brow—
> Such as creation's dawn beheld, thou rollest now.
> (2:185)

Acknowledging the ocean's power, Byron shares it. He thereby regains, for the moment, the imaginative insights romantics associate with youth: "For I was as it were a child of thee, / And trusted to thy billows far and near, / And laid my hand upon thy mane—as I do here" (2:186). The consequence of this past recaptured is "not apocalypse but that radically equivocal and human thing—glory."[12]

Some stanzas before *Childe Harold*'s glorious apostrophe to the sea, Byron, having ignored his title character throughout most of canto 4, at last invokes him—for dismissal:

> But where is he, the Pilgrim of my song,
> The being who upheld it through the past?
> Methinks he cometh late and tarries long.

He is no more—these breathings are his last;
His wanderings done, his visions ebbing fast,
And he himself as nothing.
                                        (*CPW,* 2:179)

The intermittently composed long poem had served Byron well, but when he next had need of the genre it was time for a change. On 3 July 1818, having settled into a congenial mode of life in Italy, Byron exchanged English Spenserian verse for Italian ottava rima, the form he had first tried out in the verse tale *Beppo* in the months following the completion of *Childe Harold* 4. He replaced the invented Childe Harold with the appropriated Don Juan, the narratorial pose of world-weary pilgrim with that of rueful laughing philosopher. Beginning *Don Juan,* Byron struck a vein of gold comparable to but even richer than that of *Childe Harold.* Again he hit upon an indefinitely sustainable poetic vehicle for self-expression through a volatile blend of concealment and confession, a delightfully mystifying tissue of apparent sincerity, blatant falsehood, and every nuance between. Byron's first plan was to follow but revise the classical model in a 12-canto modern epic that was "to be a little quietly facetious upon every thing" (*BLJ,* 6:67), but his professed intentions for *Don Juan* varied widely over time.

His actual intentions also changed, modified by circumstance, advice, and mood. Finally his "plan" was an endorsement of planlessness, felicitous possibilities, unforeseen consequences. From the moment he began the poem until 1823, when he abandoned it a few stanzas into canto 17 to sail for Greece and a freedom fighter's life or death, Byron made *Don Juan* both an intensely personal work, packed with his own opinions, adventures, relationships, loves, and loathings, and an extensively public work that assimilates and meditates upon the culture, politics, and history of his age, roughly the period from the American Revolution to the Greek Revolution. Although *Don Juan*'s cant-defying brilliance struck many contemporary readers as licentious immorality, Shelley and many readers in subsequent generations have deemed it the greatest long poem since *Paradise Lost.* It is a masterpiece whose subject, as Hazlitt shrewdly noticed, is its own making. Taken another way, its subject is the whole world. Given the poem's nature, its critics soon discover the truth of McGann's claim that "*Don Juan* encourages almost endless commentary but frustrates almost every sort of formal analysis."[13]

The first stanza of the first canto of Byron's modern epic begins with an extraordinary proposition:

> I want a hero: an uncommon want,
>   When every year and month sends forth a new one,
> Till, after cloying the gazettes with cant,
>   The age discovers he is not the true one;
> Of such as these I should not care to vaunt,
>   I'll therefore take our ancient friend Don Juan,
> We all have seen him in the pantomime
> Sent to the devil, somewhat ere his time.
>
> (*CPW,* 5:8)

Don Juan's ground rules are discernible from the start. Here, readers glimpse the poem's apparently improvisational but actually artful mode of proceeding, its narrator-composer's ruling passion (hatred of cant), its protagonist's antiheroic status (as a comically mispronounced English pantomime version of a legendary Spanish libertine), and its age's unworthiness to offer appropriately epic material. Unlike the mythic past that furnished many a classical hero, the real world of Byron's (and George III's, Wellington's, Castlereagh's, Napoléon's, the Lake Poets') day is seen, bloody and warlike though it may be, as containing no worthy contenders. In the next two stanzas, however, Byron will prove deft enough at incorporating a parade of the rejected names, gazette fashion, into his poem. This epic catalog continues the prolepsis, for *Don Juan* will be, among other things, its own refutation—a work that notices by purporting to ignore, continues by pretending to conclude, gossips by professing to keep silent.

Though Byron claims to take "our ancient friend" from contemporary English pantomime, Don Juan is of course an archetypal figure from much further back and from another country. First presented in Tirso da Molina's *El Burlador de Sevilla* of 1630, later put onstage by Molière, Mozart, and Goldoni, among others, the traditional Don Juan is a mature, deliberate seducer and deceiver of women from all ranks and nations. His amorous success and eventual downfall are equally spectacular. Having killed the father of one of his victims, he invites the man's memorial statue to dine with him. The stone effigy turns up—a

most effective *coup de théâtre*—and drags Don Juan down to hell. Byron's
Don Juan is an ingenious transformation of the archetype. First
glimpsed as the well-born but ill-raised child of parents as mismatched
as Byron's own or as Byron and Annabella, Juan is a youth of 16 when
the main action of canto 1 begins. Sheltered and naive, attractive and
sensitive, he is ripe for being seduced rather than seducing—and his
successive seduction is the leitmotif of Byron's poem. The young man's
picaresque adventures in various nations and cultures always end up the
same way: with Juan in the arms, or bed, of a woman older (whether by
a few months or many years) and more powerful than he is.

The series of liaisons begins in Seville, where Juan's hypocritical
mother, Donna Inez, seems to have set in motion an adulterous farce
involving the adolescent Juan with Donna Julia, "married, charming,
chaste, and twenty-three," who happens to be the wife of Inez's former
lover the 50-year-old Don Alfonso. Caught in the act by the cuckolded
Alfonso, Juan flees naked in the night and subsequently is packed off to
travel. Struck by a tempest, his ship sinks in the Gulf of Lyons. Juan and
a few others escape with very little food to a long-boat, where most of
the starving survivors are driven to cannibalism and gorge themselves
on Juan's tutor, Pedrillo. Ultimately only Juan survives to wash up on
the rocky coast of an Aegean isle where the pirate Lambro's beautiful
daughter, Haidée, nurses him back to strength and makes him lord of
her heart and hearth until her "piratical papa," whom she had presumed
dead, returns home and dispatches Juan to a slave ship.

Purchased in the Constantinople slave market by the sultan's favorite
wife, Gulbayez, Don Juan is dressed as a woman and smuggled into the
harem, where he high-mindedly resists the sultana's amorous commands but yields to the charms of an odalisque, Dudù. In the company
of a fellow slave, an older man who is his English namesake (John Johnson), Juan escapes from Constantinople and ends up in battle, as soldier
in a Russian force laying siege to the Turkish city Ismail. Distinguished
for valor, Juan carries news of the victory to Catherine, "whom glory still
adores / As greatest of all sovereigns and w____s" (*CPW,* 5:327).
Favored as the ardent empress's romantic plaything until his constitu-
tion begins to suffer, Juan is dispatched to England on diplomatic business. There he experiences first the urban delights and follies of London
in the season, then the rural pleasures of Norman Abbey. There the bro-
ken-off poem leaves Juan subject to the competing charms of three different and dangerous women, the sensuous Duchess of Fitz-Fulke, the
prim heiress Aurora Raby, and Lady Adeline Amundeville, the brilliant

political hostess who shows promise of being "the fair most fatal Juan ever met."

In some ways, suspension amid rival beauties seems the best situation in which to leave Don Juan. Much earlier, however, Byron had professed to have other plans for his protagonist. A few months before putting the poem aside at Teresa Guiccioli's purported request, he wrote to Murray, still his publisher, about his intentions. "I meant to take him the tour of Europe—with a proper mixture of siege—battle—and adventure—and to make him finish as *Anarchsis Cloots*—in the French revolution. . . . I meant to have made him a Cavalier Servente in Italy and a cause for a divorce in England—and a Sentimental 'Werther-faced man' in Germany." Byron had not decided whether to have Juan end up "in Hell—or in an unhappy marriage," the former being "probably only an Allegory of the other state" (*BLJ,* 8:78). If we credit the allusion to Jean Baptiste Clootz, guillotined by Robespierre in 1794, Juan, who had survived the battle of Ismail in 1790, had only a few more years to live when left at the Norman Abbey breakfast table. Nevertheless, Byron could have stretched the adventures of those years to fill many more cantos—certainly the 24 of classical tradition, perhaps even the 100 he facetiously promises in canto 12 (*CPW,* 5:511).

The chief reason for this infinite expandability is that the adventures of Don Juan are only somewhat more important to the poem than are the protagonist's travels to *Childe Harold's Pilgrimage.* As Anne Barton has pointed out, Byron's Don Juan differs from other versions of the character in having no comic servant to accompany and comment upon him. Instead, the poem offers a narrator, initially dramatized as a Spanish bachelor personally acquainted with Juan's family but soon largely conflated with Byron himself. Despite Juan's strenuously epic adventures in love, war, travel, and shipwreck, the narrator's digressive remarks constitute the most engaging feature of the poem. Ironic, serious, sentimental, outraged, amused, disingenuous, candid, narrowly self-absorbed, broadly speculative, the ever-changeable narrator unifies his errant poem. The unity provided, as critics long have recognized, is "that of Byron's own extraordinary personality."[14]

Before Don Juan appears on the scene, that "extraordinary personality" makes itself felt in two preliminaries to the epic: a prose preface and a verse dedication, both suppressed during Byron's life. The preface, a dazzling fragment of romantic irony, parodies the text from which it derives, "a note or preface (I forgot which) by Mr. W. Wordsworth to a poem," which happens to be "The Thorn" from *Lyrical Ballads.* Much as

Wordsworth had hoped to establish plausibility by requesting that his reader imagine a retired sea captain as teller of his rustic tale, Byron mockingly asks that "[t]he Reader who has acquiesced in Mr. W. Wordsworth's supposition that his 'Misery oh Misery' is related by the 'Captain of a small &c.' is requested to suppose by a like exertion of Imagination that the following epic narrative is told by a Spanish Gentleman in a village in the Sierra Morena on the road between Monasterio and Seville—sitting at the door of a posada with the curate of the hamlet on his right hand" (*CPW,* 5:82–83). Though it sets a context for the tale of Don Juan, the chief effect of this unfinished preface is to ridicule the principles and practices of Wordsworth and his fellow Lake Poet Southey, a task Byron found he could do yet more devastatingly in verse. Accordingly, he put away the preface and instead wrote an ottava rima dedication, which he described to Thomas Moore as "good, simple, savage verse upon the [laureate's] politics, and the way he got them" (*BLJ,* 6:68). The dedication, an amazingly concise, fiercely opinionated dissertation on the close connection between language and politics, denounces the squalid nature of both in contemporary Britain. Byron addresses his chief target immediately: "Bob Southey! You're a poet—poet Laureate. / And representative of all the race" (*CPW,* 5:3). The secondary target (or as Anne Mellor aptly characterizes him, the "other Bob")[15] of the dedication is Robert Stewart, viscount Castlereagh and foreign secretary of the Tory government whose policies Byron found repressive at home, in Ireland, and on the Continent alike. Southey's fellow Lakists Wordsworth and Coleridge, who like him passed from radical youth to Tory middle age, also sustain hits. As George Orwell would do more than a century later in "Politics and the English Language," Byron acknowledges the intimate connection between verbal utterances and political acts. He denounces the Lakists for their tuneless, foggy ravings as well as for their turncoat Toryism, Castlereagh for both his policies and the "set trash of phrase" that marks his oratory. The antithesis to all these Regency Tories is Milton, a man and poet as sublime in his song as he was unchanging in his antimonarchial politics: "*He* did not loathe the sire to laud the son, / But closed the tyrant-hater he begun" (5:6).

Byron enhances his chief targets' poetical and political inadequacy by associating both with sexual impotence. Each "Bob" is less than manly. Byron denounces Castlereagh as an "intellectual eunuch" who warrants no pronoun but "it" and, in a famously scurrilous innuendo that burlesques Bellerophon riding Pegasus or Icarus falling from heaven, represents Southey's poetical hubris in terms of a flying fish "[g]asping on deck, because you soar too high, Bob, / And fall, for lack of moisture, quite adry, Bob!" (*CPW,* 5:3–4). Along with the other Lake Poets, Southey is obliquely accused of intellectual incest, a charge enriched by Southey's and Coleridge's marriage to sisters, Edith and Sarah Fricker, and by the Coleridges' longtime sharing of the Southeys' house at Keswick:

> You, Gentlemen! By dint of long seclusion
>   From better company have kept your own
> At Keswick, and through still continued fusion
>   Of one another's minds at last have grown
> To deem as a most logical conclusion
>   That Poesy has wreaths for you alone;
> There is a narrowness in such a notion
> Which makes me wish you'd change your lakes for ocean.
>
>   (5:4)

This stanza economically settles an old score with Southey, whom Byron suspected of having done as much as anyone to spread rumors of a Byron-Shelley "league of incest" at Villa Diodati in the summer of 1816. It also faithfully predicts the cosmopolitan freedom of *Don Juan,* a work in which English concerns—poetic, political, and all the rest—will be important but not all-engrossing to the broad-minded composing presence who resists authority, undercuts order, transgresses limits, and lives at ease with the ocean and the wide world.

The dedication's contrast between the deplored insularity of the Lake Poets and Byron's own implied cosmopolitanism continues into the poem itself. The first canto is, like *Beppo,* a self-sufficient ottava rima tale contrasting the manners and morals of its Mediterranean locale with those prevailing on its immediate audience's "tight little island." The poem's hybrid nature—English words, Italian form—proves highly appropriate, given this thematic preoccupation, as does its recurrent strategy of comic mispronunciation. The first thing a reader notices, and then most likely accepts without analyzing, is the contortion of the protagonist's name from "Hwan" to "Joo-un," a mispronunciation first evident in stanza 1, where it rhymes with "new one" and "true one." Byron goes out of his way to do similar things with other Spanish proper nouns in the canto: Juan's father becomes Jóse (JO-zee) rather than José (Ho-ZAY). His mother's name, Inez, rhymes with "fine as." His birthplace, Seville, rhymes with "revel"; the stream running through it, the Guadalquivir, with "river"; Cadiz with "ladies."

Similarly, though canto 1's farcical story of cuckoldry and discovery is on its surface generic and Mediterranean—as the narrator facetiously generalizes, "What men call gallantry, and gods adultery, / Is much more common where the climate's sultry" (*CPW,* 5:29)—the characters and situations have relevance to Byron's England, particularly to his own life there. Donna Inez, for instance, is a marvelous portrait of pretension along the lines of Chaucer's Prioress, but she also bears telling resemblances to the Regency tribe of Bluestockings and especially to one such "lady intellectual," Annabella Milbanke: "Her favourite science was the mathematical, / Her noblest virtue was her magnanimity" (1:12). The recognizable reality of this magnificently drawn hypocrite who hounds her errant spouse to "death or Doctors' Commons"—the latter an English alternative, not a Spanish one—was likely, Hobhouse correctly predicted, to rally British support for Annabella. Byron replied, "She is not meant for Clytemnestra [one of his stock epithets for his wife]—and if She were—would you protect the fiend?" (*BLJ,* 6:131).

Here, as he does so often, Byron tells a partial truth. Inez portrays Annabella—but more broadly, she embodies a distinctive English form of false prudery, just as pubescent Juan wandering "by the glassy brooks / Thinking unutterable things" is at once a distinctive literary character, a 16-year-old Everyman, and a representation of the sexual blindness Byron associates with his poetical foes the Lakists. Infatuated with Julia but pursuing "self-communion with his own high soul," young Juan turns "without perceiving his condition, / Like Coleridge, into a metaphysician" (*CPW,* 5:37). This Lakist obliviousness to physical desire suits him well to pair with the object of his affections, whose lush beauty and hot Moorish blood (which Julia shares with the poem's second heroine, Haidée) pull against her Catholic piety and her naive trust in platonic love. In the world Byron describes, the real and the ideal both have their power, but the latter is bound to triumph. His anatomizing of the struggle in Julia's mind is both sympathetic and amused as she finds herself in a garden rendezvous with Juan at the charming (if prosaically specified) time of "the sixth of June, about the hour / Of half-past six—perhaps still nearer seven" (5:41):

> Julia had honour, virtue, truth, and love,
>   For Don Alfonso; and she inly swore,
> By all the vows below to powers above,
>   She never would disgrace the ring she wore,
> Nor leave a wish which wisdom might reprove;
>   And while she ponder'd this, besides much more,
> One hand on Juan's carelessly was thrown,
> Quite by mistake—she thought it was her own."
> (1:43)

Byron's acute psychological study of amorous self-deception continues for several stanzas until Julia capitulates in a couplet whose last line might be taken as an epitome for human nature as it exists in the world of *Don Juan:* "A little still she strove, and much repented, / And whispering 'I will ne'er consent'—consented" (1:46).

That a poem called *Don Juan* would represent and sympathize with a love-smitten woman's perspective is itself revisionist. That the woman is the agent, not object, of seduction takes the transformation still further. That the self-deceiving female platonist of "the sixth of June" has become, by November, a splendidly resourceful deceiver of her husband is equally candid and comic. Romantic love in a garden gives way to adultery in a matrimonial bedroom, where the wily Julia can batter her husband with outraged words even as her lover is concealed beneath the bedclothes:

> "Yes, search and search," she cried,
> "Insult on insult heap, and wrong on wrong!
> It was for this that I became a bride!
> For this in silence I have suffer'd long
> A husband like Alfonso at my side."
> (*CPW,* 5:55)

The flood of righteous rhetoric continues and overwhelms the wronged husband. Only the irrefutable fact of Don Juan's shoes, over which Alfonso stumbles, can silence Julia's pretensions to innocence. Such is Byron's sense of where romantic love leads in a real world. With the affair discovered, the road forks for the guilty. Julia, as married woman, is banished to a convent; Juan, as unmarried man, is sent on travels "[t]o mend his former morals, or get new [ones]" (5:70). Clear-sighted at last, Julia bids him farewell by letter and recognizes that though she will cherish their love, he will forget it: " 'Man's love is of his life a thing apart, / 'Tis woman's whole existence' " (5:71). In that contrast lies the practical truth and moral point of the Don Juan myth as Byron understands it.

Byron sent the first canto and its preliminaries to England at the end of 1818. His manuscript's first English audience—his witty, worldly confreres Hobhouse, Scrope Davies, and Douglas Kinnaird, plus John Hookham Frere, who had introduced English ottava rima in his work *The Monks and the Giants*—realized that the poem would outrage the wider readership and in January 1819 argued against publication while at the same time admiring "the genius, wit, poetry, satire" of the "singular style" that, they granted, might be Byron's "real forte."[16] In spite of his friends' advice against publication and Murray's obvious reluctance, Byron was determined to bring out the poem and wrote a second canto to appear with the first.

If canto 1 offers comic farce, canto 2 presents equal measures of realism (shipwreck) and romance (idyllic love), with Juan arriving "half senseless, from the sea" on Lambro's island at the precise midpoint of the canto. Byron, self-styled friend of the Mediterranean at the conclusion of *Childe Harold* 4, here does no romantic projecting of attributes on "the vast, salt, dread, eternal deep." Rather, he takes pride in drawing his fictive wreck from factual accounts: especially Dalyell's *Shipwrecks and Disasters at Sea* (1812) but also other sources, including the narratives of Captain Bligh and of his own seagoing grandfather, "Foul Weather Jack" Byron. The accurately rendered storm that swamps the *Trinidada* is no more malevolent than the succeeding rainbow, "airy child of vapour and the sun," is a sign of God's blessing. Juan and the other survivors find themselves adrift in a merely natural world, where their spiritual resources may endure, but their physical needs are undeniable. One of the passages least acceptable to Byron's cant-ridden public turned out to be a couplet reporting the double nature of loss the survivors in the long-boat feel as a companion vessel goes down: "They grieved for those who perish'd with the cutter, / And also for the biscuit casks and butter" (*CPW,* 5:108). Mourning the destruction of human lives does not preclude the survivors from also lamenting the loss of food that might furnish human livelihood.

Throughout the first half of canto 2, amoral nature makes itself most unromantically felt in just this way. Juan, declaiming his fidelity to Julia, is silenced by seasick retching. When the survivors tear up his cherished relic, Julia's letter, for lots and settle on his tutor, Pedrillo, as cannibal sacrifice, they are presented as hungry animals, not sinful souls: "None in particular had sought or plann'd it, / 'Twas nature gnaw'd them to this resolution" (*CPW,* 5:112). Juan's success in reaching shore depends less on heroic skill—the talent for swimming that he shares with Byron—than on natural randomness (and of course literary necessity): a shark that might have preyed on Juan "carried off his neighbor by the thigh," and a wave washes a piece of flotsam by "[j]ust as his feeble arms could strike no more" (5:122). When at mid-canto Juan comes ashore somewhere in the Cyclades, Byron's source texts change: factual accounts of shipwreck give way to *The Odyssey* and *The Tempest*. But natural law continues to prevail. Juan's recovery depends on being fed by practical Zoë, not on being loved by beautiful Haidée: "some good lessons / Are also learnt from Ceres and from Bacchus, / Without whom Venus will not long attack us" (5:141–42).

When at the entire poem's romantic high point the narrative leaves a restored Juan slumbering in the arms of Haidée, biblical and classical allusions suggest the pair's pristine isolation. Civilization is never further away. Haidée is "Nature's bride" and Juan's natural love—but the attentive reader should remember what Nature is and does. The lovers' "natural" refuge is a cave formed by the sea that wrecked the *Trinidada* and littered the picturesque coast with the remnants of similarly destroyed vessels. That same sea surrounds the island where the lovers fancy themselves alone. On that sea Haidée's sharklike father plies his trade: the economic basis of Haidée's seeming island paradise is Lambro's piracy. Thus as the canto closes both nature and society impinge, though as yet but lightly, on the lovers' apparently timeless idyll. The narrator acknowledges that "[l]ove, constant love" has another foe as potent and mutable as the sea. Wordsworth got it partly right: nature and human nature are inextricably linked—and for Byron, that is the problem.

> The heart is like the sky, a part of heaven,
> But changes night and day too, like the sky;
> Now o'er it clouds and thunder must be driven,
> And darkness and destruction as on high.
> (*CPW,* 5:156)

Recognizing the inextricable connection of *Don Juan*'s most brilliant touches with its most blasphemous features, John Murray, like Byron's literary advisers, resisted publishing the manuscript in unexpurgated form. A series of negotiations with Byron resulted in the removal of the dedication. Byron ultimately agreed that to include the ad hominem attack on Southey would be wrong, given that the poem was to appear anonymously. Other deletions unauthorized by Byron (of references to syphilis or "the pox" and to the recent suicide of Lady Byron's attorney, Sir Samuel Romilly) toned down some of the most provocative passages. Even so, some members of the reading public did, as anticipated, take offense on religious and moral grounds. The absence of the author's and publisher's names may in fact have increased their outrage, as Hobhouse half-seriously predicted: "This will make our wiseacres think that there is poison for King Queen & Dauphin in every page and will irritate public pruriency to a complete priapism."[17] *Don Juan*'s deluxe quarto edition did not sell out, and anonymous publication left it unprotected by copyright law and vulnerable to pirated editions.

Nevertheless, Murray could not be said to suffer financially from *Don Juan*. He brought out cheaper editions that, along with the pirated versions, allowed the poem to circulate widely among less prosperous readers.[18] Even while counting his profits, a discreet Tory of Murray's stamp was bound to feel less than comfortable about a work its own author conceded to be "as free as La Fontaine—& bitter in politics—too" (*BLJ*, 6:76). The publisher did not encourage Byron's continuation of the poem, though he brought out the next three cantos, 3 through 5, in August 1821. This installment succeeded with the buying and reading public but not with Byron himself, who was indignant over the many misprints and errors in the text and disappointed at what he considered the "tediousness" of his own writing, even though he resourcefully and hilariously incorporated confession of that supposed fault into the poem itself, at the point where he divided the original canto 3 into two shorter ones: "I feel this tediousness will never do— / 'Tis being *too* epic, and I must cut down / (In copying) this long canto into two" (*CPW,* 5:200).

If Byron found cantos 3, 4, and 5 tedious, it may have been because they inevitably involved continuation. He had to bring Juan and Haidée's story to its tragic conclusion, and doing so involved a return to subject matter long familiar to him, what Elizabeth Boyd terms "the nexus of oriental fiction ancient and modern."[19] The third and fourth cantos in some ways reenact, at the opposite end of the Mediterranean, the progress of Juan's love affair with Julia. When we first glimpse Juan and Haidée in canto 3, some time has passed since the seaside consummation of their love. With the passage of time "Haidée forgot the island was her sire's" (*CPW,* 5:165) and installed Juan in Lambro's house where, richly attired, they feast with attendant revelers. Having left their cave and entered society, the young lovers, previously described as "a group that's quite antique, / Half naked, loving, natural, and Greek," no longer seem timeless and innocent, though to the last the narrator asserts the absolute intensity of their love, a state "[o]h beautiful! And rare as beautiful!" that "was in them their nature, or their fate" (5:149, 208, 209).

The narrator's unqualified sympathy for pure young love leads him to a strategic deployment of tedium: delaying Lambro's entry on the scene. Like the disguised Odysseus returning to Ithaca, the piratical "fisher of men" or "sea-attorney" comes ashore in stanza 20 of canto 3. He arrives in "the house no more his home" in stanza 51 and in stanza 61 stands unseen "within his hall at eventide." Eighty-five stanzas of "tediousness" separate this arrival from Lambro's self-disclosure, as Haidée awakens from troubled dreams: "Oh! Powers of Heaven! What dark eye meets she there? / 'Tis—'tis her father's—fix'd upon the pair!" (*CPW,* 5:214). Before this dramatic reunion, the Byronic narrator is at his most discursive—piling digression on digression, dividing the one long canto into two (which necessitates a conclusion and a new beginning), interjecting all sorts of self-conscious rhetorical traffic-direction ("But to resume," "Meanwhile Apollo plucks me by the ear," "But let me to my story," "But I'm digressing"). The psychological motive behind all this obstruction and errancy, as Anne Barton points out, is Byron's profound reluctance to bring Haidée and Juan's idyll to "its inevitable tragic end" (Barton, 37). High romantic love may have been a commonplace of Byron's pen, but here he could not cut it short without a sigh and thousands of delaying words.

With Lambro's return comes the end of young love—and of Haidée, who goes mad when parted from Juan and dies self-starved—but also the introduction of a topic crucial to Byronic Orientalism, the subjection of individuals and nations. Patient, temperate, brave, and resourceful, a man like Lambro has no acceptable place in his native Greece under Turkish despotism. He can live as a slave within the law, or go outside the law and become an enslaver. Similarly, when canto 5 finds Juan enslaved and conducted to the sultan's palace at Constantinople—a pleasure dome where "wealth had done wonders, taste not much"—all his natural and social attributes are veiled. Free, Occidental, male, and Christian, Juan is obliged (or encouraged, in the last case, by the eunuch

Baba, who earnestly recommends Islamic circumcision) to give up all these attributes and to play the role of "Juanna" so that he may be smuggled into the harem at the fancy of the sultana Gulbayez, in whom the powers of love and despotism combine. Beautiful though she may be, this creature of the palace is herself in bondage to her position, as if to illustrate an insight voiced by Juan's companion John Johnson: "Most men are slaves, none more so than the great, / To their own whims and passions, and what not" (*CPW,* 5:248). As prisoner of her exalted position, Gulbayez does not understand how to win a heart: "Something imperial, or imperious, threw / A chain o'er all she did. . . .And rapture's self will seem almost a pain / With aught which looks like despotism in view" (5:276). Still mourning Haidée, Juan is able to resist the implied command in the sultana's " 'Christian, canst thou love?' " and answers the question by bursting into tears (5:278). This response proves both natural and unnatural enough to rouse the woman in the sultana.

His second response, an indignant lecture that begins " 'The prison'd eagle will not pair, nor I / Serve a sultana's sensual phantasy" and ends with " 'Heads bow, knees bend, eyes watch around a throne, / And hands obey—our hearts are still our own" (*CPW,* 5:281–82), does still more. Though the milieu of canto 5 is a blatantly artificial world where a Spanish speaker's eloquence is intelligible to a Turkish auditor, Juan's speech evokes a psychologically convincing, and utterly human, series of potential reactions in the spoiled sultana.

> Her first thought was to cut off Juan's head;
>   Her second, to cut only his—acquaintance;
> Her third, to ask him where he had been bred;
>   Her fourth, to rally him into repentance;
> Her fifth, to call her maids and go to bed;
>   Her sixth, to stab herself; her seventh, to sentence
> The lash to Baba:—but her grand resource
> Was to sit down again, and cry of course.
>   (5:285)

This "grand resource" proves just what is needed to soften Juan's resolve, which was prepared to withstand a tyrant's threats: "But all his great preparatives for dying / Dissolved like snow before a woman crying" (5:286). Only the sultan's fortuitous arrival saves the weakening

Juan from Gulbayez's bed. The canto ends with the sultana burdened with her lord, its last note blending the themes of love and slavery in an explicit criticism of the East and an equally sharp, if implicit, jab at the West:

> Thus in the East they are extremely strict,
>   And *Wedlock* and a *Padlock* mean the same;
> Excepting only when the former's pick'd
>   It ne'er can be replaced in proper frame;
> Spoilt, as a pipe of claret is when prick'd:
>   But then their own Polygamy's to blame;
> Why don't they knead two virtuous souls for life
> Into that moral centaur, man and wife?
>
>   (5:291)

His own wedlock broken, Byron closes canto 5, the last segment of Don Juan's story published by Murray, where the first canto opened—with the monster called marriage.

Byron blamed a different heterosexual convention, Italian extramarital *serventismo*, for the yearlong lapse of *Don Juan*. In July 1821 he informed Murray that the lady whose *cavalier servente* he was, Countess Guiccioli, disliked the poem, which she had read in a French translation, and had extracted his promise to refrain from continuing it. Byron's explanation may have contained truth, but it was not the whole truth. He had also been discouraged by how his friends, his reviewers, and the reading public reacted to the poem's first cantos. Increasingly involved in Italian revolutionary politics and in obliquely or overtly political writing (his historical verse dramas and *The Vision of Judgment*), he regretted the omissions that had diluted the bitter political insights of *Don Juan*. He may have found the prospect of spinning out further variations on the theme of Don Juan's amours less than exciting at a time when life was full of other, more compelling challenges. Nonetheless, as McGann's textual research has shown, he resumed *Don Juan* in secret at the start of 1822. Only in July did he tell Murray that his "Dictatress" had allowed him to continue the poem; but beneath the manuscript's inked-out dates, infrared and ultraviolet technology disclose the truth. Canto 6 was begun in January, and canto 7 was completed by the end of June

(*CPW,* 5:715). From then on, Byron's interest in *Don Juan* was keen and his rate of composition swift. By March 1823 cantos 8 through 16 were complete.

When he first eased back into the writing of *Don Juan,* Byron returned to the light vein of romantic satire. Gulbayez's drearily dutiful hours with the sultan contrast tellingly with Don Juan's night in the seraglio, amid an assemblage of love-starved women whose diverse nationalities and varied types of beauty call to mind the Mozartian Don Giovanni's list of conquests all brought together in one room. The odalisques are attracted to Juan/Juanna without exactly knowing why. Dudù, the Georgian "sleepy Venus" who shares her bed with the newcomer, discovers the reason for Juanna's magnetism with a delighted shriek in the night and then, as Julia had earlier done, glibly covers for Don Juan. Her "dream" of plucking a delectable golden apple, then being stung by a bee issuing from the fruit, is, like Haidée's dream, evidence that Byron had no need of psychoanalytic theory to represent the workings of the conscious and subconscious alike. Next morning Gulbayez, on discovering what has transpired in the harem, orders "the Georgian and her paramour" dispatched to a fate familiar to readers of Byron's Eastern tales: " 'Let the boat / Be ready by the secret portal's side: / You know the rest' " (*CPW,* 5:333). And here, "trusting Juan may escape the fishes," Byron ends the canto with a promise that "The Muse will take a little touch at warfare" (5:335).

The battlefield is where the new direction of *Don Juan* urged Byron's muse to go. Canto 6 had been a tentative warm-up exercise. By the time he had completed canto 7, Byron had regained confidence in his epic intentions and had determined that his poem was headed from love to war. Furthermore, he had found a suitable engagement, and with it a date that would, from that point in the poem onward, ground Don Juan's adventures in a specific European social and political context, at the start of the revolutionary era still continuing as Byron wrote his poem. Byron's source of detail on the siege of Ismail, a small city on the Danube contested by Ottoman defenders and Russian attackers in 1790, was the Marquis de Castlenau's *Essai sur l'Histoire ancienne et moderne de la Nouvelle Russie* (1820). But the perspective is pure Byron: *Don Juan*'s savagely indignant presentation of modern warfare's brutality and folly is an ironic countertext to Castlenau's saber-rattling.[20]

When Juan, along with that seasoned soldier of fortune John Johnson, escapes from Turkish slavery and enlists as a mercenary in Suwarrow's Russian troops besieging Ismail, he merely becomes a pawn for the other side. Byron's presentation of battlefield details compares to the unflinching realism of his account of shipwreck. At Ismail, as aboard the *Trinidada* and its long-boat, there are individual moments of courage and nobility, among them Juan's rescue of the orphan girl Leila from his Cossack comrades in arms and the vignette of a Tartar Khan and his five sons all fighting to the death against insurmountable odds. Byron can even admire the sangfroid of the old pasha who "sits among some hundreds dead, / Smoking his pipe quite calmly" or the manic effectiveness of Suwarrow inspiring and drilling his troops: "Now Mars, now Momus, and when bent to storm / A fortress, Harlequin in uniform" (*CPW,* 5:394, 354). Mostly, however, Byron's sympathies are reserved for those ordinary people whose lives are lost or ruined because Russia's empress and Turkey's sultan had an itch for confrontation. Furthermore, Byron leaves his contemporary readers no room to imagine that his case against militarism and imperialism is any less valid in 1822 than it had been in 1790. At a time when the European allies who had beaten Napoléon and dismantled the French Empire were congratulating themselves and restoring the regimes he had toppled, Byron's eloquent invective proved deeply shocking to many. We can perhaps best appreciate the triumph of his point of view by recognizing how self-evident his claims now seem to many of us:

> 123
> All that the mind would shrink from of excesses;
>   All that the body perpetrates of bad;
> All that we read, hear, dream of man's distresses;
>   All that the Devil would do if run stark mad;
> All that defies the worst which pen expresses;
>   All by which Hell is peopled, or as sad
> As Hell—mere mortals who their power abuse,—
> Was here (as heretofore and since) let loose.

> 124
> If here and there some transient trait of pity
>   Was shown, and some more noble heart broke through
> Its bloody bond, and saved perhaps some pretty
>   Child, or an aged, helpless man or two—

What's this in one annihilated city,
   Where thousand loves, and ties, and duties grow?
Cockneys of London! Muscadins of Paris!
   Just ponder what a pious pastime war is:

125
Think how the joys of reading a Gazette
   Are purchased by all agonies and crimes:
Or if these do not move you, don't forget
   Such doom may be your own in after times.
Meantime the taxes, Castlereagh, and debt,
   Are hints as good as sermons, or as rhymes.
Read your own hearts and Ireland's present story,
Then feed her famine fat with Wellesley's glory.

No need to fear that famine will approach the throne of Britain: "Though Ireland starve, great George weighs twenty stone" (5:402–3).

The plight of abject Ireland, birthplace of Byron's foes and Britain's pillars Wellington and Castlereagh, also appears in the preface to cantos 6, 7, and 8, a ferocious attack on the detested foreign minister (who had recently cut his own throat) and a denunciation of *Don Juan*'s cant-spouting critics, the "degraded and hypocritical mass which leavens the present English generation" (*CPW,* 5:296). As he explained to Moore, Byron felt obliged "in the present clash of philosophy and tyranny, to throw away the scabbard. I know it is against fearful odds; but the battle must be fought; and it will eventually be for the good of mankind" (*BLJ,* 9:191). This letter's take-no-prisoners attitude also entailed asking Moore to send him the deleted stanzas on Wellington—or "Vilainton," which would furnish an introductory apostrophe for canto 9.

John Murray found the new cantos and the materials surrounding them "so outrageously shocking that I would not publish them if you were to give me your Estate—Title and Genius."[21] He was unable to persuade Byron to moderate the cantos, and so ended Byron's increasingly troubled relationship with the respectable Tory who had been his publisher since *Childe Harold;* from cantos 6, 7, and 8 on, Byron's works would be published by the radical John Hunt. Later in *Don Juan* Byron fancifully describes the loss of his "foolscap subjects," a change in market status plainly suggested in his move from a mainstream publisher to a fringe one, in terms of being deposed as "grand Napoleon of the realms of rhyme": "But Juan was my Moscow, and Faliero / My Leipsic, and my Mont Saint Jean seems Cain" (*CPW,* 5:482). The analogy does not hold in all its details. Whereas Napoléon finally had to retreat from Moscow, Byron never backed down on cantos 6 through 8, and keeping the poem true to his bitter politics made him the epic poet he wanted to be. He points this out toward, but not at, the end of canto 8: "You have now / Had sketches of love, tempest, travel, war— / All very accurate, you must allow, / And *Epic*, if plain truth should prove no bar" (5:407). Unusually, though Byron typically concludes his cantos with self-reflexive considerations of just this sort, canto 8 proceeds a few stanzas further and ends with his eye on the story, not the storyteller. The last words of this powerful canto, which has had so much to say about the devastation of war, concern a small act of human kindness amid the carnage, the rescue of orphaned Leila: "—And Juan wept, / And made a vow to shield her, which he kept" (5:408).

Byron's move from John Murray to John Hunt was not solely the effect of his uncompromising devotion to publishing the plain truth as he saw it. Daily connection with expatriate radicals (notably Shelley and Leigh Hunt, whom Byron and Shelley had brought to Italy to edit *The Liberal*, a new periodical to which both poets would contribute) had pushed Byron beyond the limits of decorum as understood back in Britain, where tastes had grown tamer in the years of Byron's absence. *Don Juan*'s Russian interlude—during which Juan, "Love turned a Lieutenant of Artillery" (*CPW,* 5:422), couples with Catherine the Great, "the grand Epitome / Of that great Cause of war, or peace, or what / You please" (5:426)—is stuffed with outrageous sexual innuendo. As Anne Barton observes, "That Murray should have severed his connection . . . seems less surprising than John Hunt daring to print at all" (Barton, 62). Once Juan arrives on English shores, however, the tone modulates. Byron's digressions on his native land mingle contempt and nostalgia as Juan catches his first sight of "Albion's chalky belt":

> I have no great cause to love that spot of earth,
>   Which holds what *might have been* the noblest nation;
> But though I owe it little but my birth,
>   I feel a mixed regret and veneration
> For its decaying fame and former worth.
>
>   (5:456–57)

The ensuing cantos will superimpose three different moments in the recent British past: Juan's experience of England in 1791 (at which time Byron, a child of three, still lived in Scotland), Byron's "Years of Fame," 1812 to 1816 (the source of his recollections of life in the Great World), and the time of composition, 1822 to 1823 (when Byron's impressions of England were secondhand). The consequence is that the final phase of *Don Juan* derives less from literature and more from life. As Elizabeth Boyd notes, "Although the circumstances of plot and character are thoroughly fictionalized, the thoughts, the feelings, and the situations are largely Byron's at firsthand."[22] Having by this time stopped work on his *Memoirs*, Byron now put the personal materials they might have contained into *Don Juan*. Not inappropriately, then, as he turns his eye on England Byron alludes to the catastrophic geologist Cuvier's theory of successive creations and destructions and imagines a time when George IV might be "dug up" as a fossil treasure, a mammoth or Titan to astound the denizens of a new and diminished world. Byron's retrospective evocation is an excavation in which he unearths an English world dead to him in certain senses yet in other senses vitally attractive. Condensing past and present, distilling real people into combinable essences, he mythifies the very facts he preserves.

The English Cantos fall into two parts that offer the long-established contrast of city and country, *urbs* and *rus*.[23] Juan's first view of metropolitan London is a vista from Shooter's Hill, where his naive effusion on "[f]reedom's chosen station," "chaste wives, pure lives," and "laws all inviolate" has been shattered by a highwayman's interjection of a knife and a demand: " 'Damn your eyes! your money or your life!' " (*CPW*, 5:467–68). The smoky capital Juan glimpses seems "the 'Devil's drawing-room' " (5:461). And so it is, in a shrunken way: a place entered by a macadamized highway smooth and easy like the road to perdition, lit by flames (the city's recently introduced gaslights), and featuring, in the fashionable neighborhood where Juan will roost, "some Hotels, / St. James's Palace, and St. James's 'Hells' " (5:474). Not for nothing is Don Juan called "our young diplomatic sinner" in the same stanza! But if King George's capital seems a trivialized version of Satan's Pandemonium, it likewise reflects and diminishes the Heavenly City. The word "Paradise" is repeatedly invoked, materialized, and cheapened in this part of the poem, in which the suburbs contain " 'Rows' most modestly called 'Paradise,' / Which Eve might quit without much sacrifice," (a West End ballroom is "[a]n earthly Paradise of 'Or Molu,' " and the smoothly monotonous Great World of fashion itself is a "Paradise of Pleasure and

Ennui" (5:471, 486, 563). Candidly presenting that gaudy, gilded "microcosm on stilts," Byron digs up a tawdry but fascinating past world that, all professions to the contrary, he has loved all too well. As fashionable London's sights pass before Juan's pseudo-Spanish eyes, Byron's elegiac *ubi sunt* passage concludes canto 11 by displaying his buried but undead emotional ties, "all those butterflies he has loved and hated, sought and scorned," in McGann's memorable phrase:[24]

> "Where is the world," cries Young, "at *eighty?* Where
> The world in which a man was born?" Alas!
> Where is the world of eight years past? 'Twas there
> I look for it—'tis gone, a Globe of Glass!
> Cracked, shivered, vanished, scarcely gazed on, ere
> A silent change dissolves the glittering mass.
> Statesmen, chiefs, orators, queens, patriots, kings,
> And dandies, all are gone on the wind's wings.
>
> (5:488)

This phase of the poem ends with the narrator offering Juan the generic advice of *ubi sunt* convention (" 'Carpe diem,' Juan, 'Carpe, carpe!' ") and some strictures specifically relevant to his new English milieu ("Be hypocritical, be cautious, be / Not what you *seem* but always what you *see*"), then bluntly addressing the natives of this realm where Juan needs prudence and pretense: "You are *not* a moral people, and you know it / Without the aid of too sincere a poet" (*CPW,* 5:491). Such an assertion would have struck many of Byron's contemporary readers as counterintuitive. To them Don Juan, having been dispatched on his travels for moral improvement, would seem to have passed through progressively ascending circles of morality and civilization: from elemental existence in the long-boat to pirate's island, Eastern despotism, Westernizing despotism, and finally British constitutional monarchy. Arriving in England, Juan moves to what they would consider the apex of civilization: from Dover through Kent to London, where he enters the best circles. Once "[t]he English winter—ending in July, / to recommence in August" is done (5:537), he migrates with a group of fashionable birds of passage to the most civilized setting in the modern world, a great English country house, where the impeccably elite Lord Henry and Lady Adeline Amundeville include him among their guests.

Taking the country house party as his subject, Byron becomes almost novelistic, as has been often noted.[25] But the genre he claims for himself is that well-established antithesis to the novel, the sermon:

> The portion of this world which I at present
>   Have taken up to fill the following sermon,
> Is one of which there's no description recent:
>   The reason why, is easy to determine:
> Although it seems both prominent and pleasant,
>   There is a sameness in its gems and ermine,
> A dull and family likeness through all ages,
> Of no great promise for poetic pages.
>   (*CPW*, 5:563)

The narrator goes on to deplore the reigning monotony of manner that puts "[a] sort of varnish over every fault" and also smoothes over more desirable differences (5:563). Such deprecation of the fashionable world is itself a fashionable attitude, a sign that the speaker has been an insider long enough to become bored. It is also a shrewd way of enhancing artistic achievement. The task of making an unpromising subject sparkle on "poetic pages" is bound to be harder than presenting naturally dazzling material.

Whether *Don Juan* is construed as verse novel or as sermon, its last completed phase is a ghost story in several ways. The action of the Norman Abbey episode leads up to what is literally the tale of a revenant, the ghostly Black Friar haunting the cloister that had belonged to his order until Henry VIII's dissolution of the monasteries. But the corporeal characters of this section are also revenants, in two senses. They bring back traits and circumstances of Juan's earlier acquaintances (Julia, Alfonso, Haidée) and with him enact variations on patterns already delineated in the poem. The minor characters evoke remembered celebrities from Byron's Years of Fame, individuals boiled down to their essential features and given allusively generic names clearly conveying their purposes in the story: Longbow, Strongbow, Miss Giltbedding, Jack Jargon, Dick Dubious. The central characters likewise derive features from real people with whom Byron mingled in 1812 and thereafter. The world walked by all these revenants is itself Byron's past recaptured and transformed; for Norman Abbey, the seat of the Amundevilles, is nothing but Newstead Abbey revised and improved.

An old, old monastery once, and now
Still older mansion, of a rich and rare
Mixed Gothic, such as Artists all allow
Few specimens yet left us can compare
Withal.

"[E]mbosom'd in a happy valley, / Crown'd by high woodlands, where the Druid oak / Stood"—before it, "a lucid lake, / Broad as transparent"—adjacent, "[a] glorious remnant of the Gothic pile" that had been the Black Friars' (*CPW,* 5:541–42).

This mansion and its estate, revealing England as it has existed through the ages, can be seen as a kind of time-lapse portrait in stone and land. The details also represent Byron's personal history as he might have liked it to be. Norman Abbey has architectural distinction beyond the actual Newstead's. Norman Abbey's ancient trees still stand, but Newstead's oaks had been cut and sold by the cash-hungry "Wicked Lord," Byron's predecessor. Inside, the same improvement is evident. Family portraits indicate a degree of national eminence to which the Byrons never rose until the poet's day. The mansion holds a distinguished collection of paintings Byron might have admired but never owned, and comfortable furnishings—implied but not listed, for with a modest fear that "Dan Phoebus takes me for an auctioneer," the nonchalantly aristocratic narrator tactfully tells his readers, "I spare you then the furniture and plate" (*CPW,* 5:546)—notably lacking during his tenure as seventh lord. Further, Norman Abbey is, unlike Newstead, a political power house, a stronghold of the grand Whig tradition that, in Pitt's day, held both tyranny and anarchy at a distance. A rural center of industry, prosperity, and hospitality under the patronage of its competent and responsible (if chilly) master and its intelligent and gracious (if repressed) mistress, Norman Abbey seems a ghostly paradise from the vantage point of 1822. In a Europe that has had its fill of autocratic centralized regimes and revolutions that brought no real progress, the political and cultural model offered at Norman Abbey is, as Malcolm Kelsall observes, "the best that is on offer."[26]

The Byronic blend of self-presentation through revision and masquerade pervades the last romantic situation faced by Don Juan—the English Cantos' reenactment of the mythical judgment of Paris, with Juan's three rival goddesses, Aurora Raby, Lady Adeline Amundeville, and the Duchess of Fitz-Fulke. Though the poem's narrator has by this point so closely converged with Byron that the two seem nearly identical, the protagonist's situation amid desirable women resembles Byron's London "Years of Fame" or Venetian Carnival weeks in ways his contemporaries would not miss. But the three women are likewise cut from cloth shot through with Byronic threads. The virginal heiress Aurora Raby has some of Annabella's cool self-possession (not to mention a surname connecting her with the Milbankes), but in her deeming, "that fallen worship far more dear / Perhaps because 'twas fallen" (*CPW,* 5:602) can be detected Byron's idealist side, his love of a lost or losing cause, his professed attraction for Catholicism above all Protestant faiths. In the duchess, who, disguised as the Black Friar, gives Juan a practical lesson in the difference between appearance and reality at the end of the last completed canto, we see Byron's penchants for monastic impersonation and for *tracasserie.* Her very name "Fitz-Fulke" suggestively combines in its two syllables, one Norman and one Saxon, Byron's pride in his lofty descent and in his erotic energy. Lady Adeline, who can be seen as playing Lady Caroline Lamb to Lord Henry's William Lamb and Don Juan's Byron, also resembles Byron, in more particulars than having a cloistered abbey for a country house. Like Byron, she favors Whig politics and Pope's poetry. Like Byron in his period of composing *Don Juan* and like the *Don Juan* narrator himself, she is a poet-chameleon, a liar with a lyre. The author-performer of a ballad ("Beware! beware of the Black Friar!") she sings to oblige her husband, entertain her guests, and bewitch Don Juan at a political dinner, Adeline deploys poetry to express, without confessing, her sincere feelings. Don Juan's response to her changeable nature is to doubt "how much of Adeline was *real*" (5:648). The narrator's more charitable inclination is to see her as a creature of mobility, that essential quality of actors, artists, romancers, speakers, bards, diplomats, dancers. The mobility shared by the real Lord Byron and the fictive Lady Adeline is

> A thing of temperament and not of art,
>   Though seeming so, from its supposed facility;
>   And false—though true; for surely they're sincerest,
>   Who are strongly acted on by what is nearest.
>   (5:649)

"False though true" is the perfect epithet for the English Cantos' *amour à quatre,* whether we read it historically as a continuation of the Don Juan

myth, biographically as a masquerade of the Lord Byron myth, or psy-
choanalytically as a narcissistic tableau of a poet's protagonist making
love to his composite anima. Whatever the case, Don Juan and his three
English ladies all combine features of their author with attributes clearly
distinct from his. They are ghosts of Byron's past come into the present
through the portal of literature. The barely begun canto 17 leaves all sus-
pended in the morning aftermath of Juan and Fitz-Fulke's "tender
moonlight situation"—but though he put it aside and sailed for Greece,
the unextinguishable poem itself was a ghost that haunted Byron to the
end. In the last weeks of his life, Byron received Moore's report of news
that "instead of pursuing heroic and warlike adventures, he was residing
in a delightful villa, continuing 'Don Juan.' "[27]

Despite the overwhelming number and contradictory nature of the
narrative clues and authorial statements of intent, *Don Juan*'s readers cannot resist speculating on how this remarkably errant poem by a man of
radical mobility might have closed.[28] Jerome McGann points out that
from canto 7 on the narrative's sequence of time and event precisely coincides with Byron's professed plan of ending Juan's life in the French
Reign of Terror—but also acknowledges that Byron's intentions were so
continually mutable that the dominant note seems to have been that of
"an epic with no plan." Andrew Rutherford, who draws on Byron's comments to Hunt, Lady Blessington, Parry, and others, believes that Byron
abandoned or indefinitely postponed Don Juan's death by guillotine and
planned to prolong the poem almost indefinitely—that among his alternatives might have been turning Juan Methodist or taking him to Greece
as a revolutionary. Cecil Y. Lang has argued that Juan would end up with
Aurora "in the hell of an unhappy marriage." M. K. Joseph guesses that
Byron intended to involve Juan and Adeline in a scandal that would
shatter the Amundeville marriage and preclude Juan's union with
Aurora, but he concedes that the poem's appropriate end is the narrator's
demise, not the protagonist's. Echoing Joseph, Bernard Beatty points out
that the poem is "inherently unfinished": its necessary conclusion will
finish off author, not text. Elizabeth Boyd also claims that the narrative
stops because it has to—because Byron had advanced the story to a point
where his skepticism and ambivalence could no longer carry the tale. She
believes that Byron's principles and experience would have had to change
before the narrative could continue. Endorsing the value of incompletion,
Michael Cooke describes the "unfinishable poem" as "a signal romantic
contribution to the form and vital entelechy of poetry itself." Anne Bar-

ton points out that *Don Juan* has an afterlife beyond Byron's authorial control in the series of continuations, imitations, and fictional extrapolations that prove the continued vitality of story and style alike. "Is it not *life*, is it not *the thing?*" Byron wrote in an impassioned defense of *Don Juan* (*BLJ*, 6:232). A cloud of witnesses—critics, poets, novelists, and readers—continue to testify that it is.

Notes and References

Preface

　　1.　L. J. Swingle, "On Reading Romantic Poetry," *PMLA* 86 (1971): 974–81.

Chapter One

　　1.　Lord Byron, *Don Juan,* canto 10, stanza 17, in *Complete Poetical Works,* ed. Jerome J. McGann, seven vols. (Oxford: Clarendon, 1980–1993), 5:442. Throughout this book, I have tried to balance the competing claims of clear reading with those of thorough annotation by citing the sources of substantial quotations from Byron but not citing short phrases, mere epithets, and the like. Passages quoted from Byron's poetry refer to this text and are parenthetically cited as *CPW,* followed by volume and page numbers. Citations from Byron's letters and journals are from *Byron's Letters and Journals,* ed. Leslie A. Marchand, 12 vols. (Cambridge, Mass.: Harvard, 1974–1982), hereafter cited in the text as *BLJ,* followed by volume and page numbers.

　　2.　The phrase was recalled by Washington Irving, who had been allowed to read Byron's autobiographical memoir, later burned. Quoted in Leslie A. Marchand, *Byron: A Biography* (New York: Knopf, 1957), 2:510.

Chapter Two

　　1.　All quotations from Byron's poetry refer to *The Complete Poetical Works,* ed. Jerome J. McGann (Oxford: Clarendon, 1980–1993), hereafter cited in the text as *CPW,* followed by volume and page numbers. In all cases, poems' titles are those appearing in *CPW.* When enclosed in square brackets, these titles have been added by the editor.

　　2.　M. H. Abrams, "Structure and Style in the Greater Romantic Lyric," in *From Sensibility to Romanticism,* ed. Gordon Haight and Harold Bloom (New Haven: Yale University Press, 1965), 527.

　　3.　Andrew Rutherford, *Byron: A Critical Study* (Stanford: Stanford University Press, 1961), 15–16.

　　4.　Jerome J. McGann, "Byron and the Anonymous Lyric," *Byron Journal* 20 (1992): 40. Similarly, Brian Nellist finds that the Eastern tales, *Childe Harold,* and *Don Juan* read like multiple lyrics. See Nellist, "Lyric Presence in Byron from the Tales to Don Juan," in *Byron and the Limits of Fiction,* ed. Bernard Beatty and Vincent Newey (Liverpool: Liverpool University Press, 1988), 39–77.

5. Lord Byron, *Byron's Letters and Journals,* ed. Leslie A. Marchand (Cambridge, Mass.: Harvard University Press, 1973–1982), 3:179, hereafter cited in the text as *BLJ.*

6. Henry Brougham, unsigned review, *Edinburgh Review* 40 (January 1808): 285–89, reprinted in *Byron: The Critical Heritage,* ed. Andrew Rutherford (New York: Barnes and Noble, 1970), 28, 32.

7. James Soderholm, "Byron's Ludic Lyrics," *Studies in English Literature* 34, no. 4 (Autumn 1994): 740–51. Hereafter cited in the text.

8. McGann, "Byron and the Anonymous Lyric," 33.

9. Thomas L. Ashton, *Byron's Hebrew Melodies* (Austin: University of Texas Press, 1972), 102. Ashton's book offers a full account of the genesis of *Hebrew Melodies.*

10. Jerome Christensen, *Lord Byron's Strength: Romantic Writing and Commercial Society* (Baltimore: Johns Hopkins University Press, 1993), 78. Hereafter cited in the text.

11. For a fuller discussion of these lyrics, see Peter W. Graham, *Don Juan and Regency England* (Charlottesville: University Press of Virginia, 1990), 135–38, 190–93. Hereafter cited in the text.

12. John Clubbe discusses the interrelationships of Byron's 1816 poems in " 'The New Prometheus of New Men': Byron's 1816 Poems and MAN-FRED," in Clyde de L. Ryals et al., eds., *Nineteenth-Century Literary Perspectives* (Durham, N.C.: Duke University Press, 1974), 17–47.

13. On the sources of "Darkness," see McGann's notes to *CPW,* 4:459–60; R. J. Dingley, " 'I had a dream.' Byron's 'Darkness,' " *Byron Journal* 9 (1981): 20–33; and, on the literary importance of 1816's dismal summer weather, John Clubbe, "The Tempest-toss'd Summer of 1816: Mary Shelley's *Frankenstein,*" *Byron Journal* 19 (1991): 26–40.

14. Malcolm Kelsall, *Byron's Politics* (Brighton, England: Harvester, 1987), 5. Hereafter cited in the text.

15. For the composition and publishing history of the additional stanzas, see *CPW,* 3:456–57.

16. Hobhouse's Paris letters to Byron appear in *Byron's Bulldog: The Letters of John Cam Hobhouse to Lord Byron,* ed. Peter W. Graham (Columbus: Ohio State University Press, 1984), 120–29, 184–220.

17. Thérèse Tessier, "Byron and Thomas Moore: A Great Literary Friendship," *Byron Journal* 20 (1992): 48.

18. In *Byron and Greek Love: Homophobia in Nineteenth-Century England* (Berkeley: University of California Press, 1985), 312–37. Louis Crompton meticulously traces the autobiographical circumstances surrounding these final poems and the details of their posthumous publication. Hereafter cited in the text.

19. Pietro Gamba, *Lord Byron's Last Journey to Greece* (London: John Murray, 1825), 125.

Chapter Three

1. Although critical studies of Byron's satires usually include extensive discussions of *Don Juan,* I have chosen to reserve it for a later chapter that also considers *Childe Harold's Pilgrimage.* Both long works contain satirical interludes, *Don Juan* significantly more than *Childe Harold.* But both are complex, multifaceted texts whose essence is to resist, and finally transcend, generic categories. My general approach to Byron as satirist is informed by Frederick L. Beaty, *Byron the Satirist* (DeKalb: Northern Illinois University Press, 1985); Michael G. Cooke, *The Blind Man Traces the Circle* (Princeton: Princeton University Press, 1969); and Robert F. Gleckner, "From Selfish Spleen to Equanimity: Byron's Satires," *Studies in Romanticism* 18 (Summer 1979): 173–206.

2. See Hobhouse's 5 January 1819 letter to Byron; Hobhouse, 256–62.

3. Frederick L. Beaty, *Byron the Satirist* (DeKalb: Northern Illinois University Press, 1985), 34. Hereafter cited in the text.

4. Quoted in Marchand, 1:278.

5. William St. Clair, *Lord Elgin and the Marbles* (Oxford: Oxford University Press, 1983), 189.

6. Moore, the recipient of a colonial sinecure in Bermuda, had become liable for £6,000 that his Bermuda deputy had embezzled. Unable to repay the money, Moore fled abroad to Paris, where he lived from 1819 until 1822. The Tory newspaper *John Bull* attacked him on 1 and 12 August 1821.

7. Quoted in Henry Crabb Robinson, *Diary, Reminiscences, and Correspondence,* ed. Thomas Sadler (London: Macmillan, 1869), 2:437.

8. Compare *CPW,* 5:188–93. "The Isles of Greece!" falls between stanzas 86 and 87 of canto 3 of *Don Juan;* see especially stanzas 9 and 10 of the lyric.

9. See Moore's journal entry of 9 September 1821: "A good deal of talk about the Royal visit in Ireland—the good sense with which the King has acted, and the bad, servile style in which poor Paddy has received him—Mr. O Connel pre-eminent in Blarney & inconsistency—Many *good* results, however, likely to arrive from the whole affair, if the King but continues in the same state of temperature towards Ireland in which he is at present." *The Journal of Thomas Moore,* ed. Wilfred S. Dowden et al. (Newark: University of Delaware Press, 1984), 2:484.

10. For instance, one might compare the opinions of two contemporary readers who discussed literary matters with one another, Henry Crabb Robinson and Goethe. The former read "The Vision of Judgment" in *The Liberal* and pronounced it "as dull as it is profligate. . . . The trash is not redeemed by a single passage of poetry, sense, or wit." In contrast, Goethe considered Byron's *Vision* "the utmost of which he was capable." Both quoted in Andrew Rutherford, ed., *Byron: The Critical Heritage* (New York: Barnes and Noble, 1970), 251–52.

11. Informative discussions of the literary or political dimensions of the satire appear in Beaty, 180–95; Rutherford, 215–37; Kelsall, 119–45; and Stuart Peterfreund, "The Politics of 'Neutral Space' in Byron's *Vision of Judgment*," *Modern Language Quarterly* 40 (1979): 275–91.

12. Malcolm Kelsall, *Byron's Politics* (Brighton, England: Harvester, 1987), 119. Hereafter cited in the text.

13. Psalms 100: 4–5

Chapter Four

1. Caroline Franklin, *Byron's Heroines* (Oxford: Oxford University Press, 1992), 14–17. Hereafter cited in the text.

2. Jerome J. McGann, *The Beauty of Inflections : Literary Investigations in Historical Method and Theory* (Oxford: Oxford University Press, 1988), 262.

3. For appraisal of the rumor, see M. K. Joseph, *Byron the Poet* (London: Gollancz, 1964), 65n. 16. Later in Byron's writing career, Don Juan will rescue a young Muslim girl called Leila at Ismail.

4. Leslie A. Marchand, *Byron: A Biography* (New York: Knopf, 1957), 1:419.

5. Daniel Watkins, *Social Relations in Byron's Eastern Tales* (Cranbury, N.J.: Associated University Presses, 1987), 52.

6. Andrew Rutherford, *Byron: A Critical Study* (Stanford: Stanford University Press, 1961), 16. Hereafter cited in the text. The *locus classicum* for more extensive treatment of the character is Peter L. Thorslev, *The Byronic Hero: Types and Prototypes* (Minneapolis: University of Minnesota Press, 1962).

7. Among the many considerations of the political dimension of Byron's Eastern tales are Watkins, cited previously; Jerome J. McGann, *Fiery Dust: Byron's Poetic Development* (Chicago: University of Chicago Press, 1968); Robert F. Gleckner, *Byron and the Ruins of Paradise* (Baltimore: Johns Hopkins University Press, 1967); Peter J. Manning, "Tales and Politics: The Corsair, Lara, and The White Doe of Rylstone," in *Byron: Poetry and Politics,* ed. James Hogg (Salzburg, Vienna: Institut für Anglistik & Amerikanistik, Universität Salzburg, 1981); Jerome Christensen, *Lord Byron's Strength* (Baltimore: Johns Hopkins University Press, 1993).

8. Samuel Taylor Coleridge, "Limbo," in *The Portable Coleridge,* ed. I. A. Richards (New York: Viking Penguin, 1977), 205–6.

9. Jerome J. McGann, *Shelley and His Circle, 1773–1822*, ed. Donald H. Reiman (Cambridge: Harvard University Press, 1986), 8:247; Peter J. Manning, *Reading Romantics: Texts and Contexts* (Oxford: Oxford University Press, 1990), 147.

10. Quoted in Andrew Rutherford, ed., *Byron: The Critical Heritage* (New York: Barnes and Noble, 1970), 122.

11. Ibid., 126.

12. Ibid., 128–29.

13. McGann, *Shelley and His Circle,* 8:246; Manning, 148.

Chapter Five

1. Leslie A. Marchand, *Byron: A Biography* (New York: Knopf, 1957), 1:363.

2. The ensuing discussion of Byron's dramatic poems is informed by the following texts: Anne Barton, " 'A Light to Lesson Ages': Byron's Political Plays," in John Jump, ed., *Byron: A Symposium* (London: Macmillan, 1975), 138–62; Jerome Christensen, *Lord Byron's Strength* (Baltimore: Johns Hopkins University Press, 1993); David V. Erdman, "Byron's Stage Fright: The History of His Ambition and Fear of Writing for the Stage," *ELH* 6 (September 1939): 219–43; Richard Lansdown, *Byron's Historical Dramas* (Oxford: Oxford University Press, 1992); Peter J. Manning, *Byron and His Fictions* (Detroit: Wayne State University Press, 1978); Jerome J. McGann, *Fiery Dust: Byron's Poetic Development* (Chicago: University of Chicago Press, 1968); Barry Weller, "The Stage History of Byron's Plays," *CPW,* 6:579–96.

3. In a review of *Manfred* translated for Byron in 1820, Goethe wrote, "Byron's tragedy, *Manfred,* was to me a wonderful phenomenon, and one that closely touched me. This singular intellectual poet has taken my *Faustus* to himself, and extracted from it the strangest nourishment for his hypochondriac humour. He has made use of the impelling principles in his own way, for his own purposes, so that no one of them remains the same." Quoted in Andrew Rutherford, ed., *Byron: The Critical Heritage* (New York: Barnes and Noble, 1970), 119.

4. Francis Jeffrey, unsigned review of *Sardanapalus, The Two Foscari,* and *Cain, Edinburgh Review* 36 (February 1822): 413–52. Quoted in Rutherford, ed., 231.

5. Francis Jeffrey, unsigned review of *Marino Faliero, Edinburgh Review* 35 (July 1821): 271–85. Quoted in Rutherford, ed., 211.

6. McGann surveys the historical texts that served as sources for *Marino Faliero* in *CPW,* 5:524–26.

7. John Spalding Gatton, " 'Pretensions to Accuracy': Byron's Manipulation of History in the Venetian Dramas," in *Byron e la Cultura Veneziana,* ed. Giulio Marra et al. (Venice: Universita degli Studi de Venezia, 1986), 60–63. Hereafter cited in the text.

8. Malcolm Kelsall, *Byron's Politics* (Brighton, England: Harvester, 1987), 91. Hereafter cited in the text.

9. Jeffrey, review of *Sardanapalus,* qtd. in Rutherford, ed., 229.

10. Richard Lansdown, *Byron's Historical Dramas* (Oxford: Oxford University Press, 1992), 150.

11. Michael G. Cooke, "The Restoration Ethos of Byron's Classical Plays," *PMLA* 79 (December 1964): 569–78.

12. Philip W. Martin, *Byron: A Poet before His Public* (Cambridge: Cambridge University Press, 1982), 164–68.

13. Edward E. Bostetter, "Byron and the Politics of Paradise," *PMLA* 75 (1960): 571.

14. Quoted in Malcolm Elwin, *Lord Byron's Wife* (New York: Harcourt Brace and World, 1963), 263

15. William Hazlitt, *The Spirit of the Age* (Oxford: Oxford University Press, 1970), 111.

16. Charles Robinson, "The Devil as Doppelgänger in *The Deformed Transformed:* The Sources and Meaning of Byron's Unfinished Drama," *Bulletin of the New York Public Library* 76 (March 1970): 177–202.

Chapter Six

1. The following texts have influenced this chapter's discussion of *Childe Harold:* Jerome Christensen, *Lord Byron's Strength* (Baltimore: Johns Hopkins University Press, 1993); M. K. Joseph, *Byron the Poet* (London: Gollancz, 1964); Peter J. Manning, *Byron and His Fictions* (Detroit: Wayne State University Press, 1978); Jerome McGann, "The Book of Byron and the Book of the World," in *The Beauty of Inflections, Fiery Dust,* and *The Romantic Ideology* (Chicago: University of Chicago Press, 1983); Vincent Newey, "Authoring the Self: *Childe Harold* III and IV," in *Byron and the Limits of Fiction,* ed. Bernard Beatty and Vincent Newey (Liverpool: Liverpool University Press, 1988), 148–90; Andrew Rutherford, *Byron: A Critical Study*. Besides the works mentioned in note, the commentary on *Don Juan* is particularly informed by Anne Barton, *Byron Don Juan* (Cambridge: Cambridge University Press, 1992); Bernard Beatty, *Byron's "Don Juan"* (Totowa, N.J.: Barnes and Noble, 1985); Frederick L. Beaty, *Byron the Satirist* (DeKalb: Northern Illinois University Press, 1985); Elizabeth Boyd, *Byron's "Don Juan": A Critical Study* (New York: The Humanities Press, 1958); Michael G. Cooke, "Byron's *Don Juan:* The Obsession and Self-Discipline of Spontaneity," *Studies in Romanticism* 14, no. 3 (Summer 1975): 290–300; Jerome J. McGann, *Don Juan in Context* (Chicago: University of Chicago Press, 1976); Susan J. Wolfson, " 'Their She Condition': Cross-Dressing and the Politics of Gender in *Don Juan,*" in *Romantic Poetry: Recent Revisionary Criticism,* ed. Karl Kroeber and Gene W. Ruoff (New Brunswick, N.J.: Rutgers University Press, 1993), 267–89. Some of the points made here derive from my *Don Juan and Regency England* (Charlottesville: University Press of Virginia, 1990).

2. Compare Byron's letter of 19 January 1819 to Hobhouse and Kinnaird, an epic list of his recent conquests (*BLJ,* 6:92) with Leporello's aria "Madamina! Il catalogo è questo," which lists for the vengeful Donna Elvira the international army of women seduced by Don Giovanni: 640 Italians, 231 Germans, 100 French, 91 Turks, and 1,003 Spaniards.

3. For discussion of the triple time scheme of *Don Juan,* see McGann's introduction to the Oxford *Don Juan* (*CPW,* 5:xxiii–xxiv), and Peter Manning, *Byron and His Fictions* (Detroit: Wayne State University Press, 1978), 279n. 3.

4. Marchand, *Byron: A Biography,* 1:212; John Galt, *Letters from the Levant* (London: 1813), 51–56.

5. McGann, *Fiery Dust,* 76.

6. Walter Scott to Joanna Baillie, 4 April 1812, quoted in *Byron: The Critical Heritage,* ed. Andrew Rutherford (New York: Barnes and Noble, 1970), 36–37.

7. Joseph, 23.

8. Christensen's thoughts on the commercial and cultural nuances of Byromaniacal celebrity-making appear throughout his treatments of *Childe Harold* 1 and 2, 65–78.

9. See Francis Jeffrey's unsigned review of the third canto in *Edinburgh Review* 27 (December 1816): 277–310, reprinted in Rutherford, *Byron: The Critical Heritage,* 98–109.

10. For the early reactions of Hobhouse, Gifford, John Wilson Croker, and Elizabeth Duchess of Devonshire, see Rutherford, *Byron: The Critical Heritage,* 81–83. Henry Crabb Robinson writes that Byron "palpably imitated" Wordsworth in *Henry Crabb Robinson on Books and Their Writers.* His comment is extracted in Rutherford, 109n. 1. Thomas Moore heard firsthand of Wordsworth's impression of "Byron's plagiarisms from him—the whole third Canto of Childe Harold's founded on his style & sentiments." Thomas Moore, *The Journal of Thomas Moore,* ed. Wilfred S. Dowden (Newark: University of Delaware Press, 1983), 1:355.

11. The fascinating story of Davies's trunk and the manuscripts it contained appears in T. A. J. Burnett, *The Rise and Fall of a Regency Dandy: The Life and Times of Scrope Berdmore Davies* (London: John Murray, 1981).

12. Jerome J. McGann, *Fiery Dust: Byron's Poetic Development* (Chicago: University of Chicago Press, 1968), 138.

13. Jerome J. McGann, *Don Juan in Context* (Chicago: University of Chicago Press, 1976), 107.

14. Anne Barton, *Byron Don Juan* (Cambridge: Cambridge University Press, 1992), 7. Hereafter cited in the text.

15. Anne K. Mellor, *English Romantic Irony* (Cambridge, Mass.: Harvard University Press, 1980), 56.

16. For the complete argument developed in this letter of 5 January 1819, see John Cam Hobhouse, *Byron's Bulldog: The Letters of John Cam Hobhouse to Lord Byron,* ed. Peter W. Graham (Columbus: Ohio State University Press, 1984), 256–62.

17. Hobhouse, 275.

18. On publishing choices, piracy, and Byron's readers, see *CPW,* 5:666–67; Hugh J. Luke Jr., "The Publishing of Byron's *Don Juan,*" *PMLA* 80

(1965): 199–209; William St. Clair, "The Impact of Byron's Writings," in *Byron: Augustan and Romantic,* ed. Andrew Rutherford (London: Macmillan, 1990); Christensen, 237–40.

19. Elizabeth French Boyd, *Byron's "Don Juan": A Critical Study* (New York: The Humanities Press, 1958), 121.

20. Peter G. Vassallo, "Casti's *Animali Parlanti,* the Italian Epic, and *Don Juan:* the Poetry of Politics," in *Byron: Poetry and Politics,* ed. E. A. Sturzl and J. Hogg (Salzburg: Institut für Anglistik und Amerikanistik, Universität Salzburg, 1981), 166–203.

21. The letter of 29 October 1822 is extracted in Marchand, 3:1040.

22. Boyd, 150.

23. This topos is well treated in Ernest J. Lovell Jr., *Byron: The Record of a Quest* (Austin: University of Texas Press, 1949), and in Malcolm M. Kelsall, *The Great Good Place: The Country House in English Literature* (London: Harvester, 1993), 115–23.

24. Jerome J. McGann, *The Romantic Ideology* (Chicago: University of Chicago Press, 1983), 145.

25. See Andreas Horn, *Byron's "Don Juan" and the Eighteenth-Century English Novel* (Berne: Swiss Studies in English no. 51, 1960); A. B. England, *Byron's "Don Juan" and Eighteenth-Century Literature* (Lewisburg, Penn.: Bucknell University Press, 1975); Boyd, 150–59.

26. Kelsall, *Byron's Politics,* 179.

27. Quoted in Marchand, *Byron: A Biography* (New York: Knopf, 1957), 3:1196.

28. For the critical opinions on *Don Juan*'s ending mentioned here, see McGann, *Don Juan in Context,* 1–4; Rutherford, 238–41; Lang, "Narcissus Jilted: Byron, *Don Juan,* and the Biographical Imperative," in *Historical Studies and Literary Criticism,* ed. Jerome J. McGann (Madison: University of Wisconsin Press, 1985), 176; Joseph, 186, 304; Beatty, 8; Boyd, 160–61; Cooke, 285–86; Barton, 84–89, 98–101.

Selected Bibliography

The following list, by no means comprehensive, offers a starting point for further reading. For additional guidance, consult the bibliographies cited. The books and shorter pieces included here represent a range of topics and approaches; on-line materials and fictional accounts are not included. Where a work's title seems sufficiently self-explanatory, no descriptive annotation is given.

PRIMARY WORKS

Poetry

Byron. Ed. Jerome J. McGann. Oxford. Oxford University Press, 1986. A volume in the Oxford English Authors series, with texts from the definitive edition of Byron's poetry.

Byron's "Don Juan": A Variorum Edition. Ed. T. G. Steffan and W. W. Pratt. Austin: University of Texas Press, 1957. Four vols. Variorum text with notes and extensive information on the making of the poem.

The Complete Poetical Works. Ed. Jerome J. McGann. Oxford: Clarendon, 1980–1993. Seven vols. The definitive edition, with annotations and concise but thorough discussion of textual, historical, and critical matters.

The Works of Lord Byron: Poetry. Ed. E. H. Coleridge. London: John Murray, 1898–1904. Seven vols. Still useful for its extensive annotations.

Prose

Byron's Letters and Journals. Ed. Leslie A. Marchand. London: John Murray, 1973–1982. Twelve vols., including index. The definitive edition.

The Complete Miscellaneous Prose. Ed. Andrew Nicholson. Oxford: Clarendon, 1991. An annotated gathering of speeches, reviews, essays, inscriptions, lists, and other prose writings.

"What comes uppermost": Byron's Letters and Journals. Ed. Leslie A. Marchand. Newark: University of Delaware Press, 1994. Further letters that have come to light since the publication of the Murray edition.

The Works of Lord Byron: Letters and Journals. Ed. R. E. Prothero. London: John Murray, 1898–1901. Six vols. As with the Coleridge edition of the poems, still useful for its annotations.

SECONDARY WORKS

Books

Barton, Anne. *Byron. Don Juan.* Cambridge: Cambridge University Press, 1992. Concise and lucid introduction to the poem and its background.

Beatty, Bernard. *Byron's "Don Juan."* Totowa, N.J.: Barnes and Noble, 1985. Reads *Don Juan* as a work whose essence is process, not content.

───── and Vincent Newey, eds. *Byron and the Limits of Fiction.* Liverpool: Liverpool University Press, 1988. A collection of British bicentennial essays.

Beaty, Fredrick L. *Byron the Satirist.* DeKalb: Northern Illinois University Press, 1985. Admirable, accessible treatment of the satiric mode in Byron's poetry.

Blessington, Marguerite. *Lady Blessington's Conversations of Lord Byron.* Ed. Ernest J. Lovell. Princeton: Princeton University Press, 1969. Insightful, sometimes imaginative, contemporary account.

Boyd, Elizabeth F. *Byron's "Don Juan": A Critical Study.* New York: The Humanities Press, 1958. On the sources and significance of Byron's masterpiece.

Christensen, Jerome. *Lord Byron's Strength.* Baltimore: Johns Hopkins University Press, 1993. Ambitiously theoretical assessment of "Byron" as construct and commodity in a commercial society.

Cooke, Michael. *The Blind Man Traces the Circle.* Princeton: Princeton University Press, 1969. Important work on the intellectual patterns and philosophy of Byron's poetry.

Crompton, Louis. *Byron and Greek Love.* Berkeley: University of California Press, 1985. Historical and cultural study of Byron's bisexuality in the context of early-nineteenth-century homophobia.

Elledge, W. Paul. *Byron and the Dynamics of Metaphor.* Nashville: Vanderbilt University Press, 1968. Examination of Byron's poetic artistry, especially in the nonsatiric works.

Elfenbein, Andrew. *Byron and the Victorians.* Cambridge: Cambridge University Press, 1995. Reception and perception of Byron in middle- and later-nineteenth-century British culture.

Elwin, Malcolm. *Lord Byron's Wife.* New York: Harcourt Brace & World, 1963. Life of Lady Byron drawing on the Lovelace Papers, Byroniana passed down through the Byrons' daughter, Ada, countess of Lovelace.

Fleming, Anne. *Bright Darkness.* London: Nottingham Court Press, 1983. An accessible introduction to Byron's poetry in relation to his life and times.

Franklin, Caroline. *Byron's Heroines.* Oxford: Clarendon Press, 1992. Perceptive and persuasive historically grounded feminist study.

Gleckner, Robert F. *Byron and the Ruins of Paradise.* Baltimore: Johns Hopkins University Press, 1967. The dark side of Byron's works through 1816.

Graham, Peter W. *Don Juan and Regency England*. Charlottesville: University Press of Virginia, 1990. Reads *Don Juan* in various historical, cultural, and literary contexts.

Grosskurth, Phyllis. *Byron: The Flawed Angel*. Boston: Houghton Mifflin, 1997. Newest biography; psychoanalytic approach.

Hoagwood, Terence A. *Byron's Dialectic*. Lewisburg, Penn.: Bucknell University Press, 1993. Analytical and historical appraisal of Byron's skeptic philosophy as presented in his works.

Hobhouse, John Cam. *Byron's Bulldog: The Letters of John Cam Hobhouse to Lord Byron*. Ed. Peter W. Graham. Columbus: Ohio State University Press, 1984. Letters from Byron's closest lifelong friend.

Joseph, M.K. *Byron the Poet*. London: Gollancz, 1964. A sound general account; excellent introductory reading.

Kelsall, Malcolm. *Byron's Politics*. Brighton, England: Harvester Press, 1987. A consideration of Byron's roots in, and adaptation of, the liberal Whig tradition.

Lansdown, Richard. *Byron's Historical Dramas*. Oxford: Clarendon Press, 1992. Examines both form and content of the dramas based on historical materials.

Levine, Alice, and Robert N. Keane, eds. *Rereading Byron*. New York: Garland, 1993. Selected essays from Hofstra University's Byron Bicentennial Conference.

Longford, Elizabeth. *The Life of Byron*. Boston: Little, Brown, and Co., 1976. Readable one-volume biography.

Manning, Peter J. *Byron and His Fictions*. Detroit: Wayne State University Press, 1978. One of the strongest and most persuasive psychoanalytic interpretations.

Marchand, Leslie A. *Byron: A Biography*. New York: Knopf, 1957. Three vols. A masterwork in its genre; still the definitive Byron biography.

———. *Byron: A Portrait*. New York: Knopf, 1970. Excellent one-volume life.

McGann, Jerome J. *"Don Juan" in Context*. Chicago: University of Chicago Press, 1976. Traces the influences shaping Byron's mature sensibility, particularly as expressed in *Don Juan*.

———. *Fiery Dust: Byron's Poetical Development*. Chicago: University of Chicago Press, 1968. A seminal critical study that considers Byron's self-expressive and self-constructive "poetry of sincerity."

———. *The Romantic Ideology*. Chicago: University of Chicago Press, 1983. Discusses romantic poetry, including Byron's, and romantic criticism as self-reproducing cultural products.

Medwin, Thomas. *Conversations of Lord Byron*. Ed. Ernest J. Lovell. Princeton: Princeton University Press, 1966. Firsthand account of the last phase of Byron's life.

Moore, Doris Langley. *The Late Lord Byron*. Philadelphia: Lippincott, 1961. Fascinating study of Byron's posthumous influence on the friends and relations who survived him.
————. *Lord Byron: Accounts Rendered*. London: John Murray, 1974. Insights into Byron's life chiefly through the history of his finances.
Moore, Thomas. *Letters and Journals of Lord Byron, with Notices of His Life*. London: Longmans, 1830. First life and letters, produced by Byron's designated biographer, recipient of the notorious memoirs burned at John Murray's.
Ridenour, George M. *The Style of "Don Juan."* New Haven: Yale University Press, 1960. The masterpiece assessed in terms of the myth of the fall and the classical rhetorical styles.
Robinson, Charles. *The Snake and the Eagle Wreathed in Flight*. Baltimore: Johns Hopkins University Press, 1976. Appraises the relationship and mutual influences of Byron and Shelley.
Rutherford, Andrew. *Byron: A Critical Study*. Stanford: Stanford University Press, 1961. Insightful and readable survey.
————, ed. *Byron: The Critical Heritage*. New York: Barnes and Noble, 1970. Collection of contemporary reviews and later-nineteenth-century critical assessments of Byron's works.
Shilstone, Frederick W. *Byron and the Myth of Tradition*. Lincoln: University of Nebraska Press, 1988. Conflict between self and tradition as played out in the poetry and prose.
Soderholm, James. *Fantasy, Forgery, and the Byron Legend*. Lexington: University of Kentucky Press, 1996. Lively interpretation of the Byron myth and how women close to him collaborated in its making.
St. Clair, William. *That Greece Might Still Be Free*. Oxford: Oxford University Press, 1983. Historical account of nineteenth-century Philhellenism and Byron's part in the movement.
Thorslev, Peter L. *The Byronic Hero*. Minneapolis: University of Minnesota Press, 1962. Urtext on the famous character type.
Watkins, Daniel P. *Social Relations in Byron's Eastern Tales*. Cranbury, N.J.: Associated University Presses, 1987. Political reading of the ostensibly "escapist" tales.
Young, Ione Dodson. *A Concordance to the Poetry of Byron*. Austin, Texas: Pemberton Press, 1965.

Articles, Essays, Chapters

Barton, Anne. " 'A Light to Lesson Ages': Byron's Political Plays." In *Byron: A Symposium*. Ed. John Jump. London: Macmillan, 1975. Fine introduction to the political plays.
Bone, Drummond. *"Beppo:* The Liberation of Fiction." In *Byron and the Limits of Fiction*. Ed. Bernard Beatty and Vincent Newey. Liverpool: Liverpool

University Press, 1988. A sophisticated yet nontechnical analysis of the poem's complex texture.

———. "The Rhetoric of Freedom." In *Byron: Wrath and Rhyme*. Ed. Alan Bold. Totowa, N.J.: Barnes and Noble, 1983. Well-blended theory and explication in this treatment of a Byronic preoccupation.

Bostetter, Edward. "Masses and Solids: Byron's View of the External World." *Modern Language Quarterly* 35 (1974): 257–71. Byron as empiricist among the romantics.

Butler, Marilyn. "The Orientalism of Byron's *Giaour*." In *Byron and the Limits of Fiction*. Ed. Bernard Beatty and Vincent Newey. Liverpool: Liverpool University Press, 1988. Historically grounded account of Orientalism in the first of the Eastern tales.

Clubbe, John, and Ernest J. Lovell. "Byron as a Romantic Poet." In *English Romanticism: The Grounds of Belief*. DeKalb: Northern Illinois University Press, 1983. Argues that Byron is a more typical romantic poet than modern critical consensus has seen him to be.

Cooke, Michael G. "Byron's *Don Juan:* The Obsession and Self-Discipline of Spontaneity." *Studies in Romanticism* 14, no. 3 (Summer 1975): 285–302. Subtle reading of the phenomenon of "improvisation" as practiced by Byron.

Erdman, David V. "Lord Byron as Rinaldo." *PMLA* 57 (March 1942): 189–231. Account of Byron's brief parliamentary career.

Hazlitt, William. "Lord Byron." In *The Spirit of the Age*. Oxford: Oxford University Press, 1970. This vigorously opinionated appraisal by one of Byron's contemporaries remains compelling.

Hofkosh, Sonia. "The Writer's Ravishment: Women and the Romantic Author— The Example of Byron." In *Romanticism and Feminism*. Ed. Anne K. Mellor. Bloomington: Indiana University Press, 1988. Appraises Byron's notion of autonomy as threatened by his female readers.

Lang, Cecil Y. "Narcissus Jilted: Byron, *Don Juan,* and the Biographical Imperative." In *Historical Studies and Literary Criticism*. Ed. Jerome J. McGann. Madison: University of Wisconsin Press, 1985. A well-calculated blend of historical investigation and critical assessment.

Manning, Peter. "The Nameless Broken Dandy and the Structure of Authorship." In *Reading Romantics: Text and Context* (Oxford: Oxford University Press, 1990). A chapter focusing on the complex motives of authorship in *Beppo*. Sociopolitical contextualizing enriches a subtle critical reading.

McGann, Jerome. "The Book of Byron and the Book of a World." In *The Beauty of Inflections: Literary Investigations in Historical Method and Theory*. Oxford: Clarendon Press, 1985. Chapter on the interaction of the personal and the public in Byron's art and life.

———. "Byron and the Anonymous Lyric." *Byron Journal* 20 (1992): 27–45. An account of the reading of Byron McGann has evolved over almost 30 years of editorial and critical involvement with his works.

Mellor, Anne. "Byron: Half Dust Half Deity." In *English Romantic Irony*. Cambridge, Mass.: Harvard University Press, 1980. Posits that Byron's mature works are the most masterful expressions of English romantic irony.

St. Clair, William. "The Impact of Byron's Writings." In *Byron: Augustan and Romantic*. Ed. Andrew Rutherford. London: Macmillan, 1990. Well-substantiated reception study.

Tessier, Thérèse. "Byron and Thomas Moore: A Great Literary Friendship." *Byron Journal* 20 (1992): 46–58. A sympathetic survey of one of Byron's most important literary and personal relations.

Wolfson, Susan J. " 'Their She Condition': Cross-Dressing and the Politics of Gender in *Don Juan*." *ELH* 54 (1987): 586–617. Reversal of gender roles as exemplifying cultural contradictions in Byron's work.

Bibliographies

Clubbe, John. "George Gordon Lord Byron." In *English Romantic Poets: A Review of Research*. Ed. Frank Jordan. New York: MLA, 1985. Thorough, judicious critical bibliography building on previous essays by Samuel Chew and Ernest J. Lovell and assessing the state of Byron scholarship through 1985.

Goode, Clement Tyson. *George Gordon, Lord Byron: A Comprehensive, Annotated Research Bibliography of Secondary Materials in English, 1973–1994*. Lanham: Scarecrow Press, 1997.

Keats-Shelley Journal. Annual critical bibliography on Byron.

MLA International Biography. Annual listing of the year's publications.

Santucho, Oscar José. *Lord Byron: A Comprehensive Bibliography of Secondary Materials in English, 1807–1974*. Metuchen, N.J.: Scarecrow Press, 1977. Bibliography supplemented by a critical review of research by Clement Tyson Goode.

Index

The Author

Peter W. Graham is professor of English at Virginia Polytechnic Institute and State University. His writing and teaching centers on nineteenth-century British literature and culture and on the medical humanities. Among his other publications are *Byron's Bulldog: The Letters of John Cam Hobhouse to Lord Byron; Don Juan and Regency England; Articulating the Elephant Man: Joseph Merrick and His Interpreters* (with Fritz Oehlschlaeger); and *The Portable Darwin* (with Duncan M. Porter).

The Editor

Herbert Sussman is professor of English at Northeastern University. His publications in Victorian literature include *Victorian Masculinities: Manhood and Masculine Poetics in Early Victorian Literature and Art; Fact into Figure: Typology in Carlyle, Ruskin, and the Pre-Raphaelite Brotherhood;* and *Victorians and the Machine: The Literary Response to Technology.*

ISBN 0-8057-7065-8

9 780805 770650

2/09